42.10
29
1ST ED
1958

VACUUM-TUBE AND
SEMICONDUCTOR ELECTRONICS

McGraw-Hill Electrical and Electronic Engineering Series
FREDERICK EMMONS TERMAN, *Consulting Editor*
W. W. HARMAN and J. G. TRUXAL, *Associate Consulting Editors*

Vacuum-tube and Semiconductor Electronics

JACOB MILLMAN, Ph.D.

Professor of Electrical Engineering
Columbia University

McGRAW-HILL BOOK COMPANY, INC.

New York   Toronto   London

1958

VACUUM-TUBE AND SEMICONDUCTOR ELECTRONICS

III

42382

THE MAPLE PRESS COMPANY, YORK, PA.

1-46 $x = -1.76$ cm, $y = 1.04$ m.

1-47 b 13.2 n gauss.

1-48 0.27, 0.55, -0.89 cm.

1-49 0.87 cm.

Chapter 2

2-1 a 6.50×10^{-4} m/sec; b 0.622 gauss; c 7.30 gauss.

2-2 a 3.66 cm; d 56.5 volts.

2-3 a 33.0 gauss; b 2.58 cm.

2-5 a $y = 0.224$ cm, $z = 0.313$ cm; b $y = -0.039$ cm, $z = 0.558$ cm.

2-6 a 4.67×10^8 cps; b 6.42×10^{-8}.

2-7 3.39 om.

2-8 3.90 cm.

2-9 b 4.67×10^8 cps.

2-11 7.2 %

2-14 a 1.21 cm; b 2.07 cm; c 1.04 cm.

2-17 1.79 cm.

2-18 0.49 cm

2-19 0.162 webers/m^2

2-20 a 3.40×10^8 m/sec; b 2.25×10^8 m/sec; c 1.51 .

2-22 a $B = m\mu/e\rho$; b $l = \rho$; c $t = \pi\rho/2\mu + D/\mu$; d $v = \mu$.

2-23 a 13.8 Mc; b 3.62 μsec; c 3.40×10^7 m/sec, 39.1 cm.

2-24 a 19.4 Mc; b 19.7 Mev; c 154 kev.

2-25 a 5.38 Mev; b 430 ev; c 12,500.

2-27 a 5.30; b 7.38 cm; c 610 cps; d 1.86×10^{-9} sec; e 1.02×10^5 m.

Chapter 3

3-2 4.70×10^7 (ohm-m)$^{-1}$

3-3 0.10 m^2/(volt-sec)

3-4 a 1.78×10^{-4} m/sec; b 4.17×10^{-3} m^2/(volt-sec) c 5.62×10^7 (ohm-m)$^{-1}$

3-5 <u>a</u> 0.143 cm; <u>b</u> 1.88 X 10^8 cm/sec.

3-8 <u>a</u> 0.25 ev; <u>b</u> 1 ev.

3-9 <u>a</u> No; <u>b</u> 1.68 X 10^{-8} sec; <u>c</u> 0.

3-11 <u>a</u> 2.00 X 10^{27} electrons/m^3; <u>b</u> 1.73 X 10^{27} electrons/m^3.

3-12 <u>a</u> 11.6 ev; <u>b</u> 5.50 ev.

3-14 4.45 ev.

3-15 <u>a</u> 21.4 % ; <u>b</u> 2,370° K.

3-16 28.7 %

3-17 0.40 volts.

3-18 0.235 .

3-19 1.00 cm.

3-21 <u>a</u> 0.21 μa; <u>b</u> 0.20 v accelerating; <u>c</u> 9.3 X 10^{-6}

3-22 3,240 volts/m.

3-23 <u>a</u> $\cong$ 0 ; <u>b</u> $\cong$ 0 ; <u>c</u> 2.2 X 10^3 amperes/m^2; <u>d</u> 9.6 X 10^{10} amps/m^2.

3-26 5.3 %

3-27 7.7 %

3-29 <u>a</u> 51,000 ohm-cm; <u>b</u> 9.6 ohm-cm.

3-30 <u>a</u> 5.8 X 10^{12} electrons/cm^3, 1.06 X 10^{14} holes/cm^3, p-type; <u>b</u> p = n = 2.5 X 10^{13} cm^{-1}, intrinsic; <u>c</u> 1.43 X 10^{15} electrons/cm^3, 1.53 X 10^{15} holes/cm^3.

3-31 3.47 X 10^{17} holes/cm^3, 1.80 X 10^9 electrons/cm^3

3-32 1.65 X 10^{14} electrons/cm^3, 3.78 X 10^{12} holes/cm^3

3-33 52.3 ma/cm.

Chapter 4

4-1 1,900° K.

4-2 1.03 amps.

4-3 11.5 watts, 0.575 amp, 50 ma/watt.

4-4 1,200° K, 0.98 amp.

4-5 2.10 ev.

4-6 4.50 ev.

4-10 159 volts, 28.3 ma, 80 ma.

4-11 1.57×10^{-6} coulombs/m^3

4-12 242 volts.

4-13 25 v, 2.5 ma; b 150 v, 20 ma; c 20 ma, 100 v, 200 v.

4-14 1.56, 1.46.

4-15 a 2,330 watts/m^2; b 32 ; c 545° K, 1270° K.

4-16 400 volts.

4-17 0.70 amp/m^2

4-18 a 153 ma; b 150 μa; c 150 μa.

4-19 a 1.91 watts; b 83 μa; c 83 μa.

4-20 26.7 ma.

4-21 a 57.5 ma; b 136 volts.

4-25 a ≅ 280 ohms, ≅ 190 ohms; b 500 ohms, 350 ohms.

4-26 a 105 ma, 34 v; b 190 ma, 51 v; c 240 ma, 60 v; d 0 ma, 0 v.

4-27 a 124 ma, 58 v; b 200 ma, 80v; c 350 ma, 120 v; d 0 ma, 0 volts.

4-29 a 1,000 ohms, 667 ohms; b 1410 ohms, 940 ohms.

Chapter 5

5-1 a - 0.060 v0lts; b - 68.3 ; c 0.455 ma, 21.7 ma, 1.01 amp.

5-3 a 0.018, 4.98 volts; b 228 μa.

5-4 a 5×10^{44} amp; b 27.7 ma.

5-5 a 29.8 ma; b- 10 μa; c 29.8 ma, - 20 ma.

5-6 a 33.6 ohms; b 3.88 Meg.

5-7 70.8 μμf.

5-9 a 7.75×10^{-6} m; b 1.33×10^{-6} m; c 7.68×10^{-7} m; d 18.3, 107, 185 μμf.

5-13 a 0.149 volts; b 0.463 volts.

5-16 8.34 μa.

5-17 1,415

5-18 a 10.7 % ; b 15.4 % .

Chapter 6

6-1 _a_ 3.30×10^5 m/sec; _b_ no emission; _c_ 2.29×10^6 m/sec, 1.94×10^6 m/sec.

6-2 2.25 ev, 3.60×10^{-19} joules.

6-3 9.30 volts.

6-4 _a_ 4.42 ev; _b_ 2,800 A.

6-5 291 electrons.

6-6 1.17 μa.

6-11 _a_ 104 ft-candles; _b_ 2.7 Meg.

6-12 11.

6-13 5.95 .

6-14 _a_ 33.6 gauss; _b_ 1.43 cm.

Chapter 7

7-4 _a_ 6.5 ma; _b_ - 2.5 volts.

7-5 _a_ - 6 volts; _b_ 210 volts.

7-6 _a_ 31 ma; _b_ 2.5 K; _c_ 2.8 millimhos.

7-7 _a_ 1.31, 2.5×10^{-2} ; _b_ 7.55 K, 2.64 millimhos.

7-8 _a_ 7.3 K, 20.5, 2.8 m-mhos.

7-14 _a_ 23.0, 8.5, 2.7 ma; _b_ 250, 165, 115 volts; _c_ 7.5 K; _d_ 40 volts.

7-15 _a_ 310, 370, 490 v; 3.20, 2.53, 2.00, 0, 0.20, 0.50 .

7-17 _a_ 1.5 v; _b_ 99.5 v; _c_ 84.5 v; _d_ - 1.5 v.

7-18 _a_ 0, - 3.2 volts; _b_ 170 volts.

7-20 _a_ - 4.5 v; _b_ - 33.3 v; _c_ - 2 v.

7-22 0.70 K, 110 v.

7-23 _a_ 6.2 ma; _b_ 68.5 v.

Chapter 8

8-2 _a_ 1.49 K; _b_ 424 v; _c_ 5.25 v rms; _d_ 137.5° lag.

8-3 _a_ 3.33 K, 10 ; _b_ 950 v; _c_ 14.5 $\underline{/166°}$ v.

8-6 - 18.7 .

8-7 - 1.11 .

8-8 1.57 $\underline{/91.7^\circ}$.

8-10 10.6 $\underline{/-137.7^\circ}$.

8-11 $\underline{a}$ 3 K; $\underline{b}$ 8.35 ; $\underline{c}$ 174° lagging.

8-12 10.15 volts.

8-13 33.1 μa.

8-15 $E_0 = \dfrac{-\mu(\mu + 1)E_1 - \mu E_2}{R_L + (\mu + 2)r_p}$

8-16 $\underline{a}$ - 0.50; $\underline{b}$ 0.928 .

8-18 - 0.477E_1 + 0.161E_2

8-19 $\underline{a}$ 4.75 ; $\underline{b}$ 15 K.

8-24 $\underline{b}$ 13.5 Meg.

8-25 100.5 - j2.6 K.

8-30 $\underline{a}$ - 58.5 + j 8.78 , (1.32 + j 9.23) X 10^{-5} mhos;
- 59.8 , j 9.45 X 10^{-8} mhos; $\underline{b}$ 75.7 K, 147 μμf;
infinite, 151 μμf.

8-31 $\underline{a}$ Infinite, 38.5 μμf; 10.3 K, 28.0 μμf; $\underline{b}$ -20.8
Meg, 43.5 μμf; 8.83 K, 34.1 μμf.

8-32 5.22 K

8-33 $\underline{e}$ 0.0176 to 0.0557 μf; 1.56 to 0.52 K.

8-34 $\underline{b}$ $Y_i = Y_p + (1 + g_m R)Y_{LR}$; $\underline{c}$ $L_i = (1 + \alpha^2)/\omega \alpha g_m$,
$R_i = r_p(1 + \alpha^2)/(1 + \alpha^2 + \mu)$; $\underline{d}$ $(L_i)_{max} = 2/\omega g_m$,
$(R_i)_{max} = 2r_p/(2 + \mu)$; $\underline{e}$ 0.0578 to 0.0182 h;
1.56 to 0.52 K.

8-37 R between 1.58 and 7.9 Meg.

8-38 5 μa, 4.1 ma.

8-39 $\underline{a}$ 30 ft-c; $\underline{b}$ 5.0 ma; $\underline{c}$ outside the region
27.8°< α < 152.2° .

Chapter 9

9-2 $\underline{c}$ 0.138 μa, - 2.00 μa, - 0.116 v.

9-3 $\underline{a}$ 80 a,$\underline{b}$0.164 v, 0.0624 v, - 0.0624v, - 0.164
v, 0.102 v; $\underline{c}$ 0.167, 0.110, - 0.110, - 0.167,
0.057 volts; $\underline{d}$ V_C, V_E and V_{CE} are unchanged;
V_{CB}: - 0.0824, - 0.160 v; V_{EB}: -0.184, -0.217 v.

9-12 $\underline{a}$ - 2.05 v, - 20.5 μa, - 1.0 ma; $\underline{b}$ 24.2 .

9-13 $\underline{a}$ 3.7, 2.8 ma; $\underline{b}$ 1.2, 1.7 ma.

9-16 5.0 ma, 9.5 volts, 95 μa.

9-18 0.49, 8.31, 43.8; $\underline{b}$ 0.49, 1.20, 8.00 K.

9-19 $\underline{a}$ 3.31 ; $\underline{b}$ - 30 μa, -1.58 v, - 1.43 ma; $\underline{c}$ 3.92;
 - 1.59 v, - 1.42 ma, - 30μa.

Chapter 10

10-16 - 38.6 .

10-17 $\underline{a}$ 44.8 ohms, 1.80 K, 401 K; $\underline{b}$ 1.96 Meg, 40.8 K.
 1.025 K.

10-18 20.6 K.

10-19 $\underline{a}$ 10.3 K; $\underline{b}$ 205 ohms.

10-20 $\underline{a}$ 4 ohms; $\underline{b}$ 200 ohms.

10-21 $\underline{c}$ 45; 60 K.

10-24 $\underline{a}$ 26.9 K; 26.5 K.

10-26 0.263 .

10-30 + 0.88; 1.0 Meg; - 3 ohms; 7.33; 120 K.

10-31 60; 0.984; 2.5 Meg; 1,250 ohms; 40 ohms; 40 K.

10-32 39.6 ohms; 3.9 X 10^{-4}; - 0.98; 0.5 μmhos.

10-34 $y_{11} = (r_e + r_d)/\Delta \qquad y_{12} = - r_e/\Delta$
 $y_{21} = (a_e r_d - r_e)/\Delta \quad y_{22} = (r_b + r_e)/\Delta$
 where $\Delta = r_b(r_e + r_d) + r_e r_d(1 + a_e)$

Chapter 11

11-5 $\underline{a}$ 1 Meg; $\underline{b}$ 4.0 millimhos; $\underline{d}$ 3.4 millimhos.

11-6 $\underline{a}$ 5.5 m-mhos; $\underline{b}$ 2.73 K; $\underline{c}$ 66 ohms; $\underline{d}$ 23 K.

11-12 $\underline{a}$ 5.7 Mc; $\underline{b}$ 48 kc.

11-13 7.1 X 10^{-3} cm.

Chapter 12

12-1 3.23 X 10^{16} molecules/m^3.

12-2 490 mm Hg.

12-4 8.45 X 10^{20} molecules/m^3.

12-6 $\underline{a}$ 9.16 X 10^{-3} m; $\underline{b}$ 1.97 X 10^4 collisions/sec;
  $\underline{c}$ 1.35 amps/m^2.

12-7 3.98 X 10^6 collisions/sec.

12-8 72.

12-12 5,770 A.

12-13 1,560 A.

12-14 18,800, 6,600, 1,220, 1,030, 4,880 A.

12-15 $\underline{a}$ 22,200, 5,896 A; $\underline{b}$ 3.75 to 3.19 ev; 2.10 to
  0 ev.

12-17 $\underline{a}$ 8.61 X 10^5 m/sec; $\underline{b}$ no.

12-18 $\underline{a}$ 2.75 X 10^6 m/sec; $\underline{b}$ 5.20 X 10^{15} cps.

12-19 $\underline{a}$ 24,800 volts; $\underline{b}$ 0.207 A.

12-20 1.11 X 10^{-18} joules.

12-21 1.51 X 10^6 m/sec.

12-22 0.9 ev.

12-26 $\underline{a}$ 177.5 m^{-1}, 0.00091 ; $\underline{b}$ 3.94 cm, 630 volts.

12-31 4 X 10^6 volts/m.

12-36 1.8 amp/m^2.

12-37 $\underline{a}$ 106 volts; $\underline{b}$ 1.10 μa; $\underline{c}$ 3.44 cm^2.

12-38 0.0143 cm.

Chapter 13

13-1 $\underline{a}$ 662 cps; $\underline{b}$ 174 volts; $\underline{c}$ 400 ohms.

13-3 $\underline{a}$ 15 v; $\underline{b}$ 0.005 μf; $\underline{c}$ 200 ohms.

13-5 8 volts; 90 μμf.

13-6 Greater than 0.05 lumens.

13-7 $\underline{b}$ 21 volts, 2.3 volts.

13-10 $\underline{a}$ 43 volts; $\underline{c}$ 1 % ; $\underline{d}$ 417 cps.

13-11 $\underline{a}$ 200 ma; $\underline{b}$ 800 ma.

13-12 $\underline{a}$ 1.88 K; $\underline{b}$ 20 ma; $\underline{c}$ 20.2 ma.

13-13 $\underline{a}$ 2 K; $\underline{b}$ 215 to 285 volts.

13-16 $\underline{a}$ 20 volts; $\underline{b}$ 376 cps; $\underline{c}$ 12.5 % .

13-17 $\underline{a}$ 0.19 Meg; $\underline{b}$ 1 K.

13-18 $\underline{a}$ 112.5 volts; $\underline{b}$ 230 volts.

13-19 a 38 μa; b 96 vOlts; c 81 volts; d 0.24

Chapter 14

14-1 a 0.354 amps; b 0.113 amps; c 0.177 amp; d -113
volts; e 37.7 watts; f 33.8 % ; g 20 % .

14-4 a 101 ma; b 50.5 ma; c 358 volts; d 20.4 watts;
e 64.8 % ; f 25 % .

14-8 a 0.188 amp; b 0.298 amp; c - 94.3 v; d 156 v;
e 46.3 watts; f 38.2 % .

14-9 a 0.33 amp; b 45°, 135°; c 0.055 amp; d 0.12 amp;
e 0.045 watts; f 5.1 % .

14-10 a 7.65 ohms; b 4.17 % ; 17.3 ohms, 4.73 % ;
19.0 ohms, 5 % .

14-12 5.56 volts.

14-14 a E_m, $2E_m$; b $2E_m$, $2E_m$; c 0, $2E_m$.

14-15 b 0, $2E_m$, $2E_m$, $4E_m$.

14-18 a $I_{rms} = (E_m/2R_L)(-\frac{\pi - \varphi}{\pi} + \frac{sin2\varphi}{2\pi})^{\frac{1}{2}}$

b $E_{rms} = (E_m/2)\left[(\pi + \varphi)/\pi - sin2\varphi/2\pi\right]^{\frac{1}{2}}$

c $P = (E_m^2/4\pi R_L)(\pi - \varphi + \frac{1}{2}sin2\varphi)$

14-19 a 1.98 amps; b 1.85 amps; c 1.98 amps.

14-20 a $\pi/2$; b 0.0992 amp; c 0.198; e 60°, 0.149 amp,
0 to 0.198 amp.

14-21 b 0.192 amp; c 199 volts.

14-22 b 0.674 amp; c 0 ; d 0.337 amp.

14-23 c R: 0 to infinity; 0 to 0.99 amp.

14-24 b R = 0; 1.49 amps; c 0.745 amp; d 12.1 K;
e R infinite, 1.49 amps; 1.64 K, 0.745 amp.

14-25 b R infinite; 0.90 amp; c 306 volts.

14-26 a 70 volts; c 1.64 ma.

14-27 a 1.58 amps; b 1.65 amps; c 1.06 amps.

14-28 a 30°; c 0.158 amp.

14-29 a 4.10 amps; b 136 volts; c - 281 volts.

14-30 a 0.180 amp, 70.7 volts; b 0.168 amp; c -141.4
volts.

<u>14-35</u> <u>b</u> 0.126 amp; <u>c</u> 0.135 amp, 155 v, 423 v.

<u>14-37</u> $\underline{b_2}$ $I_{rms} = (E_m/\pi^{\frac{1}{2}}R_L)\left\{\left[\frac{1}{2} + (E_o/E_m)^2\right](\pi - \varphi_o - \varphi)\right.$

$$+ (1/4)(\sin 2\varphi_o + \sin 2\varphi)$$

$$\left. - (2E_o/E_m)(\cos\varphi_o + \cos\varphi)\right\}^{\frac{1}{2}}$$

$\underline{b_3} = (I_{dc}^2 R_L)/(I_{rms}^2 R_L + E_o I_{dc})$

<u>14-38</u> <u>b</u> 2.53 amps; <u>c</u> 1,300 watts.

<u>14-39</u> <u>b</u> 1.39 amp.

<u>14-42</u> <u>a</u> 700 watts; <u>b</u> 7.50 watts; <u>c</u> 8,400 watts; <u>d</u> 8.7×10^{-4}.

<u>14-44</u> <u>a</u> 1.25 amps; <u>b</u> 25 watts; <u>c</u> 422 watts; <u>d</u> 2.81 amps; <u>e</u> 397 watts.

<u>14-45</u> <u>a</u> 14.3 amps; <u>b</u> 8.59 amps; <u>c</u> 229 volts; <u>d</u> - 128 volts; <u>e</u> 215 v; <u>f</u> 129 v; <u>g</u> 129 watts; <u>h</u> 1,110 watts; <u>i</u> 3,220 watts; <u>j</u> 34.4 % .

<u>14-48</u> $(E_{dc} - E_o)(1 - 2\varepsilon^{-t/2RC})$ equals the rising portion of the voltage. E_{dc} is the d-c input voltage, E_o is the tube drop and R is the effective resistance reflected into each half of the output transformer. It is assumed that the input choke keeps the line current constant and that a steady voltage is reached in each half cycle.

<u>14-49</u> <u>c</u> 306 volts; <u>d</u> 159 volts; <u>f</u> 326 v, 176 v.

Chapter 15

<u>15-3</u> <u>a</u> 7.86 cps; <u>b</u> 267 kc; <u>c</u> 19.1; 25.6 dbv; <u>d</u> -21.45° <u>e</u> 36.8°.

<u>15-4</u> <u>a</u> 36.4; 31.2 dbv; <u>b</u> 69.5 kc; <u>c</u> 0.0031 µf.

<u>15-5</u> 39.3 cps to 10.2 kc.

<u>15-7</u> 10.2 cps, 39.4 kc.

<u>15-8</u> <u>a</u> 0.0621 µf; <u>b</u> 0.090 µf; <u>c</u> 317 kc; <u>d</u> 1,240.

<u>15-9</u> <u>a</u> 1,270; 62.1 dbv; <u>b</u> 305 cps; <u>c</u> 600 cps; <u>d</u> 636 kc; <u>e</u> 324 kc.

15-10 <u>a</u> 11.5 K; <u>b</u> 10.1, 102; <u>c</u> 18.3 μμf; <u>d</u> 15.8 cps;
    <u>e</u> 895 kc, 1.69 Mc; <u>f</u> 31.3 cps, 855 kc.

15-11 I. <u>a</u> 2.94 K; <u>b</u> 15.9 cps; <u>c</u> 3.22 Mc.
    II. <u>a</u> 23.3 K; <u>b</u> 15.8 cps; <u>c</u> 366 kc.

15-13 <u>a</u> 40.0 ohms, 54.6 ohms; <u>c</u> 1.35, 181; <u>d</u> 245.

15-14 4.0 cps, 0.30 cps, 10 kc.

15-15 <u>a</u> - 13.2, - 18.0; <u>b</u> - 13.2, - 43.2; <u>c</u> 569.

15-18 <u>a</u> 1.60 K; <u>b</u> - 11.9, - 5.11; <u>c</u> 9.3 μf.

15-19 <u>a</u> 24.2 K; <u>b</u> 60.5 K; <u>c</u> 131 ohms.

Chapter 16

16-3 <u>a</u> 20 ma rms; <u>b</u> 4.8 % ; <u>c</u> 44.5 ma.

16-4 <u>a</u> 7.7 K; <u>b</u> - 6 v; <u>c</u> 6.5 ma; <u>d</u> 11.8 % ; 9.25; in-
    finite power gain.

16-6 <u>a</u> 301 v; <u>b</u> 8.4 v; <u>c</u> 72 v; <u>d</u> 12 v; <u>e</u> 75 ma.

16-7 14.6 %

16-13 <u>a</u> 4.22 watts, 14.0 watts, 15.0 % ; <u>b</u> 260 v;
    <u>c</u> 4.22 watts, 14.0 watts, 23.2 % .

16-14 <u>a</u> 1.2 watts, 15 %, 18 % ; <u>b</u> 2.0 watts, 3.1 % ,
    11 % .

16-20 <u>a</u> 4 : 1; 5.52 milliwatts; <u>c</u> 0.037 % ; <u>d</u> 8 : 1,
    23.4 %.

16-21 <u>a</u> 3.8 watts; <u>b</u> ≅ 80 ma; <u>c</u> 20 watts.

16-22 <u>c</u> = 11 %, 0.5 %, 1 % ; ≅ 12 %, 8 %, 1 % .

16-23 21 %, 1.9 %, 0.95 %.

16-26 <u>a</u> 3.8 K; <u>b</u> 2.8 K.

16-27 <u>a</u> 3.0 K; <u>b</u> 4.6 watts; <u>c</u> 8.4 watts; <u>d</u> 35.4 % .

16-28 <u>a</u> 25.5 ma; <u>b</u> 34 ma; <u>c</u> 20 %, 1.9 %; <u>d</u> 2.3 watts;
    <u>e</u> 2.4 watts.

16-29 <u>a</u> 25.5 ma; <u>b</u> 28.8 ma; <u>c</u> 7 %, 11 %; <u>d</u> 4.4 watts;
    <u>e</u> 4.5 watts.

16-30 <u>b</u> 890 ohms, 330 v; 725 ohms, 250 v; <u>c</u> 30 v rms;
    <u>d</u> 3.28 watts; <u>e</u> 20 dbv, 38.1 dbp; 9.60 dbv,
    14.5 dbp; 29.6 dbv, 52.6 dbp.

16-34 <u>c</u> 2.9 watts; <u>d</u> 0 ; <u>e</u> 72 ma; <u>f</u> 16 % .

16-35 <u>c</u> 3.5 watts; <u>d</u> 2.5 % ; <u>e</u> 40 ma; <u>f</u> 35 %.

16-37 <u>c</u> 9.0 watts; <u>d</u> 8 % ; <u>e</u> 75 ma; <u>f</u> 40 % .

16-38 <u>a</u> 24 ; <u>b</u> 6.4 % ; <u>c</u> 62 ma.

16-39 <u>a</u> 45 watts; <u>b</u> 5.7 ma rms; <u>c</u> 197 ma; <u>d</u> 57 % .

16-43 0.246 watts.

16-44 <u>a</u> 9.6 %, 1.3 %, 0.3 %; <u>b</u> 1.36 watts; <u>c</u> 39 % .

16-47 <u>a</u> 4.30 watts; <u>b</u> 39 % ; <u>c</u> 6.2 % .

Chapter 17

17-1 <u>a</u> 9.90 ; <u>b</u> 101, 0.0099 ; <u>c</u> 0.198 cps, 5.05 Mc.

17-2 <u>a</u> 2.19 v; <u>b</u> 0.196 v.

17-3 <u>a</u> $- 2.07 \times 10^4$; 1.41 K; <u>b</u> $- 8.44$; 1.41 K.

17-6 <u>a</u> $e_{pn} = (e_a)\left[r_p + (\mu + 1)R_k\right]/\left[r_p + (\mu + 1) R_k + R_L\right]$

    <u>b</u> $e_{kn} = e_a R_k/\left[r_p + (\mu + 1)R_k + R_L\right]$

    <u>c</u> $e_{pn} = -(\mu + 1)R_L e_k/\left[r_p + R_L + (\mu + 1)R_k\right]$

    $e_{kn} = (r_p + R_L)e_k/\left[r_p + R_L + (\mu + 1)R_k\right]$

17-7 <u>a</u> 83.3 K; <u>b</u> + 48 v, $-$ 202 v; <u>c</u> 8.47 Meg; <u>d</u> 10.3 kv.

17-8 <u>a</u> $- 0.499$; <u>b</u> 0.931 .

17-12 $-$ 309 volts, 101 K.

17-13 $-$ 0.367 mv.

17-14 <u>a</u> 50 K, 46.7 K; <u>b</u> 0.19 % .

17-18 <u>a</u> 3.17 ; <u>b</u> 6.67 K.

17-24 126.5 v, $-$ 2 v, 1.9 ma.

17-25 3.6 ma, 201.9 v.

17-26 <u>a</u> 167 v.

17-27 <u>a</u> 12.7 ma; <u>b</u> 147 K; <u>c</u> $r_p/(\mu + 2) = 404$ ohms.

17-29 <u>b</u> 67 ohms.

17-32 $0.99 \angle 90.57°$

17-33 $e_o = - (E/RC)\left[t + (L/R)(\varepsilon^{-Rt/L} - 1)\right]$

Chapter 18

18-5 <u>a</u> $\beta = 1/3 + j(\omega RC - 1/\omega RC)$; <u>c</u> $f = 1/2_\pi RC$; <u>d</u> 3

18-6 $\beta = 1/(1 - \alpha^2 - j\,3\alpha)$ where $\alpha = 1/\omega RC$

18-7 <u>a</u> $\beta = 1/\left[1 - 5\gamma^2 + j(6\gamma - \gamma^3)\right]$ where $\gamma = \omega RC$

    <u>b</u> $Z_i = -(j/\omega C)\left[1 - 5\gamma^2 + j(6\gamma - \gamma^3)\right] /$

                $(3 - \gamma^2 + j\,4\gamma)$

    <u>c</u> $f = 6^{1/2}/2_\pi RC$; A $>$ 29

18-13 <u>a</u> $\omega = (LC)^{-1/2}$; $A_{min} = (R_3 + R)/R_3$; <u>b</u> $A_{min} = 1/\beta$

    where $\beta = (R_3)/(R_3 + R) - (R_2)/(R_1 + R_2)$

18-14 <u>a</u> 3,180 cps; <u>b</u> 3.12 K.

18-20 <u>a</u> $\omega^2 C_3 (L_1 + L_2) = \dfrac{1 + r_2/R_0}{1 + \dfrac{(r_1 L_2 + r_2 L_1)(1 + \mu)}{R_0(L_1 + L_2)}}$

    <u>b</u> $R_0 = \dfrac{(\mu L_1 - L_2)L_2}{(r_1 + r_2)C(L_1 + L_2)}$ for small r_1 & r_2.

18-21 $\omega^2 = (L_2 C_3)^{-1}$

18-22 <u>c</u> 1 % .

18-23 <u>a</u> 1.09 Mc; <u>b</u> 3.3 % ; <u>c</u> 410 .

18-27 3.41

18-29 0.134, 2.24, 0.368 .

Chapter 19

19-4 <u>a</u> 105° ; <u>b</u> 36°, 715 ma; <u>c</u> 93.8°, 58°, 1.75 amps

19-7 <u>a</u> $E_{dc} = E_m/(1 + I_{dc}/4fCE_m) - I_{dc}R$ where R is
the resistance of the inductor; <u>b</u> $r = 2^{1/2}(X_C/X_L)$.

19-8 <u>a</u> 30.2 henrys; <u>b</u> 345 volts.

19-10 <u>a</u> 0.88 v; <u>b</u> 0.077 v; <u>c</u> 0.044 v.

19-13 <u>a</u> 244 v; 0.031; <u>b</u> 481 v; 0.0353; <u>c</u> 244 v;
6.5 X 10^{-4}; <u>d</u> 244 v; 1.42 X 10^{-5}; <u>e</u> 400 v;
1.6 X 10^{-4}.

19-14 $r = 2^{1/2}(X_C/R_L)(X_{C1}/X_{L1})$

19-15 368 v; 0.515

19-16 250 ohms, 10.0 henrys.

19-17 a_1 270 v; a_2 424 v; a_3 270 v; a_4 424 v;
b_1 270 v; b_2 382 v; b_3 270 v; b_4 270 v;
c_1 const.; c_2 incr.; c_3 decr.; c_4 from zero current to the critical current r increases. Beyond the critical current r remains constant;
d 848 v for all cases.

19-18 316 v, 495 v.

19-19 382 v, 764 v.

19-20 + 316 v, - 990 v.

19-21 a - 424 v, + 424 v; b 848 v; c 270 v; d 402 v.

19-25 ≅ 15 volts.

ANSWERS TO PROBLEMS IN

VACUUM-TUBE AND SEMICONDUCTOR ELECTRONICS

By

Jacob Millman

Chapter 1

1-1 <u>a</u> 1.88×10^7 m/sec; <u>b</u> 3.26×10^5 m/sec.

1-2 <u>a</u> 8.52×10^{-10} sec; <u>b</u> 0.428 cm; <u>c</u> 285 volts.

1-3 <u>a</u> 1.065×10^{-9} sec; <u>b</u> 2.08×10^{-7} sec.

1-4 <u>a</u> 4.40×10^5 m/sec; <u>b</u> 0.732 cm; <u>c</u> 1.58×10^6 m/sec

1-5 <u>a</u> Yes; 625 volts.

1-6 <u>a</u> $x = \left(v_o - \dfrac{e}{m} \dfrac{E_m}{d\omega} \right)t + \dfrac{e}{m} \dfrac{E_m}{d\omega^2} \sin \omega t$;

<u>b</u> $\mathcal{E} = \left(\dfrac{v_o m E_m \omega}{ed}\right)^{\frac{1}{2}} \left(2 - \dfrac{v_o m d\omega}{e E_m}\right)^{\frac{1}{2}}$

1-7 <u>a</u> 3.0×10^{-8} sec; <u>b</u> 7.91×10^5 m/sec.

1-8 <u>a</u> 1.42 volts; <u>b</u> bottom; <u>c</u> 1.58×10^{-7} sec;
   <u>d</u> $- 4.09 \times 10^6$ m/sec.

1-9 0.354 cm.

1-10 $x = \dfrac{eE_o}{2md}(t - t_o)^2 - \dfrac{eE_1}{md\omega^2}(\sin\omega t - \sin\omega t_o) +$

   $v_o(t - t_o) + \dfrac{eE_1}{md\omega}(t - t_o)\cos\omega t_o$

1-11 4.02×10^{-8} sec.

1-12 <u>a</u> 2.00 cm; <u>b</u> $45°$.

1-13 <u>a</u> 5.84×10^{-9} sec; <u>b</u> 3.24 cm; <u>c</u> 0.24 cm.

1-14 $t = \dfrac{3d^{1/3}}{(2ek/m)^{\frac{1}{2}}}$

1-15 <u>a</u> 255,000 volts; <u>b</u> 2.24×10^8 m/sec.

1-16 4.92, 1.001.

McGraw-Hill Book Co., Inc.   Printed in U.S.A.

1-17 $v = at/(1 + a^2t^2/c^2)^{1/2}$

$x = -\dfrac{c^2}{a} \left[(1 + a^2t^2/c^2)^{1/2} - 1 \right]$ where $a \equiv e\mathcal{E}/m_o$

1-18 a 1.82 volts; b 128 kv.

1-19 4.46 X 10^{-4} m/sec.

1-20 3.84 gauss.

1-21 a $x = 1.16$ cm, $z = 0$; b $v_x = -2.97$ X 10^6 m/sec, $v_y = -5.14$ m/sec, $v_z = 0$.

1-22 a 0.338 cm; b 0.676 cm.

1-23 3.10n milliweber/m^2.

1-24 - 0.94, 2.50, - 1.18 cm.

1-25 a $5.0°$; b $0.80°$.

1-26 16.7, 33.4 gauss.

1-27 1.43, 2.86, 4.29 amps.

1-30 2.0 X 10^{-5} volts/m, 33.7 m/sec.

1-31 a 0.845, 1.6, 0.153 cm; b 4.81 X 10^6 m/sec, 10.4 X 10^6 m/sec, 1.79 X 10^6 m/sec; c 0.998, 1.6, 0.216 cm; 4.68 X 10^6, 7.14 X 10^6, 2.10 X 10^6 m/sec.

1-32 a 2 X 10^{-8} sec; b 0, 4, 3.82 cm; - 3 X 10^6, 0, 0 m/sec.

1-33 a $x = 0.226$ cm, $z = 0.207$ cm; b 0.348 X 10^6, 5.94 X 10^6, 3.98 X 10^6 m/sec.

1-34 61.8 cm.

1-35 122 gauss.

1-36 $n_\pi \mathcal{E} = Bv_o \cos\theta$ where n is an integer

1-37 a 3.52 X 10^{-7} sec; b 5, 11.9, 3.10 cm; c 2.27 X 10^{-7} sec; 3.60, 5, 1.23 cm; d 4.91 X 10^{-7} sec; 5.82, 23.2, 5 cm.

1-38 a 0.36 cm; b 3.54 X 10^{-9} sec.

1-39 a 47.7 gauss, out of the plane of the paper; b 4.20 X 10^6 m/sec.

1-40 a 1.75, 14, - 12.1 cm; b ions do not strike the plate; c 1.89, 22.5, - 14 cm.

1-44 a $v_{oz} = -\mathcal{E}_x/B$; b $y = \frac{1}{2}(e/m)\mathcal{E}_y t^2$, $z = -\mathcal{E}_x t/B$; c parabola.

2

PREFACE

AT COLUMBIA UNIVERSITY the undergraduate electrical engineering curriculum contains a two-year sequence in electronics. This book is intended to serve as the text covering approximately the first year of this course. The sequence then continues with a study of pulse circuits using about one-half of the material in Millman and Taub, "Pulse and Digital Circuits." The rest of the course is devoted to the teaching of communication circuits (a-m and f-m modulation and detection, etc.) and to electronic systems generally.

The text has three primary objectives. The first aim is to present a clear, consistent picture of the internal physical behavior of vacuum, gaseous, and semiconductor devices. A study of physical electronics leads to an appreciation of the usefulness and also the limitations of these devices. Furthermore, it is only through such basic knowledge, particularly of solid-state physics, that one can understand the new electronic devices that are being developed in the research and industrial laboratories.

The second goal is to integrate the study of semiconductor devices with that of vacuum tubes. The integrated nature of the presentation may be noted from the following. The consideration of the electronic theory of a metal leads immediately into a discussion of the nature of a semiconductor. After the analysis of the vacuum diode, the p-n junction is given careful consideration. The treatment of vacuum photocells is followed directly by that of semiconductor photodevices. A study of vacuum-triode characteristics and equivalent circuits is immediately followed by a corresponding analysis of transistors, etc.

The third objective is to teach electronic circuit theory in such a manner as to provide an intimate understanding of, and intuitive feeling for, each vacuum-tube or semiconductor device as a circuit element. Methods of analysis and characteristics which are common to many different devices and circuits are emphasized. For example, a good deal of attention is given to the concept of the load line and the bias curve, to input and output impedances, to small-signal equivalent circuits, to Thévenin's and Norton's representations, to large-signal nonlinear distortions, to frequency response, to the effects of feedback, etc. However, in order that the student may appreciate the different applications of the various circuits, the basic building blocks (such as rectifiers, untuned voltage

vii

amplifiers, audio power amplifiers, feedback amplifiers, and oscillators) are each discussed in a separate chapter. In designing or analyzing a complex electronic system it must be resolved into its component parts according to function, and hence the above arrangement of material is of practical importance.

Approximately 600 homework problems are included at the end of the book. Some of these are theoretical and others are numerical. They have been chosen to illustrate some physical principle, technique, or circuit discussed in the text.

Special mention must be made of the freedom with which the author drew on his text "Electronics" (by J. Millman and S. Seely, McGraw-Hill Book Company, Inc., New York, 1951). With the permission of Dr. Seely a great deal of the material parallels that in the earlier book.

The author is grateful to the many companies who supplied technical data and to the following persons for their assistance: Professor R. C. Retherford of the University of Wisconsin offered constructive criticism of "Electronics." Mr. M. G. Scheraga of the A. B. Du Mont Laboratories, Inc., supplied data on cathode-ray tubes and multiplier phototubes. Mr. L. B. Lambert of Columbia University and Mr. J. F. Ossanna, Jr., of the Bell Telephone Laboratories supplied valuable information on semiconductor electronics. Mr. P. T. Mauzey of Columbia University read a good deal of the text, and his criticism was most helpful.

The author is particularly indebted to Professor H. Taub of The City College of New York for many interesting discussions and for the suggestions he offered on many specific topics. A number of the sections are based upon notes written originally in collaboration with him.

The author wishes to express his gratitude to Mr. A. Vigants and, in particular, to Miss S. Silverstein of The City College of New York for their assistance in the preparation of the manuscript and to Mr. P. Demetriou and Mr. M. I. Rackman for their help with the instructor's problem solutions manual.

J. MILLMAN

CONTENTS

ix

CHAPTER 1

MOTION OF CHARGED PARTICLES IN ELECTRIC AND MAGNETIC FIELDS

THIS chapter will present the fundamental physical and mathematical theory of the motion of particles in electric and magnetic fields of force. The succeeding chapter will give many important applications based upon these analyses.

The motion of a charged particle in electric and magnetic fields will be discussed, starting with simple paths and proceeding to more complex motions. First a uniform electric field will be considered, and then the analysis will be given for motions in a uniform magnetic field. This discussion will be followed in turn by the motion in parallel electric and magnetic fields and in perpendicular electric and magnetic fields. Some discussion is included of nonuniform fields.

1-1. Charged Particles. The charge or quantity of negative electricity of the electron has been found by numerous experiments to be 1.602×10^{-19} coulomb. The values of many important physical constants are given in Appendix I. Some idea of the number of electrons per second that represent currents of the usual order of magnitude is readily possible. For example, since the charge per electron is 1.602×10^{-19} coulomb, the number of electrons per coulomb is the reciprocal of this number, or approximately 6×10^{18}. Further, since a current of 1 amp is the flow of 1 coulomb/sec, then a current of only 1 $\mu\mu$a (1 micromicroamp or 10^{-12} amp) represents the motion of approximately 6 million electrons per second. Yet a current of 1 $\mu\mu$a is so small that considerable difficulty is experienced in attempting to measure it.

In addition to its charge, the electron possesses a definite mass. A direct measurement of the weight of an electron cannot be made, but the ratio of the charge to the mass e/m has been determined by a number of experimenters using independent methods. The most probable value for this ratio is 1.759×10^{11} coulombs/kg. From this value of e/m and the value of e, the charge on the electron, the mass of the electron is calculated to be 9.1085×10^{-31} kg.

The charge of a positive ion will be an integral multiple of the charge of the electron, although it is of opposite sign. For the case of singly ionized

1

particles, the charge is equal to that of the electron.   For the case of doubly ionized particles, the ionic charge is twice that of the electron.

The mass of an atom is expressed as a number that is based on the choice of the atomic weight of oxygen equal to 16.   The mass of a hypothetical atom of atomic weight unity is, by this definition, one-sixteenth that of the mass of monatomic oxygen.   This has been calculated to be 1.660×10^{-27} kg.   Hence, *in order to calculate the mass in kilograms of any atom, it is necessary only to multiply the atomic weight of the atom by 1.660×10^{-27} kg.*   A table of atomic weights is given in Appendix III.

The radius of the electron has been estimated as 10^{-15} m and that of an atom as 10^{-10} m.   These are so small that all charges will be considered as mass points in the following sections.

1-2. The Force on Charged Particles in an Electric Field.   *The force on a unit positive charge at any point in an electric field is,* by definition, *the electric-field intensity $\mathcal{E}$ at that point.*   Consequently, the force on a positive charge q in an electric field of intensity $\mathcal{E}$ is given by $q\mathcal{E}$, the resulting force being in the direction of the electric field.   Thus,

$$\mathbf{f}_q = q\mathcal{E} \qquad \text{newtons} \tag{1-1}$$

where q is in coulombs and $\mathcal{E}$ is in volts per meter.   Boldface type will be employed wherever vector quantities (those having both magnitude and direction) are encountered.

The mks (meter-kilogram-second) rationalized system of units will be found most convenient for the subsequent studies.   Therefore, unless otherwise stated, this system of units will be employed.   Appendix IV lists the names of the most common quantities in the mks system.   Conversions from the electrostatic (esu) and the electromagnetic (emu) systems of units to the mks system of units are listed in Appendix II.

In order to calculate the path of a charged particle in an electric field, the force, given by Eq. (1-1), must be related to the mass and the acceleration of the particle by Newton's second law of motion.   Hence,

$$\mathbf{f}_q = q\mathcal{E} = m\frac{d\mathbf{v}}{dt} \qquad \text{newtons} \tag{1-2}$$

acceleration of particle

where m is in kilograms and $\mathbf{v}$ is in meters per second.   The solution of this equation, subject to appropriate initial conditions, will give the path of the particle resulting from the action of the electric forces.   If the magnitude of the charge on the electron is e, then the force on an electron in the field is

$$\mathbf{f} = -e\mathcal{E} \qquad \text{newtons} \tag{1-3}$$

The minus sign denotes that the force is in the direction opposite to the field.

In investigating the motion of charged particles which are moving in externally applied force fields of electric and magnetic origin, it will be implicitly assumed that the number of particles is so small that their presence will not alter the field distribution.

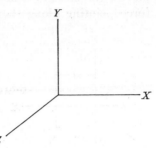

FIG. 1-1. Cartesian coordinate axes.

Since the electronic motion will take place, in general, in space, the motion will be specified mathematically with respect to the customary three mutually perpendicular Cartesian axes, illustrated in Fig. 1-1. The system of notation to be employed throughout the text is the following:

x = position of the particle along the X axis, m
y = position of the particle along the Y axis, m
z = position of the particle along the Z axis, m
v = magnitude of the velocity of the particle, m/sec
v_x, v_y, v_z = velocity components along the X, Y, and Z axes, respectively, m/sec
a = magnitude of the acceleration of the particle, m/sec^2
a_x, a_y, a_z = components of the acceleration along the X, Y, and Z axes, respectively, m/sec^2

Similar subscript notation will be used for other vector components. For example,

f_y = component of the force along the Y direction, newtons
$\mathcal{E}_z$ = component of the electric-field intensity along the Z axis, volts/m

It should be kept in mind that any or all of the foregoing quantities may be functions of time.

The exact motion of a particle in a given force field cannot be determined unless the initial values of velocity and displacement are known. The term "initial" represents the value of the specified quantity at the time $t = 0$. The subscript 0 will be used to designate such initial values. For example,

x_0 = initial displacement of the particle along the X axis
v_{0z} = initial component of velocity in the Z direction

In every case the path will be determined from an analysis of Eq. (1-2) subject to appropriate specified initial conditions.

1-3. Constant Electric Field. Suppose that an electron is situated between the two plates of a parallel-plate capacitor which are contained in an evacuated envelope, as illustrated in Fig. 1-2. A difference of potential is applied between the two plates, the direction of the electric field in the region between the two plates being as shown. If the distance between the plates is small compared with the dimensions of the plates, the electric field may be considered to be uniform, the lines of force pointing along the negative X direction. That is, the only field that is present is $\mathcal{E}$ along the $-X$ axis. It is desired to investigate the characteristics of the motion, subject to the initial conditions

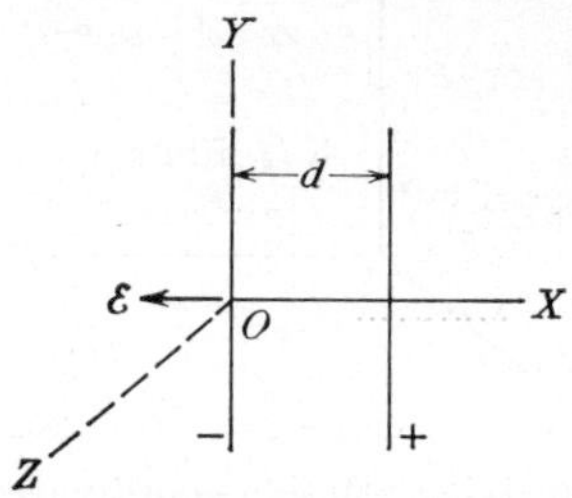

$$\left.\begin{array}{l} v_x = v_{0x} \\ x = x_0 \end{array}\right\} \quad \text{when } t = 0 \qquad (1\text{-}4)$$

This means that the initial velocity is chosen along $\mathcal{E}$, the lines of force.

Since there is no force along the Y or Z directions, Newton's law states that the acceleration along these axes must be zero. However, zero acceleration means constant velocity; and since the velocity is initially zero along these axes, the particle will not move along these directions. That is, the only possible motion is one-dimensional, and the electron moves along the X axis.

FIG. 1-2. The one-dimensional electric field between the plates of a parallel-plate capacitor.

Newton's law applied to the X direction yields

$$e\mathcal{E} = ma_x$$

or

$$a_x = \frac{e\mathcal{E}}{m} = \text{const} \qquad (1\text{-}5)$$

where $\mathcal{E}$ represents the *magnitude* of the electric field. This analysis indicates that the electron will move with a constant acceleration in a uniform electric field. Consequently, the problem is analogous to that of a freely falling body in the uniform gravitational field of the earth. The solution of this problem is given by the well-known expressions for the velocity and displacement, *viz.*,

$$v_x = v_{0x} + a_x t \qquad x = x_0 + v_{0x}t + \tfrac{1}{2}a_x t^2 \qquad (1\text{-}6)$$

provided that $a_x = \text{const}$, independent of the time.

It is to be emphasized that, if the acceleration of the particle is not a constant but depends upon the time, then Eqs. (1-6) are no longer valid. Under these circumstances the motion is determined by integrating the equations

$$\frac{dv_x}{dt} = a_x \quad \text{and} \quad \frac{dx}{dt} = v_x \qquad (1\text{-}7)$$

These are simply the definitions of the acceleration and the velocity, respectively. Equations (1-6) follow directly from Eqs. (1-7) by integrating the latter equations subject to the conditions of a constant acceleration.

Example. A sinusoidal potential having a frequency of 1 million cycles per second (1 megacycle) and whose maximum value is 10 volts is applied to the plates of a parallel-plate capacitor which are 2 cm apart. If an electron is released from one plate at an instant when the applied potential is zero and increasing in the positive direction, find the position of the electron at any subsequent time t. Assume that the initial velocity of the electron is 10^6 m/sec along the lines of force.

Solution. Assume that the plates are oriented with respect to a Cartesian system of axes as illustrated in Fig. 1-2. The magnitude of the electric-field intensity is

$$\varepsilon = \frac{10}{0.02} \sin 2\pi ft = 500 \sin (6.28 \times 10^6 t) \qquad \text{volts/m}$$

whence

$$a_x = \frac{dv_x}{dt} = \frac{f_x}{m} = \frac{e\varepsilon}{m} = 1.76 \times 10^{11} \times 500 \sin (6.28 \times 10^6 t)$$
$$= 8.80 \times 10^{13} \sin (6.28 \times 10^6 t) \qquad \text{m/sec}^2$$

This becomes, upon integration,

$$v_x = -1.40 \times 10^7 \cos (6.28 \times 10^6 t) + A$$

where A = constant of integration. A is determined from the initial condition that

$$v_x = 10^6 \text{ m/sec} \qquad \text{when } t = 0$$

Thus,

$$A = 1.50 \times 10^7 \text{ m/sec}$$

so that the velocity is given by

$$v_x = 1.50 \times 10^7 - 1.40 \times 10^7 \cos (6.28 \times 10^6 t) \qquad \text{m/sec}$$

Integration with respect to t, subject to the condition that $x = 0$ when $t = 0$, yields

$$x = 1.50 \times 10^7 t - 2.23 \sin (6.28 \times 10^6 t) \qquad \text{m}$$

1-4. Potential. The discussion to follow need not be restricted to uniform fields, but ε_x may be a function of distance. However, it will be assumed that ε_x is *not a function of time*. Then, from Newton's second law

$$-\frac{e\varepsilon_x}{m} = \frac{dv_x}{dt} \qquad \text{PROVIDED}$$

Multiply this equation by $dx = v_x \, dt$, and integrate. This leads to

$$-\frac{e}{m} \int_{x_0}^{x} \varepsilon_x \, dx = \int_{v_{0x}}^{v_x} v_x \, dv_x \qquad (1\text{-}8)$$

The definite integral

$$\int_{x_0}^{x} \varepsilon_x \, dx$$

is an expression for the work done by the field in carrying a unit positive charge from the point x_0 to the point x.

By definition, *the potential V of point x with respect to point x_0 is the work done against the field in taking a unit positive charge from x_0 to x.*   Thus,*

$$V \equiv - \int_{x_0}^{x} \mathcal{E}_x \, dx \qquad \text{volts} \tag{1-9}$$

By virtue of Eq. (1-9), Eq. (1-8) integrates to

$$eV = \tfrac{1}{2}m(v_x^2 - v_{0x}^2) \qquad \text{joules} \tag{1-10}$$

This shows that an electron that has "fallen" through a certain difference of potential V in going from point x_0 to point x has acquired a specific value of kinetic energy and velocity, independent of the form of the variation of the field distribution between these points and depending only upon the magnitude of the potential difference V.

Although this derivation supposes that the field has only one component, namely, $\mathcal{E}_x$ along the X axis, the final result given by Eq. (1-10) is simply a statement of the law of conservation of energy.   This is known to be valid even if the field is multidimensional.   This result is extremely important in electronic devices.   Consider any two points A and B in space, with point B at a higher potential than point A by V_{BA} volts. Stated in its most general form, Eq. (1-10) becomes

ONLY if GOOD if t = CONSTANT

$$qV_{BA} = \tfrac{1}{2}mv_A^2 - \tfrac{1}{2}mv_B^2 \qquad \text{joules} \tag{1-11}$$

where q is the charge in coulombs and v_A and v_B are the corresponding initial and final speeds in meters per second at the points A and B, respectively.   By definition, *the potential energy between two points equals the potential multiplied by the charge in question.*   Thus, the left-hand side of Eq. (1-11) is the *rise* in *potential energy* from A to B.   The right-hand side represents the *drop* in *kinetic energy* from A to B.   Thus, Eq. (1-11) states that the rise in potential energy equals the drop in kinetic energy, which is equivalent to the statement that the total energy remains unchanged.

It must be emphasized that *Eq. (1-11) is not valid if the field varies with time*.

If the particle is an electron, then $-e$ must be substituted for q.   If the electron starts at rest, then its final speed v, as given by Eq. (1-11) with $v_A = 0$, $v_B = v$, and $V_{BA} = V$, is

$$v = \left(\frac{2eV}{m}\right)^{\frac{1}{2}} \qquad \text{m/sec} \tag{1-12}$$

or

$$v = 5.93 \times 10^5 V^{\frac{1}{2}} \qquad \text{m/sec} \tag{1-13}$$

Thus if an electron "falls" through a difference of only 1 volt, its final speed is 5.93×10^5 m/sec, or approximately 370 miles/sec.   Despite this

* The symbol $\equiv$ is used to designate "equal to by definition."

tremendous speed, the electron possesses very little kinetic energy, because of its minute mass.

It must be emphasized that *Eq. (1-13) is valid only for an electron starting at rest*. If the electron does not have zero initial velocity or if the particle involved is not an electron, then the more general formula [Eq. (1-11)] must be used.

1-5. The ev Unit of Energy. The joule is the unit of energy in the mks system. In some engineering power problems this unit is very small, and a factor of 10^3 or 10^6 is introduced to convert from watts (joules per second) to kilowatts or megawatts, respectively. However, in other problems, the joule is too large a unit, and a factor of 10^{-7} is introduced to convert from joules to ergs. For a discussion of the energies involved in electronic devices even the erg is much too large a unit. This is not to be construed to mean that only minute amounts of energy can be obtained from electron tubes. It is true that each electron possesses a tiny amount of energy, but as previously pointed out (see Sec. 1-1), an enormous number of electrons is involved even in a small current so that considerable power may be represented.

The new unit of work or energy, called the *electron volt* (ev), is defined as follows:

$$1 \text{ ev} = 1.60 \times 10^{-19} \text{ joule}$$

Of course, any type of energy, whether it be electrical, mechanical, thermal, etc., may be expressed in electron volts.

The name "electron volt" arises from the fact that if an electron falls through a potential of one volt its kinetic energy will increase by the decrease in potential energy or by

$$eV = (1.60 \times 10^{-19} \text{ coulomb})(1 \text{ volt}) = 1.60 \times 10^{-19} \text{ joule} \equiv 1 \text{ ev}$$

However, as mentioned above, the electron-volt unit may be used for any type of energy and is not restricted to problems involving electrons.

The abbreviations Mev and Bev are used to designate 1 million and 1 billion electron volts, respectively.

It is common practice to designate energies in terms of "volts" although it must be clearly understood that the terms "volt" and "electron volt" are being used synonymously. For example, the phrase "a 5-volt mercury ion" means simply that the ion has a kinetic energy of $5 \times 1.60 \times 10^{-19}$ joule. Similarly, the phrase "0.1-ev thermal energy" means an amount of thermal energy of $0.1 \times 1.60 \times 10^{-19}$ joule.

1-6. Relationship between Field Intensity and Potential. The definition of potential is expressed mathematically by Eq. (1-9). If the electric field is uniform, the integral may be evaluated to the form

$$- \int_{x_0}^{x} \mathcal{E}_x \, dx = -\mathcal{E}_x(x - x_0) = V \qquad \text{volts}$$

which shows that the electric-field intensity resulting from an applied potential difference V between the two plates of the capacitor illustrated in Fig. 1-2 is given by

$$\mathcal{E}_x = \frac{-V}{x - x_0} = -\frac{V}{d} \quad \text{volts/m} \tag{1-14}$$

where d is the distance between plates, in meters.

In the general case where the field may vary with the distance, this equation is no longer true, and the correct result is obtained by differentiating Eq. (1-9).   It is

$$\mathcal{E}_x = -\frac{dV}{dx} \tag{1-15}$$

The minus sign shows that the electric field is directed from the region of higher potential to the region of lower potential.

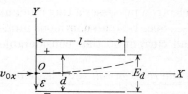

FIG. 1-3. Two-dimensional motion in a uniform electric field.

1-7. Two-dimensional Motion. Suppose that an electron enters the region between the two parallel plates of a parallel-plate capacitor which are oriented as shown in Fig. 1-3, with an initial velocity in the $+X$ direction. It will again be assumed that the electric field between the plates is uniform.   Then, as chosen, the electric field $\mathcal{E}$ is in the direction of the $-Y$ axis, no other fields existing in this region.

The motion of the particle is to be investigated, subject to the initial conditions

$$\left.\begin{array}{ll} v_x = v_{0x} & x = 0 \\ v_y = 0 & y = 0 \\ v_z = 0 & z = 0 \end{array}\right\} \quad \text{when } t = 0 \tag{1-16}$$

Since there is no force in the Z direction, the acceleration in that direction is zero.   Hence, the component of velocity in the Z direction remains constant.   Since the initial velocity in this direction is assumed to be zero, the motion must take place entirely in one plane, the plane of the paper.

For a similar reason, the velocity along the X axis remains constant and equal to v_{0x}.   That is,

$$v_x = v_{0x}$$

from which it follows that $\tag{1-17}$

$$x = v_{0x}t$$

On the other hand, a constant acceleration exists along the Y direction, and the motion is given by Eqs. (1-6), with the variable x replaced by y.

$$v_y = a_y t \qquad y = \tfrac{1}{2}a_y t^2 \tag{1-18}$$

where

$$a_y = -\frac{e\mathcal{E}_y}{m} = \frac{eE_d}{md} \qquad (1\text{-}19)$$

and where the potential across the plates is $V = E_d$. These equations indicate that in the region between the plates the electron is accelerated upward, the velocity component v_y varying from point to point, whereas the velocity component v_x remains unchanged in the passage of the electron between the plates.

The path of the particle with respect to the point O is readily determined by combining Eqs. (1-17) and (1-18), the variable t being eliminated. This leads to the expression

$$y = \left(\frac{1}{2}\frac{a_y}{v_{0x}^2}\right)x^2 \qquad (1\text{-}20)$$

which shows that the particle moves in a parabolic path in the region between the plates.

Example. A source introduces 500-volt potassium ions (atomic weight 40) into the region between two parallel plates oriented as shown in Fig. 1-4. The ions leave point A at an angle of 30 deg with the horizontal. There is a fixed voltage E_d across the plates, and the top plate is positive. Discuss the resultant motion. In particular, answer the following:

a. How long will it take an ion to reach point B on the negative plate at a distance of 10 cm away from A?

b. What must be the value of E_d, if the ion is to pass through B?

c. What is the highest point of ascent of the ion?

Solution. From the above theory, it follows that the path is a parabola as shown by the dashed curve in Fig. 1-4. This problem is analogous to the firing of a gun in the earth's gravitational field. The bullet will travel in a parabolic path, first rising because of the muzzle velocity of the gun and then falling because of the downward attractive force of the earth. Because of this analogy, the study of the motion of charged particles in a field of force is called *electron ballistics.* The source of the charged particles is called an "electron gun" or an "ion gun."

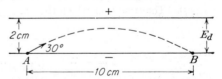

FIG. 1-4. The path of a charged particle in a uniform electric field is a parabola, provided that there exists a component of velocity normal to the field.

The initial components of velocity will now be found. The mass of the potassium ion is $40 \times 1.66 \times 10^{-27} = 6.64 \times 10^{-26}$ kg (see Sec. 1-1). The initial energy of the ion is $500 \times 1.60 \times 10^{-19} = 8.00 \times 10^{-17}$ joule. Hence the initial velocity is given by

$$\tfrac{1}{2}mv_0^2 = 8.00 \times 10^{-17} \text{ joule}$$

$$v_0^2 = \frac{2 \times 8.00 \times 10^{-17}}{6.64 \times 10^{-26}} = 2.41 \times 10^9 \text{ m}^2/\text{sec}^2$$

$$v_0 = 4.91 \times 10^4 \text{ m/sec}$$

$$v_{0x} = v_0 \cos 30° = 4.91 \times 10^4 \times 0.866 = 4.26 \times 10^4 \text{ m/sec}$$

$$v_{0y} = v_0 \sin 30° = 4.91 \times 10^4 \times 0.500 = 2.46 \times 10^4 \text{ m/sec}$$

a. Since the horizontal velocity is constant, the time t_1 to travel a distance $x = 10$ cm $= 0.10$ m is

$$t_1 = \frac{x}{v_{0x}} = \frac{0.1}{4.26 \times 10^4} = 2.35 \times 10^{-6} \text{ sec}$$

b. If the ion passes through point B, then its vertical displacement is zero. The vertical motion is one of constant acceleration of *magnitude a* downward with an initial velocity v_{0y} upward. Hence

$$v_y = v_{0y} - at$$

and

$$y = v_{0y}t - \tfrac{1}{2}at^2$$

If

$$y = 0 \quad \text{for } t = t_1$$

then

$$v_{0y}t_1 - \tfrac{1}{2}at_1{}^2 = 0$$

or

$$a = \frac{2v_{0y}}{t_1} = \frac{2 \times 2.46 \times 10^4}{2.35 \times 10^{-6}} = 2.09 \times 10^{10} \text{ m/sec}^2$$

But

$$a = \frac{qE_d}{md}$$

where q is the charge on the ion (which is equal to the electronic charge for a singly ionized atom) and d is the separation of the plates.   Hence

$$E_d = \frac{mda}{q} = \frac{6.64 \times 10^{-26} \times 0.02 \times 2.09 \times 10^{10}}{1.60 \times 10^{-19}}$$
$$= 173.5 \text{ volts}$$

c. At the highest point of ascent, the ion is traveling neither up nor down, whence $v_y = 0$. The time t_2 at which this takes place is given by

$$v_y = 0 = v_{0y} - at_2$$

or

$$t_2 = \frac{v_{0y}}{a} = \frac{2.46 \times 10^4}{2.09 \times 10^{10}} = 1.18 \times 10^{-6} \text{ sec}$$

Note that $t_2 = t_1/2$.   This means that the time of ascent is half the total time, or that the ion takes the same time traveling upward as it does traveling downward. The maximum vertical displacement y_m is given by

$$
\begin{aligned}
y_m &= v_{0y}t_2 - \tfrac{1}{2}at_2{}^2 \\
&= (2.46 \times 10^4)(1.18 \times 10^{-6}) - \tfrac{1}{2} \times 2.09 \times 10^{10} \times (1.18 \times 10^{-6})^2 \\
&= 2.90 \times 10^{-2} - 1.45 \times 10^{-2} = 1.45 \times 10^{-2} \text{ m} = 1.45 \text{ cm}
\end{aligned}
$$

The same result may be obtained by using the theorem of the conservation of energy. If the potential energy is taken as zero at point A, it is $y_m \mathcal{E}_y q$ at the highest point, or

$$y_m \frac{E_d}{d} q = \frac{173.5 \times 1.60 \times 10^{-19}}{0.02} \qquad y_m = 1.39 \times 10^{-15} y_m$$

This must equal the change in kinetic energy.   Since the horizontal component of velocity is unchanged and since there is no vertical component of velocity at the highest point, then the change in kinetic energy just equals

$$\tfrac{1}{2}mv_{0y}{}^2 = \tfrac{1}{2}(6.64 \times 10^{-26})(2.46 \times 10^4)^2 = 2.02 \times 10^{-17}$$
$$y_m = \frac{2.02 \times 10^{-17}}{1.39 \times 10^{-15}} = 1.45 \times 10^{-2} \text{ m} = 1.45 \text{ cm}$$

as above.

1-8. Relativistic Variation of Mass with Velocity.   The theory of relativity postulates an equivalence of mass and energy according to the relationship

$$W = mc^2 \tag{1-21}$$

where W is the total energy in joules, m is the mass in kilograms, and c is the velocity of light in vacuum, in meters per second.   According to this theory, the mass of a particle will increase with its energy and hence with its speed.

If an electron starts at the point A with zero velocity and reaches the point B with a velocity v, then the increase in energy of the particle must be given by the expression eV joules, where V is the difference of potential between the points A and B.   Hence,

$$eV = mc^2 - m_0c^2 \quad \text{joules} \tag{1-22}$$

where m_0c^2 is the energy possessed at the point A.   The quantity m_0 is known as the *rest mass* or the *electrostatic mass* of the particle and is a constant independent of the velocity.   The total mass m of the particle is given by

$$m = \frac{m_0}{\sqrt{1 - v^2/c^2}} \tag{1-23}$$

This result, which was originally derived by Lorentz and then by Einstein as a consequence of the theory of special relativity, predicts an increasing mass with an increasing velocity, the mass approaching an infinite value as the velocity of the particle approaches the velocity of light.   From Eqs. (1-22) and (1-23), the decrease in potential energy, or, equivalently, the increase in kinetic energy, is

$$eV = m_0c^2 \left(\frac{1}{\sqrt{1 - v^2/c^2}} - 1 \right) \tag{1-24}$$

This expression enables one to find the velocity of an electron after it has fallen through any potential difference V.   By defining the quantity v_N as the velocity that would result if the relativistic variation in mass were neglected, *i.e.*,

$$v_N \equiv \sqrt{\frac{2eV}{m_0}} \tag{1-25}$$

then Eq. (1-24) can be solved for *v, the true velocity of the particle.* The result is

$$v = c \left[1 - \frac{1}{(1 + v_N^2/2c^2)^2} \right]^{\frac{1}{2}} \tag{1-26}$$

This expression looks imposing at first glance. It should, of course, reduce to $v = v_N$ for small velocities. That it does so is seen by applying the binomial expansion to Eq. (1-26). The result becomes

$$\boldsymbol{v = v_N \left(1 - \frac{3}{8} \frac{v_N^2}{c^2} + \cdots \right)} \tag{1-27}$$

From this expression, it is seen that, if the speed of the particle is much less than the speed of light, the second and all subsequent terms in the expansion can be neglected, and then $v = v_N$, as it should. This equation also serves as a criterion to determine whether the simple classical expression or the more formidable relativistic one must be used in any particular case. For example, if the speed of the electron is one-tenth of the speed of light, Eq. (1-27) shows that an error of only three-eighths of 1 per cent will result if the speed is taken as v_N instead of v.

For an electron, the potential difference through which the particle must fall in order to attain a velocity of $0.1c$ is readily found to be 2,560 volts. Thus, if an electron falls through a potential in excess of about 3 kv, the relativistic corrections should be applied. If the particle under question is not an electron, the value of the nonrelativistic velocity is first calculated. If this is greater than $0.1c$, then the calculated value of v_N must be substituted in Eq. (1-26) and the true value of v then calculated. In cases where the speed is not too great, the simplified expression (1-27) may be used.

The accelerating potential in high-voltage cathode-ray tubes is sufficiently high to require that relativistic corrections be made in order to calculate the velocity and mass of the particle. Other devices employing potentials that are high enough to require these corrections are X-ray tubes, the cyclotron, the betatron, and other particle-accelerating machines. Unless specifically stated otherwise, nonrelativistic conditions will be assumed in what follows.

1-9. Force in a Magnetic Field. To investigate the force on a moving charge in a magnetic field, the well-known "motor law" is recalled. It has been verified by experiment that, if a conductor of length L meters, carrying a current of I amperes, is situated in a magnetic field of intensity B webers per square meter,* the force acting on this conductor is BIL newtons. This assumes that the directions of $\mathbf{I}$ and $\mathbf{B}$ are perpendicular to each other. The direction of this force is perpendicular to the plane of $\mathbf{I}$ and $\mathbf{B}$ and has the direction of advance of a right-handed screw which is placed at O and is rotated from $\mathbf{I}$ to $\mathbf{B}$ through 90 deg, as illustrated in Fig. 1-5. *If $\mathbf{I}$ and $\mathbf{B}$ are not perpendicular to each other, then only the component of $\mathbf{I}$ perpendicular to $\mathbf{B}$ contributes to the force.* This simple way of finding the direction of the force is equivalent to the well-known left-hand rule of Fleming.

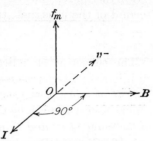

Fig. 1-5. Pertaining to the determination of the direction of the force f_m on a charged particle in a magnetic field.

Some caution must be exercised with regard to the meaning of Fig. 1-5. If the particle under consideration is a positive ion, then $\mathbf{I}$ is to be taken along the direction of its motion. This is so because the conventional direction of the current is taken in the direction of flow of positive charge. Since the current is generally due to the flow of electrons, the direction of $\mathbf{I}$ is to be taken as opposite to the direction of the motion of the electrons. If, therefore, a negative charge moving with a velocity $\mathbf{v}^-$ is under consideration, one must first draw $\mathbf{I}$ antiparallel to $\mathbf{v}^-$ as shown and then apply the "direction rule."

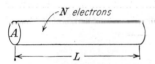

Fig. 1-6. Pertaining to the determination of the magnitude of the force on a charged particle in a magnetic field.

If N electrons are contained in a length L of conductor (see Fig. 1-6) and if it takes an electron a time T seconds to travel a distance of L meters in the conductor, then the total number of electrons passing through any cross section of wire in unit time is N/T. Thus the total charge per second passing any point, which is the current, by definition, is

$$I = \frac{Ne}{T} \quad \text{amp} \quad (1\text{-}28)$$

The force on a length L meters (or the force on the N conduction charges

---

* One weber per square meter equals 10^4 gauss. A unit of more practical size in most applications is the milliweber per square meter, which equals 10 gauss. Other conversion factors are given in Appendix II.

The SUN Commission of the International Union of Pure and Applied Physics recommends the "weber per square meter," whereas the International Electrotechnical Commission has adopted the "tesla" for the unit of magnetic-field intensity.[1]†

† Superscript numbers refer to numbered References at the end of each chapter.

contained therein) is

$$BIL = \frac{BNeL}{T} \quad \text{newtons} \tag{1-29}$$

Furthermore, since L/T is the average, or *drift*, speed v meters per second of the electrons, then the force per electron is

$$f_m = evB \quad \text{newtons} \tag{1-30}$$

The subscript m indicates that the force is of magnetic origin.   To summarize: *The force on a negative charge e (coulombs) moving with a component of velocity v^- (meters per second) normal to a field B (webers per square meter) is given by ev^-B (newtons) and is in a direction perpendicular to the plane of v^- and B, as noted in Fig. 1-5.*

1-10. Current Density.   Before proceeding with the discussion of possible motions of charged particles in a magnetic field, it is convenient to introduce the concept of current density.   This concept will be very useful in many later applications.   By definition, the current density, denoted by the symbol J, is the current per unit area of the conducting medium.   That is, assuming a uniform current distribution,

$$J \equiv \frac{I}{A} \quad \text{amp/m}^2 \tag{1-31}$$

where A is the cross-sectional area of the conductor.   This becomes, by Eq. (1-28),

$$J = \frac{Ne}{TA}$$

But it has already been pointed out that $T = L/v$.   Then

$$J = \frac{Nev}{LA} \tag{1-32}$$

From Fig. 1-6 it is evident that LA is simply the volume containing the N electrons, and so N/LA is the electron concentration n.   Thus

$$n \equiv \frac{N}{LA} \quad \text{electrons/m}^3 \tag{1-33}$$

and Eq. (1-32) reduces to

$$J = nev = \rho v \quad \text{amp/m}^2 \tag{1-34}$$

where $\rho \equiv ne$ is the charge density, in coulombs per cubic meter, and v is in meters per second.

This derivation is independent of the form of the conducting medium. Consequently, Fig. 1-6 does not necessarily represent a wire conductor. It may represent equally well a portion of a gaseous-discharge tube or a volume element in the space-charge cloud of a vacuum tube.   Furthermore, neither ρ nor v need be constant but may vary from point to point in space or may vary with time. Numerous occasions will arise later in the text when reference will be made to Eq. (1-34).

1-11. Motion in a Magnetic Field. The path of a charged particle that is moving in a magnetic field will be investigated. Consider an electron to be placed in the region of the magnetic field. If the particle is at rest, $f_m = 0$ and the particle remains at rest. If the initial velocity of the particle is along the lines of the magnetic flux, then there is no force acting on the particle, in accordance with the rule associated with Eq. (1-30). Hence, *a particle whose initial velocity has no component normal to a uniform magnetic field will continue to move with constant speed along the lines of flux.*

Now consider an electron moving with a speed v_0 to enter a constant uniform magnetic field normally as shown in Fig. 1-7. Since the force $\mathbf{f}_m$ is perpendicular to $\mathbf{v}$ and so to the motion at every instant, then *no work is done on the electron.* This means that its kinetic energy is not increased, and so its speed remains unchanged. Further, since $\mathbf{v}$ and $\mathbf{B}$ are each constant in magnitude, then $\mathbf{f}_m$ is constant in magnitude and perpendicular to the direction of motion of the particle. This type of force results in motion in a circular path with constant speed. It is analogous to the problem of a mass tied to a rope and twirled around with constant speed. The force (which is the tension in the rope) remains constant in magnitude and is always directed toward the center of the circle, and so is normal to the motion.

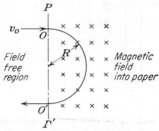

FIG. 1-7. Circular motion of an electron in a transverse magnetic field.

To find the radius of the circle, it is recalled that a particle moving in a circular path with a constant speed v has an acceleration toward the center of the circle of magnitude v^2/R, where R is the radius of the path. Then

$$\frac{mv^2}{R} = evB$$

from which

$$R = \frac{mv}{eB} \quad \text{m} \tag{1-35}$$

The corresponding angular velocity is given by

$$\omega = \frac{v}{R} = \frac{eB}{m} \quad \text{rad/sec} \tag{1-36}$$

The time for one complete revolution, called the "period," is

$$T = \frac{2\pi}{\omega} = \frac{2\pi m}{eB} \quad \text{sec} \tag{1-37}$$

For an electron, this reduces to

$$T = \frac{3.57 \times 10^{-11}}{B} \quad \text{sec} \quad \quad \text{(1-38)}$$

In these equations, e/m is in coulombs per kilogram and B in webers per square meter.

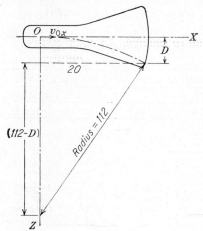

It is noticed that the radius of the path is directly proportional to the speed of the particle. Further, *the period and the angular velocity are independent of speed or radius.* This means, of course, that faster-moving particles will traverse larger circles in the same time that a slower particle moves in its smaller circle. This very important result is the basis of operation of numerous devices, for example, the cyclotron and magnetic focusing apparatus.

FIG. 1-8. The circular path of an electron in a cathode-ray tube resulting from the earth's transverse magnetic field (normal to the plane of the paper). This figure is not drawn to scale.

Example. Calculate the deflection of a cathode-ray beam caused by the earth's magnetic field. Assume that the tube axis is so oriented that it is normal to the field, the strength of which is 0.6 gauss. The anode potential is 400 volts; the anode-screen distance is 20 cm (see Fig. 1-8).

Solution. According to Eq. (1-13), the velocity of the electrons will be

$$v_{0x} = 5.93 \times 10^5 \sqrt{400} = 1.19 \times 10^7 \text{ m/sec}$$

Since 1 weber/m^2 = 10^4 gauss, then $B = 6 \times 10^{-5}$ weber/m^2. From Eq. (1-35) the radius of the circular path is

$$R = \frac{v_{0x}}{(e/m)B} = \frac{1.19 \times 10^7}{1.76 \times 10^{11} \times 6 \times 10^{-5}} = 1.12 \text{ m} = 112 \text{ cm}$$

Furthermore, it is evident from the geometry of Fig. 1-8 that (in centimeters)

$$112^2 = (112 - D)^2 + 20^2$$

from which it follows that

$$D^2 - 224D + 400 = 0$$

The evaluation of D from this expression yields the value $D = 1.8$ cm.

This example indicates that the earth's magnetic field can have a large effect on the position of the cathode-beam spot in a low-voltage cathode-ray tube. If the anode voltage is higher than the value used in this example or if the tube is not oriented normal to the field, the deflection will be less than that calculated. In any event, this calculation indicates the advisability of carefully shielding a cathode-ray tube from stray magnetic fields.

1-12. Magnetic Focusing.   As another application of the theory developed in the previous section, one method of measuring e/m will be discussed.   The essentials of a cathode-ray tube needed for this purpose are shown in Fig. 1-9.   The hot cathode K emits electrons which are accelerated toward the anode by the potential E_a.   Those electrons which are not collected by the anode pass through the tiny anode hole and strike the end of the glass envelope.   This has been coated with a material that fluoresces when bombarded by electrons.   Thus the positions where the electrons strike the screen are made visible to the eye.   A more detailed discussion of the cathode-ray tube will be given in the next chapter.

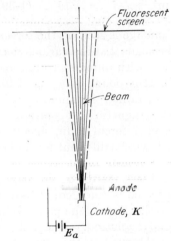

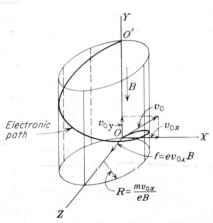

Fig. 1-9. The cathode, anode, and fluorescent screen of a cathode-ray tube. The unfocused electron beam is shown.

Fig. 1-10. The helical path of an electron introduced at an angle (not 90 deg) with a constant magnetic field.

Imagine that the cathode-ray tube is placed in a constant longitudinal magnetic field, the axis of the tube coinciding with the direction of the magnetic field.   A magnetic field of the type here considered is obtained through the use of a long solenoid, the tube being placed within the coil. An inspection of Fig. 1-10 reveals the motion.   The Y axis represents the axis of the cathode-ray tube.   The origin O is the point at which the electrons emerge from the anode.   The velocity at the origin is $\mathbf{v}_0$, the initial transverse velocity due to the mutual repulsion of the electrons being v_{0x}. It will now be shown that the resulting motion is a helix, as illustrated.

The electronic motion can most easily be analyzed by resolving the velocity into two components v_y and v_θ along and transverse to the magnetic field, respectively.   Since <u>the force is perpendicular to $\mathbf{B}$, then there is no acceleration in the Y direction.</u>   *Hence v_y is constant and equal to v_{0y}.* A force $ev_\theta B$ normal to the path will exist, resulting from the transverse velocity. *This force gives rise to circular motion,* the radius of the circle being mv_θ/eB, with v_θ a constant, and equal to v_{0x}. *The resultant path is a helix* whose axis is parallel to the Y axis and displaced from it by a distance R along the Z axis, as illustrated.

The pitch of the helix, which is defined as the distance traveled along the direction of the magnetic field in one revolution, is given by

$$p = v_{0y}T$$

where T is the period, or the time for one revolution. It follows from Eq. (1-37) that

$$p = \frac{2\pi m}{eB} v_{0y} \quad \text{m} \tag{1-39}$$

If the electron beam is defocused, then a smudge is seen on the screen when the applied magnetic field is zero. This means that the various electrons in the beam pass through the anode hole with different transverse velocities v_{0x} and so strike the screen at different points (see Fig. 1-9). This accounts for the appearance of a broad, faintly illuminated area instead of a bright point on the screen. As the magnetic field is increased from zero, the electrons will move in helixes of different radii, since the velocity v_{0x} that controls the radius of the path will be different for different electrons. However, the period or the time to trace out the path is independent of v_{0x}, and so the period will be the same for all electrons. If, then, the distance from the anode to the screen is made equal to one pitch, all the electrons will be brought back to the Y axis (the point O' in Fig. 1-10) since they all will have made just one revolution. Under these conditions an image of the anode hole will be observed on the screen.

As the field is increased from zero, the smudge on the screen resulting from the defocused beam will contract and will become a tiny sharp spot (the image of the anode hole) when a critical value of the field is reached. This critical field is that which makes the pitch of the helical path just equal to the anode-screen distance, as discussed above. By continuing to increase the strength of the field beyond this critical value, the pitch of the helix decreases, and the electrons travel through more than one complete revolution. The electrons then strike the screen at various points so that a defocused spot is again visible. A magnetic-field strength will ultimately be reached at which the electrons make two complete revolutions in their path from the anode to the screen, and once again the spot will be focused on the screen. This process may be continued, numerous foci being obtainable. In fact, the current rating of the solenoid is the factor that generally furnishes a practical limitation to the order of the focus.

The foregoing considerations may be generalized in the following way: If the screen is perpendicular to the Y axis at a distance L from the point of emergence of the electron beam from the anode, then, for an anode-cathode potential equal to E_a, the electron beam will come to a focus at the center of the screen provided that L is an integral multiple of p. Under these conditions, Eq. (1-39) may be rearranged to read

$$\frac{e}{m} = \frac{8\pi^2 E_a n^2}{L^2 B^2} \quad \text{coulombs/kg} \qquad (1\text{-}40)$$

where n is an integer representing the order of the focus. It is assumed, in this development, that $eE_a = \frac{1}{2}mv_{0y}^2$ or that the only effect of the anode potential is to accelerate the electron along the tube axis. This implies that the transverse velocity v_{0x}, which is variable and unknown, is negligible in comparison with v_{0y}. This is a justifiable assumption.

This arrangement was suggested by Busch[2] and has been used[3] to measure the ratio e/m for electrons very accurately.

1-13. Parallel Electric and Magnetic Fields. Consider the case where both electric and magnetic fields exist simultaneously, the fields being in the same or in opposite directions. If the initial velocity of the electron either is zero or is directed along the fields, then *the magnetic field exerts no force on the electron* and the resultant motion depends solely upon the electric-field intensity $\mathcal{E}$. In other words, the electron will move in a direction parallel to the fields with a constant acceleration. If the fields are chosen as in Fig. 1-11, the complete motion is specified by

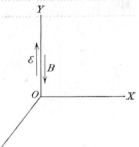

Fig. 1-11. Parallel electric and magnetic fields.

$$v_y = v_{0y} - at \qquad y = v_{0y}t - \tfrac{1}{2}at^2 \qquad (1\text{-}41)$$

where $a = e\mathcal{E}/m$ is the magnitude of the acceleration. The negative sign results from the fact that the direction of the acceleration of an electron is opposite to the direction of the electric-field intensity $\mathcal{E}$.

If, initially, a component of velocity v_{0x} perpendicular to the magnetic field exists, this component, together with the magnetic field, will give rise to circular motion, the radius of the circular path being independent of $\mathcal{E}$. However, because of the electric field $\mathcal{E}$, the velocity along the field changes with time. Consequently, the resulting path is helical with a pitch that changes with the time. That is, the distance traveled along the Y axis per revolution increases with each revolution.

Example. Given a uniform electric field of 10^4 volts/m parallel to and opposite in direction to a magnetic field of 5 milliwebers/m². An electric gun, directed at an angle of 30 deg with the direction of the electric field, introduces 400-volt electrons into the region of the fields (see Fig. 1-12).   Give a quantitative description of the electronic motion.

Solution.   As discussed above, the path is a helix of variable pitch.   The plane determined by $\mathcal{E}$ and v_0 is chosen as the XY plane.   From Eq. (1-13),

$$v_0 = 5.93 \times 10^5 \sqrt{400} = 1.19 \times 10^7 \text{ m/sec}$$
$$v_{0x} = v_0 \sin 30° = 5.93 \times 10^6 \text{ m/sec}$$
$$v_{0y} = v_0 \cos 30° = 1.03 \times 10^7 \text{ m/sec}$$

$$a = \frac{e\mathcal{E}}{m} = 1.76 \times 10^{15} \text{ m/sec}^2$$

along the $-Y$ direction.   Hence, from Eq. (1-35),

$$R = \frac{mv_{0x}}{eB} = \frac{5.93 \times 10^6}{1.76 \times 10^{11} \times 5 \times 10^{-3}} = 6.75 \times 10^{-3} \text{ m}$$

Thus, the projection of the path on the XZ plane is a circle of radius 0.675 cm.   An application of the direction rule shows that the circle is being traversed in the counterclockwise direction (when looking along the $+Y$ direction).   The path is essentially that illustrated in Fig. 1-10 except that the velocity along the fields is not constant but is given by Eqs. (1-41), *viz.*,

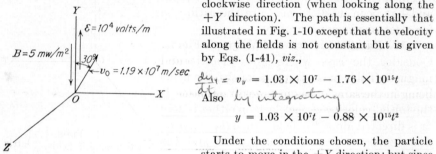

$$\frac{dy}{dt} = v_y = 1.03 \times 10^7 - 1.76 \times 10^{15}t$$

Also by integrating

$$y = 1.03 \times 10^7 t - 0.88 \times 10^{15}t^2$$

FIG. 1-12. A problem illustrating helical electronic motion of variable pitch.

Under the conditions chosen, the particle starts to move in the $+Y$ direction; but since the acceleration is along the $-Y$ direction, the velocity will shortly be reduced to zero, and the particle will then reverse its Y-directed motion.   This reversal will occur at the time t' for which $v_y = 0$, namely,

$$t' = \frac{1.03 \times 10^7}{1.76 \times 10^{15}} = 5.86 \times 10^{-9} \text{ sec}$$

The distance traveled in the $+Y$ direction to the position at which the reversal occurs is

$$y' = 1.03 \times 10^7 \times 5.86 \times 10^{-9} - 0.88 \times 10^{15}(5.86 \times 10^{-9})^2$$
$$= (6.04 - 3.04) \times 10^{-2} \text{ m} = 3.00 \text{ cm}$$

It should be kept in mind that the term "reversal" refers only to the Y-directed motion, not to the direction in which the electron traverses the circular component of its path.   The rotation in this circular component is determined entirely by the quantities B and v_{0x}.   Furthermore, only one reversal is made, the Y-directed motion continuing in the $-Y$ direction with an ever-increasing linear velocity, even though the angular velocity remains constant and equal to

$$\omega = \frac{eB}{m} = 1.76 \times 10^{11} \times 5 \times 10^{-3} = 8.80 \times 10^8 \text{ rad/sec}$$

By using either the relationship $T = 2\pi/\omega$ or Eq. (1-38), there is obtained $T = 7.14 \times 10^{-9}$ sec for the period.

Since $t' < T$, then less than one revolution is made before the reversal.

The point P' in space at which the reversal takes place is obtained by considering the projection of the path in the XZ plane (since the Y coordinate y' is already known). Refer to Fig. 1-13. The angle θ through which the electron has rotated about the Y axis is

$$\theta = \omega t' = 8.80 \times 10^8 \times 5.86 \times 10^{-9}$$
$$= 5.17 \text{ rad} = 296°$$

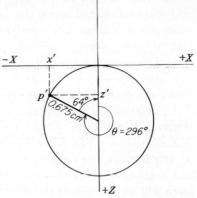

From the figure it is clear that

$$x' = -0.675 \sin 64° = -0.608 \text{ cm}$$

and

$$z' = 0.675 - 0.675 \cos 64° = 0.317 \text{ cm}$$

The time t'' that it takes the electron to return to the XZ plane is obtained by setting y equal to zero. Thus,

$$t'' = \frac{1.03 \times 10^7}{0.88 \times 10^{15}} = 1.17 \times 10^{-8} \text{ sec}$$

FIG. 1-13. The projection of the path in the XZ plane is a circle.

Since $t'' = 2t'$, it takes the electron just as long to travel from the XZ plane to the point of reversal as it does to return to this plane. The point to which the electron returns in the XZ plane may be obtained by using for θ the value $\omega t'' = 2\omega t' = 592°$ in Fig. 1-13. The result is

$$x'' = -0.532 \text{ cm} \qquad \text{and} \qquad z'' = 1.09 \text{ cm}$$

It should be noted that the electron does *not* return to the origin.

1-14. Perpendicular Electric and Magnetic Fields. The directions of the fields are shown in Fig. 1-14. The magnetic field is directed along the $-Y$ axis, and the electric field is directed along the $-X$ axis. The force on an electron due to the electric field is directed along the $+X$ axis. Any force due to the magnetic field is always normal to **B** and hence lies in a plane parallel to the XZ plane. Thus there is no component of force along the Y direction, and the Y component of acceleration is zero. Hence the motion along Y is given by

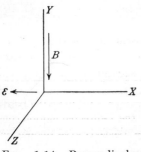

FIG. 1-14. Perpendicular electric and magnetic fields.

for this case only will lie in diff. plane if B & E have diff direction

$$f_y = 0 \qquad v_y = v_{0y} \qquad y = v_{0y}t \qquad (1\text{-}42)$$

assuming that the electron starts at the origin.

If the initial velocity component parallel to **B** *is zero, then the path lies entirely in a plane perpendicular to* **B**.

It is desired to investigate the path of an electron *starting at rest* at the origin. The initial magnetic force is zero, since the velocity is zero. The electric force is directed along the $+X$ axis, and the electron will be accelerated in this direction. As soon as the electron is in motion, the magnetic force will no longer be zero. There will then be a component of this force which will be proportional to the X component of velocity and will be directed along the $+Z$ axis. The path will thus bend away from the $+X$ direction toward the $+Z$ direction. Clearly, the electric and magnetic forces interact with one another. In fact, the analysis cannot be carried along further profitably in this qualitative fashion. The arguments given above do, however, indicate the manner in which the electron starts on its path. This path will be shown to be a cycloid.

To determine the path of the electron quantitatively, the force equations must be set up. The force due to the electric field $\mathcal{E}$ is $e\mathcal{E}$ along the $+X$ direction. The force due to the magnetic field is found as follows: At any instant, the velocity is determined by the three components v_x, v_y, and v_z along the three coordinate axes. Since **B** is in the Y direction, no force will be exerted on the electron due to v_y. Because of v_x, the force is ev_xB in the $+Z$ direction, as can be verified by the direction rule of Sec. 1-9. Similarly, the force due to v_z is ev_zB in the $-X$ direction. Hence Newton's law, when expressed in terms of the three components, yields

$$f_x = m\frac{dv_x}{dt} = e\mathcal{E} - ev_zB \qquad f_z = m\frac{dv_z}{dt} = ev_xB \qquad (1\text{-}43)$$

$f_y = 0$

By writing for convenience

$$\omega \equiv \frac{eB}{m} \qquad \text{and} \qquad u \equiv \frac{\mathcal{E}}{B} \qquad (1\text{-}44)$$

then the foregoing equations may be written in the form

$$\frac{dv_x}{dt} = \omega u - \omega v_z \qquad \frac{dv_z}{dt} = +\omega v_x \qquad (1\text{-}45)$$

A straightforward procedure is involved in the solution of these equations. In order to evaluate the velocity components, the first equation of (1-45) is differentiated and combined with the second, *viz.*,

$$\frac{d^2v_x}{dt^2} = -\omega\frac{dv_z}{dt} = -\omega^2v_x \qquad (1\text{-}46)$$

The solution of this differential equation is

$$v_x = A\cos\omega t + C\sin\omega t \qquad (1\text{-}47)$$

where A and C are arbitrary constants. In order to evaluate these constants, the initial conditions, $v_{0x} = v_{0z} = 0$ when $t = 0$, are imposed on

this equation. Thus,

$$v_x = 0$$

and, from Eqs. (1-45),

$$\frac{dv_x}{dt} = \omega u \quad \Bigg\} \quad \text{when } t = 0$$

From these, it is found that

$$A = 0 \quad \text{and} \quad C = u \tag{1-48}$$

so that

$$v_x = u \sin \omega t$$

The first equation of (1-45) and the solution for v_x give

$$v_z = u - \frac{1}{\omega} \frac{dv_x}{dt} = u - u \cos \omega t$$

Thus, the solutions of Eqs. (1-45) are

$$v_x = u \sin \omega t \qquad v_z = u - u \cos \omega t \tag{1-49}$$

In order to find the coordinates x and z from these expressions, each equation must be integrated. Thus

$$x = \int v_x \, dt = \int u \sin \omega t \, dt$$

or

$$x = - \frac{u}{\omega} \cos \omega t + D$$

Since $x = 0$ when $t = 0$, then

$$D = \frac{u}{\omega}$$

In a similar way, from Eqs. (1-49)

$$z = \int v_z \, dt = ut - \frac{u}{\omega} \sin \omega t$$

the constant of integration being zero since $z = 0$ at $t = 0$.

The complete solution of this problem is, therefore,

$$x = \frac{u}{\omega} (1 - \cos \omega t) \qquad z = ut - \frac{u}{\omega} \sin \omega t \tag{1-50}$$

If, for convenience,

$$\theta \equiv \omega t \quad \text{and} \quad Q \equiv \frac{u}{\omega} \tag{1-51}$$

then

$$x = Q(1 - \cos \theta) \qquad z = Q(\theta - \sin \theta) \tag{1-52}$$

where u and ω are as defined in Eqs. (1-44).

It will now be shown that these are the parametric equations of a *common cycloid*, defined as *the path generated by a point on the circumference*

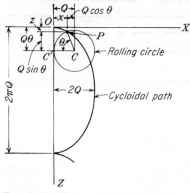

FIG. 1-15. The cycloidal path of an electron in perpendicular electric and magnetic fields when the initial velocity is zero.

of a circle of radius Q which rolls along a straight line, the Z axis. This is illustrated in Fig. 1-15. The point P whose coordinates are x and z $(y = 0)$ represents the position of the electron at any time. The dark curve is the locus of the point P. The reference line CC' is drawn through the center of the generating circle parallel to the X axis. Since the circle rolls on the Z axis, then OC' represents the length of the circumference that has already come in contact with the Z axis. This length is evidently equal to the arc PC' (and equals $Q\theta$). The angle θ gives the number of radians through which the circle has rotated.   From the diagram, it readily follows that

$$x = Q - Q \cos \theta \qquad z = Q\theta - Q \sin \theta \qquad (1\text{-}53)$$

which are identical with Eqs. (1-52), thus proving that the path is cycloidal as predicted.

The physical interpretation of the symbols introduced above merely as abbreviations is as follows:

ω *represents the angular velocity of rotation of the rolling circle.*

θ *represents the number of radians through which the circle has rotated.*

Q *represents the radius of the rolling circle.*

Since $u = \omega Q$, then u *represents the velocity of translation of the center of the rolling circle.*

From these interpretations and from Fig. 1-15 it is clear that the maximum displacement of the electron along the X axis is equal to the diameter of the rolling circle, or $2Q$.   Also, the distance along the Z axis between cusps is equal to the circumference of the rolling circle, or $2\pi Q$.   At each cusp the speed of the electron is zero, since at this point the velocity is reversing its direction (see Fig. 1-15).   This is also seen from the fact that each cusp is along the Z axis and hence at the same potential.   Therefore the electron has gained no energy from the electric field, and its speed must again be zero.

If an initial velocity exists that is directed parallel to the magnetic field, then the projection of the path on the XZ plane will still be a cycloid but the particle will now have a constant velocity normal to the plane.   This

might be called a "cycloidal helical motion." The motion is described by
Eqs. (1-52) with the addition of Eqs. (1-42).

There is one other special case of importance. Suppose that the electron is released perpendicular to both the electric and magnetic fields so that $v_{0x} = v_{0y} = 0$ and $v_{0z} \neq 0$. The electric force is $e\mathcal{E}$ along the $+X$ direction (see Fig. 1-14), and the magnetic force is $ev_{0z}B$ along the $-X$ direction. If the net force on the electron is zero, then it will continue to move along the Z axis with the constant speed v_{0z}. This condition is realized when

$$e\mathcal{E} = eBv_{0z}$$

or

$$v_{0z} = \frac{\mathcal{E}}{B} = u \tag{1-54}$$

from Eqs. (1-44).

This gives another interpretation to u. It represents that velocity with which an electron may be injected into perpendicular electric and magnetic fields and suffer no deflection, *the net force being zero*. Note that this velocity u is independent of the charge or mass of the ions. Such a system of perpendicular fields will act as a *velocity filter* and allow only those particles whose velocity is given by the ratio $\mathcal{E}/B$ to be selected.

Example. A magnetic field of 0.01 weber/m² is applied along the axis of a cathode-ray tube. A field of 10^4 volts/m is applied to the deflecting plates. If an electron leaves the anode with a velocity of 10^6 m/sec along the axis, how far from the axis will it be when it emerges from the region between the plates? The length l of the deflecting plates along the tube axis is 2.0 cm.

Solution. Choose the system of coordinate axes illustrated in Fig. 1-14. Then,

$$v_{0x} = v_{0z} = 0 \qquad v_{0y} = 10^6 \text{ m/sec}$$

As shown above, the projection of the path is a cycloid in the XZ plane, and the electron travels with constant velocity along the Y axis. The electron is in the region between the plates for the time

$$\frac{l}{v_{0y}} = 2 \times 10^{-8} \text{ sec}$$

Then, from Eqs. (1-44) and (1-51), it is found that

$$\omega = \frac{eB}{m} = 1.76 \times 10^9 \text{ rad/sec}$$

$$u = \frac{\mathcal{E}}{B} = 10^6 \text{ m/sec}$$

$$Q = \frac{u}{\omega} = 5.68 \times 10^{-4} \text{ m} = 0.0568 \text{ cm}$$

$$\theta = \omega t = (1.76 \times 10^9)(2 \times 10^{-8}) = 35.2 \text{ rad}$$

Since there are 2π rad/revolution, the electron goes through five complete cycles and enters upon the sixth before it emerges from the plates. Thus

$$35.2 \text{ rad} = 10\pi + 3.8 \qquad \text{rad}$$

Since 3.8 rad equals 218 deg, then Eqs. (1-52) yield

$$x = Q(1 - \cos \theta) = 0.0568(1 - \cos 218°) = 0.103 \text{ cm}$$
$$z = Q(\theta - \sin \theta) = 0.0568(35.2 - \sin 218°) = 2.03 \text{ cm}$$

so that the distance from the tube axis is

$$r = \sqrt{x^2 + z^2} = 2.03 \text{ cm}$$

If the initial velocity component in the direction perpendicular to the magnetic field is not zero, it can be shown[4] that the path is a *trochoid*.[5] This curve is the locus of a point on a "spoke" of a wheel rolling on a straight line, as illustrated in Fig. 1-16. If the length Q' of the spoke is greater than the radius Q of the rolling circle, the trochoid is called a *prolate cycloid*[5] and has subsid-

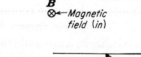

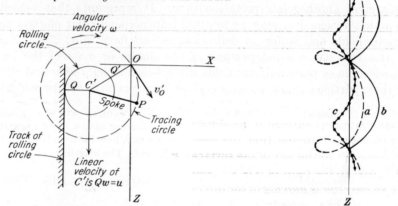

Fig. 1-16. The locus of the point P at the end of a "spoke" of a wheel rolling on a straight line is a trochoid.

Fig. 1-17. The trochoidal paths of electrons in perpendicular electric and magnetic fields.

iary loops (Fig. 1-17a). If $Q' = Q$, the path is called a *common cycloid* and is illustrated in Fig. 1-15 or 1-17b. If Q' is less than Q, the path is called a *curtate cycloid*[5] and has blunted cusps, as indicated in Fig. 1-17c.

1-15. Nonuniform Fields. If the fields are not constant, it is still possible to write down the differential equations of motion but it is seldom possible to obtain an exact solution. The particular case in which the tube possesses cylindrical symmetry is amenable to analysis. However, in most practical tubes the fields themselves are seldom known exactly, but only the voltages applied to a certain electrode configuration are given. Because of the importance of this type of problem, approximate graphical, numerical, and experimental methods of solution have been devised.[6]

One direct experimental method for finding the path of an electron in a given two-dimensional electrode configuration (without first finding the field) is called the "rubber-model" method. In this method, a large-scale model is made of the electrode assembly, the height of the various electrodes being adjusted to be in proper proportion to the negative potential of the electrodes. A rubber membrane is pressed down over this configuration in such a way that it makes contact with the top of every electrode. The surface of the diaphragm is then no longer flat but has an elevation that is proportional to the potential at each point in space. A small ball is projected onto this model with an initial speed and direction appropriate to the original electronic problem, and the subsequent path of the rolling ball is photographed with a motion-picture camera. It can be shown that the motion of the ball rolling on the stretched diaphragm under the action of the earth's gravitational field (subject to certain conditions usually approximated in practice) is identical with that of the electron in the original electrode configuration.[7]

1-16. Electron Optics. Because of the close analogy that exists between the paths of charged particles in electric and magnetic fields and the path of light rays in passing through lenses or through media of varying index of refraction, the foregoing analyses may be called "geometrical electron optics." To note this close analogy,[8] consider the regions on both sides of an equipotential surface S, as shown in Fig. 1-18. Suppose that the electric potential to the left of the surface is V^-, that to the right of S is V^+, and that an electron is moving in the direction PQ with a velocity v_1. At the surface S a force exists in the direction normal to the equipotential. Because of this force, the velocity of the electron increases to v_2 after it has passed S.

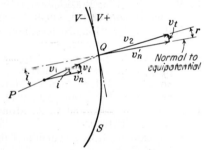

FIG. 1-18. Demonstration of the similarity between "geometrical electron optics" and "geometrical light optics."

Only the normal component of velocity v_n changes, since no work is done by moving the particle along an equipotential. That is, the tangential component of the velocity v_t on both sides of the equipotential remains unchanged. It follows from Fig. 1-18 that

$$v_t = v_1 \sin i = v_2 \sin r$$

where i and r may be considered as the angles of incidence and refraction of the electron ray, respectively. Then

$$\frac{\sin i}{\sin r} = \frac{v_2}{v_1} \tag{1-55}$$

In geometrical light optics the ratio of the velocities of propagation in two media is called the *index of refraction* μ. This resultant equation is then recognized as Snell's law of refraction, $\sin i / \sin r = \mu$. It therefore follows that the refraction of an electronic beam at an equipotential surface obeys the same law as the bending of a light beam at a refracting surface. Because of this, the electron-lens system and an optical-lens system may be considered to be roughly analogous. It must be kept in mind, however, that electron lenses cannot be sharply defined, the region actually being one of continuously varying index of refraction. Furthermore, the index of refraction of the electron lens can readily be varied by changing the potentials applied to the electrodes that constitute the lens. This is the electron-lens arrangement for focusing the electron beam in a cathode-ray tube and will be further discussed in Sec. 2-5.

REFERENCES

1. NIELSEN, H. N., "Symbols and Units," *Phys. Today*, **9**, 23–27, November, 1956.
   SWEZEY, K. M., "Nikola Tesla," *Elec. Eng.*, **75**, 786–790, September, 1956.
2. BUSCH, H., "Eine neue Methode zur e/m-Bestimmung," *Physik. Z.*, **23**(20/21), 438–441, 1922.
3. WOLF, F., "Eine Präzisionsmessung von e/m_0 nach der Methode von H. Busch," *Ann. Physik*, **83**(14), 849–883, 1927.
   GOEDICKE, E., "Eine Neubestimmung der spezifischen Ladung des Electrons nach der Methode von H. Busch," *ibid.*, **36**(1), 47–63, 1939.
4. MILLMAN, J., and S. SEELY, "Electronics," 2d ed., p. 35, McGraw-Hill Book Company, Inc., New York, 1951.
5. JAMES, G., and R. C. JAMES, "Mathematics Dictionary," D. Van Nostrand Company, Inc., Princeton, N.J., 1949.
6. ZWORYKIN, V. K., and G. A. MORTON, "Television," John Wiley & Sons, Inc., New York, 1940.
   SPANGENBERG, K. R., "Vacuum Tubes," McGraw-Hill Book Company, Inc., New York, 1948.
7. ZWORYKIN, V. K., and G. A. MORTON, "Television," p. 83, John Wiley & Sons, Inc., New York, 1940.
   BRÜCHE, E., and A. RECKNAGEL, "Über Modelle elektrischer und magnetischer Felder der Elektronenoptik," *Z. tech. Phys.*, **17**(4), 126–134, 1936.
8. ZWORYKIN, V. K., G. A. MORTON, E. G. RAMBERG, J. HILLIER, and A. W. VANCE, "Electron Optics and the Electron Microscope," John Wiley & Sons, Inc., New York, 1945.

CHAPTER 2

APPLICATIONS OF THE MOTION OF PARTICLES IN APPLIED FIELDS

This chapter will present a discussion of a number of the more important electronic devices that depend for their operation on the theory developed in the preceding chapter.

2-1. Electrostatic Deflection in Cathode-ray Tubes. The essentials of a cathode-ray tube for electrostatic deflection are illustrated in Fig. 2-1. A more detailed discussion of the elements of the tube will follow later.

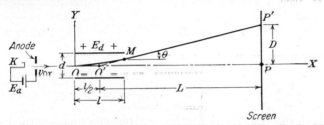

Fig. 2-1. Electrostatic deflection in a cathode-ray tube.

It will be assumed that a constant voltage E_d is applied between the deflecting plates as shown. The initial velocity of the electrons v_{0x} results from the application of an accelerating potential E_a. The magnitude of this velocity is given by Eq. (1-12), *viz.*,

$$v_{0x} = \sqrt{\frac{2eE_a}{m}} \quad \text{m/sec} \tag{2-1}$$

on the assumption that the initial velocities of emission of the electrons from the cathode are negligible.

Since no field is supposed to exist in the region from the anode to the point O, the electrons will move with a constant velocity v_{0x} in a straight-line path. In the region between the plates the electrons will move in the parabolic path given by $y = \frac{1}{2}(a_y/v_{0x}^2)x^2$ according to Eq. (1-20). The path is a straight line from the point of emergence M at the edge of the plates to the point P' on the screen, since this region is field-free.

The straight-line path in the region from the deflecting plates to the screen is, of course, tangent to the parabola at the point M. The slope

29

of the line at this point, and so at every point between M and P', is [from Eq. (1-20)]

$$\tan \theta = \left. \frac{dy}{dx} \right]_{x=l} = \frac{a_y l}{v_{0x}{}^2}$$

From the geometry of the figure, the equation of the straight line MP' is found to be

$$y = \frac{a_y l}{v_{0x}{}^2} \left(x - \frac{l}{2} \right) \tag{2-2}$$

since $x = l$ and $y = \frac{1}{2} a_y l^2 / v_{0x}{}^2$ at the point M.

When $y = 0$, $x = l/2$, which indicates that when the straight line MP' is extended backward it will intersect the tube axis at the point O', the center point of the plates.   This result means that O' is, in effect, a virtual cathode, and, regardless of the applied potentials E_a and E_d, the electrons appear to emerge from this "cathode" and move in a straight line to the point P'.

At the point P', $y = D$, and $x = L + \frac{1}{2} l$.   Equation (2-2) reduces to

$$D = \frac{a_y l L}{v_{0x}{}^2}$$

By inserting the known values of a_y $(= eE_d/dm)$ and v_{0x}, this becomes

$$D = \frac{l L E_d}{2 d E_a} \tag{2-3}$$

This result shows that the deflection on the screen of a cathode-ray tube is directly proportional to the deflecting voltage E_d applied between the plates.   Consequently, a cathode-ray tube may be used as a linear-voltage indicating device.

The *electrostatic-deflection sensitivity* of a cathode-ray tube is defined as the deflection (in meters) on the screen per volt of deflecting voltage. Thus

$$S \equiv \frac{D}{E_d} = \frac{l L}{2 d E_a} \quad \text{m/volt} \tag{2-4}$$

The *deflection factor* of the tube is, by definition, the reciprocal of the sensitivity and is, therefore,

$$G \equiv \frac{1}{S} = \frac{2 d E_a}{l L} \quad \text{volts/m} \tag{2-5}$$

This expression gives a measure of the potential that must be applied to the deflecting plates in order to give unit deflection on the screen.

An inspection of Eq. (2-4) shows that the sensitivity is independent of both the deflecting voltage E_d and the ratio e/m.   Furthermore, the sensitivity varies inversely with the accelerating potential E_a.

The idealization made in connection with the foregoing development, *viz.*, that the electric field between the deflecting plates is uniform and does not extend beyond the edges of the plates, is never met in practice. Consequently, the effect of fringing of the electric field may be enough to necessitate corrections amounting to as much as 40 per cent[1] in the results obtained from an application of Eqs. (2-4) and (2-5).

Typical values of deflection factors range from approximately 25 to 250 volts/in., corresponding to sensitivities of 1.0 to 0.1 mm/volt.

2-2. Experimental Determination of Sensitivity. The simplest procedure for determining the sensitivity of a cathode-ray tube experimentally is to apply an a-c (60-cycle) voltage to the deflecting plates. As far as an individual electron is concerned, this is equivalent to a constant potential since, during the time interval in which it is in the region between the plates, the potential remains substantially constant. To verify this, one need only recall that, if the electron were accelerated even by an anode potential of only 100 volts, its speed would be 5.93×10^6 m/sec. The length of time it would be in the region between plates 1 cm long would be $l/v = 0.01/(5.93 \times 10^6)$, or less than 10^{-8} sec. Certainly the 60-cycle voltage may be considered to remain unchanged for such a short time interval.

This analysis furnishes the justification for determining the electrostatic sensitivity by means of an alternating instead of a static field between the plates. It must be noted that the expression for the deflection sensitivity must be modified when the time of passage of an electron between the plates is comparable with the period of the a-c deflecting voltage. However, since the time of passage of the electron between the plates is of the order of 10^{-8} sec, the deflection sensitivity is independent of frequency for frequencies less than about 10 megacycles/sec.

What will be seen on the screen when the deflecting voltage is sinusoidal? Since each succeeding electron in the cathode-ray stream arrives between the plates at a different phase of the applied voltage, then the deflecting voltage will be different in magnitude for the different electrons. This circumstance results in different deflections so that the electrons, instead of striking one spot on the screen, will be spread out, the image on the screen being a line. The eye cannot, of course, detect the individual rain of electrons on the screen but owing to the persistence of vision sees only the integrated result, a line. Since the applied a-c potential reverses twice each cycle, the electron beam will be deflected upward during one half period and downward during the other half period. The total length of the line will correspond to that resulting from the application of a d-c voltage equal to $2E_m$, where E_m is the maximum value of the applied a-c potential.

It is a very simple matter to measure the length of the resulting line with a transparent scale, particularly since the end points appear brighter than the rest of the line.   The bright end points result from the fact that more electrons are deflected toward these points than to any other point in the line because the voltage is in the neighborhood of its maximum or its minimum value for a large portion of its period.

If the applied deflecting potential is not a pure sinusoidal wave but contains harmonics, the resulting line on the screen will possess, in accordance with the foregoing discussion, gradations in intensity.   The brightest portions of the line will correspond to regions where the magnitude of the applied potential wave is changing least with respect to the time, and more electrons are acted upon by this field strength than by any other.

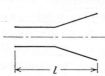

Fig.   2-2.   Inclined plates in a cathode-ray tube.

If the deflecting voltage is large enough, it is possible for the electrons to strike the deflecting plates and so never reach the screen.   In order to avoid this difficulty and thus allow for larger deflections on the screen, the plates of the deflecting system are often bent with respect to one another, as illustrated in Fig. 2-2.

It is found that the electron beam is defocused as it is deflected.   This effect can be minimized by properly shaping the deflection plates.   For the most uniform focusing the plates are bent in a parabolic form approximating the path which the electron beam follows.

2-3. The Intensifier Tube.   It is shown in Sec. 2-1 that the sensitivity varies inversely with the accelerating potential E_a.   Consequently, greater sensitivity prevails for smaller values of E_a.   However, smaller values of E_a cause a decrease of the luminosity of the spot on the screen, since the luminosity depends upon the energy carried by the beam of electrons (Sec. 2-8).   It is therefore necessary to reach a compromise between luminosity and sensitivity in the design of a cathode-ray tube.

It is, however, possible to obtain high sensitivity and at the same time high luminosity by the use of an additional electrode called the *intensifier*,[2] *postaccelerating electrode*, or *third anode* which is placed close to the screen.   The general appearance of such a tube is shown in Fig. 2-3. This extra electrode I is usually in the form of a conducting ring on the inner surface of the glass near the screen.   It serves to give the electrons an added acceleration toward the screen subsequent to their deflection by the deflecting plates.   Thus the sensitivity is increased through the use of a lower

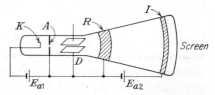

Fig. 2-3. A cathode-ray tube provided with a postaccelerating electrode.

accelerating potential E_{a1} prior to the deflection of the beam, and the intensity of the spot on the screen is increased through the use of the intensifier voltage E_{a2}, which speeds up the electrons subsequent to the deflection. As usually operated, the potential between the intensifier electrode and the accelerating anode is approximately equal to that between the anode and the cathode. This provides full brilliance with a sensitivity approximately twice that of a tube not provided with the intensifier electrode. In order to avoid a loss in sensitivity resulting from an axial acceleration in the region of the deflecting plates caused by the field of the intensifier electrode, the anode is connected to a conducting ring R painted on the inner surface of the glass beyond the deflecting

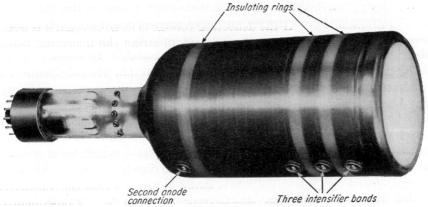

Fig. 2-4. Type 5RP multiband intensifier tube.   (*Courtesy of A. B. Du Mont Laboratories, Inc.*)

plates (Fig. 2-3). This ring may take the form of an aquadag coating extending over quite a region on both sides of the deflecting plates. This ring renders the deflecting plate space free from an axial component of force. Such an axial force would, of course, shorten the time the electron would be under the influence of the deflecting voltage and would give a decreased deflection.

If the ratio of intensifier to anode potential is much greater than 2:1, then it is found that distortions are introduced.[3] These are due in a large measure to the nonaxial components of electric field caused by the intensifier. The distortions are minimized by changing the shape of the envelope from a tapered to a cylindrical form and by applying the intensifier voltage in several equal steps. Figure 2-4 shows such a tube operating satisfactorily at an intensifier-to-anode voltage of 10:1. The electrons are accelerated through a potential of 20 kv before striking the screen and yet the sensitivity is as high as 0.15 mm/volt. This tube has sufficient intensity to allow photographing of very rapid transients, *writing speeds* (Sec. 2-8) as high as 400 in./μsec having been recorded. Before the advent of the intensifier-type tube this could be done only with a demountable-type tube in which the photographic plate was placed inside of the tube envelope so that the electron beam exposed it directly.[4] This required that the system be connected continually to vacuum pumps, a distinct disadvantage over the sealed-off intensifier-type tube.

A second application of the intensifier tube is as a projection oscillograph.

The A. B. Du Mont Laboratories, Inc., has developed a postaccelerating tube in which the gap-type intensifier rings of Fig. 2-4 are replaced by a continuous band in the form of a spiral. This *spiral intensifier* gradually raises the potential from the second anode to the final postaccelerating voltage at the screen. The over-all result is less distortion, less defocusing of the spot at the limits of deflection, and a more uniform distribution of the secondary electrons that bombard the screen.

By improving production techniques, the A. B. Du Mont Laboratories, Inc., has found it possible to maintain much closer tolerances in a cathode-ray-tube assembly. By decreasing the deflection-plate spacing, increasing the length of the plates, and increasing the beam current it is possible to obtain the same sensitivity and intensity as with a postaccelerating tube. Such a *mono-accelerator*[5] *tube* operates at a much lower voltage than the intensifier tube but has none of the disadvantages of the latter type.

2-4. Magnetic Deflection in Cathode-ray Tubes. The illustrative example in Sec. 1-11 immediately suggests that a cathode-ray tube may employ a magnetic as well as an electric field in order to accomplish the deflection of the electron beam. However, as it is not feasible to use a field extending over the entire length of the tube, a short coil furnishing a transverse field in a limited region is employed, as shown in Fig. 2-5. The magnetic field is taken as pointing out of the paper, and the beam is deflected upward. It is assumed that the magnetic-field intensity B is uniform in the restricted region shown and is zero outside of this area. Hence, the electron moves in a straight line from the cathode to the boundary O of the magnetic field. In the region of the uniform magnetic field the electron experiences a force of magnitude evB, where v is the speed.

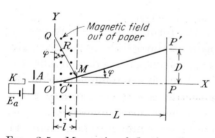

FIG. 2-5. Magnetic deflection in a cathode-ray tube.

The path OM will be the arc of a circle whose center is at Q. The speed of the particles will remain constant and equal to

$$v = v_{0x} = \sqrt{\frac{2eE_a}{m}} \quad \text{m/sec} \tag{2-6}$$

The angle φ is, by definition of radian measure, equal to the length of the arc OM divided by R, the radius of the circle, or approximately

$$\varphi \cong \frac{l}{R} \tag{2-7}$$

where, by Eq. (1-35),

$$R = \frac{mv}{eB} \quad \text{m} \tag{2-8}$$

In most practical cases, L is very much larger than l, so that little error will be made in assuming that the straight line MP', if projected backward, will pass through the center O' of the region of the magnetic field. Then

$$D \cong L \tan \varphi \tag{2-9}$$

These assumed conditions presuppose that the angle φ is a small quantity, thereby permitting the approximation $\tan \varphi \cong \varphi$. By Eqs. (2-6), (2-7), and (2-8), Eq. (2-9) now becomes

$$D \cong L\varphi = \frac{lL}{R} = \frac{lLeB}{mv} = \frac{lLB}{\sqrt{E_a}} \sqrt{\frac{e}{2m}}$$

The deflection per unit magnetic-field intensity, D/B, given by

$$\frac{D}{B} = \frac{lL}{\sqrt{E_a}} \sqrt{\frac{e}{2m}} \quad \text{m/(weber/m}^2) \tag{2-10}$$

is called the *magnetic-deflection sensitivity* of the tube. It is observed that this quantity is independent of B. This condition is analogous to the electric case for which the electrostatic sensitivity is independent of the deflecting potential. However, in the electric case the sensitivity varies inversely with the anode voltage, whereas it here varies inversely with the square root of the anode voltage. Another important difference is in the appearance of e/m in the expression for the magnetic sensitivity, whereas this ratio did not enter into the final expression for the electric case. Because the sensitivity increases with L, the deflecting coils are placed as far down the neck of the tube as possible, usually directly after the accelerating anode.

2-5. Focusing the Beam. The essentials of a high-vacuum tube are illustrated in Fig. 2-6. (The pressure is about 10^{-6} mm Hg.) The electrons are emitted from the indirectly heated oxide-coated cathode K, the filament power being supplied to the heater H. The heater is generally noninductively wound. The intensity of the beam is controlled by varying the negative bias on the grid G, which is usually a nickel cylinder provided with a small, centrally located hole coaxial with the tube axis.

Because of the mutual repulsion of the electrons a method for focusing the beam into a small spot must be provided. The electrostatic method of doing this is indicated in Fig. 2-6. The electrode A_3 is a metal cylinder that contains several baffles in order to collimate the beam and accelerate it to its final velocity. The electrodes A_1 and A_2 are cylinders coaxial with A_3. The cylinder A_2 is electrically connected to A_3, but A_1 is at a lower voltage. Focusing of the electron beam is accomplished by varying the potential between A_1 and A_2, thereby changing the index of refraction

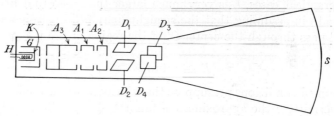

FIG. 2-6. The elements of a high-vacuum cathode-ray tube. (*Courtesy of A. B. Du Mont Laboratories, Inc.*)

of the electron rays (Sec. 1-16). Because of this, A_1 is referred to as the "focusing electrode" or the "first anode," A_2 is called the "second anode," and A_3 is known as the "preaccelerating electrode." The combination of H, K, G, A_1, A_2, and A_3 is called an "electron gun,"[6] an appropriate name because of the analogy with ordinary ballistics. A complete picture of an electrostatic cathode-ray tube is given in Fig. 2-7. The lens action of the electron gun on the electron beam is clearly indicated in the diagram. Many cathode-ray tubes are manufactured with a flat rather than a curved face.

In addition to the electrostatic method of focusing, just described, it is possible to focus the beam magnetically. The method of Sec. 1-12 employing a longitudinal magnetic field over the entire length of the tube is not too practical. Hence, a short coil is placed over the neck of the tube. One type of coil and the corresponding magnetic lines are shown in Fig. 2-8. There are two components of force on the electron, one due to the axial component of velocity and the radial component of field and the second due to the radial component of the velocity and the axial component of field. Because the axial component of velocity is so much greater than the transverse component, then, to a good approximation, only the former force need be taken into account. The analysis is complicated,[7]

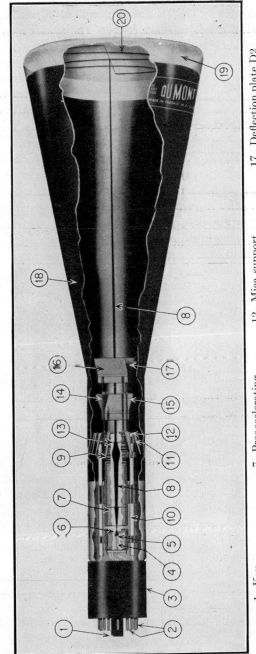

1. Key
2. Pins
3. Base
4. Heater element
5. Cathode
6. Control grid
7. Preaccelerating electrode
8. Electron beam
9. Focusing electrode
10. Ceramic support
11. Spider support
12. Mica support
13. Accelerating electrode
14. Deflection plate D3
15. Deflection plate D4
16. Deflection plate D1
17. Deflection plate D2
18. Internal conductive coating
19. Fluorescent screen material
20. Pattern

Fig. 2-7. Complete modern electrostatic cathode-ray tube. (*Courtesy of A. B. Du Mont Laboratories, Inc.*)

but it can be seen qualitatively that the motion will be a rotation about the axis of the tube and, if conditions are correct, the electron on leaving the region of the coil may be turned sufficiently so as to move in a line toward the center of the screen. A rough adjustment of the focus is obtained by positioning the coil properly along the neck of the tube. The fine adjustment of focus is made by controlling the coil current.

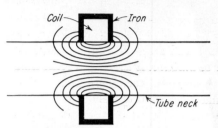

FIG. 2-8. Magnetic-focusing coil.

A picture of a tube with magnetic deflection and focus is shown in Fig. 2-9. For television the tube face is usually rectangular in shape. Note that the preaccelerating electrode and the focusing electrode of the electrostatic tube are missing and instead an electrode called the "screen grid" is used. This is held at a fixed positive voltage, usually 250 volts,

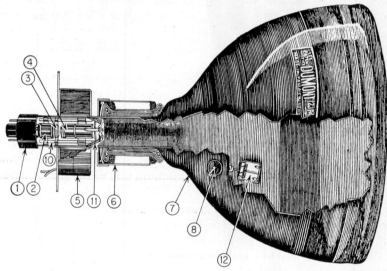

1. Base
2. Control electrode (Grid No. 1) (G$_1$)
3. Screen grid (Grid No. 2) (G$_2$)
4. Accelerating electrode (anode) (A)
5. Focusing coil
6. Deflection yoke

7. Anode conductive coating
8. Anode terminal
9. Fluorescent screen
10. Ceramic gun support
11. Mount support spider
12. Getter

FIG. 2-9. Typical cathode-ray tube with magnetic focusing and deflection. (*Courtesy of A. B. Du Mont Laboratories, Inc.*)

with respect to the cathode and allows the tube to be operated over a wide range of accelerating voltages without appreciably changing the control-grid characteristics of the tube.

2-6. Charges in a Cathode-ray Tube. There is the likelihood of the accumulation of electrons on the surface of the glass in a cathode-ray tube. If these charges are not symmetrically distributed, they may cause spurious deflections of the electron beam. In order to assist in the removal of undesirable stray charges, the inside surface of the glass envelope of most tubes is given a coating of a conducting material, which is then electrically connected to the second anode (Figs. 2-7 and 2-9). Usually an aqueous solution of graphite, known as *aquadag* or *dixonac*, is used. In some magnetic tubes the anode is dispensed with entirely, the conducting coating on the glass walls being used as the final accelerating electrode.

Since both the screen material and the uncoated portion of the glass envelope are good electrical insulators, what happens when the electron beam strikes the screen? The answer is found in the secondary-emission properties (Sec. 3-13) of the screen material and the glass on which it is deposited. For the materials usually employed, between one and two secondary electrons are emitted for each incident electron. However, in the equilibrium state as many electrons must leave the screen as reach it. Experimentally, it is found that for low beam current densities the screen acquires a potential of 1 or 2 volts positive with respect to the second anode. Thus, although more secondary electrons are emitted than the number contained in the primary beam, not all of these can surmount the retarding field between the screen and the second anode and some will return to the screen. Thus, the equilibrium condition of zero net current to the screen is attained.

If the current density in the beam is high, then the screen potential is found[8] to be at a few volts below the anode potential. However, the secondary electrons are still subjected to a retarding field because under this condition there exists a potential minimum due to the space charge in the beam (Sec. 4-3).

In addition to electrons, many types of *negative* ions (oxygen, carbon, chlorine, etc.) have been discovered[9] in the cathode-ray tube. The chief source of these ions is the oxide-coated cathode. In Sec. 2-4 it is shown that the deflection due to a magnetic field varies as $(e/m)^{\frac{1}{2}}$, where m is the mass of the particle. Since these ions are thousands of times heavier than the electron, they are deflected very little and hence they continually strike a small area at the center of the screen. This soon results in the appearance of a dark stain or blemish. This "ion burn" is found principally in tubes with electrostatic focusing and magnetic deflection. If magnetic focusing is used, then the coil current for proper focusing depends upon the mass of the particle. If the electron beam is focused, then the ions are not in focus and they spread out over a considerable portion of the screen. Hence, the concentration is usually not great enough to cause a severe ion burn.

It is shown in Sec. 2-1 that the electrostatic deflection of a particle is independent of e/m. Hence, in a tube with electrostatic focusing and electrostatic deflection the ions travel with the electrons. The ions are not concentrated at the center of the screen and do not produce an ion burn.

In order to avoid this ion difficulty, several forms of "ion trap" have been invented.[10]   The simplest of these uses an electron gun inclined at an angle of about 30 deg with respect to the tube axis. A magnetic field transverse to the gun bends the electrons back to the axis but (because of their much greater mass) has very little effect on the ions so that they strike the ion trap and do not get to the screen.

In some tubes a thin aluminum film[11] is deposited over the screen after the fluorescent material has been put on the glass. It is found that a film of the proper thickness is nearly opaque to ions and hence an ion trap may not be needed. At the velocities encountered in television tubes the electrons, on the other hand, can pass through the thin metal foil with little loss in energy. Furthermore, the aluminum backing acts as a mirror and reflects the light from the bombarded side of the screen which would otherwise travel toward the rear of the tube. Hence, an aluminized screen can give an improvement in brightness (by a factor of about 2 for an anode voltage of 12 kv) over that of a nonaluminized screen. Also, the foil is connected to the second anode and hence serves as a return path for the electrons striking the screen (independent of the secondary-emission properties of the screen).

2-7. Sweep Action in a Cathode-ray Tube.   An electrostatic tube has two sets of deflecting plates which are at right angles to each other in space (as indicated in Figs. 2-6 and 2-7). These plates are referred to as the *vertical* and *horizontal* plates because the tube is oriented in space so that the potentials applied to these plates result in vertical and horizontal deflections, respectively. The reason for having two sets of plates will now be discussed.

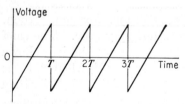

Fig. 2-10. Sweep voltage for a cathode-ray tube.

Suppose that the *saw-tooth* wave form of Fig. 2-10 is impressed across the horizontal plates. Since this voltage is used to sweep the electron beam across the screen, it is called a *sweep voltage*. The electrons are deflected linearly with time in the horizontal direction for a time T. Then the beam returns to its starting point on the screen very quickly as the saw-tooth voltage rapidly falls to its initial value at the end of each period.

If a sinusoidal voltage is impressed across the vertical plates when, simultaneously, the sweep voltage is impressed across the horizontal plates, the sinusoidal voltage, which of itself gives rise to a vertical line, will now be spread out and will appear as a sinusoidal trace on the screen. The pattern will appear stationary only if the time T is equal to or is some multiple of the time for one cycle of the wave on the vertical plates. It is then necessary that the frequency of the sweep circuit be adjusted to synchronize with the frequency of the applied wave.

Actually, of course, the voltage impressed on the vertical plates may have any wave form. Consequently, a system of this type provides an almost inertialess oscilloscope for viewing arbitrary wave shapes. This is one of the most common uses for cathode-ray tubes. If a nonrepeating sweep voltage is applied to the horizontal plates, it is possible to study transients on the screen. This requires a system for synchronizing the sweep with the start of the transient.

A magnetic tube has two coils oriented at right angles to perform the same functions as the two sets of plates in an electrostatic tube.

2-8. Screens for Cathode-ray Tubes.[12] *Luminescence* is the production of light by means other than heating (for example, by the bombardment of a screen by electrons). *Fluorescence* is luminescence during excitation, and *phosphorescence* is luminescence after the excitation has stopped (when the electron beam has been turned off). The phosphorescence, or persistence, of a screen material may be classified generally as short (microseconds), medium (milliseconds), or long (seconds).

Standard cathode-ray tubes are classified with a phosphor code designation such as P1, P2, etc. The characteristics of some of the most important phosphors are summarized in Table 2-1.

TABLE 2-1

STANDARD RETMA PHOSPHORS

Designation	Fluorescent	Phosphorescent	Persistence	Applications
P1	Green	Green	Medium	General-purpose oscillographs
P2	Blue-green	Green	Long	General purpose
P4	White	Yellow	Medium	Television picture tube
P7	Blue-white	Yellow	One short, one long	Radar and low-speed transients
P11	Blue	Blue	Short	Photographing high-speed transients
P16	Violet and near ultraviolet	Violet and near ultraviolet	Extremely short	Flying spot scanner

The luminous-output characteristics of the screen will depend upon a number of factors, such as the beam current, the accelerating voltage (the product of these two gives the beam power), the size of the spot, the chemical and physical make-up of the screen, the side from which the screen is viewed, and the length of time a given area on the screen is bombarded by the electrons.   In a given cathode-ray tube the luminescence can be altered by varying the energy with which the impinging electrons bombard a given spot on the screen or by controlling the number of electrons that get to the given area in a given time, *i.e.*, the electron current.   To increase the energy of the impinging electrons, one must increase the accelerating potential.   The beam current is most easily varied by means of variations of the grid-to-cathode potential.

Strictly speaking, this discussion applies to a stationary beam.   If a pattern exists on the screen, local variations in intensity may result from variations in the rate of arrival of the electrons at various points on the screen.   This rate is controlled by the wave shape of the potential applied to the deflecting plates.   It is because of this that one talks about a

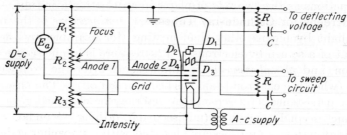

Fig. 2-11. Connections for a typical electrostatic high-vacuum cathode-ray tube.

"writing" or "tracing" speed.   If the writing rate is too great over a portion of a curve, this part may not be at all visible on the screen.   For example, with a well-designed sweep circuit, the rapid vertical fall at the end of each period should not be visible (Fig. 2-10).

2-9. Cathode-ray-tube Connections.   The connections for a typical electrostatic cathode-ray tube are shown in Fig. 2-11.   The d-c supply for the accelerating and focusing system is obtained from a thermionic-tube rectifier.   The resistors R_1, R_2, and R_3 represent a voltage divider providing the correct voltages for operation.   Focusing of the beam is accomplished by adjusting the ratio between the voltages on anodes 2 and 1. The magnitude of the voltage on the first focusing electrode is usually about one-fourth to one-fifth that of the accelerating anode A_2.   By varying the voltage on anode 2, regulation of the spot size and intensity may be accomplished.   If the voltage of anode 2 is increased, the electron speed is increased, thereby decreasing the spot size and increasing the intensity.   The current, or number of electrons per second, to anode 2 may be increased by decreasing the bias voltage applied to the control grid.   Thus, in an oscilloscope operating at a fixed accelerating voltage the intensity of the beam is controlled by adjusting the grid voltage.

It is noted that in Fig. 2-11 the final anode and one plate of each set are grounded. This means that the cathode is below ground by an amount equal to the accelerating voltage. The chief reason for this arrangement is that the wave form to be observed is applied to the plates. Hence, to protect the operator from high-voltage shock when making this connection, the plates should be near ground potential. Also, the deflecting voltages are measured with respect to ground and hence high-voltage blocking capacitors and additional shunt capacitances with respect to ground are avoided by this connection.

In applications, such as television or radar, where the signal is used to control the intensity of the picture the operator must have access to the cathode-grid region of the tube. For reasons of safety in these cases, it is customary to ground this portion of the circuit. The anodes are then at high voltages (suitably insulated) with respect to ground.

In tubes using the intensifier principle a separate high-voltage supply is ordinarily used for the intensifier electrodes.

In Fig. 2-11 one plate of each set is shown internally connected to the second anode. This reduces by two the relatively large number of external connections that must be made to the tube. However, this simplified design results in the two sets of plates not being independent of one another. Consequently defocusing of the spot and distortion of the sweep may result.[13] These difficulties are avoided by bringing out each plate lead separately and applying the deflecting voltages in a balanced manner; i.e., one plate is driven positively while the other is driven negatively the same amount with respect to ground.

Correction for astigmatism in the electron-optical system is made by adjusting the average potential of one set of plates with respect to that of the other. Positioning of the beam in one direction is accomplished by adjusting the average potential of the corresponding set of plates with respect to the second-anode potential by means of a d-c bias voltage. Neither the astigmatism control nor the X or Y positioning controls are indicated in the simplified diagram of Fig. 2-11.

2-10. Comparison of Electric and Magnetic Tubes. Electric deflection is used in all oscilloscope applications where operation over a wide range of frequency is desired. The upper frequency limit (about 10 megacycles) is determined by the capacitance between the deflecting plates (a few micromicrofarads) and the capacitance of the associated amplifier and leads. Higher frequencies can be observed by using tubes specially designed for the purpose and having very small plates brought out directly through the glass neck to coaxial connectors.

Magnetic deflection has a much smaller band pass (about 10 kc) because of the inductance of the coils. Thus, the same input voltage at different frequencies will result in different coil currents and hence different deflections.   For this reason magnetic deflection is limited essentially to tubes involving a constant sweep frequency, such as television or radar.   (In these applications the high-frequency signals are applied to the grid or to the cathode to give intensity variations of the picture.)

Electric focusing is always used with tubes equipped with deflection plates.   Such focusing requires very little power and is an insensitive function of power-supply variations.   This latter characteristic is due to the fact that the focusing-electrode voltage is obtained from a bleeder across the accelerating-voltage power supply (Fig. 2-11), and hence these two voltages will vary in proportion and the spot will stay focused for small variations in d-c supply.

In a television tube satisfactory picture brightness requires high beam current and very large values ($\cong$ 10 kv) of accelerating voltage E_a.   It has proved commercially more economical to obtain the necessary large deflections under these conditions with a magnetic-deflection tube.   [It should be recalled that electric deflection varies inversely as E_a (Eq. 2-3), whereas magnetic deflection varies inversely as $E_a^{\frac{1}{2}}$ (Eq. 2-10).]

In the past, magnetic focusing was always used with tubes equipped with deflection coils because no simple and inexpensive electron gun existed which could give good focus at high beam currents.   In 1952 this difficulty was overcome commercially with the development of the *self-focusing* electrostatic lens,[14] and many television picture tubes are now built with magnetic-deflection and electric-focusing elements.   The geometry of this lens is similar to that shown in Fig. 2-6 and is indicated in Fig. 2-12.   By adjusting the dimensions of this lens properly it is possible to ground A_1 and have the beam stay in focus for fairly wide variations in anode voltage E_a.   Hence, no focusing control is needed with such a tube, which is a distinct advantage.

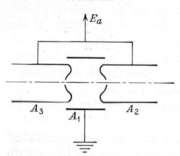

FIG. 2-12. Geometry of the self-focusing electrostatic lens.

For some applications (for example, one type of radar indicator) it is necessary to have a rotating radial deflection.   This is easily obtained with magnetic deflection since the sweep coil can be rotated mechanically around the neck of the tube.

2-11. The Magnetic and Mass Spectrographs.   The charge, mass, and velocity of electrons and ions emitted from various sources under different types of excitation have been determined experimentally by applying known electric and magnetic fields to regions through which these particles are directed and studying the subsequent motions.   Several applications of the theory of Sec. 1-11 to these problems will now be given.

Suppose that PP' (Fig. 1-7), which is reproduced in Fig. 2-13, is a photographic plate with a small opening at O through which charged particles may be introduced into the magnetic field. If the particle is an electron, it will be deflected to the right as shown (the reader should verify this by means of the direction rule) and will expose the plate at O'. The distance OO' equals the diameter of the circular path, and if e/m is known, v can be calculated with the aid of Eq. (1-35). It is in this way that the velocity of the electrons emitted from radioactive matter (the β-rays) is measured.

If, instead of the radioactive substance at O, there is a metal surface being bombarded by electrons, the velocity of the secondary electrons emitted can be measured in the manner indicated above. Similarly, if the surface at O has radiation, either visible or invisible, falling on it, then the velocity of the emitted photoelectrons can be studied. An apparatus of the type here considered is known as a *magnetic spectrograph*.

If the particles entering the field at O have a known energy, for example, if the potential through which they have fallen is known, it is then possible from the setup of Fig. 2-13 to determine the mass of the particle, provided that the charge of the particle is known. If, therefore, particles possessing the same charge but differing slightly in mass are accelerated through the same potential, the photographic plate will reveal several different spots. It was shown in essentially this way that most chemical elements consist, not entirely of particles of one mass, but rather of a mixture of atoms of slightly different

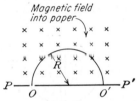

FIG. 2-13. The principle of the magnetic or the mass spectrograph.

mass. Atoms of the same element that possess the same electronic charge and differ but slightly in mass are known as *isotopes*. The instruments used to measure the masses of the isotopes that are based upon these considerations, although they may differ widely in detail, are known as *mass spectrographs*.[15]

Commercial application has been made of mass spectrographs for the quantitative and qualitative measurement of the components of gaseous mixtures[16] and for the detection of leaks in large vacuum systems.[17] In the latter application the mass spectrograph is connected to the vacuum chamber, and a stream of helium is played over the surface of the system where a leak is suspected. If there actually is a leak at this point, a reading is obtained on an output meter. The mass spectrograph contains an electron gun for ionizing the helium atoms and a voltage supply for accelerating the ions before they enter the magnetic field. The sensitivity of such a system is claimed to be one part helium to a few hundred thousand parts air.

If ions of a known mass and velocity are under consideration, then this magnetic analysis can be used to determine the charge on the ions. The method has been used to study the various stages of ionization in a discharge tube.

2-12. The Cyclotron. The principles of Sec. 1-11 were first employed by Lawrence and Livingston[18] to develop an apparatus called a *magnetic resonator* or *cyclotron*. This device imparts very high energies (tens of millions of electron volts) to positive ions. These high-energy positive ions are then allowed to bombard some substances which then become radioactive and generally disintegrate. Because of this, the cyclotron has popularly become known as an *atom smasher*.

The basic principles upon which the cyclotron operates are best understood with the aid of Fig. 2-14. The essential elements are the "dees," the two halves of a shallow, hollow, metallic "pillbox" which has been split along a diameter as shown; a strong magnetic field which is parallel to the axis of the dees; and a high-frequency a-c potential applied to the dees.

A moving positive ion released near the center of the dees will be accelerated in a semicircle by the action of the magnetic field and will reappear at point 1 at the edge of dee I. Assume that dee II is negative at this instant with respect to dee I. Then the ion will be accelerated from point 1 to point 2 across the gap and will gain an amount of energy corresponding to the potential difference between these two points. Once the ion passes inside the metal dee II, the electric field is zero, and the magnetic field causes it to move in the semicircle from point 2 to point 3. If the frequency of the applied a-c potential is such that the potential has reversed in the time necessary for the ion to go from point 2 to point 3, then dee I is now negative with respect to dee II and the ion will be accelerated across the gap from point 3 to point 4. With the frequency of the accelerating voltage properly adjusted to this "resonance" value, the ion continues to receive pulses of energy corresponding to this difference of potential again and again.

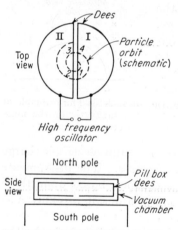

FIG. 2-14. The cyclotron principle.

Thus, after each half revolution the ion gains energy from the electric field, resulting, of course, in an increased velocity. The radius of each semicircle is then larger than the preceding one, in accordance with Eq. (1-35), so that the path described by the whirling ion will approximate a planar spiral.

Example. Suppose that the oscillator that supplies the power to the dees of a given cyclotron imparts 50,000 volts to heavy hydrogen atoms (deuterons), each of atomic number 1 and atomic weight 2.0147, at each passage of the ions across the accelerating gap. Calculate the magnetic-field intensity, the frequency of the oscillator, and the time that it will take for an ion introduced at the center of the chamber to emerge at the rim of the dee with an energy of 5 million electron volts (5 Mev). Assume that the radius of the last semicircle is 15 in.

Solution. The mass of the deuteron is

$$m = 2.01 \times 1.66 \times 10^{-27} = 3.34 \times 10^{-27} \text{ kg}$$

The velocity of the 5-Mev ions is given by the energy equation

$$\tfrac{1}{2}mv^2 = (5 \times 10^6)(1.60 \times 10^{-19}) = 8.00 \times 10^{-13} \text{ joule}$$

or

$$v = \left(\frac{2 \times 8.00 \times 10^{-13}}{3.34 \times 10^{-27}}\right)^{\frac{1}{2}} = 2.20 \times 10^7 \text{ m/sec}$$

The magnetic field, given by Eq. (1-35),

$$B = \frac{mv}{eR} = \frac{(3.34 \times 10^{-27})(2.20 \times 10^7)}{(1.60 \times 10^{-19})(15 \times 2.54 \times 0.01)} = 1.20 \text{ webers/m}^2$$

is needed in order to bring these ions to the edge of the dees.

The frequency of the oscillator must be equal to the reciprocal of the time of revolution of the ion. This is, from Eq. (1-37),

$$f = \frac{1}{T} = \frac{eB}{2\pi m} = \frac{1.60 \times 10^{-19} \times 1.20}{2\pi \times 3.34 \times 10^{-27}}$$
$$= 9.15 \times 10^6 \text{ cps} = 9.15 \text{ megacycles/sec}$$

Since the ions receive 5 Mev energy from the oscillator in 50-kv steps, they must pass across the accelerating gap 100 times. That is, the ion must make 50 complete revolutions in order to gain the full energy. Thus, from Eq. (1-37), the time of flight is

$$t = 50T = \frac{50 \times 1}{9.15 \times 10^6} = 5.47 \times 10^{-6} \text{ sec}$$

In order to produce a uniform magnetic field of 1.2 webers/m² over a circular area whose radius is at least 15 in., with an air gap approximately 6 in. wide, an enormous magnet is required, the weight of such a magnet being of the order of 60 tons. Also, the design of a 50-kv oscillator for these high frequencies and the method of coupling it to the dees present some difficulties, since the dees are in a vacuum-tight chamber. Further, means must be provided for introducing the ions into the region at the center of the dees and also for removing the high-energy particles from the chamber, if desired, or for directing them against a target.

The bombardment of the elements with the high-energy protons, deuterons, or helium nuclei which are normally used in the cyclotrons renders the bombarded elements radioactive. These radioactive elements are of the utmost importance to physicists, since they permit a glimpse into the constitution of nuclei. They are likewise of extreme importance in medical research, since they offer a substitute for radium. Radioactive substances can be followed through any physical or chemical changes by observing their emitted radiations. This "tracer" or "tagged-atom" technique is used in industry, medicine, physiology, and biology.

It is shown in Sec. 1-8 that if an electron falls through a potential of more than 3 kv a relativistic mass correction must be made, indicating that its mass increases with its energy. Thus, if electrons were used in a cyclotron, their angular velocity would decrease as their energy increased, and they would soon fall out of step with the high-frequency field. For this reason electrons are not introduced into the cyclotron.

For positive ions whose mass is several thousand times that of the electron the relativistic correction becomes appreciable when energies of a few tens of millions of electron volts are reached. For greater energies than these the ions will start to make their trip through the dees at a slower rate and slip behind in phase with respect to the electric field. This difficulty is overcome in the *synchro-cyclotron* or *f-m cyclotron* by decreasing the frequency of the oscillator (frequency modulation) in accordance with the decrease in the angular velocity of the ion. With such an f-m cyclotron, deuterons, α particles, and protons have been accelerated to several hundred million electron volts.[19]

It is possible to give particles energies in excess of those for which the relativistic correction is important even if the oscillator frequency is fixed, provided that the magnetic field is slowly increased in step with the increase in the mass of the ions so as to maintain a constant angular velocity. Such an instrument is called a *synchrotron*. The particles are injected from a gun, which gives them a velocity approaching that of light. Since the radius of the orbit is given by $R = mv/Be$ and since the ratio m/B is kept constant and v changes very little, there is not much of an increase in the orbit as the energy of the electron increases. The vacuum chamber is built in the form of a "doughnut" instead of the cyclotron "pillbox." The magnet has the form of a hollow cylinder since there is need for a magnetic field only transverse to the path. This results in a great saving in weight and expense. The dees of the cyclotron are replaced by a single-cavity resonator. Electrons have been accelerated to 70 Mev[20] and protons to several billion electron volts (Bev)[21] in synchrotrons. The larger the number of revolutions the particles make, the higher will be their energy. The defocusing of the beam limits the number of allowable cycles. With the discovery of *alternating-gradient magnetic-field focusing*,[22] higher-energy particle accelerators are expected. A general discussion of cyclotrons and problems and trends in their design in 1956 is given in Ref. 23.

2-13. The Betatron.[24]   In Sec. 1-11 it is shown that no energy can be gained by a particle in a magnetic field that is constant in time. However the situation is completely different if the field changes with time. Consider an electron moving with a speed v in a magnetic field whose instantaneous value is B_0.   If the rate of change of the magnetic field is small compared with the time required for the electron to traverse its path, this path will be almost circular, with a radius r_0, where

$$r_0 = \frac{mv}{eB_0} \tag{2-11}$$

An amount of flux Φ (webers) is enclosed by the electron in traversing this path, and as this flux is changing with time, an emf equal to $d\Phi/dt$ (volts) is induced, in accordance with Faraday's law of induction.   From the definition of potential (Sec. 1-4) it follows that an effective tangential electric field $\mathcal{E}$ must exist around the circumference of the circle of radius r_0 and that the emf must equal $2\pi r_0 \mathcal{E}$.   Hence $\mathcal{E}$ is given by

$$\mathcal{E} = \frac{1}{2\pi r_0} \frac{d\Phi}{dt} \tag{2-12}$$

Since the energy of the particle increases as it traverses its orbit, the tangential velocity will change, and as a result the radius will change.

A particle in such a field will spiral outward as the magnetic field increases, picking up energy as it continues in its path.   However, if the radial variation of the magnetic field is properly chosen, the radius r_0 of the electron orbit can be made to remain unchanged.   If the magnetic-field intensity were constant in space, then the total flux included within the orbit would be $\Phi = \pi r_0^2 B_0$. It turns out that in order to have a stable path the flux density must be nonuniform in such a manner that the total flux must equal just twice the above value. . This principle is referred to as the 1:2 condition for orbit stability and is satisfied by having a strong central field and a tapered weaker field at the electron orbit.

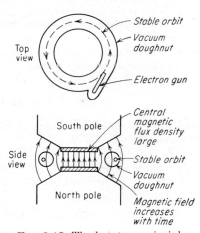

FIG. 2-15. The betatron principle.

The concepts discussed above are made use of in the *betatron*[24] invented by Kerst.   The essential features of the betatron are shown in Fig. 2-15. The particles are injected into the doughnut-shaped vacuum chamber from an electron gun at energies of about 50 kv, near the equilibrium orbit.   This gun is triggered for a few microseconds at the beginning of each cycle of the magnetic field.   The electrons are accelerated during the time the magnetic field passes from zero to its peak value, or one-quarter of the cycle of the field current.   If the electrons were to remain in the tube during the second quarter cycle when the field is decreasing, they would be decelerated and would give up their energy. They must be removed before this happens, which requires destroying the 1:2 condition, in order to have the electrons leave the equilibrium orbit. It is accomplished by applying a short pulse to an auxiliary system of coils on the pole faces at the end of the first quarter cycle. This disturbance causes the electrons to spiral away from their orbit and hit a tungsten target, which then emits very penetrating X rays. The betatron is used as an X-ray tube for radiographing metal sections several feet thick.

It is customary now to apply a steady d-c biasing field which is equal to the peak value of the a-c field. The electrons are injected when the d-c and a-c fields cancel each other, and they remain in the accelerating chamber for one-half cycle (from peak to peak) instead of one-quarter cycle. Consequently the energy possible with the biased betatron is twice that of the unbiased type.

Example. The diameter of the orbit of an unbiased betatron is 66 in. The peak flux density at the orbit is 0.4 weber/m². The magnetic field varies at a 60-cycle rate.

a. What is the maximum energy acquired by the electrons?

b. What is the average energy imparted to an electron in each trip around the doughnut?

c. How many revolutions does the electron make?

d. What is the average transit time of the electron?

Solution. *a.* The energy is given by the relativistic equation (1-22),

$$eV = mc^2 - m_0c^2$$

and hence we must first find the maximum mass of the electron. From Eq. (2-11) the maximum momentum is

$$mv = eB_0r_0$$

and from Eq. (1-23)

$$m = \frac{m_0}{\sqrt{1 - v^2/c^2}}$$

so that

$$\frac{m_0v}{\sqrt{1 - v^2/c^2}} = eB_0r_0 \qquad\qquad (2\text{-}13)$$

If the abbreviation $\beta \equiv v/c$ is introduced, then

$$\frac{\beta}{\sqrt{1 - \beta^2}} = \frac{eB_0r_0}{m_0c} = \frac{(1.76 \times 10^{11})(0.4)(33 \times 2.54 \times 10^{-2})}{3 \times 10^8} = 197$$

Solving for β, a value very close to unity is obtained. Thus, the maximum electronic velocity is almost exactly equal to the velocity of light.

Putting $\beta = 1$ in the numerator of the above equation gives

$$\frac{1}{\sqrt{1 - \beta^2}} = 197$$

and from Eq. (1-23) this equals m/m_0.   Hence, the mass of the electron after acceleration is 197 times its mass at injection!   Its final energy is

$$V = \frac{mc^2 - m_0c^2}{e} = \frac{m_0c^2}{e}\,(197 - 1)$$

$$= \frac{9 \times 10^{16} \times 196}{1.76 \times 10^{11}} = 10^8 \text{ ev, or 100 Mev}$$

b. The energy in electron volts given to the electron per trip around the doughnut is
$d\Phi/dt$.   The average value of this is the peak flux divided by the time it takes the flux
to build up to this maximum value, which in this example is one-quarter of a cycle.
By the 1:2 condition the peak flux is

$$2\pi r_0{}^2 B_0 = 2\pi(33 \times 2.54 \times 10^{-2})^2(0.4) = 1.80 \text{ webers}$$

and the time the flux takes to reach this value is $\frac{1}{4} \times \frac{1}{60} = \frac{1}{240}$ sec.   Hence, the average voltage per trip is $1.80 \times 240 = 430$ volts.   Since the flux varies sinusoidally with
time, the voltage per trip varies from revolution to revolution.   It is a maximum at
injection and drops to zero at the end of the electronic journey.   The average voltage
per trip is the 430 volts calculated above.
c. The number of revolutions made by each electron during its acceleration cycle is

$$\frac{10^8 \text{ volts}}{430 \text{ volts/trip}} = 230{,}000 \text{ revolutions}$$

d. The average transit time is the

$$\left(\frac{1}{240} \text{ sec}\right)\left(\frac{1}{230{,}000 \text{ revolutions}}\right) = 1.79 \times 10^{-8} \text{ sec/revolution}$$

The transit time per revolution remains almost constant throughout the electron's
journey.   This can be seen as follows: As soon as the electron acquires an energy of
1 Mev, its velocity is 94 per cent that of light.   Hence, as its energy increases from 1 to
100 Mev, its velocity changes by only 6 per cent (the increased energy manifesting
itself in an increased mass rather than an increased speed).   The transit time is given
by $2\pi r_0/v$, and since r_0 and v are almost constant, so is the time.   For example, the
transit time at the end of its journey is

$$\frac{2\pi r_0}{c} = \frac{2\pi(33 \times 2.54 \times 10^{-2})}{3 \times 10^8} = 1.75 \times 10^{-8} \text{ sec}$$

which agrees well with the average time calculated above.

The above illustrative example applies to the General Electric Co.[25]
100-Mev betatron.   The steel in the magnet of this instrument weighs
130 tons!   It is of some interest to note that it is desirable to correct for
the poor power factor which exists because the magnet is such a large
inductive load.   A tremendous bank of capacitors is used for this purpose.
These constitute a large fraction of the total cost and space.
Since the electrons make 230,000 revolutions, then the effects of the
mutual repulsions of the electrons and the scattering of the electrons by

residual gases must be counterbalanced.   It has been shown[26] that proper focusing can be obtained if the magnetic-field intensity in the region of the orbit varies as $1/r^n$, where $0 < n < 1$, provided that the field at the center of the magnet is so chosen as to satisfy the 1:2 condition.

In the synchrotron discussed in Sec. 2-12 the magnetic field varies with time, and hence some betatron action takes place in this instrument also.

2-14. The Magnetron.   Consider a long, straight filament of radius r_k and a coaxial cylindrical plate of radius r_a which is maintained at a positive potential E_b with respect to the cathode.   Assume that the electrons that leave the filament do so with zero initial velocities.   A magnetic field parallel to the axis of the filament is superposed upon the electric field.   This is the so-called *magnetron* arrangement, first introduced by Hull.[27] This longitudinal magnetic field may be obtained by placing a long solenoid directly over the tube, the strength of the magnetic field being varied by controlling the current through the solenoid.

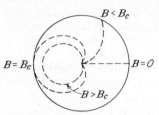

FIG. 2-16. The electronic path in a magnetron for several values of magnetic field.

The electronic paths will now be investigated qualitatively.   Suppose the magnetic field is reduced to zero.   The electron starts from rest at the cathode and is accelerated radially outward toward the plate by the electric field.   If a weak magnetic field is present, the electronic path will be curved, although the electron will strike the plate.   These conditions are illustrated in Fig. 2-16.

As the field is further increased, the path becomes more and more curved until a critical value B_c is reached, when the electronic path becomes tangent to the plate.   If the field is increased beyond this value, the electron does not strike the plate at all but instead returns to the filament.

A quantitative analysis of this problem leads to the following expression involving the critical field:

$$E_b = \frac{B_c{}^2 e r_a{}^2}{8m}\left(1 - \frac{r_k{}^2}{r_a{}^2}\right)^2 \tag{2-14}$$

Assume that a fixed potential E_b is applied between the cathode and the anode and that the plate current is read as a function of the applied magnetic field.   If B is less than the critical value B_c given by Eq. (2-14), the plate current should be unaffected, whereas for values of B greater than B_c the current should suddenly drop to zero, as illustrated by the curve of Fig. 2-17a.   Since a reversal of the direction of the magnetic field simply reverses the direction of travel of the electrons about the tube axis, the same current should be obtained for a given positive value of B as for an equal negative value of B as observed in Fig. 2-17.

In a practical tube the plate-current cutoff will not take place abruptly at a definite value B_c of magnetic field but will resemble that shown in Fig. 2-17b. This curve results mainly from the fact that the commercial tubes do not possess the ideal geometrical arrangement assumed in the mathematical discussion; that is, the cathode may not be coaxial with the anode and the plate is not a perfect cylinder. The theory assumes an infinitely long emitter and collector, a condition never satisfied in a commercial tube, although it can be approximated by using special tubes

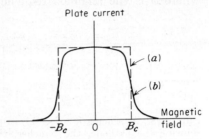

Fig. 2-17. Magnetron characteristics. (a) Ideal plate-current curve. (b) Actual.

with "guard rings." Also, if the tube contains an appreciable amount of gas, the plate-current characteristic will deviate appreciably from the ideal curve.

Very little practical use has been made of the static magnetron discussed here. However, it has been found that, if the anode is formed into a series of resonant cavities, the tube will perform efficiently as a very high-power oscillator of centimeter waves (microwaves).[28] One most important application of such tubes is in radar systems.

2-15. Velocity Modulation and Bunching.[12,29] All electrons leaving an electron gun have approximately the same velocity, that corresponding to the anode voltage. If they then pass through a region known as the *buncher* in which the potential varies with time, they will emerge from this second region with a speed that will depend upon the energy that they have acquired. Each electron will have a slightly different velocity from the preceding one, and the beam is said to be *velocity modulated*.

If the modulated beam is allowed to drift in a field-free space, then it is possible for a fast-moving electron to catch up with a slower-moving one that left the modulating region at some earlier time. The density of the electron stream will then no longer be uniform with distance along the drift space, and the beam is said to be *density modulated*. It is possible for this modulation to be intense enough for the electrons to form in bunches along the drift space. This process is called *bunching*.

These principles are made use of in the klystron, a microwave oscillator. The general characteristics of the modulating portion of such a tube are illustrated in Fig. 2-18. A quantitative discussion of the processes mentioned above follows.

The effect of a superimposed a-c buncher potential on the d-c gun voltage is to give the electrons a speed v as follows:

$$\tfrac{1}{2}mv^2 = e(E_a + E_b \sin \omega t) \tag{2-15}$$

where ω is the angular frequency of the a-c buncher potential. It is

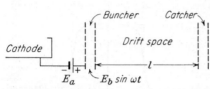

FIG. 2-18. A schematic of a klystron, showing the cathode, the buncher, the drift space, and the catcher.

assumed that the buncher grids are so close together that the electrons pass through this region in a time very short compared with one cycle of the modulating voltage. The velocity of the electron at the buncher entrance is

$$v_0 \equiv \sqrt{\frac{2eE_a}{m}} \tag{2-16}$$

and the expression for the velocity beyond the buncher is

$$v = v_0 \sqrt{1 + \alpha \sin \omega t} \tag{2-17}$$

where α is the ratio E_b/E_a. It is possible in principle for α to be greater than unity, although velocity-modulation tubes ordinarily operate with α much less than 1.

Subject to the limitations that α is small, the expression under the square-root sign may be expanded by the binomial expansion, and we find that v is approximately given by

$$v = v_0 \left(1 + \frac{\alpha}{2} \sin \omega t \right) \tag{2-18}$$

We see clearly that the electrons are velocity modulated at the buncher frequency.

At a distance l from the buncher along the drift tube there is a second pair of grids, called the *catcher*. The time of arrival t_2 at the catcher of an electron that passed the buncher at the time t_1 is

$$t_2 = t_1 + \frac{l}{v} \tag{2-19}$$

or, from Eq. (2-18),

$$t_2 = t_1 + \frac{l}{v_0[1 + (\alpha/2) \sin \omega t_1]}$$

Upon expanding the denominator there results, to the same approximation as before,

$$t_2 = t_1 + \frac{l}{v_0} \left(1 - \frac{\alpha}{2} \sin \omega t_1 \right) \tag{2-20}$$

It is convenient to multiply this equation by ω, and then all transit times are converted into transit angles. Introducing

$$\tau_1 \equiv \omega t_1 \qquad \tau_2 \equiv \omega t_2 \qquad \tau_0 \equiv \frac{\omega l}{v_0} \quad \text{rad} \qquad (2\text{-}21)$$

where τ_1 is called the *departure angle*, τ_2 the *arrival angle*, and τ_0 the *transit angle of an electron passing through the buncher when the modulating voltage is zero*, and

$$k \equiv \frac{\omega a l}{2 v_0} = \frac{\omega E_b l}{2 E_a v_0} \equiv \text{bunching parameter} \qquad (2\text{-}22)$$

the above equation takes the form

$$\tau_2 = \tau_1 + \tau_0 - k \sin \tau_1 \quad \text{rad} \qquad (2\text{-}23)$$

This equation is most important in bunching theory. Its significance can be seen by plotting τ_2 as a function of τ_1 for various values of the

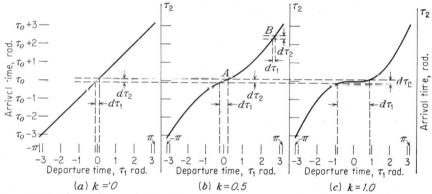

Fig. 2-19. Arrival time as a function of departure time (in radians). These curves illustrate the formation of a bunch.

parameter k. In Fig. 2-19a, $k = 0$, which means that there is no modulation. We see that a group of electrons arriving in the angular interval $d\tau_2$ came from an angular interval of equal size, namely, $d\tau_1 = d\tau_2$. This means that the catcher current equals the buncher current and there is no bunching, an obviously correct conclusion since the modulation is zero.

In Fig. 2-19b, $k = 0.5$, the same-size arrival interval $d\tau_2$ is taken, but it is seen that the interval from which the electrons departed depends upon the time τ_1. In the vicinity of the zero reference angle (region A) electrons are collected from a longer interval, $d\tau_1 > d\tau_2$ (as a matter of fact, $d\tau_1 = 2\,d\tau_2$). This means that the catcher current is greater than the buncher current, or that a *bunch* is being formed. Physically, this comes about because the faster electrons are catching up with the slower ones which left at an earlier time. In region B, however, $d\tau_1 < d\tau_2$, which means a smaller catcher current than buncher current. It should be clear that a plot of catcher current vs. time has a peak (greater than the electron-gun current) near the zero reference time and tapers off on both sides to a value below the beam current, as shown in Fig. 2-20.

In Fig. 2-19c, $k = 1.0$, the same-size arrival interval $d\tau_2$ is again taken. It is now seen that, near the origin, the electrons are collected from a very large interval $d\tau_1$, that is, $d\tau_1 \gg d\tau_2$. This condition represents a very large catcher current. As a matter of fact, if the interval $d\tau_2$ were taken very, very small (approaching zero), electrons would still be collected from a nonzero interval $d\tau_1$ or a finite number of electrons would be collected in an infinitesimal time. Since current is charge per unit time, this corresponds to an infinite current, as indicated in Fig. 2-20.

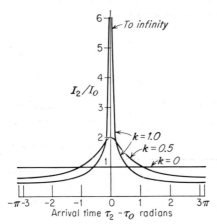

FIG. 2-20. Catcher current as a function of arrival time.

The bunching parameter k may be greater than unity. An analysis of this situation shows that electrons collected in a time $d\tau_2$ may have left the buncher in *several* discrete time intervals and that the current may contain more than one infinite peak.

The above considerations can be made quantitative as follows: If I_1 is the buncher current, then $I_1 dt_1$ is the charge leaving the buncher in the interval dt_1. If I_2 is the catcher current, then $I_2 dt_2$ is the charge entering the catcher in the interval dt_2. However, all electrons departing in the interval dt_1 arrive in the time dt_2, and hence, since there must be conservation of charge,

$$I_1 dt_1 = I_2 dt_2$$

or, since the buncher current is constant and equal to the d-c beam current I_0,

$$I_2 = I_0 \frac{dt_1}{dt_2} \tag{2-24}$$

From Eq. (2-23) this becomes

$$\frac{I_2}{I_0} = \frac{1}{1 - k \cos \tau_1} \tag{2-25}$$

This equation clearly shows the infinite value of I_2 at $\tau_1 = 0$ for $k = 1$. The value of I_2 as a function of τ_1 has no great significance, but I_2 vs. τ_2 is desired. This relationship cannot be obtained analytically since it requires solving the transcendental equation (2-23) for τ_1 in terms of τ_2. The graphs of Fig. 2-20 are obtained by assuming a value of τ_1 and then solving for τ_2 from Eq. (2-23) and for I_2/I_0 from Eq. (2-25).

REFERENCES

1. MacGregor-Morris, J. T., and V. A. Hughes, "Experimental Verification of Theory of Cathode-ray Oscillograph; and Influence of Screen Potential," *JIEE*, **79**, 454–462, October, 1936.
2. *Du Mont Lab. Comm.* 3, **19**, 33, 1939.
   Bigalke, A., "Nachbeschleunigungs-Elektronenstrahl-Oszillograph," *Z. tech. Physik*, **19**, 163–166, 1938.
   Rogowski, W., and H. Thielen, "Ueber Nachbeschleunigung bei Braunschen Roehren," *Arch. Elektrotech.*, **33**, 411–417, June, 1939.
3. Lempert, I. E., and R. Feldt, "The 5RP Multiband Tube: An Intensifier-type Cathode-ray Tube for High Voltage Operation," *Proc. IRE*, **34**, 432–440, July, 1946.
4. Nuttall, A. K., "Cathode-ray Oscillograph for Direct Measurement of High-voltage Transients," *JIEE*, **78**, 229–234, February, 1936.
   Miller, J. L., and J. E. L. Robinson, "Design and Operation of High-speed Cathode-ray Oscillograph," *ibid.*, **74**, 511–519, (discussion) 519–535, June, 1934.
5. Grossbohlin, H. W., and K. A. Hoaglund, "Improved Instrument Cathode-ray Tube Design," internal memo, A. B. Du Mont Laboratories, Inc., 1957.
6. Maloff, I. G., and D. W. Epstein, "Electron Optics in Television," 1st ed., McGraw-Hill Book Company, Inc., New York, 1938.
   Zworykin, V. K., and G. A. Morton, "Television," John Wiley & Sons, Inc., New York, 1940.
7. Cosslett, V. E., "Introduction to Electron Optics," Oxford University Press, New York, 1946.
8. Nottingham, W. B., "Electrical and Luminescent Properties of Willemite under Electron Bombardment," *J. Appl. Phys.*, **8**, 762–778, November, 1937.
   Nottingham, W. B., "Electrical and Luminescent Properties of Phosphors under Electron Bombardment," *ibid.*, **10**, 73–83, January, 1939.
   Martin, S. T., and L. B. Headrick, "Light Output and Secondary Emission Characteristics of Luminescent Materials," *ibid.*, **10**, 116–127, February, 1939.
9. Liebmann, G., "Ion Burn in Cathode Ray Tubes," *Electronic Eng.*, **18**, 289–290, September, 1946.
10. Sharpe, J., "The Ion Trap in C. R. Tubes," *Electronic Eng.*, **18**, 385–386, December, 1946.
    Bowie, R. M., "The Negative-ion Blemish in a Cathode-ray Tube and Its Elimination," *Proc. IRE*, **36**, 1482–1486, December, 1948.
11. Epstein, D. W., and L. Pensak, "Improved Cathode-ray Tubes with Metal-backed Luminescent Screens," *RCA Rev.*, **7**, 5–10, March, 1946.
12. Spangenberg, K. R., "Vacuum Tubes," 1st ed., McGraw-Hill Book Company, Inc., New York, 1948.
13. Du Mont, A. B., "Elimination of Distortion in Cathode-ray Tubes," *Electronics*, **8**, 16–17, January, 1935.
    Fleming-Williams, B. C., "Single-valve Time-base Circuit," *Wireless Eng.*, **17**, 161–163, April, 1940.
    Millman, J., and S. Seely, "Electronics," 1st ed., McGraw-Hill Book Company, Inc., New York, 1941.

14. BENTLEY, A. Y., K. A. HOAGLAND, and H. W. GROSSBOHLIN, "Self-focusing Picture Tube," *Electronics*, **25**, 107–109, June, 1952.

15. ASTON, F. W., "Mass-Spectra and Isotopes," Longmans, Green & Co., Inc., New York, 1933.
    DEMPSTER, A. J., "New Methods in Mass Spectroscopy," *Proc. Am. Phil. Soc.*, **75**, 755–767, 1935.
    BAINBRIDGE, K. T., and E. B. JORDAN, "Mass Spectrum Analysis," *Phys. Rev.*, **50**, 282–296, August, 1936.
    SAMPSON, M. B., and W. BLEAKNEY, "A Mass-spectrograph Study of Ba, Sr, In, Ga, Li, and Na," *ibid.*, **50**, 456–460, September, 1936.

16. HIPPLE, J. A., D. J. GROVE, and W. M. HICKAM, "Electronics of the Mass Spectrometer," *Elec. Eng.*, **64**, 141–145, April, 1945.

17. WORCESTER, W. G., and E. G. DOUGHTY, "High Vacuum Leak Testing with the Mass Spectrometer," *Elec. Eng.*, **65**, 946–955, December, 1945.
    THOMAS, H. A., T. W. WILLIAMS, and J. A. HIPPLE, "A Mass Spectrometer Type of Leak Detector," *Rev. Sci. Instr.*, **17**, 368–372, October, 1946.
    NIER, A. O., C. M. STEVENS, A. HUSTRULID, and T. A. ABBOTT, "Mass Spectrometer for Leak Detection," *J. Appl. Phys.*, **18**, 30–33, January, 1947.

18. LAWRENCE, E. O., and M. S. LIVINGSTON, "The Production of High Speed Light Ions without the Use of High Voltages," *Phys. Rev.*, **40**, 19–35, April, 1932.
    LAWRENCE, E. O., and M. S. LIVINGSTON, "The Multiple Acceleration of Ions to Very High Speeds," *ibid.*, **45**, 608–612, May, 1934.
    LIVINGOOD, J. J., "Radioactivity by Bombardment," *Electronics*, **8**, 421–423, 474, November, 1935.
    MANN, W. B., "The Cyclotron," Chemical Publishing Company, Inc., New York, 1940.
    WILSON, R. R., "Theory of the Cyclotron," *J. Appl. Phys.*, **11**, 781–796, December, 1940.
    LIVINGSTON, M. S., "The Cyclotron. I," *ibid.*, **15**, 2–19, January, 1944, and "The Cyclotron. II," *ibid.*, **15**, 128–147, February, 1944.
    LIVINGSTON, M. S., Particle Accelerators, in "Advances in Electronics," Vol. 1, pp. 269–316, Academic Press, Inc., New York, 1948.

19. BROBECK, W. M., E. O. LAWRENCE, K. R. MACKENZIE, E. M. McMILLAN, R. SERBER, D. C. SEWELL, K. M. SIMPSON, and R. L. THORNTON, "Initial Performance of the 184-inch Cyclotron of the University of California," *Phys. Rev.*, **71**, 449–450, April, 1947.

20. ELDER, F. R., A. M. GUREWITSCH, R. V. LANGMUIR, and H. C. POLLOCK, "A 70-Mev Synchrotron," *J. Appl. Phys.*, **18**, 810–818, September, 1947.

21. LIVINGSTON, M. S., J. P. BLEWETT, G. K. GREEN, and L. J. HAWORTH, "Design Study for a Three-Bev Proton Accelerator," *Rev. Sci. Instr.*, **21**, 7–22, January, 1950.

22. COURANT, E. D., M. S. LIVINGSTON, and H. S. SNYDER, "The Strong-focusing Synchrotron—A New High Energy Accelerator," *Phys. Rev.*, **88**, 1190–1196, December, 1952.

23. LIVINGSTON, R. S., "Trends in Cyclotron Design," *Ind. Eng. Chem.*, **48**(8), 1231–1237, August, 1956.

24. KERST, D. W., "The Acceleration of Electrons by Magnetic Induction," *Phys. Rev.*, **60**, 47–53, July, 1941.
    WANG, T. J., "The Betatron," *Electronics*, **18**, 128–134, June, 1945.

25. WESTENDORP, W. F., and E. E. CHARLTON, "A 100-Million Volt Induction Electron Accelerator," *J. Appl. Phys.*, **16**, 581–593, October, 1945.

26. KERST, D. W., and R. SERBER, "Electronic Orbits in the Induction Accelerator," *Phys. Rev.*, **60**, 53–58, July, 1941.

WANG, T. J., "The Betatron," *Electronics*, **18**, 128–134, 1945.

27. HULL, A. W., "The Effect of a Uniform Magnetic Field on the Motion of Electrons between Coaxial Cylinders," *Phys. Rev.*, **18**, 31–57, July, 1921.

28. FISK, J. B., H. D. HAGSTRUM, and P. L. HARTMAN, "The Magnetron as a Generator of Centimeter Waves," *Bell System Tech. J.*, **25**, 167–348, April, 1946.

COLLINS, G. B., "Microwave Magnetrons," 1st ed., Radiation Laboratory Series, Vol. 6, McGraw-Hill Book Company, Inc., New York, 1948.

29. HAMILTON, D. R., J. K. KNIPP, and J. B. H. KUPER, "Klystrons and Microwave Triodes," Radiation Laboratory Series, Vol. 7, McGraw-Hill Book Company, Inc., New York, 1948.

BRONWELL, A. B., and R. E. BEAM, "Theory and Application of Microwaves," 1st ed., McGraw-Hill Book Company, Inc., New York, 1947.

CHAPTER 3

METALS AND SEMICONDUCTORS

In this chapter we present physical "pictures" of the inside of a metal and a semiconductor. The nature of conduction in a solid and the laws governing the emission of electrons from the surface of a metal are considered.

3-1. Free Electrons in Metals. X-ray and other studies reveal that most metals and semiconductors are crystalline in structure. A crystal consists of a space array of atoms or molecules (strictly speaking, ions) built up by regular repetition in three dimensions of some fundamental structural unit. In a metal the outer electrons of the atom are as much associated with one ion as with another, so that the electron attachment to any individual atom is practically zero. Depending upon the metal, at least one and sometimes two or three electrons per atom are free to move throughout the interior of the metal under the action of applied forces.

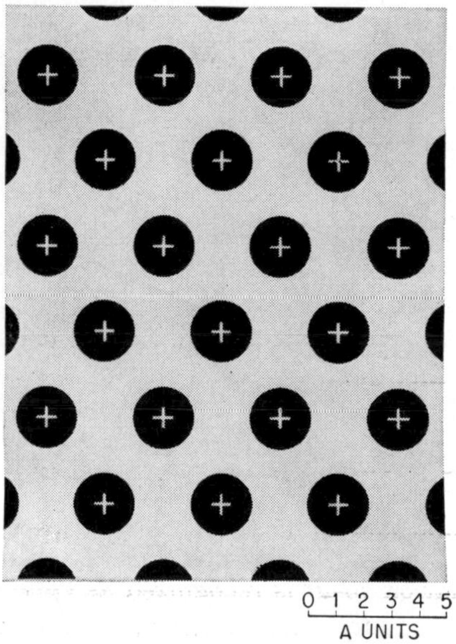

Figure 3-1 shows the charge distribution within a metal, specifically, sodium. The plus signs represent the heavy positive sodium nuclei of the individual atoms. The heavily shaded regions represent the electrons in the sodium atom that are tightly bound to the nucleus. These are inappreciably disturbed as the atoms come together to form the metal. The light shading represents the outer, or valence, electrons in the atom; and it is these electrons that cannot be said to belong to any particular atom. Instead, they have completely lost their individuality and can

FIG. 3-1. Arrangement of the sodium atoms in one plane of the metal. (*W. Shockley, J. Appl. Phys.*, **10**, 543, 1939.)

wander freely about from atom to atom in the metal. Thus a metal is visualized as a region containing a periodic three-dimensional array of heavy, tightly bound ions permeated with a swarm of electrons that may move about quite freely. This picture is known as the "electron-gas" description of a metal.

3-2. Mobility and Conductivity. According to the electron-gas theory of a metal, the electrons are in continuous motion, the direction of flight being changed at each collision with the heavy (almost stationary) ions. The average distance between collisions is called the *mean free path.* Since the motion is random, then, on an average, there will be as many electrons passing through unit area in the metal in any direction as in the opposite direction in a given time. Hence, the average current is zero. ɪɴ ᴛʜᴇ ᴍᴇᴛᴀʟ.

Let us now see how the situation is changed if a constant electric field of magnitude ε volts per meter is applied to the metal. As a result of this electrostatic force the electrons would be accelerated and the velocity would increase indefinitely with time, were it not for the collisions with the ions. However, at each inelastic collision with an ion an electron loses energy, and a steady-state condition is reached where a finite value of *drift speed v* is attained. This drift velocity is in the direction opposite to that of the electric field, and its magnitude is proportional to ε. Thus,

$$v = \mu\varepsilon \tag{3-1}$$

where μ square meters per volt-second is called the *mobility* of the electrons.

According to the above theory, a steady-state drift speed has been superimposed upon the random thermal motion of the electrons. Such a directed flow of electrons constitutes a current. If the concentration of free electrons is n electrons per cubic meter, then the current density J amperes per square meter is (Sec. 1-10)

$$J = nev = ne\mu\varepsilon = \sigma\varepsilon \tag{3-2}$$

where

$$\sigma = ne\mu \quad \text{(ohm-meter)}^{-1} \tag{3-3}$$

is the *conductivity* of the metal. Equation (3-2) is recognized as Ohm's law: namely, the conduction current is proportional to the applied voltage. As already mentioned, the energy which the electrons acquire from the applied field is, as a result of collisions, given to the lattice ions. Hence, power is dissipated within the metal by the electrons, and the power density (Joule heat) is given by $J\varepsilon = \sigma\varepsilon^2$ watts per cubic meter.

3-3. The Energy Method of Analyzing the Motion of a Particle. A method is considered in Chap. 1 by which the motion of charged particles may be analyzed. It consists of the solution of Newton's second law in which the forces of electric and magnetic origin are equated to the product of the mass and the acceleration of the particle. Obviously, this method is not applicable when the forces are as complicated as they must be in a metal. Furthermore, it is neither possible nor desirable to consider what happens to each individual electron.

It is necessary, therefore, to consider an alternative approach. This method employs the law of the conservation of energy, use being made of the potential-energy curve corresponding to the field of force. The principles involved may best be understood by considering specific examples of the method.

Example. An idealized diode consists of plane-parallel electrodes, 5 cm apart. The anode A is maintained 10 volts negative with respect to the cathode K. An electron leaves the cathode with an initial energy of 2 ev. What is the maximum distance it can travel from the cathode?

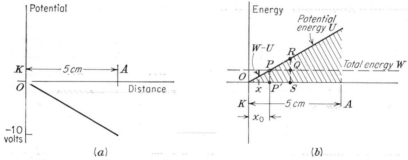

Fig. 3-2. Illustration of the potential-energy barrier encountered by an electron in a retarding field.

Solution. This problem will be analyzed by the energy method. Figure 3-2a is a linear plot of potential vs. distance, and in Fig. 3-2b is indicated the corresponding potential energy vs. distance. Since potential is the potential energy per unit charge (Sec. 1-4), curve b is obtained from curve a by multiplying each ordinate by the charge on the electron (a negative number). Since the total energy W of the electron remains constant, it is represented as a horizontal line. The kinetic energy at any distance x equals the difference between the total energy W and the potential energy U at this point. This difference is greatest at O, indicating that the kinetic energy is a maximum when the electron leaves the cathode. At the point P this difference is zero, which means that no kinetic energy exists, so that the particle is at rest at this point. This distance, x_0, is the maximum that the electron can travel from the cathode. At point P it comes momentarily to rest and then reverses its motion and returns to the cathode. From geometry it is seen that $x_0/5 = \frac{2}{10}$ or $x_0 = 1$ cm.

Consider a point such as S which is at a greater distance than 1 cm from the cathode. Here the total energy QS is less than the potential energy RS, so that the difference, which represents the kinetic energy, is negative. This is an impossible physical condition, however, since negative kinetic energy ($\frac{1}{2}mv^2 < 0$) implies an imaginary velocity. We must conclude that the particle can never advance a distance greater than OP' from the cathode.

The foregoing analysis leads to the very important conclusion that the shaded portion of Fig. 3-2b can never be penetrated by the electron. Thus, at point P the particle acts *as if* it had collided with a solid wall, hill, or barrier and the direction of its flight had been altered. *Potential energy barriers* of this sort will play important roles in the analyses to follow.

It must be emphasized that the words "collides with" or "rebounds from" a potential "hill" are convenient descriptive phrases and that an actual encounter between two material bodies is not implied.

As a second illustration, consider a mathematical pendulum of length l, consisting of a "point" bob of mass m that is free to swing in the earth's gravitational field. If the lowest point of the swing (point O, Fig. 3-3) is chosen as the origin, then the potential energy of the mass at any point P corresponding to any angle θ of the swing is given by

$$U = mgy = mgl(1 - \cos \theta) \tag{3-4}$$

where g is the acceleration of gravity. This potential-energy function is illustrated graphically in Fig. 3-4.

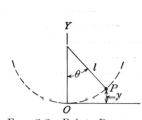

FIG. 3-3. Point P represents the mass m of a mathematical pendulum swinging in the earth's gravitational field.

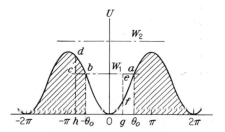

FIG. 3-4. The potential energy of the bob in Fig. 3-3 plotted as a function of the angle of swing.

Consider the resultant motion of the bob if it is given a potential energy U_1 by raising it through an angle θ_0 and releasing it with zero initial velocity. If dissipation is neglected, the particle will swing back and forth through the angle $2\theta_0$, going from θ_0 on one side to θ_0 on the other side of the vertical axis. How might we analyze the motion of the physical system if only the potential-energy field of Fig. 3-4 were given without specifying the physical character of the system?

The procedure is the same as that followed in the simple diode problem considered above. A horizontal line *aebc* is drawn at a height equal to the total energy W_1 of the particle. At any point, such as e, the total energy is represented by $eg = W_1$, and the potential energy is represented by fg. The difference between these two, namely, ef, represents the kinetic energy of the particle when the angle of swing, given by the intercept of eg on the axis, corresponds to Og. In other words, the difference between the total-energy line and the potential-energy curve at any angle represents the kinetic energy of the particle under these conditions. This difference is greatest at O, indicating that the kinetic energy is a maximum at the bottom of the swing, an almost evident result. At the points a and b this difference is zero. This condition means that no kinetic energy exists, or that the particle is at rest at these points. This result is evident, since corresponding to the points a ($\theta = \theta_0$) and b ($\theta = -\theta_0$), the particle is about to reverse its motion.

Consider a point in the shaded region outside the range $-\theta_0$ to $+\theta_0$, such as h. Here the total energy ch is less than the potential energy dh. This impossible condition is interpreted by our previous reasoning to mean that the particle whose total energy is W_1 can never swing to the angle Oh, so that the motion must be confined to the region ab. The shaded portions of Fig. 3-4 represent the potential barrier which can never be penetrated by the bob, if its total energy is no greater than W_1. This type of constrained motion about a point O is closely analogous to that of the so-called "bound" electrons in a metal, as will be seen later.

Now consider the case when the bob has a total energy equal to W_2, which is greater than the maximum of the potential-energy curve. Clearly from Fig. 3-4 the horizontal line corresponding to this energy cannot intersect the curve at any point. Consequently, the particle does not "collide" with the potential barrier, and its course is never altered, so that it moves through an ever-increasing angle. Of course, its kinetic energy varies over wide limits, being maximum for $\theta = 0, 2\pi, 4\pi, \ldots$ and minimum for $\theta = \pi, 3\pi, 5\pi, \ldots$. Physically, this type of motion results when the bob has enough energy to set it spinning completely around in a circular path. This type of motion is somewhat analogous to that experienced by the so-called "free" electrons in a metal.

This simple but powerful energy method facilitates the discussion of the motion of a particle in a conservative field of force, such as that found in the body of a metal. It will also be applied to many other types of problem. For example, the method of analysis just considered is extremely useful in determining whether electrons will possess sufficient energy to pass through grids and reach the various electrodes in a vacuum tube, whether or not electrons or ions will be able to penetrate electron clouds in a vacuum tube or ion sheaths in a gaseous-discharge tube, and whether charge carriers can cross a semiconductor junction. This method will now be applied to the analysis of the motion of electrons in metals.

3-4. The Potential-energy Field in a Metal. It is desired to set up the potential-energy field for the three-dimensional array of atoms that exists in the interior of a metal and to discuss the motion of electrons in this field. The resultant potential energy at any point in the metal is simply the sum of the potential energies produced at this point by all the ions of the lattice. To determine the potential energy due to one ion, it is noted that an atom of atomic number Z has a net positive charge Ze on its nucleus. Surrounding this nucleus is an approximately spherical cloud, or shell, of Z electrons. By Gauss's law the potential at a point at a distance r from the nucleus varies inversely as r and directly as the total charge enclosed within a sphere of radius r. Since the potential V equals the potential energy U per unit charge (Sec. 1-4), then $U = -eV$. The minus sign is introduced since e represents the magnitude of the (negative) electronic charge.

The potential of any point may be chosen as the zero reference of potential because it is only differences of potential that have any physical significance. For the present discussion it is convenient to choose zero potential at infinity, and then the potential energy at any point is negative. Enough has been said to make plausible the potential-energy

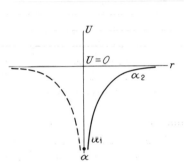

FIG. 3-5. The potential energy of an electron as a function of radial distance from an isolated nucleus.

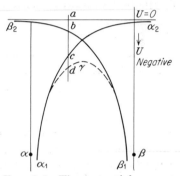

FIG. 3-6. The potential energy resulting from two nuclei α and β.

curve illustrated in Fig. 3-5. Here α represents a nucleus, the potential energy of which is given by the curve $\alpha_1\alpha_2$. The vertical scale represents U, and the horizontal scale gives the distance r from the nucleus. It must be emphasized that r represents a radial distance from the nucleus and hence can be taken in any direction. If the direction is horizontal but to the left of the nucleus, then the dashed curve represents the potential energy.

To represent the potential energy at every point in space requires a four-dimensional picture, three dimensions for the three space coordinates and a fourth for the potential-energy axis. This difficulty is avoided by plotting U along some chosen line through the crystal, say through a row of ions. From this graph and the method by which it is constructed it is easy to visualize what the potential energy at any other point might be. In order to build up this picture, consider first two adjacent ions, and neglect all others. The construction is shown in Fig. 3-6. $\alpha_1\alpha_2$ is the U curve for nucleus α, and $\beta_1\beta_2$ is the corresponding U curve for the adjacent nucleus β. If these were the only nuclei present in the metal, the resultant U curve in the region between α and β would be the sum of these two curves, as shown by the dashed curve $\alpha_1\gamma\beta_1$ (since $ad = ab + ac$). It is seen that the resultant curve is very nearly the same as the original curves in the immediate vicinity of a nucleus, but it is lower and flatter than either individual curve in the region between the nuclei.

Let us now single out an entire row of nuclei α, β, γ, δ, ϵ, . . . from the metallic lattice (Figs. 3-1 and 3-7) and sketch the potential energy as we proceed along this line from one nucleus to the other, until the surface of the metal is reached. Following the same type of construction as above, but considering the influence of other nearby nuclei, an energy distribution somewhat as illustrated in Fig. 3-7 is obtained.

According to classical electrostatics, which does not take the atomic structure into account, the interior of a metal is an equipotential region.

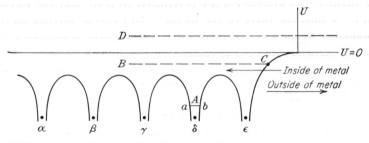

FIG. 3-7. The potential-energy distribution within and at the surface of a metal.

The present, more accurate, picture shows that the potential energy varies appreciably in the immediate neighborhoods of the nuclei and actually tends to $-\infty$ in these regions. However, the potential is approximately constant for the greatest *volume* of the metal, as indicated by the slowly varying portions of the diagram in the regions between the ions.

Consider the conditions that exist near the surface of the metal. It is evident, according to the present point of view, that the exact position of the "surface" cannot be defined. It is located at a small distance from the last nucleus ϵ in the row. It is to be noted that, since no nuclei exist to the right of ϵ, there can be no lowering and flattening of the potential-energy curve such as prevails in the region between the nuclei. This leads to a most important conclusion, *viz.: A potential-energy "hill," or "barrier," exists at the surface of the metal.*

3-5. Bound and Free Electrons. The motion of an electron in the potential-energy field of Fig. 3-7 will now be discussed by the method given in Sec. 3-3. Consider an electron in the metal that possesses a total energy corresponding to the level A in Fig. 3-7. This electron collides with, and rebounds from, the potential walls at a and b. It cannot drift very far from the nucleus but can move about only in the neighborhood *ab* of the nucleus. Obviously this electron is strongly bound to the nucleus and so is called a *bound electron.* It is evident that these bound electrons contribute very little to the conductivity of the metal since they cannot drift in the metal, even under the stimulus of an externally applied electric field. These electrons are responsible for the heavy shading in the neighborhood of the nuclei of Fig. 3-1.

Our present interest is in the *free, or conduction,* electrons in the metal rather than in the bound ones. A free electron is one having an energy corresponding to the level B of the figure. At no point *within* the metal is its total energy entirely converted into potential energy. Hence, at no point is its velocity zero, and the electron travels more or less freely throughout the body of the metal. However, when the electron reaches the surface of the metal, it collides with the potential-energy barrier there. At the point C, its kinetic energy is reduced to zero, and the electron is turned back into the body of the metal. An electron having an energy corresponding to the level D collides with no potential walls, not even the one at the surface, and so it is capable of leaving the metal.

In our subsequent discussions the bound electrons will be neglected completely since they in no way contribute to the phenomena to be studied. Attention will be focused on the free electrons. The region in which they find themselves is essentially a potential plateau, or equipotential region. It is only for distances close to an ion that there is any appreciable variation in potential. Since the regions of rapidly varying potential represent but a very small portion of the total volume of the metal, we shall henceforth assume that the field distribution within the metal is equipotential and the free electrons are subject to no forces whatsoever. The present viewpoint is therefore essentially that of classical electrostatics.

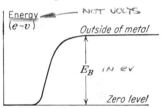

FIG. 3-8. For the free electrons, the interior of a metal may be considered an equipotential volume, but there is a potential barrier at the surface.

Figure 3-7 is redrawn in Fig. 3-8, all potential* variations within the metal being omitted, with the exception of the potential barrier at the surface. For the present discussion, the zero of energy is chosen at the level of the plateau of this diagram. This choice of the zero-energy

* This figure really represents potential energy and not potential. However, the phrase "potential barrier" is much more common in the literature than the phrase "potential-energy barrier." Where no confusion is likely to arise, these two expressions will be used interchangeably. These barriers will be measured in electron volts, and hence the symbol E will replace the U of the preceding sections. It must be emphasized that one unit of E represents 1.60×10^{-19} joule of energy.

reference level is valid since, as has already been emphasized, only difference of potential has physical significance.   The region outside the metal is now at a potential equal to E_B, the height of the potential-energy barrier in electron volts.

3-6. Energy Distribution of Electrons.   In order to be able to escape, an electron inside the metal must possess an amount of energy at least as great as that represented by the surface barrier E_B.   It is therefore important to know what energies are possessed by the electrons in a metal.   This relationship is called the *energy distribution function*.   We shall digress briefly in order to make clear what is meant by a distribution function.

Suppose that we were interested in the distribution in age of the people in the United States.   A sensible way to indicate this relationship is

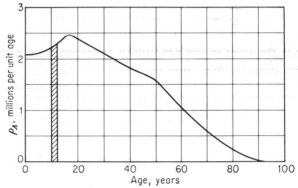

Fig. 3-9. The distribution function in age of the people in the United States.

shown in Fig. 3-9, where the abscissa is *age* and the ordinate is ρ_A, the *density* of the population in age.   This density gives the number dN_A of people whose ages lie in the range between A and $A + dA$, or

$$dN_A = \rho_A \, dA \qquad (3\text{-}5)$$

The data for such a plot are obtained from census information.   We see, for example, that the number of persons having ages between 10 and 12 years is represented by dN_A, with $\rho_A = 2.25$ million per year chosen as the mean ordinate between 10 and 12 years, and dA is taken as $12 - 10 = 2$ years.   Thus $dN_A = \rho_A \, dA = 4.50$ million.   Geometrically, this is the shaded area of Fig. 3-9.   Evidently, the total population N is given by

$$N = \int dN_A = \int \rho_A \, dA \qquad (3\text{-}6)$$

or simply the total area under the curve.

We shall now be concerned with the distribution in energy of the free electrons in a metal.   By analogy with Eq. (3-5), we may write

$$dN_E = \rho_E \, dE \qquad (3\text{-}7)$$

where dN_E represents the number of free electrons per cubic meter whose energies lie in the energy interval dE electron volts and where ρ_E gives the density of electrons in this interval. The question that immediately presents itself is: What is the mathematical expression for the density function ρ_E? Fermi,[1] and independently Dirac,[2] taking into account the quantum nature of the electron, other physical facts, and the laws of probability, deduced this most probable distribution function[3] for electrons. The application of this statistics to the theory of metals is due primarily to Sommerfeld. The Fermi-Dirac-Sommerfeld energy density function may be expressed in the form

$$\rho_E = \frac{\gamma E^{\frac{1}{2}}}{1 + \epsilon^{(E-E_M)/E_T}} \quad \text{(electrons/m}^3\text{)/ev}$$

where γ is a constant defined by

$$\gamma \equiv \frac{4\pi}{h^3}(2me)^{\frac{3}{2}} \quad \text{(electrons/m}^3\text{)/(ev)}^{\frac{3}{2}} \qquad = 6.82 \times 10^{27}$$

for electrons.

\hfill (3-8)

and where m is the mass of the electron in kilograms, h is a constant (its dimensions are joule-seconds) first introduced by Planck, ϵ is the base of natural logarithms, E is the energy of the electron in electron volts, E_M is a parameter to be discussed later, and E_T is defined by the relationship

$$eE_T \equiv kT \qquad (3\text{-}9)$$

where k is the Boltzmann gas constant in joules per degree Kelvin, T is the temperature in degrees absolute or Kelvin, and e is the electronic charge in coulombs. The quantity E_T is called the *electron-volt equivalent of temperature*[4] and is a convenient abbreviation. The numerical values of the physical constants introduced here are contained in Appendix I. Equation (3-9) becomes, upon substituting numerical values for the constants contained in the equation,

$$E_T = \frac{T}{11,600} \qquad (3\text{-}10)$$

This permits a rapid conversion from temperature to the electron-volt equivalent.

Several points must be emphasized before discussing Eq. (3-8). Since our interests are confined only to the free electrons, it will be assumed that there are no potential variations within the metal. Hence, there must be, a priori, the same number of electrons in each cubic meter of the metal. That is, the density in space (electrons per cubic meter) is a constant. However, within each unit volume of metal there will be electrons having all possible energies. It is this distribution in energy (per cubic meter of the metal) that is expressed by Eq. (3-8).

At a temperature of absolute zero, Eq. (3-8) attains a very striking form known as the *completely degenerate function.* When $T = 0°$K, then $E_T = 0$, and two possible conditions exist: (1) If $E > E_M$, then the exponential term becomes infinite, whence $\rho_E = 0$. Consequently, *there are no electrons with energies greater than E_M at absolute zero of temperature.* That is, E_M is the *maximum* energy that any electron may possess at absolute zero. This important quantity E_M is often referred to as the "Fermi characteristic energy" or the "Fermi level." (2) If $E < E_M$, then the exponential in Eq. (3-8) becomes zero. Hence

$$\left.\begin{array}{ll} \rho_E = \gamma E^{\frac{1}{2}} & \text{for } E < E_M \\ \rho_E = 0 & \text{for } E > E_M \end{array}\right\} \quad \text{when } E_T = 0 \qquad (3\text{-}11)$$

A plot of the distribution in energy given by Eqs. (3-8) and (3-11) for metallic tungsten at $T = 0°$K and $T = 2500°$K is shown in Fig. 3-10. The area under each curve is simply the total number of particles per cubic meter of the metal, whence the two areas must be equal. Also, the curves for all temperatures must pass through the same ordinate, namely, $\rho_E = \gamma E_M{}^{\frac{1}{2}}/2$, at the point $E = E_M$, as is evident from Eq. (3-8).

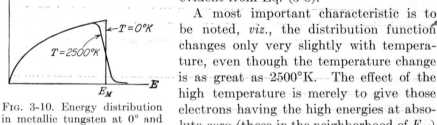

A most important characteristic is to be noted, *viz.,* the distribution function changes only very slightly with temperature, even though the temperature change is as great as 2500°K. The effect of the high temperature is merely to give those electrons having the high energies at absolute zero (those in the neighborhood of E_M) still higher energies, whereas those having

FIG. 3-10. Energy distribution in metallic tungsten at 0° and 2500°K.

lower energies have been left practically undisturbed. Since the curve for $T = 2500°$K approaches the energy axis asymptotically, a few electrons will have large values of energy.

An expression for E_M may be obtained on the basis of the completely degenerate function. The area under the curve of Fig. 3-10 represents the total number of free electrons (as always, per cubic meter of the metal). Thus

$$N = \int_0^{E_M} \gamma E^{\frac{1}{2}} \, dE = \tfrac{2}{3}\gamma E_M{}^{\frac{3}{2}}$$

or

$$E_M = \left(\frac{3N}{2\gamma}\right)^{\frac{2}{3}} \quad \text{ev} \qquad (3\text{-}12)$$

Inserting the numerical value (6.82×10^{27}) of the constant γ in this expression, there results

$$E_M = 3.64 \times 10^{-19} N^{\frac{2}{3}} \quad \text{ev} \qquad (3\text{-}13)$$

Since the density N (electrons per cubic meter) varies from metal to metal, then E_M will also vary among metals. Knowing the specific gravity, the atomic weight, and the number of free electrons per atom, it is a simple matter to calculate N, and so E_M. For most metals the numerical value of E_M is less than 10 ev.

Example. The specific gravity of tungsten is 18.8, and its atomic weight is 184.0.* Assume that there are two free electrons per atom. Calculate the numerical values of N and E_M.

Solution. A quantity of any substance equal to its molecular weight in grams is a *mole* of that substance. Further, 1 mole of any substance contains the same number of molecules as 1 mole of any other substance. This number is *Avogadro's number* and equals 6.02×10^{23} molecules per mole. Thus

$$N = 6.02 \times 10^{23} \frac{\text{molecules}}{\text{mole}} \times \frac{1 \text{ mole}}{184 \text{ g}} \times 18.8 \frac{\text{g}}{\text{cm}^3} \times \frac{2 \text{ electrons}}{\text{atom}} \times \frac{1 \text{ atom}}{\text{molecule}}$$

$$= 12.3 \times 10^{22} \frac{\text{electrons}}{\text{cm}^3} = 1.23 \times 10^{29} \frac{\text{electrons}}{\text{m}^3}$$

since for tungsten the atomic and the molecular weights are the same. Therefore, for tungsten,

$$E_M = 3.64 \times 10^{-19}(123 \times 10^{27})^{\frac{2}{3}} = 8.95 \text{ ev}$$

3-7. Work Function. In Fig. 3-11, Fig. 3-10 has been rotated 90 deg counterclockwise and combined with Fig. 3-8 so that the vertical axis represents energy for both sets of curves.[5] At $0°$K it is impossible for an electron to escape from the metal because this requires an amount of energy equal to E_B and the maximum energy possessed by any electron is only E_M. It is necessary to supply an additional amount of energy equal to the difference between E_B and E_M in order to make this escape possible. This difference, written E_W, is known as the *work function* of the metal.

$$E_W \equiv E_B - E_M \qquad (3-14)$$

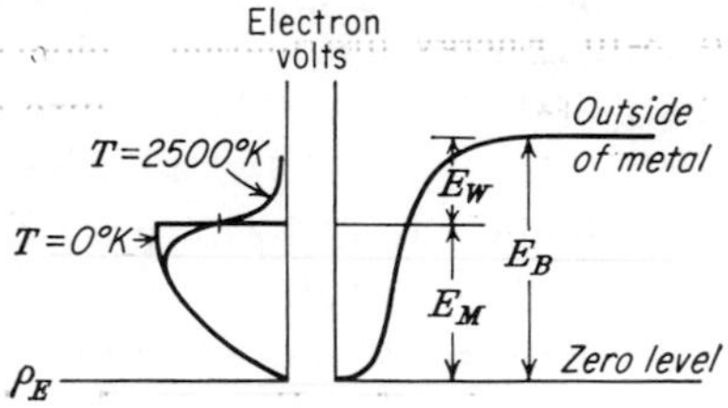

FIG. 3-11 Energy diagram used to define the work function.

Thus the work function of a metal represents the minimum amount of energy that must be given to the fastest-moving electron at the absolute zero of temperature in order for this electron to be able to escape from the metal.

The experiments of Davisson and Germer[6] and of Rupp[7] on the diffraction of electrons in passing through matter have verified the existence of the potential-energy barrier at the surface of the metal. In fact, based on the results of these experiments together with experimentally determined values of E_W, it is possible to calculate the values of E_M for the

* The atomic weights of the elements are given in the periodic table (Appendix III).

metals used. These data show fair agreement between the experimental and theoretical values.

A second physical meaning of the term "work function" may be obtained by considering what happens to an electron as it escapes from a metal, without particular regard to the conditions within the interior of the metal. A negative electron will induce a positive charge on a metal from which it escapes. There will then be a force of attraction between the induced charge and the electron. Unless the electron possesses sufficient energy to carry it out of the region of influence of this image force of attraction, it will be returned to the metal. The energy required for the electron to escape from the metal is the work function E_W (based upon this classical electrostatic model).

3-8. Thermionic Emission. The curves of Fig. 3-11 show that the electrons in a metal at absolute zero are distributed among energies which range in value from zero to the maximum energy E_M. Since an electron must possess an amount of energy at least as great as E_B in order to be able to escape, no electrons can leave the metal. Suppose now that the metal, in the form of a filament, is heated by sending a current through it. Thermal energy is then supplied to the electrons from the lattice of the heated metal crystal. The distribution of the electrons changes, owing to the increased temperature, as indicated in Fig. 3-11. As the temperature is raised, some of the electrons represented by the tail of the curve of Fig. 3-11 will have energies greater than E_B and so may be able to escape from the metal.

Using the analytical expression from the distribution function, it is possible to calculate the number of electrons which strike the surface of the metal per second with sufficient energy to be able to surmount the surface barrier and hence escape. Based upon such a calculation,[8] the thermionic current is given by

$$I_{th} = SA_0 T^2 \epsilon^{-E_W/E_T} \qquad \text{or} \qquad I_{th} = SA_0 T^2 \epsilon^{-b_o/T} \qquad \text{amp} \qquad (3\text{-}15)$$

where S = area of filament, m^2

A_0 = constant whose dimensions are amp/$(m^2)(^\circ K^2)$

T = temperature, $^\circ K$

$E_T \equiv T/11,600$ is defined in Eq. (3-9)

E_W = work function, ev

$b_o \equiv 11,600E_W$, $^\circ K$

Equations (3-15) are two forms of the equation of thermionic emission. They are sometimes referred to as the "Dushman equations" and sometimes as the "Richardson equations," since both workers developed equations of this form theoretically. The constant E_W, which has been termed the "work function," is known also as the "latent heat of evaporation of electrons" from the metal, from the analogy of electron emission with the evaporation of molecules from a liquid.

The thermionic-emission equation has received considerable experimental verification.[9] The graphical representation between the thermionic-emission current and the temperature is generally obtained by taking the logarithm of Eq. (3-15), *viz.*,

$$\log_{10} I_{th} - 2 \log_{10} T = \log_{10} SA_0 - 0.434 b_o \frac{1}{T} \qquad (3\text{-}16)$$

where the factor 0.434 represents $\log_{10} \epsilon$. Hence, if we plot $\log_{10} I_{th} - 2 \log_{10} T$ vs. $1/T$, the result should be a straight line having a slope equal to $-0.434 b_o$. The verification of this equation requires a knowledge of the cathode temperature. In those cases where the cathode is sufficiently exposed, the temperature can most accurately be determined by means of an optical pyrometer. Often, however, it is difficult or entirely impossible to see the cathode. Under these conditions a method that is based upon the energy radiated by the cathode is usually employed.

If a certain amount of power is supplied to a cathode, it will become heated and the temperature will increase until temperature equilibrium occurs. Equilibrium exists when the rate of heat removal by all causes equals the rate of heat produced as a result of the electrical input. Since the cathode is generally a thin filament in a vacuum, no convection of heat can occur. A small amount of heat will be conducted away by the leads, but most of the heat loss is due to the radiated energy. The rate at which energy is radiated from the heated surface is expressed explicitly as a function of the temperature of the body by the Stefan-Boltzmann relation

$$P = 5.67 \times 10^{-8} e_T T^4 \qquad \text{watts/m}^2 \qquad (3\text{-}17)$$

where P is the power radiated, in watts per square meter, by the surface whose emissivity is e_T; the factor 5.67×10^{-8} watt/$(m^2)(°K^4)$ is known as the Stefan-Boltzmann constant; and T is the temperature in degrees Kelvin. The value of e_T is always less than unity for all practical cases. It varies slightly with temperature and must be determined experimentally. Forsythe and Worthing[10] and Jones and Langmuir[11] have determined the temperature of tungsten as a function of the input power per square centimeter, over wide ranges of temperature. These data determine e_T. Hence, by measuring P, the temperature T is found.[12]

An early form of an emission equation suggested on the basis of the classical kinetic theory by O. W. Richardson[13] is

$$I_{th} = A' T^{\frac{1}{2}} \epsilon^{-b'/T} \qquad (3\text{-}18)$$

where A' is a quantity that depends upon the material and b' is a quantity related to, but not equal to, b_o. Experimentally, it is impossible to distinguish between Eqs. (3-15) and (3-18).   This difficulty arises from the fact that both equations predict the same *exponential* dependence upon the temperature; and since this factor is such a rapidly varying one, it overshadows the dependence upon the $T^{\frac{1}{2}}$ or the T^2 term.   For example, it follows from the second of Eqs. (3-15), by taking the derivative of the natural logarithm of this equation, that

$$- \frac{dI_{th}}{I_{th}} = \left(2 + \frac{b_o}{T}\right) \frac{dT}{T} \tag{3-19}$$

For tungsten, $b_o = 52,400$, so that at a normal operating temperature of 2400°K the fractional change in current dI_{th}/I_{th} is $2 + 22$ times the fractional change in the temperature.   It is to be noted that the term $22 \, (= b_o/T)$ arises from the exponential term in the Dushman equation, and the term 2 arises from the T^2 term.   Because of this slight dependence upon the power of the T term, it is impossible to use the experimental results as a criterion to favor one or the other equation.   We observe in passing that the thermionic current is a very sensitive function of the temperature, since a 1 per cent change in T results in a 24 per cent change in I_{th}.

It must be emphasized that Eqs. (3-15) give the electron emission from a metal at a given temperature provided that there are no external fields present.   If there are either accelerating or retarding fields at the surface, then the actual current collected will be greater or less than the emission current, respectively.   The effect of such surface fields is discussed later in this chapter.

3-9. Contact Potential.   Consider two metals in contact with each other, as at the junction C in Fig. 3-12.   The contact difference of potential between these two metals is defined as the potential difference E_{AB}, between a point A just outside metal 1 and a point B just outside metal 2.   The reason for the existence of the difference of potential is easily understood. When the two metals are joined at the boundary C, electrons will flow from the lower-work-function metal, say 1, to the other metal, 2.   This flow will continue until metal 2 has acquired so much negative charge that a retarding field has built up which repels any further electrons.   A detailed analysis[14] of the requirement that the number of electrons traveling from metal 1 across junction C into metal 2 is the same as that in the reverse direction across C leads to the conclusion that this equilibrium condition is attained when the Fermi energies E_M of the two metals are located at the same height on the energy-level diagram.   To satisfy this condition the potential-energy diagram for the

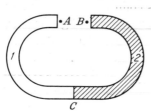

Fig. 3-12. Two metals in contact at the junction C.

two metals must be drawn as in Fig. 3-13. The barriers at the two surfaces A and B are indicated as vertical lines instead of curves as in Fig. 3-8 because the distance between the surfaces A and B is very large in comparison with atomic dimensions.

The diagram should be clear if it is recalled that $E_W = E_B - E_M$. From this figure it is seen that

$$E_{AB} = E_{W2} - E_{W1} \tag{3-20}$$

which means that *the contact difference of potential between two metals equals the difference between their work functions.* This result has been verified experimentally by numerous investigators.

If metals 1 and 2 are similar, the contact potential between them is evidently zero. If they are dissimilar metals, the metal having the lower

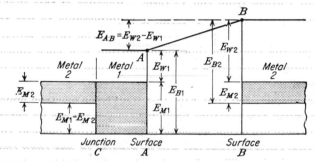

Fig. 3-13. The potential-energy system of two metals in contact.

work function becomes charged positively and the higher-work-function metal becomes charged negatively. In a vacuum tube the cathode is usually the lowest-work-function metal. If it is connected to any other electrode externally by means of a wire, then the effective voltage between the two electrodes is not zero but equals the difference in the work functions. This potential difference is in such a direction as to *repel* the electrons being emitted from the cathode. If a battery is connected between the two electrodes, then the effective potential is the algebraic sum of the applied voltage and the contact potential.

3-10. Energies of Emitted Electrons. Since the electrons inside a metal have a distribution of energies, then those which escape from the metal will also have an energy distribution. It is easy to demonstrate this experimentally. Thus consider a plane emitter and a plane-parallel collector. The current is measured as a function of the retarding voltage E_r (the emitter positive with respect to the collector). If all the electrons left the cathode with the same energy, then the current would remain constant until a definite voltage was reached and then it would fall abruptly to zero. For example, if they all had 2 ev energy, then when the retarding voltage was greater than 2 volts the electrons could not surmount the potential barrier between cathode and anode and no particles would be collected.   Experimentally no such sudden falling off of current is found, but instead there is an exponential decrease of current I_b with voltage according to the equation

$$I_b = I_{th}\epsilon^{-E_r/E_T} \tag{3-21}$$

This result may be obtained theoretically as follows: Since I_{th} is the current for zero retarding voltage, then the current obtained when the barrier height is increased by E_r is determined from the right-hand side of the first of Eqs. (3-15) by changing E_W to $E_W + E_r$.   Hence,

$$I_b = SA_0T^2\epsilon^{-(E_W+E_r)/E_T} = I_{th}\epsilon^{-E_r/E_T}$$

If E_b is the applied (accelerating) anode potential and if E' is the (retarding) contact potential, then $E_r = E' - E_b$, and Eq. (3-21) becomes

$$I_b = I\epsilon^{+E_b/E_T} \tag{3-22}$$

where

$$I \equiv I_{th}\epsilon^{-E'/E_T} \tag{3-23}$$

represents the current which is collected at zero applied voltage.   Since $E' > E_T$, this current I is a small fraction of I_{th}.   If E_b is increased from zero, the current I_b increases exponentially until the magnitude of the applied voltage E_b equals the contact potential E'.   At this voltage $E_r = 0$, and the thermionic current is collected.   If $E_b > E'$, then the field acting on the emitted electrons is in the accelerating direction and the current remains at the value I_{th}. A plot of the term $\log_{10} I$ vs. E_b should be of the form shown in Fig. 3-14. The nonzero slope of this broken-line curve is $(11{,}600 \log_{10} \epsilon)/T = 5{,}030/T$. From the foregoing considerations, the potential represented by the distance from O to O' is the contact potential E'.   Because most commercial diodes do not even approximate a plane cathode with a plane-parallel anode, the volt-ampere characteristic indicated in Fig. 3-14 is only approached in practice.   Furthermore, since the effect of space charge (Chap. 4) has been completely neglected, Eq. (3-21) is valid only for low values (microamperes) of current.   For larger values of I_b, the current varies as the three-halves power of the plate potential (Sec. 4-4).

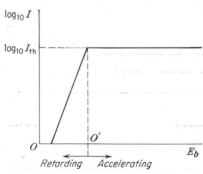

FIG. 3-14.   To verify the retarding-potential equation, $\log_{10} I$ is plotted vs. E_b.

Example. What percentage of the electrons leaving a tungsten filament at 2700°K can surmount a barrier whose height is 1 ev?

Solution. Using Eq. (3-21), with $E_r = 1$, and remembering that $E_T = T/11,600$ yields

$$\frac{I_b}{I_{th}} = \epsilon^{-(11,600\times1)/2,700} = \epsilon^{-4.28} \cong 0.014$$

Hence, only about 1.4 per cent of the electrons have energies in excess of 1 ev.

If the emitter is an oxide-coated cathode operating at 1000°K, then a calculation similar to the above gives the result that only about 0.001 per cent of the electrons have a surface-directed energy in excess of 1 ev!

A statistical analysis[15] shows that the average energy of the escaping electrons is given by the expression

$$\bar{E} = 2E_T \quad \text{ev} \tag{3-24}$$

For operating temperatures of 2700° and 1000°K the average energies of the emitted electrons are 0.47 and 0.17 ev, respectively.

These calculations demonstrate the validity of the assumption made in Chap. 1 in the discussion of the motion of electrons in electric and magnetic fields, *viz.*, that the electrons begin their motions with very small initial velocities. In most applications the initial velocities are of no consequence, but they are of significance in tubes which are operated at low electrode voltages.

3 11. Accelerating Fields. Under normal operating conditions, the field applied between the cathode and the collecting anode is accelerating rather than retarding, and so the field aids the electrons in overcoming the image force at the surface of the metal. This accelerating field tends, therefore, to lower the work function of the metal and so results in an increased thermionic emission from the metal. It can be shown[16] that the current I under the condition of an accelerating field of $\mathcal{E}$ volts per meter at the surface of the emitter is

$$I = I_{th}\epsilon^{+0.440\mathcal{E}^{\frac{1}{2}}/T} \tag{3-25}$$

where I_{th} is the zero-field thermionic current and T is the cathode temperature in degrees Kelvin. The fact that the measured thermionic currents continue to increase as the applied potential between the cathode and the anode is increased is often referred to as the *Schottky effect*, after the man who first predicted this effect. Some idea of the order of magnitude of this increase can be obtained from the following illustration.

Example. Consider a cylindrical cathode of radius 0.01 cm and a coaxial cylindrical anode of radius 1.0 cm. The temperature of the cathode is 2500°K. If an accelerating potential of 500 volts is applied between the cathode and the anode, calculate the percentage increase in the zero-external-field thermionic-emission current because of the Schottky effect.

Solution. The electric-field intensity at any point r (meters) in the region between the electrodes of a cylindrical capacitor, according to classical electrostatics, is given by the formula

$$\mathcal{E} = \frac{E_b}{\ln (r_a/r_k)} \frac{1}{r} \qquad \text{volts/m} \qquad (3\text{-}26)$$

where ln denotes the logarithm to the natural base ϵ, E_b is the plate voltage, r_a is the anode radius, and r_k is the cathode radius. Thus the electric-field intensity at the surface of the cathode is

$$\mathcal{E} = \frac{500}{2.303 \log_{10} 100} \frac{1}{10^{-4}} = 1.085 \times 10^6 \text{ volts/m}$$

It follows from Eq. (3-25) that

$$\log_{10} \frac{I}{I_{th}} = \frac{(0.434)(0.44)(1.085 \times 10^6)^{\frac{1}{2}}}{2,500} = 0.0795$$

Hence, $I/I_{th} = 1.20$, which shows that the Schottky theory predicts a 20 per cent increase over the zero-field emission current.

3-12. High-field Emission. Suppose that the accelerating field at the surface of a "cold" cathode (one for which the thermionic-emission current is negligible) is very intense. Under these circumstances the variation of the emission-current density with the strength of the electric-field intensity at the surface of the metal has been calculated by several investigators.[17] The result obtained by Fowler and Nordheim is

$$J = C\mathcal{E}^2 \epsilon^{-D/\mathcal{E}} \qquad \text{amp/m}^2 \qquad (3\text{-}27)$$

where

$$\left. \begin{array}{l} C = \dfrac{6.2 \times 10^{-6}}{E_B} \left(\dfrac{E_M}{E_W} \right)^{\frac{1}{2}} \qquad \text{amp/volt}^2 \\[2mm] D = 6.8 \times 10^9 E_W^{\frac{3}{2}} \qquad \text{volts/m} \end{array} \right\} \qquad (3\text{-}28)$$

$E_w = \dfrac{K b_o}{e}$

This equation has received direct experimental verification.[18] This effect is called *high-field, cold-cathode* or *autoelectronic emission.* The electric-field intensity at an electrode whose geometry includes a sharp point or edge may be very high even if the applied voltage is moderate. Hence, if high-field emission is to be avoided, it is very important to shape the electrodes in a tube properly so that a concentration of electrostatic lines of flux does not take place on any metallic surface. On the other hand, the cold-cathode effect has been used to provide several thousand amperes in an X-ray tube used for high-speed radiography.[19]

3-13. Secondary Emission.[20] The number of secondary electrons that are emitted from a material, either a metal or a dielectric, when subjected to electron bombardment has been found experimentally to depend upon a number of factors. Among these are the number of primary electrons, the energy of the primary electrons, the angle of incidence of the electrons on the material, the type of material, and the physical condition of the surface. The secondary-emission ratio, defined as the ratio of the number of secondary electrons per primary electron, is small for pure metals, the maximum value being between 1.5 and 2. It is increased markedly by the presence of a contaminating layer of gas or by the presence of an electropositive or alkali metal on the surface. For such composite surfaces, secondary-emission ratios as high as 10 or 15 have been detected. This ratio as a function of the energy of the impinging primary electrons on a cesium-antimony and a silver-magnesium surface is shown in Fig. 3-15.

The maximum in the secondary-emission ratio curve can be explained qualitatively. For low-energy primaries, the number of secondaries that are able to overcome the surface attraction is small. As the energy of the impinging electrons increases, more energetic secondaries are produced and the secondary-emission ratio increases. Since, however, the depth of penetration increases with the energy of the incident electron, the secondaries must travel a greater distance in the metal before they reach the surface. This increases the probability of collision in the metal, with a consequent loss of energy of these secondaries. Thus, if the primary energy is increased too much, the secondary-emission ratio must pass through a maximum.

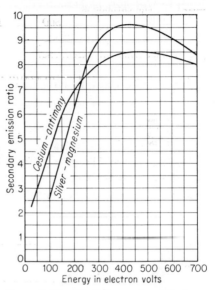

FIG. 3-15. Variation of secondary-emission ratio with primary voltage. (*Courtesy of A. B. Du Mont Laboratories, Inc.*)

Most secondary electrons are emitted with small energies. There is evidence[21] that more than 85 per cent of the secondary electrons emitted from a surface have energies of less than 3 ev. This condition is to be expected since a rapidly moving inner electron should be able to induce the same type of phenomenon as a fast-moving primary electron. The small percentage of high-energy electrons that is present is attributed to those primary electrons which have been reflected from the surface, rather than to true secondary electrons.

It is possible to induce electron emission by bombarding a surface with positive ions instead of with electrons.[22] This process is much less efficient than electron bombardment. As a result, the energies of the impinging ions must be much greater than those of electrons in order to yield a comparable secondary-emission ratio. Nevertheless, this process plays a fundamental role in some types of discharge to be discussed later.

3-14. Semiconductors.[23]   From Eq. (3-3) we see that the conductivity is proportional to the concentration n of free electrons.   For a good conductor, n is very large ($\cong 10^{28}$ electrons/m³); for an insulator, n is very small ($\cong 10^{7}$); and for a semiconductor, n lies between these two extremes. The valence electrons in a semiconductor are not free to wander about as they are in a metal but rather are trapped in a bond between two adjacent ions, as will now be explained.

Germanium and silicon are the two most important semiconductors used in electronic devices.   The crystal structure of these materials consists of a regular repetition in three dimensions of a unit cell in the form of a tetrahedron with an atom at each corner.   This structure is illustrated symbolically in two dimensions in Fig. 3-16.   Germanium has a

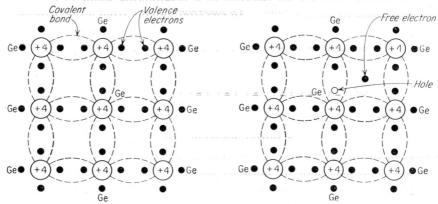

FIG. 3-16. Crystal structure of germanium, illustrated symbolically in two dimensions.

FIG. 3-17. Germanium crystal with a broken covalent bond.

total of 32 electrons in its atomic structure, and, of these, 4 are valence electrons, so that the atom is tetravalent.   The inert ionic core of the germanium atom carries a positive charge of $+4$ measured in units of the electronic charge.   The binding forces between neighboring atoms result from the fact that each of the valence electrons of a germanium atom is shared by one of its four nearest neighbors.   This *electron-pair bond*, or *covalent bond*, is represented in Fig. 3-16 by the two dashed lines which join each atom to each of its neighbors.   The fact that the valence electrons serve to bind one atom to the next also results in the valence electron being tightly bound to the nucleus.   Hence, in spite of the availability of four valence electrons, the crystal has a low conductivity.

At a low (say, 0°K) temperature the ideal structure of Fig. 3-16 is approached, and the crystal behaves as an insulator, since no free carriers of electricity are available.   However, at a higher (say room) temperature some of the covalent bonds will be broken because of the thermal energy supplied to the crystal, and conduction is made possible. This situation is illustrated in Fig. 3-17. Here an electron, which for the far greater period of time forms part of a covalent bond, is pictured as being dislodged and therefore free to wander in a random fashion throughout the crystal. The energy E_g required to break such a covalent bond is about 0.75 ev for germanium and 1.12 ev for silicon. The absence of the electron in the covalent bond is represented by the small circle in Fig. 3-17, and such an incomplete covalent bond is called a *hole.* The importance of the hole is that it may serve as a carrier of electricity which is comparable in effectiveness to the free electron.

The mechanism by which a hole contributes to the conductivity is qualitatively as follows: When a bond is incomplete so that a hole exists, it is relatively easy for an electron in a neighboring atom to leave its covalent bond to fill this hole. An electron moving from a bond to fill a

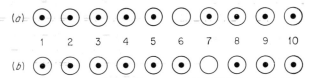

FIG. 3-18. The mechanism by which a hole contributes to the conductivity.

hole leaves a hole in its initial position. Hence, the hole effectively moves in the direction opposite to that of the electron. This hole, in its new position, may now be filled by an electron from another covalent bond, and the hole will correspondingly move one more step in the direction opposite to the motion of the electron. Here we have a mechanism for the conduction of electricity which does not involve the *free* electron. The above phenomenon is illustrated schematically in Fig. 3-18, where a circle with a dot in it represents a completed bond and an empty circle designates a hole. Figure 3-18a consists of a row of 10 ions with a broken bond, or hole, at ion 6. Now imagine that an electron from ion 7 moves into the hole at ion 6 so that the configuration of Fig. 3-18b results. If we compare this figure with Fig. 3-18a, it looks as if the hole in (a) has moved toward the right in (b) (from ion 6 to ion 7). This discussion indicates that the motion of the hole in one direction actually means the transport of a negative charge an equal distance in the opposite direction. So far as the flow of electric current is concerned, the hole behaves like a positive charge equal in magnitude to the electronic charge. We can consider that the holes are physical entities whose movement constitutes a flow of current.

In a pure semiconductor the number of holes is equal to the number of free electrons. Thermal agitation continues to produce new hole-electron pairs, while other hole-electron pairs disappear as a result of recombination.

3-15. Conductivity of a Semiconductor. With each hole-electron pair created, two current-carrying "particles" are formed. One is negative (the free electron), of mobility μ_n; and the other is positive (the hole), of mobility μ_p. These particles move in opposite directions in an electric field $\mathcal{E}$, but since they are of opposite sign the current of both is in the same direction. Hence, the current density J is given by (Sec. 3-2)

$$J = (n\mu_n + p\mu_p)e\mathcal{E} = \sigma\mathcal{E} \tag{3-29}$$

where n equals the free-electron (negative) concentration, p equals the hole (positive) concentration, and σ is the conductivity. Hence,

$$\sigma = (n\mu_n + p\mu_p)e \tag{3-30}$$

For the pure (called *intrinsic*) semiconductor considered here, $n = p = n_i$, where n_i is the intrinsic concentration.

In pure germanium at room temperature there is about one hole-electron pair for each 5×10^{10} germanium atoms. With increasing temperature, the density of hole-electron pairs increases and correspondingly the conductivity increases. If Fermi-Dirac statistics is applied to a semiconductor[24] it is found that the intrinsic concentration varies with temperature in accordance with the relationship

$$n_i^2 = A_0 T^3 \epsilon^{-E_g/ET} \tag{3-31}$$

The constants A_0, E_g, μ_n, μ_p and many other important physical quantities for germanium and silicon are given in Table 3-1.

TABLE 3-1

PROPERTIES OF GERMANIUM AND SILICON

Property	Ge	Si
Atomic number	32	14
Atomic weight	72.6	28.1
Density (g/cm³)	5.32	2.33
Dielectric constant (relative)	16	12
A_0 [Eq. (3-31)] $(cmj^{-6}(°K)^{-3}$	9.3×10^{31}	7.8×10^{32}
E_g [Eq. (3-31)] (ev)	0.75	1.12
n_i at 300°K [Eq. (3-31)] $(cm)^{-3}$	2.5×10^{13}	6.8×10^{10}
Intrinsic resistivity at 300°K (ohm-cm)*	47	230,000
μ_n (cm²/volt sec)*	3,800	1,300
μ_p (cm²/volt sec)*	1,800	500
D_n (cm²/sec) $= \mu_n E_T$	95	33
D_p (cm²/sec) $= \mu_p E_T$	45	13

* G. L. PEARSON and W. H. BRATTAIN, "History of Semiconductor Research," *Proc. IRE*, **43**, 1794–1806, December, 1955. All values not marked with an asterisk are from E. M. CONWELL, "Properties of Silicon and Germanium," *Proc. IRE*, **40**, 1327–1337, November, 1952.

The conductivity of germanium is found from Eq. (3-31) to increase approximately 5 per cent per degree increase in temperature. Such a rapid change in conductivity with temperature places a limitation upon the use of semiconductor devices in some circuits. On the other hand, for some applications it is exactly this property of semiconductors that is used to advantage. A semiconductor used in this manner is called a *thermistor*,[25] Such a device finds extensive application in thermometry, in measurement of microwave-frequency power, as a thermal relay, and in control devices actuated by changes in temperature. Silicon and germanium are not used as thermistors because their properties are too sensitive to impurities. Commercial thermistors consist of sintered mixtures of such oxides as NiO, Mn_2O_3, and Co_2O_3.

The exponential decrease in resistivity (reciprocal of conductivity) of a semiconductor should be contrasted with the small and almost linear increase in resistivity of a metal. An increase in temperature of a metal results in greater thermal motion of the ions and hence decreases slightly the mean free path of the free electrons. The result is a decrease in the mobility and hence in conductivity. For most metals the resistance increases about 0.4 per cent per degree increase in temperature. It should be noted that a thermistor has a negative coefficient of resistance, whereas that of a metal is positive and of much smaller magnitude. By including a thermistor in a metallic circuit it is possible to compensate for temperature changes over a range as wide as 100°C.

3-16. Donor and Acceptor Impurities. If, to pure germanium, a small amount of impurity is added in the form of a substance with five valence electrons, the situation results which is pictured in Fig. 3-19. The impurity atoms will displace some of the germanium atoms in the crystal lattice. Four of the five valence electrons will occupy covalent bonds, while the fifth

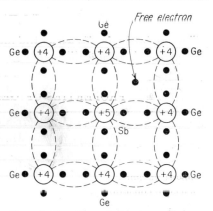

Fig. 3-19. Crystal lattice with a germanium atom displaced by an atom of a pentavalent impurity.

will be nominally unbound and will be available as a carrier of current. The energy required to detach this fifth electron from the atom is only of the order of 0.01 ev. Suitable pentavalent impurities are antimony, phosphorus, or arsenic. Such impurities donate excess negative electron carriers and are therefore referred to as *donor*, or *n*-type, impurities.

If a trivalent impurity (boron, gallium, or indium) is added, then only three of the covalent bonds can be filled, and the vacancy that exists in the fourth bond constitutes a hole. This situation is illustrated in Fig. 3-20. Such impurities make available positive carriers because they create holes which can accept electrons. These impurities are consequently known as *acceptor*, or *p*-type, *impurities*. The amount of impurity required to be added to have an appreciable effect on the conductivity is very small. For example, if a donor-type impurity is added to the extent of 1 part in 10^8, the conductivity of germanium at 30°C is multiplied by a factor of 12.

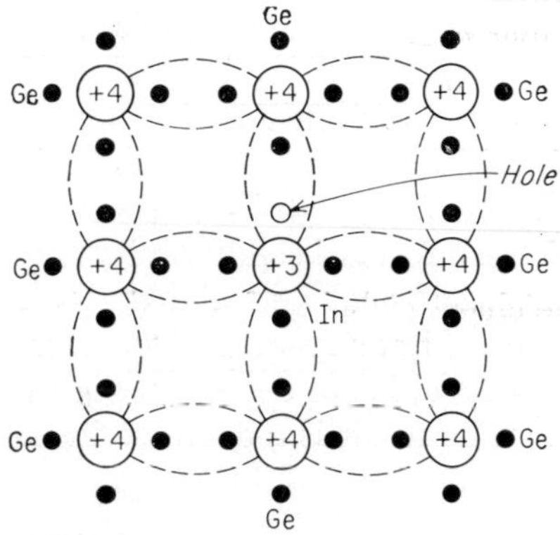

In intrinsic germanium both electrons and holes are available as carriers. The number of electrons and holes is equal, as has already been emphasized. If intrinsic germanium is "doped" with *n*-type impurities, not only does the number of electrons increase, but the number of holes decreases below that which is available in the intrinsic semiconductor. The reason for the decrease in the number of holes is that the larger number of electrons present increases the rate of recombination of holes with electrons. Similarly, the number of electron carriers in a semiconductor can be reduced by doping with *p*-type impurities.

FIG. 3-20. Crystal lattice with a germanium atom displaced by an atom of a trivalent impurity.

We have the important result that the doping of an intrinsic semiconductor not only increases the conductivity but serves also to produce a conductor in which the electric carriers are either predominantly holes or predominantly electrons. In an *n*-type semiconductor the electrons are called the *majority carriers*, and the holes are called the *minority carriers*. In a *p*-type material, the holes are the majority carriers, and the electrons are the minority carriers.

3-17. Charge Densities in a Semiconductor. Quantitatively it is found[26] that

$$np = n_i{}^2 \qquad (3\text{-}32)$$

This equation (called the *mass-action* law) gives one relationship between the electron n and the hole p concentrations. These densities are further interrelated by the law of electrical neutrality which we shall now state in algebraic form. Let N_d equal the concentration of donor atoms. Since, as mentioned above, these are practically all ionized, N_d positive charges per cubic meter are contributed by the donor ions. Hence, the total positive-charge density is $N_d + p$. Similarly, if N_a is the concentration of acceptor ions, these contribute N_a negative charges per cubic meter. The total negative-charge density is $N_a + n$. Since the semiconductor is electrically neutral, the magnitude of the positive-charge density must equal that of the negative concentration, or

$$N_d + p = N_a + n \qquad (3\text{-}33)$$

Consider an n-type material such that $N_a = 0$. Since the number of electrons is much greater than the number of holes in an n-type semiconductor ($n \gg p$), then Eq. (3-33) reduces to

$$n \cong N_d \qquad (3\text{-}34)$$

In an n-type material the free-electron concentration is approximately equal to the density of donor atoms.

In later applications we shall study the characteristics of n- and p-type materials connected together. Since some confusion may arise as to which type is under consideration at a given moment, we shall add the subscript n or p for an n-type or a p-type substance, respectively. Thus, Eq. (3-34) is more clearly written

$$n_n \cong N_d \qquad (3\text{-}35)$$

The concentration p_n of holes in the n-type semiconductor is obtained from Eq. (3-32), which is now written $n_n p_n = n_i^2$. Thus,

$$p_n = \frac{n_i^2}{N_d} \qquad (3\text{-}36)$$

Similarly, for a p-type semiconductor,

$$n_p p_p = n_i^2 \qquad p_p \cong N_a \qquad n_p = \frac{n_i^2}{N_a} \qquad (3\text{-}37)$$

3-18. Diffusion. In addition to a conduction current, the transport of charges in a semiconductor may be accounted for by a mechanism, called *diffusion*, not ordinarily encountered in metals. The essential features of diffusion will now be discussed.

We shall see later that it is possible to have a nonuniform concentration of particles in a semiconductor. Under these circumstances the concentration p of holes varies with distance x in the semiconductor, and there exists a concentration gradient dp/dx in the density of carriers. The existence of a gradient implies that, if an imaginary surface is drawn in the semiconductor, the density of holes immediately on one side of the surface is larger than the density on the other side. The holes are in a random motion as a result of their thermal energy. Accordingly, holes will continue to move back and forth across this surface. We may then expect that in a given time interval more holes will cross the surface from the more dense to the less dense side than in the reverse direction.   This net transport of charge across the surface constitutes a flow of current. It should be noted that this net transport of charge is not the result of mutual repulsion among charges of like sign but is simply the result of a statistical phenomenon.   This diffusion is exactly analogous to that which occurs in a neutral gas if there exists a pressure gradient in the gaseous container.   The diffusion hole current density is proportional to the concentration gradient and is given by

$$J_p = -eD_p \frac{dp}{dx} \quad \text{amp/m}^2 \tag{3-38}$$

where D_p (square meters per second) is called the *diffusion constant* for holes.   A similar relationship exists for the diffusion electron current [p is replaced by n, and the minus sign is replaced by a plus sign in Eq. (3-38)].   Since both diffusion and mobility are statistical thermodynamic phenomena, these two parameters are not independent.   The relationship between them is given by the Einstein equation

$$\frac{D_p}{\mu_p} = \frac{D_n}{\mu_n} = E_T \quad \text{volts} \tag{3-39}$$

where $E_T = T/11{,}600$ is defined as in Eq. (3-9).   At room temperature (300°K), $\mu = 39D$.   Measured values of μ and computed values of D for silicon and germanium are given in Table 3-1 on page 82.

3-19. The Hall Effect.[27]   If a specimen (metal or semiconductor) carrying a current I is placed in a transverse magnetic field B, an electric field $\mathcal{E}$ is induced in the direction perpendicular to both I and B.   This phenomenon, known as the *Hall effect*, is used to determine whether a semiconductor is n or p type and to find the carrier concentration. Also, by simultaneously measuring the conductivity σ, the mobility μ can be calculated.

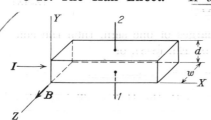

FIG. 3-21. Pertaining to the Hall effect. The carriers (whether electrons or holes) are subjected to a force in the negative Y direction.

The physical origin of the Hall effect is not difficult to find.   If in Fig. 3-21 I is in the positive X direction and B is in the positive Z direction, then a force will be exerted in the negative Y direction on the current carriers.   If the semiconductor is n type so that the current is carried by electrons, these electrons will be forced downward toward side 1 in Fig. 3-21, and side 1 becomes negatively charged with respect to side 2. Hence, a potential V_H, called the *Hall voltage*, appears between the surfaces 1 and 2.   In the equilibrium state the electric-field intensity $\mathcal{E}$ due to the Hall effect must exert a force on the carrier which just balances the magnetic force, or

$$e\mathcal{E} = Bev \tag{3-40}$$

where e is the magnitude of the charge on the carrier and v is the drift speed. From Eq. (1-14), $\mathcal{E} = V_H/d$, where d is the distance between surfaces 1 and 2. From Eq. (1-34), $J = \rho v = I/dw$, where J is the current density, ρ is the charge density, and w is the width of the specimen in the direction of the magnetic field. Combining these relationships, we find

$$V_H = Bvd = \frac{BJd}{\rho} = \frac{BI}{\rho w} \tag{3-41}$$

If V_H, B, I, and w are measured, then the charge density ρ can be determined from Eq. (3-41). If the polarity of V_H is positive at terminal 2, then, as explained above, the carriers must be electrons, and $\rho = ne$, where n is the electron concentration. If, on the other hand, terminal 1 becomes charged positively with respect to terminal 2, then the semiconductor must be p type, and $\rho = pe$, where p is the hole concentration.

It is customary to introduce the Hall coefficient R_H defined by

$$R_H \equiv \frac{1}{\rho} \tag{3-42}$$

Hence

$$R_H = \frac{V_H w}{BI} \tag{3-43}$$

If conduction is due primarily to charges of one sign, then the conductivity σ is related to the mobility μ by Eq. (3-3), or

$$\sigma = \rho\mu \tag{3-44}$$

If the conductivity is measured together with the Hall coefficient, then the mobility can be determined from

$$\mu = \sigma R_H \tag{3-45}$$

We have assumed in the above discussion that all particles travel with the mean drift speed v. Actually, the current carriers have a random thermal distribution in speed. If this distribution is taken into account, it is found that Eq. (3-43) remains valid provided that R_H is defined by $3\pi/8\rho$. Also, Eq. (3-45) must be modified to $\mu = (8\sigma/3\pi)R_H$.

3-20. Energy Bands in Solids. Quantum theory proves that in a periodic potential field such as exists in a crystal there are bands of allowed energies which may be separated by forbidden energy regions. A metal is characterized by the fact that the band occupied by the "free" or "valence" electrons is not completely filled and that there are no forbidden levels at higher energies. Recall that in a metal, at absolute zero, the energies of the electrons range from zero to a value E_M. If some additional energy is given to the crystal, the electrons are raised to higher

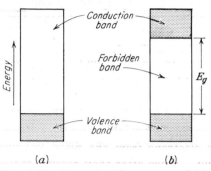

energy levels. If the energy is supplied by an externally applied voltage, conduction results and hence this energy band is also called the *conduction band*. The overlapping of the valence and conduction bands in a metal is indicated schematically in Fig. 3-22a.

The band structure of an insulator is different from that of a metal in that the valence electrons completely fill one band. The next empty band of allowed energy

FIG. 3-22. Energy-band structure of (a) a metal and (b) an insulator.

states is separated from the filled band by a forbidden region E_g which may be many electron volts high, as shown in Fig. 3-22b. The energy that can be supplied to an electron from an applied field is generally too small to carry the electron from the filled band into the empty band and hence no conduction takes place.

A semiconductor is a material in which the width of the forbidden region (the energy gap E_g) is relatively narrow ($\cong 1$ ev). Such a substance acts as an insulator at low temperatures because the electrons in

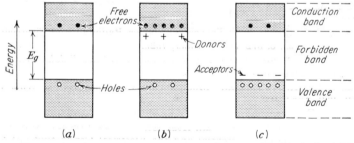

FIG. 3-23. Energy-band structure of a semiconductor. (a) Intrinsic. (b) n-type. (c) p-type.

the valence band do not have enough energy to enter the conduction band. This situation corresponds to Fig. 3-16, which shows completely filled covalent bonds.

As the temperature is increased, some of the valence electrons acquire an energy greater than E_g and hence enter the conduction band. The departing electrons leave "holes" in the valence band. This behavior of the intrinsic semiconductor is pictured in Figs. 3-23a and Fig. 3-17.

As explained in Sec. 3-14, both the electrons in the conduction band and the holes in the valence band contribute to the conductivity.

The band structure for an n-type semiconductor is indicated in Fig. 3-23b. To the diagram of the intrinsic material we have added a donor level in the forbidden region which is very closely spaced ($\cong 0.01$ ev) to the bottom edge of the conduction band. Hence, even at room temperature almost all the donors are ionized, and they contribute electrons to the conduction band. This process leaves the donor ions positively charged, as indicated by the plus signs in Fig. 3-23b. This energy diagram indicates schematically the physical behavior of the semiconductor as depicted in Figs. 3-17 and 3-19.

The band structure for a p-type material is indicated in Fig. 3-23c. The acceptor level is in the forbidden region but neighboring the valence band. The acceptor atoms can take electrons from the filled valence levels and thus leave holes in this band. Since after they receive these electrons the acceptors are negative ions, they are indicated by minus signs in Fig. 3-23c. This energy diagram corresponds to the physical pictures shown in Figs. 3-17 and 3-20.

REFERENCES

1. FERMI, E., "Zur Quantelung des idealen einatomigen Gases," *Z. Physik*, **36**, 902–912, May, 1926.
2. DIRAC, P. A. M., "On the Theory of Quantum Mechanics," *Proc. Roy. Soc. (London)*, **112**, 661–677, October, 1926.
3. SOMMERFELD, A., and H. BETHE, Elektronentheorie der Metalle, in "Handbuch der Physik," 2 Aufl., Vol. 24, Pt. 2, pp. 333–622, Verlag Julius Springer, Berlin, 1933.
   DARROW, K. K., "Statistical Theories of Matter, Radiation and Electricity," *Bell System Tech. J.*, **8**, 672–748, October, 1929.
4. DOW, W. G., "Fundamentals of Engineering Electronics," John Wiley & Sons, Inc., New York, 1937.
5. SEITZ, F., and R. P. JOHNSON, "Modern Theory of Solids. III," *J. Appl. Phys.*, **8**, 246–260, April, 1937.
6. DAVISSON, C. J., and L. H. GERMER, "Reflection and Refraction of Electrons by a Crystal of Nickel," *Proc. Natl. Acad. Sci. U.S.*, **14**, 619–627, August, 1928.
7. RUPP, E., The Internal Potential and the Electrical Conductivity of Crystals, in P. DEBYE (ed.), "The Interference of Electrons," pp. 1–11, Blackie & Son, Ltd., Glasgow, 1931.
8. MILLMAN, J., and S. SEELY, "Electronics," 2d ed., pp. 137–139, McGraw-Hill Book Company, Inc., New York, 1951.
9. DUSHMAN, S., "Thermionic Emission," *Revs. Mod. Phys.*, **2**, 381–476, October, 1930.
10. FORSYTHE, W. E., and A. G. WORTHING, "The Properties of Tungsten and the Characteristics of Tungsten Lamps," *Astrophys. J.*, **61**(3), 146–185, 1925.
11. JONES, H. A., and I. LANGMUIR, "The Characteristics of Tungsten Filaments as Functions of Temperature. Part II," *Gen. Elec. Rev.*, **30**, 354–361, July, 1927.

12. MILLMAN, J., and S. SEELY, "Electronics," 2d ed., pp. 170–171, McGraw-Hill Book Company, Inc., New York, 1951.

13. RICHARDSON, O. W., "On the Negative Radiation from Hot Platinum," *Proc. Cambridge Phil. Soc.*, **11**, 286–295, 1901.

14. MILLMAN, J., and S. SEELY, "Electronics," 2d ed., pp. 143–147, McGraw-Hill Book Company, Inc., New York, 1951.

15. MILLMAN, J., and S. SEELY, "Electronics," 2d ed., pp. 141–142, McGraw-Hill Book Company, Inc., New York, 1951.

16. MILLMAN, J., and S. SEELY, "Electronics," 2d ed., pp. 151–156, McGraw-Hill Book Company, Inc., New York, 1951.

17. FOWLER, R. H., and L. NORDHEIM, "Electron Emission in Intense Electric Fields," *Proc. Roy. Soc. (London)*, **119**, 173–181, May, 1928.

   OPPENHEIMER, J. R., "Three Notes on the Quantum Theory of Aperiodic Effects," *Phys. Rev.*, **31**, 66–81, January, 1928.

   OPPENHEIMER, J. R., "On the Quantum Theory of Autoelectric Field Currents," *Proc. Natl. Acad. Sci. U.S.*, **14**, 363–365, May, 1928.

18. MILLIKAN, R. A., and C. F. EYRING, "Laws Governing the Pulling of Electrons out of Metals by Intense Electrical Fields," *Phys. Rev.*, **27**, 51–67, January, 1926.

   MILLIKAN, R. A., and C. C. LAURITSEN, "Relations of Field-Currents to Thermionic-Currents," *Proc. Natl. Acad. Sci. U.S.*, **14**, 45–49, January, 1928.

   EYRING, C. F., S. S. MACKEOWN, and R. A. MILLIKAN, "Field Currents from Points," *Phys. Rev.*, **31**, 900–909, May, 1928.

   STERN, T. E., B. S. GOSSLING, and R. H. FOWLER, "Further Studies in the Emission of Electrons from Cold Metals," *Proc. Roy. Soc. (London)*, **124**, 699–723, July, 1929.

19. SLACK, C. M., and L. F. EHRKE, "Field Emission X-ray Tube," *J. Appl. Phys.*, **12**, 165–168, February, 1941.

20. SPANGENBERG, K. R., "Vacuum Tubes," 1st ed., McGraw-Hill Book Company, Inc., New York, 1948.

   McKAY, K. G., Secondary Electron Emission, an extensive review, in "Advances in Electronics," Vol. 1, pp. 65–130, Academic Press, Inc., New York, 1948.

   McNALL, J. W., Electron Emission, in "Industrial Electronics Reference Book," by engineers of the Westinghouse Electric Corp., pp. 10–32, John Wiley & Sons, Inc., New York, 1948.

   ZWORYKIN, V. K., and G. A. MORTON, "Television," John Wiley & Sons, Inc., New York, 1940.

21. ZWORYKIN, V. K., and G. A. MORTON, "Television," John Wiley & Sons, Inc., New York, 1940.

22. OLIPHANT, M. L. E., "The Liberation of Electrons from Metal Surfaces by Positive Ions. Part I: Experimental," *Proc. Roy. Soc. (London)*, **127**, 373–387, May, 1930.

   OLIPHANT, M. L. E., and P. B. MOON, "The Liberation of Electrons from Metal Surfaces by Positive Ions. Part II: Theoretical," *ibid.*, **127**, 388–406, May, 1930.

   MOON, P. B., "The Action of Positive Ions of Cesium on a Hot Nickel Surface," *Proc. Cambridge Phil. Soc.*, **27**, 570–577, 1931.

23. TERMAN, F. E., "Electronic and Radio Engineering," 4th ed., pp. 733–746, McGraw-Hill Book Company, Inc., New York, 1955.

   ARGUIMBAU, L. B., "Vacuum Tube Circuits and Transistors," pp. 93–110, John Wiley & Sons, Inc., New York, 1956.

24. MIDDLEBROOK, R. D., "An Introduction to Junction Transistor Theory," Chap. 4, John Wiley & Sons, Inc., New York, 1957.

25. BECKER, J. A., C. B. GREEN, and G. L. PEARSON, "Properties and Uses of Thermistors—Thermally Sensitive Resistors," *Bell System Tech. J.*, **26**, 170–212, January, 1947.

26. MIDDLEBROOK, R. D., "An Introduction to Junction Transistor Theory," John Wiley & Sons, Inc., New York, 1957.

27. SHOCKLEY, W., "Electrons and Holes in Semiconductors," D. Van Nostrand Company, Inc., Princeton, N.J., 1950.

CHAPTER 4

VACUUM-DIODE CHARACTERISTICS

THE properties of practical thermionic cathodes are discussed in this chapter. The thermionic-emission current is the maximum current that can be collected at any given temperature. In order to obtain this current an anode is placed close to the cathode in an evacuated envelope. If an accelerating field is applied, it is found that the plate current increases as the anode voltage is increased. However, if the plate potential is large enough to collect the thermionic-emission current I_{th}, then the anode current will remain constant at the value I_{th} even though the plate voltage is increased further. The limitation of the current which can be collected in a diode because of the space charge of the emitted electrons is discussed in detail in this chapter.

Finally, practical diode volt-ampere characteristics are considered, and an analysis of a circuit containing a diode is given.

4-1. Cathode Materials. The three most important practical emitters are pure tungsten, thoriated tungsten, and oxide-coated cathodes. The most important properties of these emitters will now be discussed.

Tungsten. Unlike the other cathodes discussed below, tungsten does not have an active surface layer which can be damaged by positive-ion bombardment. Hence, tungsten is used as the cathode in high-voltage high-vacuum tubes. These include X-ray tubes, diodes for use as rectifiers above about 5,000 volts, and large power-amplifier tubes for use in communication transmitters.

Tungsten has the disadvantage that the *cathode emission efficiency*, defined as the ratio of the emission current, in amperes, to the heating power, in watts, is small. However, a copious supply of electrons can be provided by operating the cathode at a sufficiently high temperature. The higher the temperature, however, the greater will be the evaporation of the filament during its operation and the sooner it will burn out. Economic considerations dictate that the temperature of the filament be about 2500°K, which gives it a life of approximately 2,000 hr. The melting point of tungsten is 3650°K. The important constants for a tungsten emitter are summarized in Table 4-1.

TABLE 4-1

COMPARISON OF THERMIONIC EMITTERS

Type of cathode	Dushman constants			Approximate operating temperature, °K	Efficiency,* amp/watt	Plate voltage, volts	Gas or vacuum tube
	$A_0 \times 10^{-4}$, amp/(m²) (°K²)	b_o, °K	E_W, ev				
Tungsten.........	60.2	52,400	4.52	2500	20–100	Above 5,000	Vacuum
Thoriated tungsten	3.0	30,500	2.63	1900	50–1,000	750–5,000	Vacuum
Oxide-coated BaO + SrO	0.01	11,600	1.0	1000	100–10,000	Below 750	Vacuum or gas

* K. R. SPANGENBERG, "Vacuum Tubes," McGraw-Hill Book Company, Inc., New York, 1948.

Thoriated Tungsten. In order to obtain copious emission of electrons at moderately low temperatures, it is necessary for the material to have a low work function. Unfortunately the low-work-function metals, such as cesium, rubidium, and barium, in some cases melt and in other cases boil at temperatures necessary for appreciable thermionic emission. However, it is possible to apply a very thin layer of low-work-function material, such as thorium, on a filament of tungsten. The base metal holds the adsorbed layer at high temperatures, even above the point at which the pure thorium would normally evaporate. Such a filament possesses emission properties that are considerably better than those of the pure tungsten.

Thoriated-tungsten filaments are obtained by adding a small amount (1 or 2 per cent by weight) of thorium oxide to the tungsten. After the tungsten is drawn and mounted in a tube, the envelope is exhausted, and the glass and the metal structure are outgassed by baking the tube in an oven. The metallic parts are further heated with a high-frequency induction furnace. Just as the tube is sealed off from the pumping system, a getter is "flashed." The getter consists of an active chemical substance, such as magnesium, which absorbs the residual gas and tends to maintain a high vacuum. This getter is usually visible in commercial tubes, it being the silvery deposit on the glass envelope of the tube.

Following the evacuation process, the filament must be activated. This process requires essentially three steps. The filament is heated to about 2800°K for several minutes. At this high temperature, the tungsten surface is cleaned and some of the thoria inside the tungsten is reduced to metallic thorium. The filament is then maintained at a temperature of 2100°K for about 30 min. At this temperature the rate of diffusion of thorium to the surface is still rather high, although the rate of evaporation from the surface is rather low. In this way an adsorbed layer, approximately one molecule thick, of thorium atoms accumulates on the surface. Finally, the temperature of the filament is reduced to the operating range, from 1800° to 2000°K.

Under the conditions of normal operation the layer of thorium atoms slowly evaporates from the filament. This evaporation is compensated for by the continued diffusion of thorium atoms to the surface. In order to increase the life of thoriated-tungsten filaments, the process of *carbonization* has been developed. A surface layer of tungsten carbide is formed which reduces the rate of evaporation of the thorium layer to about one-sixth that of noncarbonized filament.[1]

The limitation to the use of thoriated-tungsten emitters is the deactivation due to positive-ion bombardment. The effect of even a few ions is severe at high potentials, so that these filaments are confined to use in tubes that operate with potentials less than about 5,000 volts. Higher-voltage tubes use pure-tungsten filaments. Most of the "800" series of transmitting tubes use thoriated-tungsten filaments.

It is rather difficult to obtain representative values for the emission constants in the Dushman equation, since these values depend markedly upon the fraction of the surface that is covered by thorium. Though several values of A_0 and b_c are to be found in the literature, the values[2] given in Table 4-1 are representative. The presence of the monatomic layer of thorium on the surface of the tungsten does not alter the thermal properties of the tungsten, and it is possible to determine the temperature of the filament from the thermal data for pure tungsten.

Example. The saturation current from a certain thoriated-tungsten filament operating at 2000°K is 100 ma. What would be the emission from a pure-tungsten filament of the same area operating at the same temperature?

Solution. Equation (3-15) for tungsten is

$$I = (S)(60.2 \times 10^4)(2,000)^2 \epsilon^{-52,400/2,000}$$

Similarly, for thoriated tungsten, Eq. (3-15) becomes

$$100 \times 10^{-3} = (S)(3.0 \times 10^4)(2,000)^2 \epsilon^{-30,500/2,000}$$

Upon dividing these two equations, there results

$$\frac{I}{0.1} = \frac{60.2}{3.0} \epsilon^{-\frac{52,400}{2,000} + \frac{39,500}{2,000}}$$

or

$$I = 2.01 \epsilon^{-10.95}$$

This quantity can be evaluated with the aid of logarithms. Thus,

$$\begin{aligned} \log_{10} I &= \log_{10}(2.01) - (0.434)(10.95) \\ &= 0.30 - 4.75 = -4.45 = 0.55 - 5 \\ I &= 3.55 \times 10^{-5} \text{ or } 35.5\mu a \end{aligned}$$

Oxide-coated Cathodes.[3]   The modern oxide-coated cathode is the most efficient type of emitter that has been developed commercially.   It consists of a metallic base of platinum, nickel, nickel with a few per cent of cobalt or silicon, or Konal metal.   Konal metal is an alloy consisting of nickel, cobalt, iron, and titanium.   Konal-metal sleeves are used very extensively as the indirectly heated cathode of radio receiving tubes. The wire filaments or the metallic sleeves are coated with oxides of the alkaline-earth group, especially barium and strontium oxides.

Before the oxide-coated cathode shows appreciable electron emission, it must be activated.   The activation process consists essentially in operating the cathode for several minutes at a temperature which is above the normal operating temperature.   The cathode is then maintained at a lower temperature for a longer period of time, an anode potential being applied so as to draw electron current.   During this process, the emission increases rapidly to a high value.   The activation process probably results in the reduction of some oxide to the pure metallic form, which will be distributed throughout the body of the coating.

Four characteristics of the coating account for its extensive use.   The first is its long life, several thousand hours under normal operating conditions being common.   At reduced filament power several hundred thousand hours have been obtained.   The second is the fact that it can easily be manufactured in the form of the indirectly heated cathodes (Sec. 4-2).   The third is the ability to give tremendous outputs under pulsed conditions.   Thus it has been found that for (microsecond) pulses current densities in excess of 10^6 amp/m^2 may be obtained.[4]   The fourth is its very high cathode efficiency.

Oxide-coated cathodes are subject to deactivation by positive-ion bombardment and so are generally used in low-voltage tubes only.   The emission properties of an oxide-coated cathode are influenced by many factors, for example, the proportion of the contributing oxides, the thickness of the oxide coating, possibly the core material, and the details of the processing.   Hence, the emission characteristics change with the age of the cathode and vary markedly from tube to tube.   The determination of the relationship between the power input and the emissivity or temperature is very difficult.[3,5]   Hence, unique values of E_W and A_0 for oxide-coated cathodes cannot be given.   However, the mass of experimental data available indicates that a reasonable value for the work function is of the order of 1 to 1.5 volts and for A_0 of approximately 0.01×10^4 amp/(m^2)($^\circ$K^2), as given in Table 4-1.

Since the emission characteristics of oxide-coated cathodes are so variable, the reader may have wondered how tubes using these cathodes can serve satisfactorily in any circuit.   It is shown in Sec. 4-4 that tubes usually operate under conditions of space-charge limitation and not under conditions of temperature limitation. This statement means that *the current is determined by the plate voltage and not by the cathode temperature.* Thus, despite their rather unpredictable emission characteristics, oxide-coated cathodes make excellent tube elements provided only that their thermionic-emission current never falls below that required by the circuit.

Oxide-coated cathodes are used in the greatest percentage of commercial electron tubes. Almost all receiving tubes, many low-voltage transmitting tubes, and practically all gas tubes use such cathodes.

4-2. Commercial Cathodes. The cathodes used in thermionic tubes are sometimes directly heated filaments in the form of a V, a W, or a straight wire, although most tubes use indirectly heated cathodes.

The indirectly heated cathode was developed so as to minimize the hum (Sec. 15-11) arising from the various effects of a-c heater operation. The general forms of indirectly heated cathodes for use in vacuum tubes are illustrated in Fig. 4-1. The heater wire is contained in a ceramic insulator which is enclosed by a nickel or Konal-metal sleeve on which the oxide coating is placed. The cathode as a unit is so massive that its temperature does not vary appreciably with instantaneous variations in the magnitude of the heater currents. Further, since the sleeve is the emitting surface, the cathode is essentially equipotential. The heater wire within the ceramic insulator is tungsten or an alloy of tungsten and molybdenum. The ceramic insulator which acts to isolate electrically the heater wire from the cathode must, of course, be a good heat conductor. Materials that are extensively used for this purpose are the oxides of beryllium and aluminum. Under normal conditions of operation, the heater is maintained at about 1000°C, which results in the cathode temperature being at approximately 850°C.

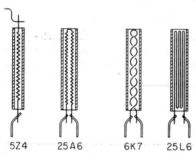

5Z4   25A6   6K7   25L6

FIG. 4-1. Typical indirectly heated cathodes. (*Courtesy of Radio Corporation of America.*)

If an excessive potential difference is maintained between the heater and the cathode, the thin layer of insulation may break down. This consideration is frequently of extreme importance in practice, where it may be desired to heat several cathodes that are at different potentials with respect to ground from the same heater circuit. Recommended practice is to limit the potential difference between the heater and the cathode to about 100 volts, unless the manufacturer specifies a larger allowable voltage. If the difference in voltage between two cathodes is greater than this recommended value, then separate heater transformers must be used.

4-3. The Potential Variation between the Electrodes. Consider a simple thermionic diode, whose cathode can be heated to any desired temperature and whose anode potential may be maintained at any desired value. It will be assumed for the present that the cathode is a plane equipotential surface and that the collecting anode is also a plane which is parallel to it. The potential variation between the electrodes is to be investigated for a given value of anode voltage.

To a first approximation, the electrons are emitted from the cathode with zero initial velocities. Under these circumstances, the curves showing the variation of potential in the interelectrode space for various temperatures of the cathode are given in Fig. 4-2. The general shape of these curves may be explained as follows: At the temperature T_1 at which no electrons are emitted, the potential gradient is constant, so that the potential variation is a linear function of the distance from the cathode to the anode. Use was made of this linear potential distribution in Chap. 1, where the motion of an electron in a constant electric field of force was under consideration.

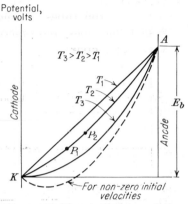

Fig. 4-2. The potential variation between plane-parallel electrodes for several values of cathode temperature.

At the higher temperature T_2, an appreciable density of electrons exists in the interelectrode space. The potential variation will be somewhat as illustrated by the curve marked T_2 in Fig. 4-2. The increase in temperature can change neither the potential of the cathode nor the potential of the anode. Hence, all the curves must pass through the fixed end points K and A. Since negative charge (electrons) now exists in the space between K and A, then, by Coulomb's law, the potential at any point will be lowered. The greater the space charge, the lower will be the potential. Thus, as the temperature is increased, the potential curves become more and more concave upward. At T_3, the curve has drooped so far that it is tangent to the X axis at the origin. That is, the electric-field intensity at the cathode for this condition is zero. One may sketch the broken curve of Fig. 4-2 to represent the potential variation at a temperature higher than T_3. This curve contains a potential minimum. Such a condition is physically impossible, if the initial velocities of the emitted electrons are assumed negligible. That this is so follows from the discussion given below.

Consider the potential-energy curves corresponding to Fig. 4-2. Since the potential energy is equal to the product of the potential V and the charge $-e$, then the curves of Fig. 4-3 are simply those of Fig. 4-2 inverted, the unit of the ordinates being changed to electron volts. It is immediately evident that the broken curve represents a potential-energy barrier at the surface of the cathode. Several such potential-energy bar-

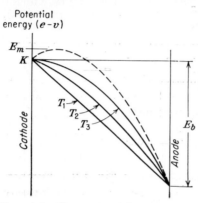

FIG. 4-3. The potential-energy variations corresponding to the curves of Fig. 4-2.

riers have already been considered in Chap. 3. On the basis of our previous discussions, it is clear that only those electrons which possess an initial energy greater than E_m, the maximum height of the barrier, can escape from the cathode and reach the anode. Consequently, the assumed condition of zero initial velocities of the emitted electrons precludes the possibility of any electrons being emitted. As a result, the barrier will be broken down, since the applied field will cause those electrons which produce the barrier to leave the interelectrode space and become part of

the anode current. This automatic growth and collapse of the potential barrier outside the cathode may be considered as a self-regulating valve that allows a certain definite number of electrons per second to escape from the cathode and reach the anode, for a given value of plate voltage.

It can be inferred from the foregoing argument that the maximum current that can be drawn from a diode for a fixed plate voltage and any temperature whatsoever is obtained under the condition of zero electric field at the surface of the cathode. Thus, for optimum conditions,

$$\mathcal{E} = -\frac{dV}{dx} = 0 \qquad \text{at } x = 0 \tag{4-1}$$

This condition is based on the assumption that the emitted electrons have zero initial energies. Because the initial velocities are not truly zero, the potential variation within the tube may actually acquire the form illustrated by the broken curve of Fig. 4-2. However since the potential minimum in Fig. 4-2 is usually small in comparison with the applied potential, it will be neglected and the condition (4-1) will be assumed to represent the true status when space-charge current is being drawn.

In the next section the analytical expression for the potential as a function of distance will be derived. The starting point in this derivation is Poisson's equation, which relates the density of electrons with the potential at any point in the interelectrode space. The derivation of this equation is given in Appendix V. It is simply a mathematical restatement of Coulomb's law relating the potential with the charge, except that the space-charge cloud is treated as a continuous volume density of charge rather than an ensemble of discrete point charges.

Poisson's equation is

$$\frac{d^2V}{dx^2} = \frac{\rho}{\epsilon_0} \tag{4-2}$$

where x is the distance from the cathode in meters, V is the potential in volts, ρ is the *magnitude* of the *electronic* volume charge density in coulombs per cubic meter, and ϵ_0 is the permittivity of free space in the mks system. The shapes of the curves in Fig. 4-2 conform to this equation. Thus, for $T = T_1$ where $\rho = 0$, Eq. (4-2) becomes

$$\frac{d^2V}{dx^2} = 0 \quad \text{or} \quad \frac{dV}{dx} = \text{const}$$

This equation represents a straight line, as shown in Fig. 4-2. Furthermore, the curve for any other temperature must be concave upward because, from Eq. (4-2), d^2V/dx^2 is a positive number. A positive second derivative means that the change in slope dV/dx, between two adjacent points, must be positive. We may readily verify that

$$\frac{dV}{dx}\bigg]_{P_2} - \frac{dV}{dx}\bigg]_{P_1}$$

is positive for any two neighboring points P_1 and P_2 of Fig. 4-2. Further, the change in slope is greater for larger values of ρ, corresponding to higher temperatures.

4-4. Space-charge Current. We shall now obtain the analytical relationship between the anode current and voltage in a diode. The electrons flowing from the cathode to the anode constitute the current. The magnitude of the current density J is given by Eq. (1-34), *viz.*,

$$J = \rho v \quad \text{amp/m}^2 \tag{4-3}$$

where v is the drift velocity of these electrons in meters per second and where ρ is the volume density of electric charge in coulombs per cubic meter. Both ρ and v are functions of the distance from the origin (the cathode). However, the product is constant, since the number of electrons passing through unit area per second must be the same for all points between a plane cathode and a parallel anode. This statement expresses the principle of *conservation of electric charge*. Therefore, at the cathode, where the velocity of the electrons is very small (the velocities being the initial velocities), the charge density must be very large. In the neighborhood of the anode, the velocity is a maximum; hence the charge density is a minimum. If the initial velocities are neglected, the velocity of the electrons at any point in the interelectrode space may be determined from the equation that relates the kinetic energy of the particle with the potential through which it has fallen, viz.,

$$\tfrac{1}{2}mv^2 = eV \tag{4-4}$$

There results, from Eqs. (4-2), (4-3), and (4-4),

$$\frac{d^2V}{dx^2} = \frac{\rho}{\epsilon_0} = \frac{J}{v\epsilon_0} = \frac{J}{[2(e/m)]^{\frac{1}{2}}\epsilon_0} V^{-\frac{1}{2}} = kV^{-\frac{1}{2}} \tag{4-5}$$

where

$$k \equiv \frac{J}{[2(e/m)]^{\frac{1}{2}}\epsilon_0} \tag{4-6}$$

is a constant, independent of x.

The solution of Eq. (4-5) is obtained as follows: Let $y \equiv dV/dx$, and this equation becomes

$$\frac{dy}{dx} = kV^{-\frac{1}{2}}$$

or

$$dy = kV^{-\frac{1}{2}}\,dx = kV^{-\frac{1}{2}}\frac{dV}{y}$$

Hence,

$$y\,dy = kV^{-\frac{1}{2}}\,dV$$

which integrates to

$$\frac{y^2}{2} = 2kV^{\frac{1}{2}} + C_1 \tag{4-7}$$

The constant of integration C_1 is zero because at the cathode $V = 0$ and $y = dV/dx = 0$, from Eq. (4-1). By taking the square root of Eq. (4-7) there results

$$y = \frac{dV}{dx} = 2k^{\frac{1}{2}}V^{\frac{1}{4}} \qquad \text{and} \qquad V^{-\frac{1}{4}}\,dV = 2k^{\frac{1}{2}}\,dx$$

This equation integrates to

$$\tfrac{4}{3}V^{\frac{3}{4}} = 2k^{\frac{1}{2}}x + C_2$$

The constant of integration C_2 is zero because $V = 0$ at $x = 0$. Finally,

$$V = (\tfrac{3}{2})^{\frac{4}{3}}k^{\frac{2}{3}}x^{\frac{4}{3}} \tag{4-8}$$

It is seen that the potential depends upon the four-thirds power of the interelectrode spacing. For example, the curve marked T_3 in Fig. 4-2 is expressed by the relation

$$V = \alpha x^{\frac{4}{3}} \tag{4-9}$$

where α is readily found in terms of constants and the current density J

from the foregoing equations.   However, α may also be written as $E_b/d^{\frac{3}{2}}$, where d is the separation of the electrodes and E_b is the plate potential. This is so because Eq. (4-9) is valid for the entire interelectrode space, including the boundary $x = d$ where $V = E_b$.

The complete expression for the current density is obtained by combining Eqs. (4-8) and (4-6).   The result is

$$J = \frac{4}{9}\left(2\,\frac{e}{m}\right)^{\frac{1}{2}} \epsilon_0 \frac{V^{\frac{3}{2}}}{x^2} \qquad \text{amp/m}^2 \tag{4-10}$$

In terms of the boundary values, this becomes, upon inserting the value of e/m for electrons and $\epsilon_0 = 10^{-9}/36\pi$,

$$J = 2.33 \times 10^{-6} \frac{E_b^{\frac{3}{2}}}{d^2} \qquad \text{amp/m}^2 \tag{4-11}$$

Therefore, *the plate current varies as the three-halves power of the plate potential.*   This result was established by Langmuir,[6] although it had been previously published in a different connection by Child.[7]   It is known by several different names, for example, the *Langmuir-Child law,* the *three-halves-power law,* or simply the *space-charge equation.*

It will be noticed that this equation relates the current density, and so the current, in terms only of the applied potential and the geometry of the tube.   The space-charge current does not depend upon either the temperature or the work function of the cathode.   Hence, no matter how many electrons a cathode may be able to supply, the geometry of the tube and the potential applied thereto will determine the maximum current that can be collected by the anode.   Of course, it may be less than the value predicted by Eq. (4-11), if the electron supply from the cathode is restricted (because the temperature is too low).   To summarize, *the plate current in a given diode depends only upon the applied potential,* provided that this current is less than the temperature-limited current.

The velocity of the electrons as a function of position between the cathode and anode can be found from Eq. (4-4) with the aid of Eq. (4-10). Then the charge density as a function of x can be found from Eq. (4-3). It is easily found (Prob. 4-7) that v varies as the two-thirds power of x and that ρ varies inversely as the two-thirds power of x.   This physically impossible result that at the cathode the charge density is infinite is a consequence of the assumption that the electrons emerging from the cathode all do so with zero initial velocity.   Actually, of course, the initial velocities are small, but nonzero, and the charge density is large, though finite.

It will be found that conditions in certain portions of a gaseous discharge (Sec. 12-21) are precisely the same as those discussed above, except that the current-carrying particles are positive ions of mass m_i instead of electrons of mass m_e. Under these conditions, the space-charge equations must be modified in order to take into account this difference in mass and, if any, the difference in charge that is carried by the ion. Equation (4-10) is to be replaced in these cases by the expression

for GASEOUS
DISCHARGE electron
m_e = mass electron + ions
m_i = mass of + ions

$$J = 2.33 \times 10^{-6} \sqrt{\frac{(e/m)_i}{(e/m)_e}} \frac{V^{\frac{3}{2}}}{x^2} \qquad \text{amp/m}^2 \qquad (4\text{-}12)$$

4-5. Cylindrical Diodes. Systems that possess plane-parallel electrodes were considered above because the simplicity of this geometry made it easy to understand the physical principles involved. However,

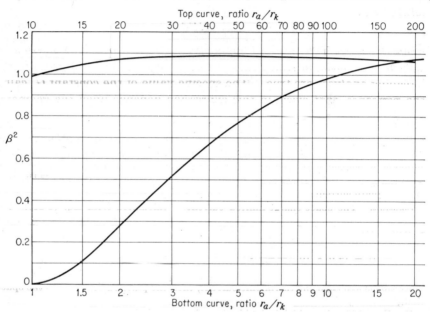

Fig. 4-4. Langmuir's space-charge parameter β^2.

such tube geometry is almost never met in practice. More frequently, tubes are constructed with cylindrical symmetry, the anode being in the form of a cylinder that is coaxial with a cathode of either the directly or the indirectly heated type. The solution of the space-charge equation for such a system, subject to the conditions that field distortion due to the end effects is negligible, that both the anode and the cathode are equipotential surfaces, and that the electrons emerge from the cathode with zero initial velocities, is found to be[8]

$$I_b = 14.6 \times 10^{-6} \frac{l}{r_a} \frac{E_b^{\frac{3}{2}}}{\beta^2} \qquad \text{amp} \qquad (4\text{-}13)$$

In this expression E_b is the plate voltage, r_a is the plate radius, l is the length of the plate, and β^2 is determined from the ratio r_a/r_k from Fig. 4-4.

A comparison of Eqs. (4-11) and (4-13) reveals that the current varies inversely as the square of the distance between the electrodes in the case of plane-parallel electrodes and varies inversely as the first power of the anode radius in the case of cylindrical electrodes, provided that the ratio r_a/r_k is sufficiently large so that β^2 may be considered approximately equal to unity.

Attention is called to the fact that the plate current depends upon the three-halves power of the plate potential for both the plane-parallel system and the one possessing cylindrical symmetry. This is a general relationship, since it is possible to demonstrate[9] that *an expression of the form*

$$I_b = GE_b^{\frac{3}{2}} \tag{4-14}$$

where I_b is the plate current, applies for any geometrical arrangement of cathode and anode, provided that the same restrictions as imposed in the foregoing analyses are true. The specific value of the constant G, called the *perveance*, that exists in this expression depends upon the geometry of the system.

Example. Given a cylindrical cathode 1.8 cm long and 0.16 cm in diameter whose thermionic emission is 40 ma at the operating temperature. An anode 1.0 cm in diameter is coaxial with this cathode. What is the plate current when the plate potential is 50 volts? If the plate potential is increased to 100 volts, what is the new value of plate current?

Solution. The space-charge-limited current is calculated from Eq. (4-13). The value of β^2 corresponding to $r_a/r_k = 0.5 \text{ cm}/0.08 \text{ cm} = 6.24$ is found from Fig. 4-4 to be 0.85. Hence

$$I_b = 14.6 \times 10^{-6} \frac{l}{r_a} \frac{E_b^{\frac{3}{2}}}{\beta^2} = (14.6 \times 10^{-6}) \left(\frac{1.8}{0.5}\right) \left(\frac{50^{\frac{3}{2}}}{0.85}\right) = 21.8 \text{ ma}$$

Since this is less than the thermionic current, then the plate current will be the space-charge current, of 21.8 ma.

For $E_b = 100$ volts, which is double the voltage used above, the three-halves-power current will be $2^{\frac{3}{2}}$ times the value just calculated, or

$$I_b = 2^{\frac{3}{2}} \times 21.8 = 61.7 \text{ ma}$$

Since this exceeds the thermionic current, then the plate current will be the thermionic current, or 40 ma.

This example emphasizes the fact that, if the thermionic and space-charge currents are calculated, the plate current will always equal the smaller of these two values.

4-6. Factors Influencing Space-charge Current. Several factors modify the equations for space charge given above, particularly at low plate voltages. Among these factors are:

1. *Filament Voltage Drop.* The space-charge equations were derived on the assumption that the cathode is an equipotential surface. This is not a valid assumption for a directly heated emitter, and the voltage

across the ends of the filament causes a deviation from the three-halves-power equation. In fact, the results depend on whether the plate current is returned to the positive or to the negative end of the filament.

If the plate current is returned to the negative end of the filament, the actual voltage of the various portions of the filament is less than the applied voltage, because of the repelling action of the filament voltage. Hence, the space-charge current is less than that which can be obtained from a geometrically similar equipotential cathode. If the cathode lead is returned to the positive end of the filament, an increased current is obtained. The effect of filament voltage drop is largely eliminated by returning the plate current to the filament mid-point, if this is available, or to a center-tapped resistor across the filament. If the filament is heated with a transformer, the plate is returned to the center tap of the secondary winding.

2. *Contact Potential.* In every space-charge equation, the symbol E_b must be understood to mean the sum of the applied voltage from plate to cathode plus the contact potential between the two. For plate voltages of only a few volts, this effect may be quite appreciable.

3. *Asymmetries in Tube Structure.* Commercial tubes seldom possess the ideal geometry assumed in deriving the space-charge equations.

4. *Gas.* The presence of even minute traces of gas in a tube can have marked effects on the tube characteristics. If the voltage is sufficiently high to cause ionization of the residual gas molecules, the plate current will rise above that demanded by the space-charge equations because the positive ions that are formed neutralize the electronic-charge density. Modern vacuum tubes are exhausted to pressures of about 10^{-6} mm Hg.

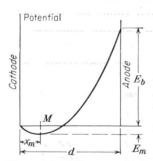

FIG. 4-5. The potential variation in a plane-parallel space-charge diode, with the initial velocities of the electrons taken into account.

5. *Initial Velocities of Emitted Electrons.* If the initial velocities of the electrons are not neglected, then the equilibrium condition will no longer be that of zero electric field at the cathode. Instead, the variation of potential with interelectrode spacing will be somewhat as depicted by the broken curve of Fig. 4-2, which is reproduced in Fig. 4-5 for convenience. This represents a potential-energy barrier at the cathode surface, and so it is only those electrons whose energies are greater than the height E_m of this barrier that can escape from the cathode. The height of this barrier is, from the results of Sec. 3-10, a fraction of 1 ev.

At a distance x_m from the surface of the thermionic emitter, the point of the potential minimum, the electric-field intensity passes through zero.

Hence the point M may be considered as the position of a "virtual" cathode. Evidently, the distance that will enter into the resulting space-charge equation will be $d - x_m$, and not d. Likewise, the effective plate potential will be $E_b + E_m$, and not E_b alone. Both of these factors will tend to increase the current above that which exists when the initial velocities are neglected.

The exact mathematical formulation of the space-charge equation taking into account the energy distribution of the electrons is somewhat involved. It can be found in the literature.[10]

To summarize, the plate current in a diode is not strictly a function only of the plate potential but does depend, to a small extent, upon the temperature of the cathode.

If all the factors discussed above are neglected, theory predicts that a plot of log I_b vs. log E_b should be a straight line having a slope equal to 1.5, since from the equation $I_b = GE_b^{\frac{3}{2}}$ we find

$$\log_{10} I_b = \log_{10} G + \tfrac{3}{2} \log_{10} E_b$$

Dishington[11] has determined this slope for 22 types of commercial diode. The values ranged from 1.24 to 1.49 with the average at 1.42.

4-7. Diode Characteristics. The discussion in this and in the preceding chapter has revealed that the two most important factors that determine the characteristics of diodes are thermionic emission and space charge. The first gives the temperature saturated value, *i.e.*, the maximum current that can be collected at a given cathode temperature, regardless of the magnitude of the applied accelerating potential. (This statement is strictly true only if the Schottky effect is neglected.) The second gives the space-charge-limited value, or the voltage saturated value, and specifies the maximum current that can be collected at a given voltage regardless of the temperature of the filament.

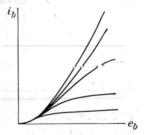

FIG. 4-6. Volt-ampere diode characteristics for various filament temperatures.

The volt-ampere characteristics obtained experimentally for an oxide-coated cathode are shown in Fig. 4-6. It should be noted that the space-charge currents corresponding to the different temperatures do not coincide but that the currents decrease slightly as the temperature decreases. Further, there is no abrupt transition between the space-charge-limited and the temperature-limited portions of the curves, but rather a gradual transition occurs. Also, the current for the temperature-limited regions gradually rises with increased anode potentials.

The temperature-current curves obtained experimentally for a tungsten-filament tube are illustrated in Fig. 4-7. The curve for $E_b = 250$ volts is actually a plot of the Dushman equation for temperatures up to about 2400°K. Beyond this temperature, the curve shows a changing curvature that indicates that the current is becoming space-charge-limited. That is, the plate voltage is not high enough to collect saturation current.

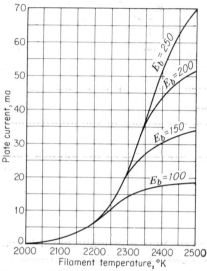

FIG. 4-7. Temperature-current curves of the General Electric FP 85 tungsten-filament diode with the plate voltage as a parameter.

The bend in the curves is much more noticeable for the lower plate voltages. Again we see that there is no abrupt change from the temperature-limited to the space-charge-limited regions. As a matter of fact, the true space-charge current is not reached at all with the higher voltages and is only approached for $E_b = 100$ volts, as is evident from the curves.

The explanation of the shapes of the diode characteristics lies in a consideration of the numerous contributing factors. For example, in the case of a directly heated cathode, the drop in potential along the cathode will cause the different portions of the cathode to be at different values of voltage saturation. Another appreciable factor affecting the shape of the curves is that the filament is not all at the same temperature. The consequence of the different temperatures existing at different parts of the cathode will result in temperature-limited currents that are limited at different values of temperature. Evidently the temperature effects are less pronounced when indirectly heated cathodes are used.

The application of the high anode potentials in order to collect the space current will give rise to an appreciable increase in current because of the Schottky effect. This effect may become particularly marked in the case of thoriated-tungsten and oxide-coated cathodes, since hot spots may result and consequently the thermionic emission may be increased.

4-8. Diode Resistance and Capacitance. An ideal diode is defined as a two-terminal circuit element having the volt-ampere characteristic shown in Fig. 4-8a. When the diode conducts, the ratio of the applied voltage e_b to the current i_b, called the *forward resistance* R_f, is zero. For negative voltages, the ratio e_b/i_b, called the *back resistance* R_b, is infinite.

The ideal diode has characteristics which are independent of temperature. Additionally, in an ideal diode, the capacitance shunting the diode is assumed to be negligible. A thermionic-diode characteristic, for voltages

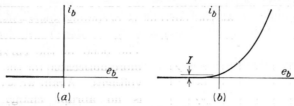

Fig. 4-8. Diode characteristics. (a) Ideal diode. (b) Thermionic diode.

below saturation, is sketched in Fig. 4-8b. This real diode differs from the ideal tube in the following respects:

1. The forward resistance is not zero, but R_f lies in the approximate range of 100 to 1,000 ohms.

2. The value of R_f is not constant but depends upon the applied voltage. It is sometimes convenient to introduce the *dynamic* or *incremental plate resistance* r_p, defined by

$$r_p = \frac{de_b}{di_b} \tag{4-15}$$

Of course, if the volt-ampere characteristic were a straight line passing through the origin, then R_f would be equal to r_p. For low values of current we have from Eq. (3-22) that

$$r_p = \frac{E_T}{I} \epsilon^{-e_b/E_T} \tag{4-16}$$

On the other hand, for space-charge-limited currents we have from Eq. (4-14) that

$$r_p = \frac{2}{3Ge_b^{\frac{1}{2}}} = \frac{2R_f}{3} \qquad G = \frac{I_b}{E_b^{3/2}} \tag{4-17}$$

3. The back resistance is not infinite although values of hundreds or even thousands of megohms are attainable even for small negative applied voltages.

4. The "break" in the characteristic (the division between the high- and low-resistance regions) is not sharp and may not occur at zero applied voltage.

5. As already mentioned in Sec. 4-6, the volt-ampere characteristic is not strictly space-charge-limited but does depend somewhat upon the filament temperature. Experiment reveals that there is a shift in the characteristic of about 0.1 *volt for a 10 per cent change in heater voltage.* The higher the filament voltage, the more the curves shift to the left,

because the increase in the initial velocities of the electrons with increase in temperature results in higher currents at a given voltage.   The shift with tube replacement or tube aging is found in practice to be of the order of ± 0.25 volt.

6. Since a diode consists of two metallic electrodes, a cathode and an anode, separated by a dielectric, a vacuum, this device constitutes a capacitor.   The order of magnitude of this capacitance is $5\mu\mu f$.   To this value must be added the wiring capacitance introduced when the diode is inserted into a circuit.

4-9. Rating of Vacuum Diodes.   The rating of a vacuum diode, *i.e.*, the maximum current that it may normally carry and the maximum potential difference that may be applied between the cathode and the anode, is influenced by a number of factors.

1. A definite limitation is set by the *cathode efficiency* (Table 4-1), which is the ratio of the emission-current to the heating power of the cathode.

2. The temperature to which the glass envelope of the tube may be safely allowed to rise also furnishes a limitation to the normal rating.   In order that the gas adsorbed by the glass walls should not be liberated, the temperature of the envelope must not be allowed to exceed the temperature to which the tube was raised in the outgassing process.

3. Probably the most important factor limiting the rating of a tube is the allowable temperature rise of the anode.   When a diode is in operation, the anode becomes heated to a rather high temperature because of the power that must be dissipated by the anode.   This power may be considered either in terms of the kinetic energy carried by the electrons and transferred to the plate when they are collected, or in terms of the product of the plate current and the plate potential.   The instantaneous power may be expressed in either of the forms

$$\tfrac{1}{2}Nmv^2 \;=\; Nee_b \;=\; i_b e_b \qquad \text{watts}$$

where N is the number of electrons per second carried by the beam, e is the charge of the electron in coulombs, m is the electronic mass in kilograms, v is the electronic velocity at the anode in meters per second, i_b is the instantaneous plate current in amperes, and e_b is the instantaneous plate potential in volts.   In addition to the power carried by the anode current, the anode will also be heated to some extent by the heat that it intercepts from the cathode.   This term depends upon the degree to which the anode surrounds the cathode and so intercepts heat radiation from it.

The temperature of the anode will rise until the rate at which the energy supplied to the anode from all sources just equals the rate at which the heat is dissipated from the anode in the form of radiation.   Consequently, for a given power supplied to the anode, the temperature to which it will rise will depend upon the area of the anode and the material of which it is constructed, in accordance with Eq. (3-17). The most common metals used for anodes are nickel and iron for receiving tubes and tantalum, molybdenum, and graphite for transmitting tubes. The surfaces are often roughened or blackened in order to increase the thermal emissivity and permit higher-power operation. These anodes may be operated at a cherry-red heat without excessive gas emission or other deleterious effects. For the larger tubes, it is necessary that the anodes be cooled. The heat is carried away either by circulating water through special cooling coils or by forced-air cooling[12] on radiator fins which are attached to the anode.

4. The voltage limitation of a high-vacuum diode is not always determined by the permissible heating of the anode. For the case of a tube in which the filament and anode leads are brought out side by side through the same glass press, conduction may take place between the filament leads and the anode lead through the glass itself, especially if the voltage between these leads is high. For this reason, high-voltage rectifiers are generally provided with filament leads and the anode lead at opposite ends of the glass envelope.

Also, the separation of the leads of high-voltage rectifiers must be large enough to preclude the possibility of flashover through the air. In fact, it is the highest voltage that may be safely impressed across the electrodes with no flow of charge that determines the safe voltage rating of a tube. Since, with an alternating potential applied between the cathode and anode, no current must exist during the portion of the cycle when the anode is negative with respect to the cathode, the maximum safe rating of a rectifying diode is known as the *peak inverse-voltage* rating.

Commercial vacuum diodes are made to rectify currents at very high voltages, up to about 200,000 volts. Such units are used with X-ray equipment, high-voltage cable-testing equipment, and high-voltage equipment for nuclear-physics research.

4-10. The Diode as a Circuit Element. The basic diode circuit of Fig. 4-9 consists of the tube in series with a load resistance R_L and an input signal source e volts. Since the heater plays no part in the analysis of the circuit, it has been omitted

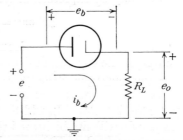

FIG. 4-9. The basic diode circuit.

from Fig. 4-9, and the diode is indicated as a two-terminal device. This circuit will now be analyzed.

The instantaneous plate current is i_b, and the instantaneous voltage across the diode is e_b, when the instantaneous input voltage is e. Evidently, by Kirchhoff's voltage law,

$$e_b = e - i_b R_L \qquad (4\text{-}18)$$

where R_L is the magnitude of the load resistance. This one equation is not sufficient to determine the two unknowns e_b and i_b in this expression. However, a second relation between these two variables is given by the

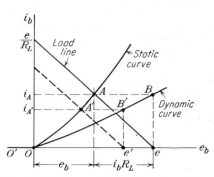

FIG. 4-10. The method of constructing the dynamic curve from the static curve and the load line.

static plate characteristic of the diode (Fig. 4-6). In Fig. 4-10 there is indicated the simultaneous solution of Eq. (4-18) and the diode plate characteristic. The straight line, which is represented by Eq. (4-18), is called the "load line." The load line passes through the points $i_b = 0$, $e_b = e$ and $i_b = e/R_L$, $e_b = 0$. That is, the intercept with the voltage axis is e and with the current axis is e/R_L. The slope of this line is determined, therefore, by R_L. It may happen that $i_b = e/R_L$ is too large to appear on the printed volt-ampere characteristic supplied by the manufacturer. If I_o does appear on this characteristic, then one point on the load line is $i_b = I_o$, $e_b = e - I_o R_L$ and the second point is $i_b = 0$, $e_b = e$.

The point of intersection A of the load line and the static curve gives the current i_A that will flow under these conditions. This construction determines the current in the circuit when the instantaneous input potential is e. This current is plotted vertically above e at point B in the diagram. If the input voltage is permitted to vary, the corresponding current will vary. Clearly, the slope of the load line does not vary since R_L is fixed. Thus, when the applied potential has the value e', the corresponding current is $i_{A'}$. This current is plotted vertically above e' at B'. The resulting curve $OB'B$ that is generated as e varies is called the "dynamic characteristic."

It is to be emphasized that, regardless of the shape of the static characteristic or the wave form of the input voltage, the resulting wave form of the current in the output circuit can always be found graphically from the dynamic characteristic. This construction is indicated in Fig. 4-11. The input-signal wave form (not necessarily sinusoidal) is drawn with its time axis vertically downward so that the voltage axis is horizontal. Suppose that the input voltage has the value indicated by the point A at an instant t'. The corresponding current is obtained by drawing a vertical line through A and noting the current a where this line intersects the dynamic curve. This current is then plotted at an instant of time

equal to t'.   Similarly, points $b, c, d, \ldots$ of the current wave form correspond to points $B, C, D, \ldots$ of the input-voltage wave form.

   The construction of Fig. 4-11 indicates that, for negative input voltages, zero output current is obtained.   If the dynamic characteristic is
linear, then the output voltage $e_o = i_b R_L$ is an exact replica of the input
voltage e except that the negative portion of e is missing.   In this application the diode acts as a *clipper.*   If the diode polarity is reversed, the
positive portion of the input voltage is clipped.   The clipping level need
not be at zero (or ground) potential.   For example, if a reference battery

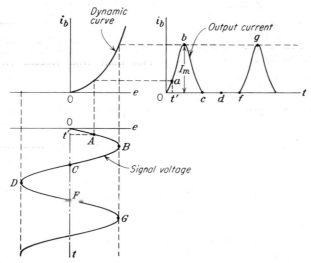

FIG. 4-11. The method of obtaining the output-current wave form from the dynamic
curve for a given input-voltage wave form.

E_R is added in series with R_L of Fig. 4-9 (with the negative battery terminal at ground), then signal voltages smaller than E_R will be clipped.
Many other wave-shaping circuits[13] employ diodes.

   One of the most important applications of a diode is rectification.   If
the input voltage is sinusoidal, then the output consists of only positive
sections (resembling half sinusoids).   The important fact to note is that,
whereas the average value of the input is zero, the output contains a
nonzero d-c value.   Hence, rectification, or the conversion from alternating to direct voltage, has taken place.   Practical rectifier circuits are
discussed in Chaps. 14 and 19.   Diodes also find extensive application in
digital computers and in circuits used to detect radio-frequency signals.

REFERENCES

1. MARSDEN, C. P., JR., "Thermionic Emission in Transmitting Tubes," *Electronics*,
    11, 22–25, 32, December, 1938.

KOLLER, L. R., "The Physics of Electron Tubes," 2d ed., p. 371, McGraw-Hill Book Company, Inc., New York, 1937.

2. DUSHMAN, S., and J. W. EWALD, "Electron Emission from Thoriated Tungsten," *Phys. Rev.*, **29**, 857–870, June, 1927.

3. Excellent reviews of oxide-coated cathodes are given by:

BLEWETT, J. P., "The Properties of Oxide-coated Cathodes," Part I, *J. Appl. Phys.*, **10**, 668–679, October, 1939; Part II, *ibid.*, **10**, 831–848, December, 1939.

BLEWETT, J. P., "Oxide Coated Cathode Literature, 1940–1945," *ibid.*, **17**, 643–647, August, 1946.

EISENSTEIN, A. S., Oxide Coated Cathodes, in "Advances in Electronics," Vol. 1, pp. 1–64, Academic Press, Inc., New York, 1948.

PRESCOTT, C. H., JR., and J. MORRISON, "The True Temperature Scale of an Oxide-coated Filament," *Rev. Sci. Instr.*, **10**, 36–38, January, 1939.

4. COOMES, E. A., "The Pulsed Properties of Oxide Cathodes," *J. Appl. Phys.*, **17**, 647–654, August, 1946.

SPROULL, R. L., "An Investigation of Short-time Thermionic Emission from Oxide-coated Cathodes," *Phys. Rev.*, **67**, 166–178, March, 1945.

5. DUSHMAN, S., "Thermionic Emission," *Revs. Mod. Phys.*, **2**, 381–476, October, 1930.

6. LANGMUIR, I., "The Effect of Space Charge and Residual Gases on Thermionic Currents in High Vacuum," *Phys. Rev.*, **2**, 450–486, December, 1913.

LANGMUIR, I., and K. B. BLODGETT, "Currents Limited by Space Charge between Concentric Spheres," *ibid.*, **24**, 49–59, July, 1924.

7. CHILD, C. D., "Discharge from Hot CaO," *Phys. Rev.*, **27**, 492–511, May, 1911.

8. LANGMUIR, I., "The Effect of Space Charge and Residual Gases on Thermionic Currents in High Vacuum," *Phys. Rev.*, **2**, 450–486, 1913.

LANGMUIR, I., and K. B. BLODGETT, "Current Limited by Space Charge between Concentric Spheres," *ibid.*, **24**, 49–59, 1911.

9. LANGMUIR, I., and K. T. COMPTON, "Electrical Discharges in Gases. Part II: Fundamental Phenomena in Electrical Discharges," *Revs. Mod. Phys.*, **3**, 191–257, April, 1931.

10. FRY, T. C., "The Thermionic Current between Parallel Plane Electrodes; Velocities of Emission Distributed According to Maxwell's Law," *Phys. Rev.*, **17**, 441–452, April, 1921.

FRY, T. C., "Potential Distribution between Parallel Plane Electrodes," *ibid.*, **22**, 445–446, November, 1923.

LANGMUIR, I., "The Effect of Space Charge and Initial Velocities on the Potential Distribution and Thermionic Current between Parallel Plane Electrodes," *ibid.*, **21**, 419–435, April, 1923.

WHEATCROFT, E. L. E., "Theory of Thermionic Diode," *JIEE*, **86**, 473–484, May, 1940.

PAGE, L., and N. I. ADAMS, JR., "Diode Space Charge for Any Initial Velocity and Current," *Phys. Rev.*, **76**, 381–388, August, 1949.

11. DISHINGTON, R. H., "Diode Circuit Analysis," *Elec. Eng.*, **67**, 1043–1049, November, 1948.

12. OSTLUND, E. M., "Air Cooling Applied to External-anode Tubes," *Electronics*, **13**, 36–39, June, 1940.

13. MILLMAN, J., and H. TAUB, "Pulse and Digital Circuits," Chaps. 4 and 13, McGraw-Hill Book Company, Inc., New York, 1956.

CHAPTER 5

SEMICONDUCTOR-DIODE CHARACTERISTICS

IN THIS chapter we demonstrate that if a junction is formed between a sample of p-type and one of n-type semiconductor this combination possesses the properties of a rectifier. The volt-ampere characteristics of such a junction are derived. A detailed study of the electron and hole currents as a function of distance is made. The capacitance across the junction is calculated. Finally, other types of semiconductor rectifiers are discussed.

Although the transistor is a triode semiconductor, it may be considered as one diode biased by the current from a second diode. Hence most of the theory developed in this chapter will be exploited later in connection with our study of the transistor.

5-1. Qualitative Theory of the p-n Junction.[1] If donor impurities are introduced into one side and acceptors into the other side of a single crystal of a semiconductor, say germanium, a p-n junction is formed. Such a system is illustrated in Fig. 5-1a. The donor ion is indicated schematically by a plus sign because after this impurity atom "donates" an electron it becomes a positive ion. The acceptor ion is indicated by a minus sign because after this atom "accepts" an electron it becomes a negative ion. Initially there are nominally only p-type carriers to the left of the junction and only n-type carriers to the right. As a result of the density gradient across the junction, holes will diffuse to the right across the junction and electrons to the left.

As a result of the displacement of these charges, an electric field will appear across the junction. When the field becomes large enough, the process of diffusion will be restrained and equilibrium will be established. The general shape of the charge distribution may be as illustrated in Fig. 5-1b. The electric charges are confined to the neighborhood ($\cong 10^{-4}$ cm) of the junction and consist of immobile ions. We see that the positive holes which neutralized the acceptor ions near the junction in the p-type germanium have disappeared as a result of combination with electrons which have diffused across the junction. Similarly, the neutralizing electrons in the n-type germanium have combined with holes which have crossed the junction from the p material. The unneutralized ions in the

113

neighborhood of the junction are referred to as *uncovered charges*. Since the region of the junction is depleted of mobile charges, it is called the *depletion region*, the *space-charge region*, or the *transition region*.

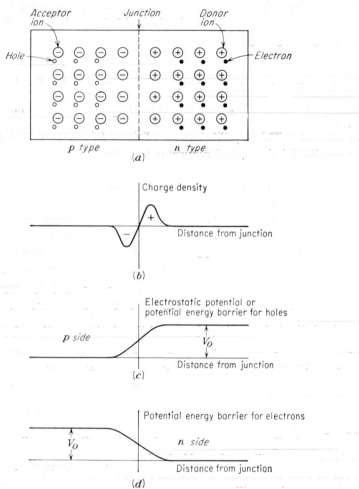

FIG. 5-1. A schematic diagram of a *p-n* junction including the charge density and potential-energy barriers at the junction.

The electrostatic potential variation in the depletion region is shown in Fig. 5-1c. This variation constitutes a potential-energy barrier against the further diffusion of holes across the barrier. The form of the potential-energy barrier against the flow of electrons from the *n* side across the junction is shown in Fig. 5-1d. It is similar to that shown in Fig. 5-1c except that it is inverted, since the electronic charge is negative.

The necessity for the existence of a potential barrier at the junction will now be considered further. Under open-circuited conditions the net hole current must be zero. If this statement were not true, the hole density at one end of the semiconductor would continue to increase indefinitely with time, a situation which is obviously physically impossible. Since the concentration of holes in the p side is much greater than that in the n side, a very large diffusion current tends to flow across the junction from the p to the n material. Hence, an electric field must build up across the junction in such a direction that a drift current will tend to flow across the junction from the n to the p side in order to counterbalance the diffusion current. This equilibrium condition of zero resultant hole current allows us to calcu-

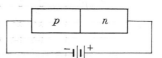

Fig. 5-2. A p-n junction biased in the reverse direction.

late the height of the potential barrier V_0 (Prob. 5-12) in terms of the donor and acceptor concentrations. The numerical value for V_0 is of the order of magnitude of a few tenths of a volt.

The essential electrical characteristic of a p-n junction is that it constitutes a diode which permits the easy flow of current in one direction but restrains the flow in the opposite direction. We consider now qualitatively how this diode action comes about. In Fig. 5-2, a battery is shown connected across the terminals of a p-n junction. The negative terminal of the battery is connected to the p side of the junction and the positive terminal to the n side. The polarity of connection is such as to cause both the holes in the p type and the electrons in the n type to move away from the junction. Consequently the region of negative-charge density is spread to the left of the junction (Fig. 5-1b), and the positive-charge-density region is spread to the right. However, this process cannot continue indefinitely, because in order to have a steady flow of holes to the left these holes must be supplied across the junction from the n-type germanium. And there are very few holes in the n-type side. Hence, nominally zero current results. Actually, a small current does flow because a small number of hole-electron pairs are generated throughout the crystal as a result of thermal energy. The holes so formed in the n-type germanium will wander over to the junction. A similar remark applies to the electrons thermally generated in the p-type germanium. This small current is the diode *reverse saturation current*, and its magnitude is designated by I_0. This reverse current will increase with increasing temperature [Eq. (5-37)], and hence the back resistance of a crystal diode decreases with increasing temperature.

The mechanism of conduction in the reverse direction may be described alternatively in the following way. When no voltage is applied to the p-n diode, the potential barrier across the junction is shown in Fig. 5-1c.

When a voltage V is applied to the diode in the direction shown in Fig. 5-2, the height of the potential-energy barrier is increased by the amount V. This increase in the barrier height serves to reduce the flow of majority carriers (*i.e.*, holes in p type and electrons in n type). However, the minority carriers (*i.e.*, electrons in p type and holes in n type), since they fall down the potential-energy hill, are uninfluenced by the increased height of the barrier. The applied voltage in the direction indicated in Fig. 5-2 is called the *reverse* or *blocking bias*.

An external voltage applied with the polarity shown in Fig. 5-3 (opposite to that indicated in Fig. 5-2) is called a *forward* bias. An ideal diode is defined as one having zero ohmic voltage drop across the body of the crystal. For such a diode the height of the potential barrier across the junction will be lowered by the applied forward voltage V. The equilibrium which was initially established between the forces tending to produce diffusion of majority carriers and the restraining influence of the potential-energy barrier at the junction will be disturbed. Hence, for a forward bias the holes cross the junction from the p type to the n type, and the electrons cross the junction in the opposite direction. These majority carriers can then travel around the closed circuit, and a relatively large current will flow.

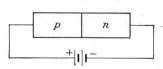

FIG. 5-3. A p-n junction biased in the forward direction.

5-2. Semiconductor-diode Volt-Ampere Characteristic. The potential barrier in Fig. 5-1 keeps the majority carriers from crossing the junction. If a potential V is applied in the forward direction, this retarding barrier is lowered by the voltage V, and the current increases exponentially in the form $A\epsilon^{V/V_T}$, where A is a constant. This situation is analogous to that which exists when the retarding potential is decreased at the surface of a thermionic emitter (Sec. 3-10). The IRE Standards on semiconductor symbols recommend V for voltage. Hence, the electron-volt equivalent of temperature, for which the symbol E_T is used in connection with a vacuum tube, is designated by V_T for a semiconductor device. By definition,

$$V_T \equiv \frac{kT}{e} = \frac{T}{11,600} \qquad (5\text{-}1)$$

where k is the Boltzmann constant in joules per degree Kelvin and e is the magnitude of the electronic charge. If a large reverse bias ($V \rightarrow -\infty$) is applied to the p-n junction, the reverse saturation current $-I_0$ is collected. Hence, the current I which flows at an applied forward voltage V is given by

$$I = A\epsilon^{V/V_T} - I_0$$

For zero applied voltage (a short-circuited junction) the current must be zero. If this statement were not true, the resultant current would generate heat in the body of the semiconductor. But there is no energy source present to supply this heat. Hence, for $V = 0$, $I = 0$, and therefore $A = I_0$, so that

$$I = I_0(\epsilon^{V/V_T} - 1) \tag{5-2}$$

The volt-ampere characteristic of a semiconductor diode with an assumed reverse saturation current of 10 μa is plotted in Fig. 5-4.

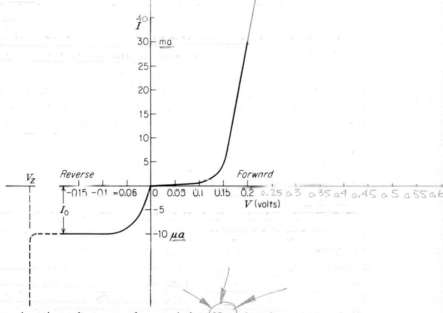

FIG. 5-4. The p-n junction volt-ampere characteristic. Note that the current scale for the forward direction is different from that for the reverse direction.

Because the forward current is so much larger than the reverse current, the vertical scale is in milliamperes in the forward direction and in microamperes in the reverse direction. It is this change of scale which accounts for the apparent discontinuity of the slope at the origin of the curves in Fig. 5-4. At 0.1 volt forward bias the current is approximately 0.5 ma, whereas at 0.2 volt it is 30 ma, which indicates the exponential behavior of current with voltage. If the forward bias is increased beyond a few tenths of a volt so as to reduce the junction barrier to zero, the above theory is no longer valid. The current is now determined by Ohm's law. We must take into account the resistance through the body of the semiconductor, the resistances of the external metallic connections to the diode, and any external resistance present. The volt-ampere characteristic now changes from that indicated by Eq. (5-2) to a linear relationship. The crystal may easily burn out if the forward voltage is too high.

We shall now consider the reverse-bias characteristic of the diode. The quantity V_T has the value 0.026 volt at room temperature (25°C). Therefore when V in Eq. (5-2) is negative and large in magnitude in comparison with 0.026 volt, the reverse current which flows is $-I_0$. However, as the magnitude of the reverse-biasing voltage is increased, a critical voltage V_z is finally reached where the diode volt-ampere characteristic exhibits an abrupt and marked departure from Eq. (5-2), as is indicated in Fig. 5-4 by the dashed portion of the curve. At this critical voltage large reverse currents flow and the diode is said to be in the breakdown region. We discuss next the physical basis for the occurrence of the breakdown.

As the reverse voltage across the diode junction increases, the height of the barrier increases and the maximum electric field encountered in the junction region also increases. When the field becomes sufficiently large, the electrons which constitute the current carriers may acquire enough velocity to produce new carriers by removing valence electrons from their covalent bonds. These new carriers may, in turn, produce additional carriers again through the process of ionization by collision, etc. This cumulative process, which is referred to as *avalanche multiplication*, results in the flow of large reverse current, and the diode is said to be in the region of *avalanche breakdown*. Even if the initially available carriers do not acquire sufficient energy to produce ionization by collision, it is possible to initiate breakdown through a direct rupture of the covalent bonds because of the existence of the strong electric field. Under these circumstances, the breakdown is referred to as a *Zener breakdown*, and the reverse voltage at which the breakdown occurs is called the *Zener voltage*, V_z. However, in either case, at breakdown, the reverse current becomes very large, and the current is largely independent of the voltage. The situation within the diode before breakdown as well as the volt-ampere characteristic after breakdown is very closely analogous to what occurs in a glow tube (Sec. 13-12).

A point of interest in connection with breakdown in junction diodes is that the diode will recover when the magnitude of the reverse voltage is reduced below the breakdown voltage, provided that the diode has not been damaged by excessive heat dissipation in the breakdown region. As a result, it has been possible to manufacture junction diodes which are suitable as voltage-reference or constant-voltage sources. The volt-ampere characteristic in the reverse direction for a typical low-voltage silicon voltage-reference diode is shown in Fig. 5-5. It should be observed that these characteristics are temperature-sensitive. Breakdown diodes are available with reference voltages in the range from several volts to several hundred volts.

The *dynamic resistance r* of a semiconductor diode (corresponding to the plate resistance r_p of a vacuum diode) is defined by

$$r \equiv \frac{dV}{dI} \tag{5-3}$$

The conductance g, which is the reciprocal of r, is given from Eq. (5-2) by

$$g \equiv \frac{dI}{dV} = \frac{I_0}{V_T} \epsilon^{V/V_T} = \frac{I + I_0}{V_T} \tag{5-4}$$

For a reverse bias greater than a few tenths of a volt (so that $|V/V_T| \gg 1$) g is extremely small and r is very large. On the other hand, for a forward bias greater than a few tenths of a volt, $I \gg I_0$, and g and r are given (approximately) by

$$g = \frac{I}{V_T} \qquad r = \frac{V_T}{I} \tag{5-5}$$

The conductance is proportional to the direct current I, and the resistance varies inversely with I. At room temperature, $V_T = 0.026$ volt and hence

$$r = \frac{26}{I} \tag{5-6}$$

where I is expressed in milliamperes and r in ohms. For a current of 26 ma the dynamic resistance is 1 ohm. The ohmic body resistance of the semiconductor may be of the same order of magnitude or may greatly exceed this value.

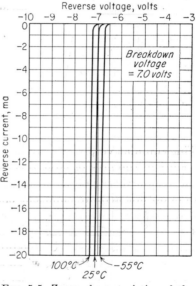

FIG. 5-5. Zener characteristics of the type 653C4 silicon diode. (*Courtesy of the Texas Instrument Company.*)

CAUSED BY REVERSE BIAS

5-3. Space-charge or Transition Capacitance C_T. As mentioned in Sec. 5-1, a reverse bias causes majority carriers to move away from the junction, thereby uncovering more immobile charges. Hence, the thickness of the space-charge layer at the junction increases with reverse voltage. This increase in uncovered charge with applied voltage may be considered a capacitive effect. We may define an incremental capacitance C_T by

$$C_T = \left| \frac{dQ}{dV} \right| \tag{5-7}$$

Mr. Mackey calls C_T the "junction capacity."

where dQ is the increase in charge caused by a change dV in voltage. It follows from this definition that a change in voltage dV in a time dt will result in a current $i = dQ/dt$ given by

$$i = C_T \frac{dV}{dt} \tag{5-8}$$

Therefore, a knowledge of C_T is important in considering a diode (or a transistor) as a circuit element. The quantity C_T is referred to as the *transition-region, space-charge, barrier,* or *depletion-region capacitance.* We shall now consider C_T quantitatively. It will turn out that this capacitance is not a constant but depends upon the magnitude of the reverse voltage. It is for this reason that C_T is defined by Eq. (5-7) rather than as the ratio Q/V.

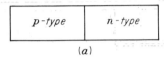

(a)

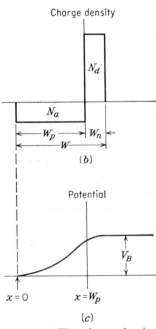

Charge density

(b)

Potential

(c)

Fig. 5-6. The charge-density and potential variation at a fusion *p-n* junction.

Consider a junction in which there is an abrupt change from acceptor ions on one side to donor ions on the other side. Such a junction is formed experimentally, for example, by placing indium, which is trivalent, against n-type germanium and heating the combination to a high temperature for a short time. Some of the indium dissolves into the germanium to change the germanium from n type to p type at the junction. Such a junction is called an *alloy* or *fusion junction.* It is not necessary that the concentration N_a of acceptor ions equal the concentration N_d of donor impurities. As a matter of fact, it is often advantageous to have an unsymmetrical junction. Figure 5-6 shows the charge density as a function of distance from an alloy junction in which the acceptor impurity density is assumed to be much smaller than the donor concentration. Since the net charge must be zero, then

$$eN_aW_p = eN_dW_n \tag{5-9}$$

If $N_a \ll N_d$, then $W_p \gg W_n$. For simplicity, we shall neglect W_n and shall assume that the entire barrier potential V_B appears across the uncovered acceptor ions. The relationship between potential and charge density is given by Poisson's equation. Starting with Coulomb's law, this relationship is derived in Appendix V and is found to be

$$\frac{d^2V}{dx^2} = \frac{eN_a}{\epsilon}$$ (5-10) *

where ϵ is the permittivity of the semiconductor. If K is the (relative) dielectric constant and ϵ_0 is the permittivity of free space (Appendix IV), then $\epsilon = K\epsilon_0$. The electric lines of flux start on the positive donor ions and terminate on the negative acceptor ions. Hence, there are no flux lines to the left of the boundary $x = 0$ in Fig. 5-6, and $\mathcal{E} = -dV/dx = 0$ at $x = 0$. Also, since the zero of potential is arbitrary, we shall choose $V = 0$ at $x = 0$. Integrating Eq. (5-10) subject to these boundary conditions yields

$$V = \frac{eN_a x^2}{2\epsilon}$$ (5-11) *

At $x = W_p \cong W$, $V = V_B$, the barrier height. Thus

$$V_B = \frac{eN_a}{2\epsilon} W^2$$ (5-12) *

to get V_0 see other book pg. 69 equa. (2-42)

If we now reserve the symbol V for the *applied* bias, then $V_B = V_0 - V$, where V is a negative number for an applied *reverse* bias and V_0 is the zero-voltage barrier height (Fig. 5-1). This equation confirms our qualitative conclusion that the thickness of the depletion layer increases with applied reverse voltage. We now see that W varies as $V_B^{\frac{1}{2}}$.

If A is the area of the junction, then the charge in the distance W is $Q = eN_a W A$. The transition capacitance C_T, given by Eq. (5-7), is

$$C_T = \left|\frac{dQ}{dV}\right| = eN_a A \left|\frac{dW}{dV}\right|$$ (5-13) *

From Eq. (5-12), $|dW/dV| = \epsilon/eN_a W$ and hence

$$C_T = \frac{\epsilon A}{W}$$ (5-14) *

It is interesting to note that this formula is exactly the expression which is obtained for a parallel-plate capacitor of area A (square meters) and plate separation W meters containing a material of permittivity ϵ. The barrier capacitance is not a constant but varies with applied voltage. The larger the reverse voltage, the larger W and hence the smaller the capacitance. Similarly, for an increase in forward bias (V positive), W decreases and C_T increases. The order of magnitude of C_T is 5 to 100 $\mu\mu$f for commercially available junction diodes. If the concentration N_d is not neglected, the above results are modified only slightly. In Eq. (5-12) W represents the total space-charge width, and $1/N_a$ is replaced by $1/N_a + 1/N_d$. Equation (5-14) remains valid.

* ALL ASSUME THE CASE WHERE $N_a \ll N_d$ or $W_p \gg W_n$
  HERE $W_p \cong W$

SEE NOTES FOR CASE WHERE W_n IS NOT NEGLECTED

A second form of junction, called a *grown junction*, is obtained by drawing a single crystal from a melt of germanium whose type is changed during the drawing process by adding first p-type and then n-type impurities. For such a grown junction the charge density varies gradually (almost linearly), as indicated in Fig. 5-7. If an analysis similar to that given above is carried out for such a junction, Eq. (5-14) is found to be valid where W equals the total width of the space-charge layer. However, it now turns out that W varies as $V_B^{\frac{1}{3}}$ instead of $V_B^{\frac{1}{2}}$ (Prob. 5-10).

5-4. Diffusion Capacitance. For a forward bias a capacitance which is much larger than that considered in the preceding section comes into play. The origin of this capacitance will now be discussed. If the bias is in the forward direction, the potential barrier at the junction is lowered and holes from the p side enter the n side. Similarly, electrons from the

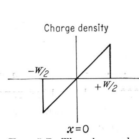

FIG. 5-7. The charge-density variation at a grown p-n junction.

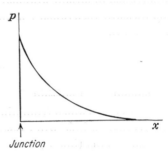

FIG. 5-8. The hole density vs. distance in the n side.

n side move into the p side. This process is called *minority-carrier injection.* Let us concentrate our attention on the holes. What happens to these after they are injected into the n side? The answer to this query is that they will diffuse away from the junction and recombine with electrons which are plentiful in the n side. As a result of this recombination, the hole density falls off exponentially with distance, as indicated in Fig. 5-8. (For a proof of this statement see Appendix VI.) The area under this curve is the charge stored at the junction (per unit cross-sectional area). As explained in Sec. 5-3, it is convenient to introduce an incremental capacitance defined as the rate of change of charge with applied voltage. This capacitance is called the *diffusion capacitance C_D* or the *storage capacitance* for holes. In Sec. 5-8 it is shown that

$$C_D = \frac{L_p^2}{D_p} g$$ (5-15)

where L_p is the mean distance that a hole travels before recombination and is called the *diffusion length* for holes. A similar expression is valid for electrons.   The symbol g is the dynamic conductance of the diode and is defined by Eq. (5-4).

For a reverse bias, g is very small and C_D may be neglected compared with C_T.   For a forward bias which is greater than a few tenths of a volt, g is given by Eq. (5-5), and we see that the conductance and hence the diffusion capacitance are proportional to the direct current.   For $L_p = 0.1$ cm and for germanium ($D_p = 45$ cm²/sec), C_D at $I = 26$ ma (at which current $g = 1$ mho) is

$$C_D = \frac{10^{-6} \times 1}{45 \times 10^{-4}} \text{ farad} \cong 220 \; \mu f$$

It should be noted that this value is far larger than the barrier capacitance C_T.   Despite this large value of C_D, the time constant rC_D (which is of importance in circuit applications) may not be excessive because the dynamic forward resistance r is small.   From Eq. (5-15), this time constant is given by

$$rC_D = \frac{L_p{}^2}{D_p} \tag{5-16}$$

and is independent of current.   For the numerical values assumed above, $rC_D \cong 220 \; \mu\text{sec}$.   Values from about 1 to 1,000 μsec have been reported.

On an average, a hole will exist for τ_p seconds before combining with a free electron.   This time τ_p is called the *mean lifetime* of the hole.   Since L_p is the average distance between recombinations and τ_p is the average time between recombinations, then these two parameters are not independent.   In Appendix VI it is shown that

$$L_p = \sqrt{D_p \tau_p} \tag{5-17}$$

Experimentally the mean lifetime is found to vary greatly between specimens which appear to be alike in all other properties.   It is concluded that the recombination process must be controlled by imperfections in the crystal.   The word *deathnium* has been introduced[2] to describe these not-too-well-understood imperfections.   It is also found that recombination takes place at the surface as well as within the body of the semiconductor, and one speaks of a *deathnium layer* at the surface.   For a specimen of small volume the surface recombination is the dominant process in determining the mean lifetime and is markedly dependent upon the physical and chemical state of the surface.   Values of τ_p of from about 1 to 1,000 μsec have been observed.[3]   For germanium we find from Eq. (5-17) that L_p lies in the range 0.007 to 0.2 cm.   Because of the above relationship between L_p and τ_p, Eq. (5-16) reduces to

$$rC_D = \tau_p \tag{5-18}$$

which states that the time constant is numerically equal to the mean lifetime.

The time constant discussed above places a serious limitation upon the use of the junction diode at high frequencies. For example, consider a diode which is conducting in the forward direction to which is suddenly applied a large negative step of voltage. This bias is in the direction to force the stored minority carriers across the junction. Hence, immediately after the application of the negative step a large reverse current flows, and it is only after the stored charge is removed that the current falls to the low reverse saturation value. The time required for the back resistance to increase to a high value is called the *back recovery time*[4] or *storage-time delay*. This recovery time depends not only upon the value of rC_D but also upon the circuit in which the diode is used. There is also a forward recovery time, but this is usually not of great importance because the forward resistance reaches a low value almost instantly even though the time to reach the final forward resistance may be relatively long.

Because of the capacitive effects discussed above, the junction diode is limited to relatively low-frequency applications, such as a rectifier to convert from alternating (up to about 50 kc) to direct voltages. An example is the 1N94 diffused-junction germanium diode, which has the following ratings: d-c output current = 500 ma, peak forward current = 1.57 amp, surge current = 25 amp, peak inverse voltage = 380 volts, and forward resistance at full load = 0.5 ohm.

5-5. Point-contact Diode. There is available commercially another type of diode, called the *point-contact* diode, which consists of a pointed tungsten or gold wire in the form of a spring which presses against a wafer of *n*-type germanium or silicon of extremely small dimensions (about 1 by 1 by 1 mm). A typical unit, the 1N34A general-purpose diode, is indicated in Fig. 5-9. The glass enclosure acts as a protection against contamination and humidity. The entire unit, exclusive of the leads, is about

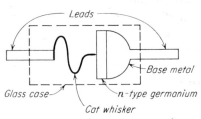

Fig. 5-9. A point-contact semiconductor diode.

0.5 in. long and 0.25 in. in diameter. In the manufacturing process a surge of current is passed through the diode and a *p-n* junction of extremely small area is formed at the point contact. The capacitances associated with this diode are much smaller than the corresponding values for the junction diode. Hence, the point-contact diode is used in high-frequency or pulse applications. For a point-contact diode the back recovery time lies in the range 0.01 to 10 μsec.

Although the point-contact diode is historically much older than the junction diode, the former is much less well understood than the latter. The volt-ampere characteristic is similar to that given in Fig. 5-4 except that the point-contact diode shows no reverse saturation. The reverse current increases with reverse voltage, probably because of the increased heating at the tiny point contact with increased voltage. It is also found that the forward current is usually larger than that predicted from Eq. (5-2).

5-6. Quantitative Theory of the p-n **Junction.** We have seen that, when a forward bias is applied to a diode, holes are injected into the n side and electrons into the p side. We show in Appendix VI that the number of these injected minority carriers falls off exponentially with distance from the junction. From the concentration gradient we can calculate the diffusion current of minority carriers. In this manner we shall find the *hole* current I_{pn} in the n-type material as a function of distance. Similarly, we shall calculate the *electron* current I_{np} in the p side as a function of distance. The sum of the hole current $I_{pn}(0)$ and electron current $I_{np}(0)$ crossing the junction ($x = 0$) equals the total current I.

$$I = I_{pn}(0) + I_{np}(0) \qquad (5\text{-}19)$$

Since the current is the same throughout a series circuit, I is independent of x. The *electron* current I_{nn} in the n material may therefore be calculated as a function of distance from

$$I = I_{pn}(x) + I_{nn}(x) \qquad (5\text{-}20)$$

A similar expression allows the *hole* current $I_{pp}(x)$ in the p side to be evaluated.

The objectives of this and the next two sections are (1) to find the four current components as a function of distance from the junction, (2) to find the total current as a function of the applied voltage (the diode volt-ampere characteristic), (3) to find the reverse saturation current as a function of the physical parameters of the semiconductor and of the temperature, and (4) to evaluate the diffusion capacitance C_D. Furthermore, the theory developed here and the results obtained will be most useful later in our study of the transistor.

Before proceeding with the analysis, a few observations will be made to help clarify the notation. *If the letters p and n both appear in a symbol, the first letter refers to the type of carrier and the second to the type of material.* For example,

$$I_{pn} = \textit{hole current in n-type semiconductor}$$
$$n_p = \textit{electron concentration in p material}$$

If a quantity is a function of distance, this fact may be indicated explicitly by inserting an x in parentheses after the symbol. For example,

$$p_n(x) = \textit{hole concentration in n side as a function of x}$$
$$p_n(0) = \textit{hole concentration in n side at the junction x} = 0$$

A subscript o indicates a thermal-equilibrium value. For example,

$$p_{no} = thermal\text{-}equilibrium\ hole\ concentration\ in\ the\ n\ side$$

The value of the concentration in excess of the thermal-equilibrium value is called the *injected concentration* and is designated by a capital letter for the type of carrier. For example,

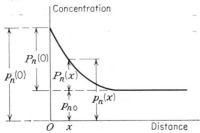

FIG. 5-10. Defining the several components of hole concentration in the n side.

$$P_n(x) \equiv p_n(x) - p_{no} \qquad (5\text{-}21)$$

where $P_n(x)$ is *the injected-hole concentration in the n material at any position x from the junction.* The various hole-concentration components in the n side are indicated in Fig. 5-10.

The diffusion length is very much larger than the depletion-layer thickness and hence we shall neglect the barrier width in the discussion to follow. The diffusion current I_{pn} is given by Eq. (3-38), namely,

$$I_{pn} = -AeD_p \frac{dp_n}{dx}$$

From Eq. (A6-13) the concentration p_n is given by

$$p_n = p_{no} + P_n(0)\epsilon^{-x/L_p}$$

and taking the derivative we obtain

$$I_{pn} = \frac{AeD_pP_n(0)}{L_p}\epsilon^{-x/L_p} \qquad (5\text{-}22)$$

This equation indicates that the hole current decreases exponentially with distance into the n side. However, since the total current I must be independent of x, then there must exist an electron current I_{nn} in the n side, given by Eq. (5-20). These current components are indicated in Fig. 5-11 for an unsymmetrically doped junction diode.

The analysis for the p side is identical to that given above for the n side, and corresponding quantities are obtained by interchanging the symbols p and n. For example, the free-electron current I_{np} in the p side is given by

$$I_{np} = \frac{AeD_nN_p(0)}{L_n}\epsilon^{-x/L_n} \qquad (5\text{-}23)$$

where L_n is the free-electron diffusion length, $N_p(0)$ is the injected-electron concentration from the n side into the p side at the junction, etc. Similarly, there is a hole current I_{pp} in the p side such that

$$I_{np} + I_{pp} = I \qquad (5\text{-}24)$$

The hole and electron currents on both sides of the junction are plotted in Fig. 5-11. Note that deep into the p side the current is a drift (conduction) current I_{pp} of holes sustained by the small electric field in the semiconductor. As the holes approach the junction, some of them recombine with the electrons which are injected into the p side from the n side. Hence, part of the current I_{pp} becomes a negative diffusion current just equal in magnitude to the diffusion current I_{np}. The current I_{pp} thus decreases toward the junction (at just the proper rate to maintain the total current constant, independent of distance). What remains of I_{pp} at the junction enters the n side and becomes the hole diffusion current I_{pn}. Similar remarks can be made with respect to current I_{nn}. Hence, in a forward-biased p-n diode the current enters the p side as a hole current and leaves the n side as an electron current of the same magnitude.

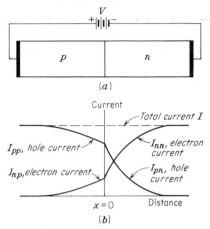

(a)

(b)

FIG. 5-11. The hole and electron-current components vs. distance in a p-n junction diode.

5-7. The Boundary Condition.[5] Before proceeding with the theory of the p-n junction it is necessary to consider the effect of the applied voltage upon the injected-carrier density. This boundary condition can be obtained from the Boltzmann relationship which states that the density N_1 of particles in a region 1 is related to the density N_2 in region 2 by the equation

$$N_1 = N_2 \epsilon^{V_{21}/V_T} \tag{5-25}$$

where V_{21} is the potential energy of region 2 with respect to region 1. This relation can be used, for example, to find the variation of atmospheric density or pressure with height above the earth's surface. In general, the particles in a solid obey Fermi-Dirac statistics but it is found that the density of holes in the valence band and of the electrons in the conduction band of a semiconductor is low enough so that the Boltzmann relation is valid to a good approximation.

Consider an open-circuited p-n junction with region 1 the p side, region 2 the n side, and holes as the particles under consideration. Then $N_1 = p_{po}$, $N_2 = p_{no}$, and $V_{21} = V_0$ so that Eq. (5-25) is equivalent to

$$p_{po} = p_{no} \epsilon^{V_0/V_T} \tag{5-26}$$

Consider now a junction biased in the forward direction by an applied voltage V. The barrier potential is $V_{21} = V_B = V_0 - V$. The hole concentration throughout the p region is constant and equal to the thermal-equilibrium value $p_{po} = N_1$. The hole concentration varies with distance from the junction in the n region, as indicated in Fig. 5-10. Hence region 2 will be considered to be just inside the n material beyond the depletion layer. Since the width of this space-charge layer is small compared with the diffusion length, we shall assume that the potential barrier has zero width. Under this assumption the concentration N_2 is the value at $x = 0$ or $N_2 = p_n(0)$. The Boltzmann relation (5-25) is, for this case,

$$p_{po} = p_n(0)\epsilon^{(V_0-V)/V_T} \tag{5-27}$$

Combining this equation with Eq. (5-26) we obtain

$$p_n(0) = p_{no}\epsilon^{V/V_T} \tag{5-28}$$

This boundary condition indicates that for $V > 0$, a forward bias, the hole concentration at the junction is greater than the thermal-equilibrium value. Equation (5-28) is one of the most fundamental relationships in junction theory.

An alternative and informative approach to the boundary condition is the following:[5] We saw in Sec. 5-1 that for an open-circuited junction the net hole current must be zero. Hence, equating the negative of the hole diffusion current to the hole drift current we have

$$eD_p \frac{dp}{dx} = e\mu_p p\mathcal{E} \tag{5-29}$$

The Einstein relation [Eq. (3-39)] is

$$\frac{D_p}{\mu_p} = V_T \tag{5-30}$$

where the electron-volt equivalent of temperature V_T is defined by Eq. (5-1). Substituting Eq. (5-30) into Eq. (5-29) and remembering the relationship Eq. (1-15) between field intensity and potential, we obtain

$$\frac{dp}{p} = \frac{\mathcal{E}\,dx}{V_T} = -\frac{dV}{V_T} \tag{5-31}$$

If this equation is integrated between limits which extend across the junction from the p- to the n-type material, the result is

$$p_{po} = p_{no}\epsilon^{V_0/V_T}$$

This equation is identical with Eq. (5-26) obtained from the Boltzmann relation. From this relationship, V_0 can be calculated in terms of the concentrations N_a and N_d, respectively, of acceptor and donor atoms and the intrinsic concentration n_i (Prob. 5-12).

By a similar argument to that given in Sec. 5-1 we conclude that the sum of the diffusion and drift *electron* currents must be zero for an open-circuited junction. This condition again leads to exactly the same relationship [Eq. (5-26)] for the barrier potential V_0.

If a junction is forward-biased, then the net hole current I_p is no longer zero. However, the diffusion and drift currents are individually very much larger than I_p. Hence, to a good approximation, we may again equate the magnitudes of the diffusion and drift currents. (If the difference between two very large numbers is a small number, the two large numbers are approximately equal to one another.) Starting with Eqs. (5-29) and (5-30) and integrating over the junction, Eq. (5-28) is again obtained.

5-8. Quantitative Theory of the p-n Junction (Continued). By making use of the boundary condition [Eq. (5-28)], we can now obtain the diode volt-ampere equation. For a forward bias V, the retarding potential barrier at the junction is lowered by V volts and more holes enter the n side. The hole concentration at the junction increases from the thermal-equilibrium value p_{no} to a new value which is $p_{no}\epsilon^{V/V_T}$. Hence, from Eq. (5-21) the hole concentration $P_n(0)$ injected into the n side at the junction is

$$P_n(0) = p_{no}(\epsilon^{V/V_T} - 1) \tag{5-32}$$

The corresponding expression for the electron density $N_p(0)$ injected into the p side at the junction is

$$N_p(0) = n_{po}(\epsilon^{V/V_T} - 1) \tag{5-33}$$

Equations (5-32) and (5-33) are also valid for reverse bias. In this case V is negative, and the injected-minority-carrier density is negative so that the concentration near the junction falls below its thermal-equilibrium value. The corresponding diffusion current will be negative, which signifies a current flow in the reverse direction. The minority-carrier densities near a p-n junction are indicated in Fig. 5-12 for both forward bias (a) and reverse bias (b).

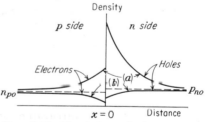

FIG. 5-12. The hole and electron concentrations vs. distance in a p-n junction diode. (a) Forward bias. (b) Reverse bias.

The total current I is found (Fig. 5-11) by adding I_{pn} and I_{np} at $x = 0$. Hence, from Eqs. (5-22) and (5-23),

$$I = \frac{AeD_pP_n(0)}{L_p} + \frac{AeD_nN_p(0)}{L_n} \tag{5-34}$$

Using Eqs. (5-32), (5-33), and (5-34), we find

$$I = I_0(\epsilon^{V/V_T} - 1) \tag{5-35}$$

where

$$I_0 = \frac{AeD_p p_{no}}{L_p} + \frac{AeD_n n_{po}}{L_n} \tag{5-36}$$

is the magnitude of the reverse saturation current (the current for $V = -\infty$ being $-I_0$). The above derivation of the diode volt-ampere characteristic justifies the somewhat heuristic proof given in Sec. 5-2.

The parameters upon which the reverse saturation depends are clearly indicated in Eq. (5-36). Another form of this equation in terms of conductivities is given in Prob. 5-15. The temperature dependence of I_0 is found from Eqs. (5-36), (3-36), (3-37), and (3-31) to be

$$I_0 = AeA_0 \left(\frac{D_p}{N_d L_p} + \frac{D_n}{N_a L_n} \right) T^3 \epsilon^{-V_g/V_T} \tag{5-37}$$

where the values of A_0 and $V_g = E_g$ are given in Table 3-1. From Eq. (5-37) it can be shown that the saturation current for germanium increases about 11 per cent per degree rise in temperature. The corresponding increase for silicon is 15 per cent. However, the value of the saturation current for silicon is very much smaller than for germanium and hence a silicon diode can be used at a very much higher temperature than can a germanium diode.

Let us make a quantitative calculation of the diffusion capacitance C_D. If the applied forward voltage increases by ΔV, the height of the barrier decreases by ΔV and the injected charge increases by ΔQ. Hence, we can define C_D by the relationship $C_D = dQ/dV$. Let us compute C_{D_p}, the diffusion capacitance due to holes. The total charge Q_p of holes injected into the n side is equal to the area under the exponential curve of Fig. 5-10 multiplied by the diode cross section A and the electronic charge e. Hence,

$$Q_p = \int_0^\infty eAP_n(0)\epsilon^{-x/L_p} \, dx = AeL_p P_n(0) \tag{5-38}$$

and

$$C_{D_p} = AeL_p \frac{dP_n(0)}{dV} \tag{5-39}$$

The hole current I_{pn} is given by the first term in Eq. (5-34), or

$$I_{pn} = \frac{AeD_p P_n(0)}{L_p} \tag{5-40}$$

and

$$\frac{dP_n(0)}{dV} = \frac{L_p}{AeD_p} \frac{dI_{pn}}{dV} = \frac{L_p}{AeD_p} g_p \tag{5-41}$$

where $g_p \equiv dI_{pn}/dV$ = conductance due to holes. Combining Eqs. (5-41) and (5-39) yields

$$C_{D_p} = \frac{L_p^2 g_p}{D_p} \tag{5-42}$$

A similar expression with p replaced by n gives the diffusion capacitance C_{D_n} due to electrons. Since the total capacitive current i is the sum of the hole and electron capacitive currents, then

$$i = C_{D_p} \frac{dV}{dt} + C_{D_n} \frac{dV}{dt} \tag{5-43}$$

Hence, it is convenient to write $i = C_D \, dV/dt$, where C_D, the total diffusion capacitance, is defined by $C_D \equiv C_{D_p} + C_{D_n}$ and is given by

$$C_D = \frac{L_p^2 g_p}{D_p} + \frac{L_n^2 g_n}{D_n} \tag{5-44}$$

or, using Eq. (5-17),

$$C_D = \tau_p g_p + \tau_n g_n \tag{5-45}$$

If the hole current is very much larger than the electron current, $g_p \gg g_n$, and

$$C_D \cong \tau_p g_p \cong \tau_p g \tag{5-46}$$

where $g = dI/dV - (I_0/V_T)\epsilon^{V/V_T}$ is the diode conductance.

In the above derivation the steady-state charge distribution of Fig. 5-10 was used. It was implicitly assumed that, after the input voltage was changed, sufficient time was allowed to pass for a new equilibrium distribution to be established before the net change in charge was calculated. If the input voltage varies with time, it may not be possible to define diffusion capacitance in a unique manner. For the important special case where the voltage varies sinusoidally with time with a frequency f, the diffusion capacitance may be obtained from the reactive component of current. Thus, if the a-c component of voltage is $V_m \epsilon^{j\omega t}$ ($\omega = 2\pi f$), then a current term in the form $j\omega C_D V_m \epsilon^{j\omega t}$ results, and this expression defines C_D. If the equation of continuity [Eq. (A6-9)] is solved for a sinusoidal input voltage (see Prob. 5-20), it is found that the diffusion capacitance is a function of frequency. The results of such an analysis are

$$C_{D_p} = \tfrac{1}{2}\tau_p g_p \qquad \text{if } \omega\tau_p \ll 1$$

and

$$C_{D_p} = \sqrt{\frac{\tau_p}{2\omega}}\, g_p \qquad \text{if } \omega\tau_p \gg 1 \tag{5-47}$$

where g_p = diode conductance due to holes at zero frequency.

5-9. Metallic Rectifiers.[6] Even prior to the discovery of the *p-n* junction diode there were in existence devices in which rectification depended upon the presence of a semiconductor. These so-called "metallic rectifiers" contain a nonohmic junction between a metal and a semiconductor rather than between two semiconductors. The elements of a metallic rectifier are illustrated in Fig. 5-13 and consist of a sandwich of a metal base plate, a semiconductor, and a metallic contact surface electrode. When the cell is formed, a thin *nonohmic, barrier,* or *blocking layer* is formed either between the base metal and the semiconductor or between the semiconductor and the metallic electrode. As a result of the nonohmic layer the cell possesses unilateral properties. In Fig. 5-13

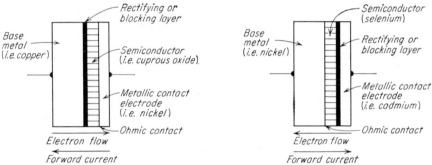

FIG. 5-13. The elements of a blocking-layer metallic-rectifier cell.

FIG. 5-14. Cross section of a selenium cell.

the semiconductor is *p* type and hence the forward (low-resistance) direction is from the semiconductor to the base metal through the blocking layer.

Two commercially important metallic-rectifier disks exist, these being known as *copper oxide cells*[7] and *selenium cells.*[8] The copper oxide cell is illustrated in Fig. 5-13. These cells are produced by heating a copper disk or plate in a furnace to approximately 1000°F and then quenching it in water. This treatment produces a thin layer of red cuprous oxide with an outer layer of black cupric oxide. The cupric oxide is then removed, leaving the cell with a layer of cuprous oxide on the base copper. Contact with the oxide surface can be made in either of two ways. One method is to use a lead disk which is held against the oxide surface at a definite pressure. The other way is to plate a metallic conductor, such as nickel, on the oxide surface. This plated film is then used as the contact surface.

The selenium cell is illustrated in Fig. 5-14. It consists of a base metal of nickel, iron, or aluminum which is covered with a thin film of selenium. An electrode of a cadmium alloy is sprayed onto the free surface of the selenium. The rectifying or blocking layer forms between the selenium and the cadmium alloy upon the application of an a-c potential.   The selenium is p type and hence the forward direction is from the semiconductor to the contact electrode through the blocking layer.

The most important characteristics of copper oxide, selenium, germanium, and silicon rectifiers are summarized in Table 5-1.   Germanium and silicon have far superior properties than the other two but are more cost'y.

TABLE 5-1

SEMICONDUCTOR RECTIFIER CHARACTERISTICS*

Characteristic	Copper oxide	Selenium	Germanium	Silicon
Back/front resistance ratio.............	10^3	10^3	4×10^5	10^6
Maximum current density, amp/in.².....	0.25	0.32	300	1,000
Maximum operating temperature, °C....	60	100	65	150
Maximum back voltage per cell, volts...	5	36	200	300

* From K. R. SPANGENBERG, "Fundamentals of Electron Devices," p. 177, McGraw-Hill Book Company, Inc., New York, 1957.

REFERENCES

1. SHOCKLEY, W., "The Theory of p-n Junctions in Semiconductors and p-n Junction Transistors," *Bell System Tech. J.*, **28**, 435–489, July, 1949.
    MIDDLEBROOK, R. D., "An Introduction to Junction Transistor Theory," pp. 115–130, John Wiley & Sons, Inc., New York, 1957.
    TERMAN, F. E., "Electronic and Radio Engineering," 4th ed., pp. 747–760, McGraw-Hill Book Company, Inc., New York, 1955.
    ARGUIMBAU, L. B., and R. B. ADLER, "Vacuum-tube Circuits and Transistors," pp. 110–125, John Wiley & Sons, Inc., New York, 1956.
2. SHOCKLEY, W., "Transistor Electronics: Imperfections, Unipolar and Analog Transistors," *Proc. IRE*, **40**, 1289–1313, November, 1952.
3. CONWELL, E. M., "Properties of Silicon and Germanium," *Proc. IRE*, **40**, 1327–1337, November, 1952.
    NAVON, D., R. BRAY, and H. Y. FAN, "Lifetime of Injected Carriers in Germanium," *ibid.*, **40**, 1342–1347, November, 1952.
4. FIRLE, T. E., M. E. McMAHON, and J. F. ROACH, "Recovery Time Measurements of Point-contact Germanium Diodes," *Trans. IRE (PGED)*, **ED-1**(2), 27–33, April, 1954.
5. MIDDLEBROOK, R. D., "An Introduction to Junction Transistor Theory," pp. 93–112, John Wiley & Sons, Inc., New York, 1957.
6. HEMISCH, H. K., "Metallic Rectifiers," Oxford University Press, New York, 1949.
7. HAMANN, C. E., and E. A. HARTY, "Fundamental Characteristics and Applications of Copper-oxide Rectifiers," *Gen. Elec. Rev.*, **36**, 342–348, August, 1933.
8. RICHARDS, E. A., "The Characteristics and Applications of the Selenium Rectifier," *JIEE*, **88**(pt. 3), 238–253, December, 1941.
    CLARKE, C. A., "Selenium Rectifier Characteristics, Applications, and Design Factors," *Elec. Commun.*, **20**, 47–66, 1941.

CHAPTER 6

PHOTOELECTRIC DEVICES

T HE liberation of electrons from matter under the influence of light is known as the *photoelectric effect*, first observed by Hertz in 1887. Today, many commercial devices are based upon this discovery.

The photoelectric effect includes (1) the liberation of electrons from a metallic surface and (2) the generation of hole-electron pairs in a semiconductor when these solids are subjected to radiation. The first phenomenon is called the *photoemissive effect* and is exploited in vacuum and gas phototubes. Photoeffects in semiconductors may be subdivided into two types: (1) the *photoconductive effect;* the electrical conductivity of a semiconductor bar depends upon the light intensity, and (2) the *junction photoeffect;* the current across a reverse-biased *p-n* junction is determined by the intensity of the illumination. If the *p-n* junction is open-circuited, then an emf is generated. This latter phenomenon is called the *photovoltaic effect.*

This chapter discusses photoelectric theory, considers practical photodevices, and shows how these are used in a circuit.

6-1. Photoemissivity. The experimental features that are characteristic of the photoemissive effect are the following:[1]

1. The photoelectrons liberated from the photosensitive surface possess a range of initial velocities. However, a definite negative potential when applied between the collector and the emitting surface will retard the fastest-moving electrons. This indicates that the emitted electrons are liberated with all velocities from zero to a definite maximum value. The maximum velocity of the emitted electrons is given by the relation

$$\tfrac{1}{2}mv_{\max}^2 = eE_r \tag{6-1}$$

where E_r is the retarding potential, in volts, necessary to reduce the photocurrent to zero. As the potential is increased, the number of electrons to the collector increases until saturation occurs. It is to be noted from Fig. 6-1, in which are plotted curves showing the variation of photocurrent I_{ph} with collector potential (the light intensity j is a parameter), that E_r and hence $v_{\max}$ are independent of the light intensity.

2. If the photoelectric current is measured as a function of the collector potential for different light frequencies f and equal intensities of the inci-

dent light, the results obtained are essentially those illustrated in Fig. 6-2.[2] It is observed that the greater the frequency of the incident light, the greater must be the retarding potential to reduce the photocurrent to zero. This means, of course, that the maximum velocity of emission of the photoelectrons increases with the frequency of the incident light. Experimentally, it is found that a linear relationship exists between E_r and f.

The experimental facts listed under 1 and 2 may be summarized in the statement that the *maximum energy of the electrons liberated photoelectrically is independent of the light intensity but varies linearly with the frequency of the incident light.*

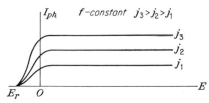

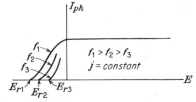

FIG. 6-1. Photocurrent vs. plate voltage with light intensity as a parameter. The frequency of the incident light is a constant.

FIG. 6-2. Photocurrent vs. plate potential with the frequency of incident light as a parameter. The light intensity is a constant.

3. If the saturation current is plotted as a function of the light intensity, we find that the photoelectric current is directly proportional to the intensity of the light.

4. The foregoing photoelectric characteristics are practically independent of temperature, within wide ranges of temperature.

5. The electrons are emitted immediately upon the exposure of the surface to light. The time lag has been determined experimentally[3] to be less than 3×10^{-9} sec.

6. Photoelectric cells are selective devices. This means that a given intensity of light of one wave length, say red light, will not liberate the same number of electrons as an equal intensity of light of another wave length, say blue light. That is, the *photoelectric yield*, defined as the photocurrent (in amperes) per watt of incident light, depends upon the frequency of the light. Alternative designations of the term "photoelectric yield" to be found in the literature are *relative response, quantum yield, spectral sensitivity, specific photosensitivity,* and *current-wave-length characteristic*. The relative response curves for the alkali metals are shown in Fig. 6-3.

Curves of these types are obtained experimentally in the following way: Light from an incandescent source is passed through the prism of a monochromator for dispersion, a narrow band of wave lengths being selected by means of an appropriately placed slit system. The current given by the photoelectric surface when exposed to the light passing through the system of slits is noted. The current given by a blackened thermopile when exposed to the same light is also noted. The ratio of these two readings is plotted vs. the wave length of the incident light. Blackened thermopiles are used because they absorb all radiation incident upon them equally, regardless of the wave length. This procedure permits a measure of the energy contained in any part of the spectrum to be made. An automatic spectral-sensitivity-curve tracer has been designed for obtaining these curves quickly with the aid of a cathode-ray tube.[4]

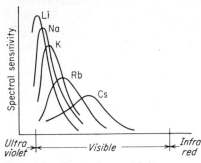

FIG. 6-3. Spectral sensitivity as a function of wave length for the alkali metals. (*E. F. Seiler, Astrophys. J.,* **52,** 129, 1920.)

6-2. Photoelectric Theory. The foregoing experimental facts find their explanation in the electronic theory of metals and in the light-quantum hypothesis of Planck. The birth of the quantum theory occurred in 1900 when Planck made the fundamental assumption that radiant energy is not continuous but can exist only in discrete quantities called *quanta* or *photons.* With the aid of this concept, Planck was able to correlate satisfactorily the theory and measurements of infrared radiation. Bohr used this same theory of photons to explain the spectra of atoms (Secs. 12-3 and 12-5). Einstein applied the same hypothesis to explain photoemission, as we shall now demonstrate. Planck's basic assumption is that *associated with light of frequency f (cycles per second) are a number of photons, each of which has an energy hf (joules)*, where h (joule-seconds) is called *Planck's constant* (Appendix I). The greater the intensity of the light, the larger is the number of photons present, but the energy of each photon remains unchanged. Of course, if the light beam is heterogeneous rather than monochromatic, then the energy of the photons therewith associated will vary and will depend upon the frequency.

If monochromatic light of frequency f falls upon a metal whose work function is E_W, the velocity of the emitted electron is, according to Einstein's equation,[5]

$$\tfrac{1}{2}mv^2 \leqq hf - eE_W \tag{6-2}$$

The significance of this equation becomes apparent when considered in the light of the electronic theory of matter. Since photoelectric devices are operated at low (room) temperatures, the completely degenerate distribution function must be employed. Figure 6-4 shows the energy distribution function at low temperatures, and also the potential-energy barrier at the surface of the metal (Fig. 3-11).

This figure indicates that the electrons within the metal exist in energy levels ranging from zero to a maximum energy, E_M electron volts, but none has energies greater than this value. If an electron possessing the energy E_M receives the photon of light energy hf and travels normal to the surface of the metal, the kinetic energy that it will have, upon escaping from the metal, will be $hf - eE_W$ joules. This follows directly from the significance of the work function E_W, which is the minimum energy that must be supplied at 0°K in order to permit the fastest-moving surface-directed electron just to surmount the potential barrier at the surface of the metal and to escape.

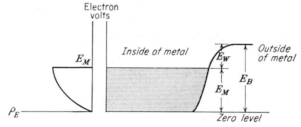

Fig. 6-4. Energy-level diagram for the free electrons within a metal. The potential-energy barrier at the surface of the metal is also shown.

Since some of the electrons which have energies less than E_M may absorb the incident photons, an energy greater in magnitude than E_W will be expended when they escape. This fact explains the inequality of Eq. (6-2).

According to this equation, the retarding potential E_r that will just repel the fastest-moving electron is given by

$$eE_r = \tfrac{1}{2}mv_{\max}{}^2 = hf - eE_W \qquad (6-3)$$

which is in agreement with the experimental facts 1 and 2. This result shows that the maximum energy of the escaping electrons varies linearly with the frequency and is independent of the light intensity. This latter condition follows from the fact that the intensity of the incident light does not enter into this expression. This equation was verified experimentally by Millikan.[6] He plotted retarding voltage vs. frequency and obtained a straight line. The slope of this line gives the value of the ratio h/e. The value of this ratio found by this method agrees very well with that from other experiments. The intercept of the Einstein line with the axis of abscissa gives E_W (provided that corrections are made for contact difference of potential). The value of the work function obtained photoelectrically agrees well with that measured thermionically for the same emitter.

The minimum frequency of light, known as the *threshold frequency* f_c, that can be used to cause photoelectric emission can be found from Eq. (6-3) by setting the velocity equal to zero.   The result is

$$f_c \doteq \frac{eE_W}{h} \tag{6-4}$$

The corresponding wave length, known as the *long-wave-length limit* or the *threshold wave length* λ_c, beyond which photoelectric emission cannot take place is

$$\lambda_c = \frac{c}{f_c} = \frac{ch}{eE_W} = \frac{12,400}{E_W} \quad A \tag{6-5}$$

where A denotes the angstrom unit (10^{-10} m) and where E_W is expressed in electron volts.   For response over the entire visible region, 4,000 to 8,000 A, the work function of the photosensitive surface must be less than 1.55 volts.   This statement follows directly from Eq. (6-5).

Example.   A tungsten surface having a work function of 4.52 ev is irradiated with the mercury line, 2,537 A.   What is the maximum speed of the emitted electrons?

Solution.   The electron-volt equivalent of the energy of the incident photons is 12,400/2,537 = 4.88 ev.   According to the Einstein equation, the maximum energy of the emitted electrons is

$$4.88 - 4.52 = 0.36 \text{ ev}$$

From Eq. (1-13) the corresponding velocity is

$$v_{\max} = 5.93 \times 10^5 \sqrt{0.36} = 3.56 \times 10^5 \text{ m/sec}$$

The fact that the photoelectric current is strictly proportional to the light intensity is readily explained.   A greater light intensity merely denotes the presence of a larger number of photons.   Further, since each photon is equally effective in ejecting electrons, the number of electrons per second ejected must be proportional to the light intensity.

If it is remembered that the distribution function of electrons in metals varies very little with temperature, then fact 4 is evident.   Strictly speaking, however, the totally degenerate distribution function applies only at the temperature 0°K.   At room temperature, therefore, a few electrons will have emission velocities greater than those predicted by Eq. (6-3). Hence no absolutely sharp long-wave-length limit exists for any substance, since the curves, such as those of Fig. 6-1, approach the axis asymptotically.   Fowler[7] investigated this matter theoretically, and this theory provides a method of determining the photoelectric work function independent of the temperature of the surface.   For most practical purposes the use of the completely degenerate distribution function even at room temperatures is quite reasonable.   Hence, it is justifiable to consider cutoff to occur sharply for frequencies below the critical value f_c.

A qualitative explanation for the shapes of the spectral response curves of Fig. 6-3 is readily found. There can be no response for frequencies below f_c; hence cutoff occurs at the point $f = f_c$. As f increases above f_c, the energy of the incident photon hf increases and some electrons in levels below the maximum energy state are permitted to escape. As a result, the response increases as the frequency increases or, correspondingly, as the wave length decreases. However, a point of maximum response must exist. This conclusion follows from the fact that if the energy of the light is W joules, then the number of photons in the light beam is W/hf. But since this number decreases with increasing frequency, the photocurrent must decrease as f increases because of the decreased number of photons present. A second peak is sometimes found to occur at the short wave lengths. This is ascribed to the interaction of the radiation with the more tightly bound conduction electrons of the matter. This *volume* photoeffect becomes significant for light in the violet or near ultraviolet. A complete quantitative explanation for the shapes of these curves has not yet been given.

6-3. Phototubes. The essential elements of a phototube are a sensitive cathode surface of large area and a collecting electrode, contained in an evacuated glass bulb. These electrodes may be arranged in numerous ways. In the older type of tube, the cathode was made by distilling the photosensitive material, generally an alkali metal (usually cesium), on the inner surface of the bulb, which first was silvered in order to ensure good conduction. The anode was made in the form of a straight wire or ring, in any case being small, so that it did not obstruct the light that was incident upon the cathode. Many of the present-day phototubes consist of a semicylindrical metallic cathode on which the photosensitive substance has been evaporated. The anode is a straight wire that is practically coaxial with the cathode. Phototubes of modern design are shown in Fig. 6-5.

The glass bulb either may be highly evacuated or may contain an inert gas at low pressure. The volt-ampere characteristics of the ordinary vacuum phototubes are shown in Fig. 6-6. The current that exists at zero accelerating potential results from the initial velocities of the electrons. Note that a retarding potential must be applied in order to reduce the current to zero.

As the anode-cathode potential is increased, the current to the anode increases very rapidly at first, the nonsaturation resulting from the possible space-charge effects, and also from the fact that some electrons are missing the wire anode on their journey from the cathode, since the attractive field is small at these low potentials. The current very soon reaches a saturation value, for the field becomes sufficient to attract all the electrons liberated from the cathode under the influence of the incident light.

The continued increase in photocurrent as the anode potential is increased results partly from the more complete collection of the electrons and possibly from the reduction of the work function of the material of the cathode surface as a consequence of the presence of the applied electric field at the cathode (the Schottky effect; Sec. 3-11).

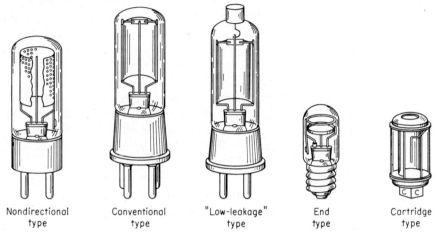

| Nondirectional | Conventional | "Low-leakage" | End | Cartridge |
| type | type | type | type | type |

FIG. 6-5. A group of typical phototubes.   (*Westinghouse Staff, "Industrial Electricity Reference Book," courtesy of John Wiley & Sons, Inc., New York*, 1948.)

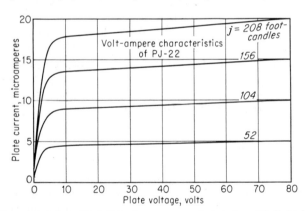

FIG. 6-6. Volt-ampere characteristics of a vacuum phototube with light intensity as a parameter.

By filling the glass envelope with an inert gas, such as neon or argon, at a pressure of the order of 0.5 mm, the current yield for a given intensity of illumination is greatly increased, as illustrated in Fig. 6-7. As described in Sec. 12-13, the increased current is produced by the field-intensified or Townsend discharge. It is important never to raise the potential across the tube to the point where a glow discharge occurs, for this will cause cathode sputtering with a consequent permanent damage to the cathode surface.

For purposes of comparison, the outputs of the vacuum and the gas-filled phototubes (specifically, the results obtained under identical experimental conditions with the General Electric PJ-22 and PJ-23 phototubes) are illustrated in Fig. 6-8. These tubes are identical in all respects,

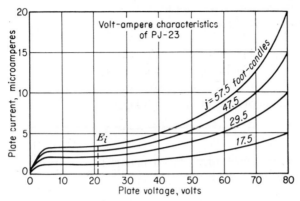

FIG. 6-7. Volt-ampere characteristics of a gas-filled phototube with light intensity as a parameter.

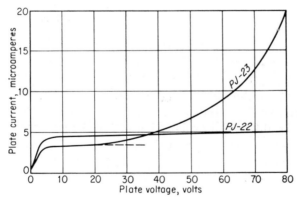

FIG. 6-8. Comparison of the volt-ampere characteristics of vacuum and gas-filled tubes with similar photosurfaces. The same light intensity was used for both tubes.

except for the fact that one is a vacuum tube and the other is an argon-filled tube. It is observed that the curves have the same shape until ionization by collision occurs in the gas tube. Beyond this point, the sensitivity of the gas tube continues to increase with increased anode potentials, owing to the contribution to the current by the electrons resulting from the ionization of the gas. The gas amplification ratio of a gas-filled tube is of the order of 4 for an anode voltage of 80 volts. From Fig. 6-8, this ratio is seen to depend upon the amount of incident light flux and upon the applied anode voltage. If an attempt is made to obtain amplification ratios larger than about 10, a glow discharge usually takes place.

6-4. Sensitivity of Phototubes. According to the above discussion, the *static* sensitivity of a phototube may be defined as the ratio of the d-c anode current to the incident radiant flux of constant value. In a similar way, the *dynamic* sensitivity of a phototube is the ratio of the alternating component of the anode current to the alternating component of the incident radiant flux. The dynamic characteristics are very important in sound projectors, television, and facsimile systems and in fact in any system which depends for its operation on changes in light intensity.

For a vacuum phototube, the two sensitivities are equal. For a gas-filled photocell, there is a falling off of sensitivity with an increase in the

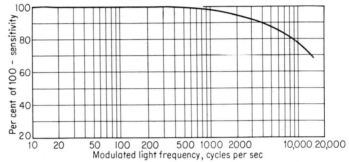

Fig. 6-9. Average sensitivity characteristic of an RCA 868 gas-filled phototube. The anode voltage is 90 volts. (*Courtesy of Radio Corporation of America.*)

frequency at which the incident light is interrupted or modulated. The average sensitivity characteristic of an RCA type 868 gas-filled phototube is shown in Fig. 6-9. The explanation of the shape of this curve lies in the amplification characteristics of the gas contained in the cell. It takes a negligible time for the photoelectrons to appear after the cathode surface has been illuminated. However, a finite amount of time is required for these electrons to build up the steady-state amplified current in the cell. This delay results from two causes. The one of minor importance is the time required[8] for the relatively slow ions that are formed by the electron-collision process to travel to the cathode. These times are measured in microseconds. The more important limitation is imposed by the diffusion times of the metastable atoms (Sec. 12-10), which move slowly, as they are electrically neutral and are not affected by the applied field. These atoms bombard the cathode and emit electrons. Such metastable diffusion times are of the order of milliseconds, so that for modulating frequencies above 1,000 cps the sensitivity will drop, as indicated in Fig. 6-9. This feature restricts such gas tubes to applications for lower frequencies of light interruption, since a sudden change in light intensity is not accompanied by corresponding instantaneous change in photocurrent.

Another disadvantage of gas-filled cells is the lack of linearity of current with incident flux.   The photocurrent increases more rapidly than the illumination for anode voltages that are higher than the ionization potential of the gas.   This is illustrated in Fig. 6-10 for the PJ-23 tube. The linear response of the PJ-22 vacuum cell is also shown.   Gas phototubes are used primarily for on-off (relay) operation or with sound-reproduction equipment, where the slight nonlinearity and the variation of dynamic sensitivity with frequency are not too important.

It should be kept in mind that the curves shown in this chapter, and also those supplied by the phototube manufacturers, are typical rather

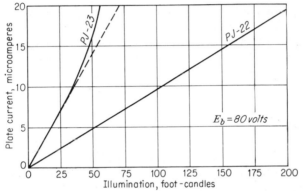

FIG. 6-10. Photocurrent as a function of illumination for a vacuum cell (PJ-22) and a gas-filled cell (PJ-23).

than specific for any particular tube type.   Large variations may exist in the characteristics of phototubes manufactured under presumably identical conditions.   This results from the fact, already noted, that the number of photoelectrons emitted for a given illumination varies appreciably for even slight changes in the surface preparation of the cathode.   For the same reason, it is often found that different portions of the same emitting surface may possess different sensitivities.   It is advisable, therefore, to illuminate a large part of the cathode uniformly whenever possible, rather than to focus the light source on only a portion of the photoemissive surface.

In any particular application, careful consideration must be given to the choice of the light source as well as to the photocell characteristics. For example, it is desirable that the source emit strongly in the frequency range in which the photocell is most sensitive, if large photocurrents are to be obtained.   Commercial phototubes are now available with photoelectric yields[9] that have peaks in various portions of the visible spectrum. Figure 6-11 shows the spectral response of the three most common photosurfaces.

Surface S-1 consists of a composite silver–cesium oxide–cesium surface. Such a surface is sensitive throughout the entire visible region and has a

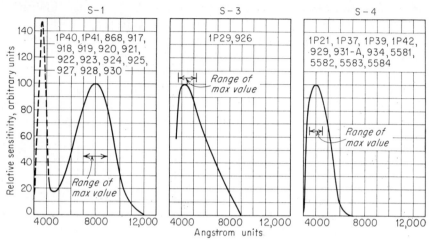

Fig. 6-11. The relative response of three commercial surfaces as a function of wave length. The phototubes using these surfaces are listed on each diagram. (*From Zworykin and Ramberg, "Photoelectricity and Its Applications," courtesy of John Wiley & Sons, Inc.*)

fair sensitivity in the infrared. As a result, this composite surface is used extensively in commercial phototubes. Surface S-3 is a silver-rubidium oxide–rubidium surface which has a sensitivity largely confined to the visible region, although it has its greatest sensitivity in the blue end of the spectrum. Surface S-4 shows the response of an antimony-cesium surface that is very sensitive to the green, blue, and near ultraviolet and is insensitive to red and infrared radiation. This is the most sensitive surface commercially available today. The tube has a sensitivity of 120 μa/lumen when daylight is used as the source. When a tungsten lamp, operating at a filament temperature of 2870°K, is the source of light, the sensitivity of the S-1 surface is 20, of the S-3 surface 6.5, and of the S-4 surface 45 μa/lumen.

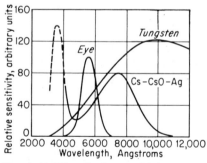

Fig. 6-12. The relative sensitivity of the eye, a Cs-CsO-Ag photosurface, and the energy distribution from an incandescent tungsten lamp as a function of wave length.

Figure 6-12 contains curves showing the spectral sensitivities of the Cs-CsO-Ag photosurface, the eye, and the energy distribution curve of the output from an incandescent tungsten lamp for purposes of comparison. It will be noticed that the Cs-CsO-Ag photosurface is sensitive over a wide range of wave lengths and so is very well adapted for use with a tungsten lamp as the source of illumination. Of course, if a photocell is desired that has a response somewhat resembling that of the human eye, the Cs-CsO-Ag surface would not be suitable.

6-5. Phototube Applications.   The basic circuit employing a phototube is shown in Fig. 6-13.   As the luminous flux that is incident on the cell varies, the output current changes and a changing voltage appears across the load resistor R_L. Although the basic circuits are the same, there are three important types of application of phototubes: (1) A definite fixed amount of illumination is to be measured.   (2) Rapid variations in light intensity are to be faithfully reproduced.   (3) A definite large change in light intensity is to be detected.

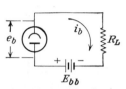

Fig. 6-13.   The basic phototube circuit.

The field of photometry and colorimetry offers many examples of the first type of application.   In such cases, R_L might simply be the internal resistance of the indicating instrument.   If the incident light is too small to be measurable directly, a d-c amplifier might be used.   In this case, R_L will be the input resistance of the amplifier.   The light beam of varying intensity that has been modulated by the sound track of a motion-picture film or by the scanning process in a television tube is of the second class.   Applications of the third type are exemplified by "on" and "off" circuits.   In such cases the phototube is used in conjunction with a relay so that some circuit is either energized or deenergized when the light intensity exceeds or falls below some preassigned value.   Many of the common applications of the "electric eye" belong to this third class.   A few illustrations are the counting or sorting of objects on a conveyer belt; the automatic opening of a door as it is approached; devices for the protection of human life; and fire-alarm systems.[10]

In order to determine the current that will flow in a phototube circuit for a given light flux, battery voltage, and load resistance, it is necessary to use the volt-ampere tube characteristics.   The straight line, expressed by the relation

$$e_b = E_{bb} - i_b R_L \qquad (6\text{-}6)$$

is superposed on this set of static characteristics.   This is the same load line that was discussed in connection with the diode rectifier in Sec. 4-10. It is drawn through the point $i_b = 0$, $e_b = E_{bb}$, and with a slope determined by the load resistor R_L, as shown in Fig. 6-14.

The intersection of the load line with each volt-ampere curve gives the current output at the value of intensity for which that curve was constructed. In this way a curve of current vs. intensity or flux for each value of load resistance can be found. The curves for $R_L = 10, 25,$ and 50 megohms and $E_{bb} = 250$ volts for the RCA 929 vacuum phototube are

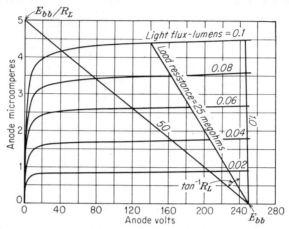

FIG. 6-14. Volt-ampere characteristics of an RCA 929 vacuum phototube. The load lines for a plate supply voltage of 250 volts and resistances of 1.0, 25, and 50 megohms are also shown. (*Courtesy of RCA Manufacturing Co.*)

reproduced in Fig. 6-15. It is noted that these curves are practically linear and almost independent of the load resistance. This results from the fact that the volt-ampere characteristics of Fig. 6-14 are essentially

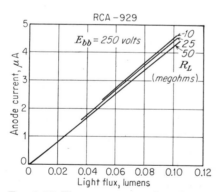

FIG. 6-15. Photocurrent as a function of light flux (dynamic curves) for load resistances of 10, 25, and 50 megohms.

horizontal lines that are equally spaced for equal intervals of light flux. Since, for a given light intensity, the plate current is nearly independent of voltage, except for small voltages, *the vacuum photocell may be considered to be a constant-current generator.* This characteristic is made use of in certain applications.

The output-voltage curves corresponding to these current curves are shown in Fig. 6-16. The voltage drop across the load resistor is plotted as a function of light flux. It is observed that a given change in light flux results in larger changes in voltage for the higher load resistances. This would seem to favor very large values of load resistances. The practical upper limit to the resistance that can be used in such a circuit is set by the leakage currents that are ever present. Thus, R_L must be kept considerably below the resistance between the cathode and anode of the phototube (and also below that between the cathode and grid of the associated amplifier, if one is used). It is desirable, therefore, to reduce the leakage currents as much as possible. In certain tubes a long leakage path is provided by bringing the leads from the electrodes through opposite ends of the glass envelope (Fig. 6-5). For very sensitive measurements, it is desirable to clean the glass surface carefully and then coat the bulb with a thin layer of ceresin wax. This reduces the leakage currents to very small values.

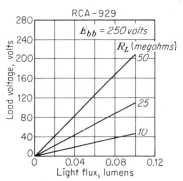

FIG. 6-16. Load voltages as a function of light flux corresponding to the current curves of Fig. 6-15.

If the load resistance is too high, or if the plate supply voltage is low, the load line will intersect the volt-ampere curves for the higher intensities in the region near the origin, where the curves are close together. Under these circumstances, a curve of current vs. light flux will no longer be linear. In fact, it will show a *saturation* value, as indicated in Fig. 6-17, and *bottoming* is said to have taken place. This expression arises from the fact that the tube voltage remains at the bottom of the characteristic (approximately zero voltage) although the excitation is increased. Where modulated light is to be translated into proportional electrical voltages, this condition is to be avoided. However, such a characteristic may be highly desirable in certain special applications.

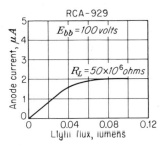

FIG. 6-17. The nonlinear dynamic curve resulting from operation at too low a supply voltage or too high a load resistance.

The analysis of a gas-phototube circuit is performed in exactly the same manner as above. Since the volt-ampere characteristics of such cells (Fig. 6-7) are no longer horizontal equidistant lines for equal intervals of light flux, the output will not, in general, be proportional to the light-flux variations, except for small variations. Furthermore, as discussed in Sec. 6-4, the graphical construction considered above is valid only at low frequencies, since the dynamic sensitivity of a gas cell decreases with the frequency.

6-6. Multiplier Phototubes. Very weak light intensities must be measured in many applications such as nuclear-radiation detection, television pickup devices, colorimetry, astronomy, and many industrial processes. A very sensitive device suitable for such applications is obtained by amplifying the current from a photoelectric surface by means of secondary emission.

The principle of operation of a photomultiplier tube is illustrated in Fig. 6-18. Light impinges upon the cathode and emits photoelectrons

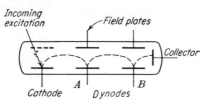

Incoming excitation — *Field plates* — *Collector* — *Cathode* — *A* — *B* — *Dynodes*

FIG. 6-18. The approximate cycloidal path in a magnetic secondary-emission electron multiplier. The magnetic field is perpendicular to the plane of the paper.

which are directed toward a plate A called a *dynode*. Upon collision with A, secondary electrons are liberated. These, in turn, travel to dynode B, where more secondary electrons are released. The charges leaving B are directed toward the next plate (if more are included), and the electrons from the last dynode are finally collected by the anode. If the ratio of the number of secondary to primary electrons is δ and if there are n dynodes, the current at the collector is

$$i = i_0 \delta^n \qquad (6\text{-}7)$$

where i_0 is the initial current at the photocathode. The over-all current gain is δ^n.

One of the earliest photomultiplier tubes[11] employed a configuration of perpendicular electric and magnetic fields both to focus and to direct the beam from dynode to dynode. In Fig. 6-18 the magnetic field is perpendicular to the plane of the paper, and the electrons move in practically cycloidal paths, as shown. However, if an electron starts from rest at the cathode it will have zero velocity when it reaches the first dynode. Under these circumstances, the electrons from the cathode could cause no secondary emission at this emitter. For this reason, an additional potential gradient must exist from the cathode to the first dynode and from the first to the second emitter, etc. The addition of this field distorts the original field, making an exact determination of the paths of the particles very difficult. The effect of the initial velocities is to cause a slight defocusing of the beam in passing from one emitter to the next. This deforming imposes a practical limitation upon the number of emitters that may be used and so upon the subsequent gain of the unit.

Because of the need for a magnetic field as well as an electric field, a great deal of attention has been given to the development of electrostatic secondary-emission multipliers. These use no magnetic field, but the shapes and the orientations of the electrodes are such that the electrons pass progressively from one dynode to the next. The development of these units has been guided to a marked extent by the rubber-model method (Sec. 1-15). Two different types of electrostatic multipliers are illustrated in Fig. 6-19.

The RCA type 931-A tube with nine dynodes has a current amplification of 200,000 and a sensitivity of 2 amp/lumen. This tube is about the size of a small receiving tube. The Du Mont tube uses an end

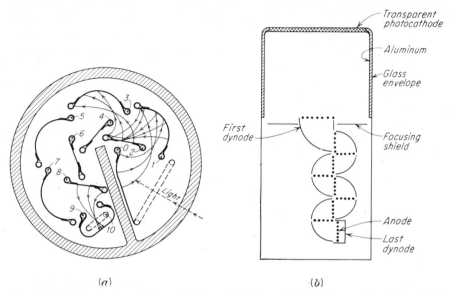

(a) (b)

FIG. 6-19. (a) A circular photomultiplier. (*Courtesy of Radio Corporation of America.*) (b) A linear photomultiplier. (*Courtesy of A. B. Du Mont Laboratories, Inc.*)

window with a semitransparent cesium-antimony photoemissive surface. Light impinges on one side, and the photoelectrons emitted from the other side are focused onto the first dynode by means of the focusing shield. The box-type dynodes are in the shape of one-fourth of a "pill box," as indicated in Fig. 6-20. The secondary-emission surfaces are of silver-magnesium for which δ equals about 3 or 4 at the recommended operating voltages. Tubes with photocathode diameters ranging from $\frac{3}{4}$ to 14 in. are available, and most of these are built with 10 secondary emitters. The dynode voltages (100 to 150 volts per stage) are obtained by means of a resistive divider arrangement from a high-voltage power supply. With these Du Mont multiplier phototubes it is possible to

FIG. 6-20. Box-type dynodes.

obtain a current amplification of 3,000,000 and a sensitivity of 100 amp/lumen.

6-7. Photoelectric Effects in Semiconductors.[12] If radiation falls upon a semiconductor, its conductivity increases. This *photoconductive effect* is explained as follows: The conductivity of a material is proportional to the concentration of charge carriers present, as indicated in Eq. (3-29).

Radiant energy supplied to the semiconductor causes covalent bonds to be broken, and hole-electron pairs in excess of those generated thermally are created. These increased current carriers decrease the resistance of the material, and hence such a device is called a *photoresistor*. The Transistor Products, Inc., type 11A photoresistor consists of an *n*-type germanium crystal of dimensions which are approximately 6 by 1 by 1 mm whose dark resistance is 4,000 ohms. For a light intensity of 300 ft-candles (lumens/ft²) the resistance of this device drops to 2,000 ohms.

If a reverse-biased *p-n* junction is illuminated, the current varies almost linearly with the light flux. This effect is exploited in the semiconductor photodiode. If a *p-n* junction is open-circuited, then an emf is generated whose magnitude depends upon the incident radiation. These junction photoeffects are discussed in detail in the next two sections.

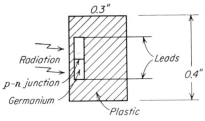

FIG. 6-21. The construction of a semiconductor photodiode.

6-8. The Semiconductor Photodiode.

A device which finds greater application than the photoresistor is the *photodiode* (sometimes called the *phototransistor*) which consists of a *p-n* germanium junction embedded in a clear plastic, as indicated in Fig. 6-21. Radiation is allowed to fall upon one surface across the junction. The remaining sides of the plastic are either painted black or enclosed in a metallic case. The entire unit is extremely small, measuring approximately 0.4 by 0.3 by 0.2 in.

If reverse voltages in excess of a few tenths of a volt are applied, then an almost constant current (independent of the magnitude of the reverse bias) is obtained. The dark current corresponds to the reverse saturation current due to the thermally generated minority carriers. As explained in Sec. 5-1, these minority carriers "fall down" the potential hill at the junction, whereas this barrier does not allow majority carriers to cross the junction. Now if light falls upon the surface, additional electron-hole pairs are formed. Since the concentration of majority carriers greatly exceeds that of minority carriers, the per cent increase in majority carriers is much smaller than the per cent increase in minority carriers. Hence, it is justifiable to ignore the increase in majority density and to consider the radiation solely as a *minority-carrier injector*. These injected minority carriers (for example, electrons in the *p* side) diffuse to the junction, cross it, and contribute to the current. Hence, when a surface is illuminated, the reverse saturation current increases in proportion to the light intensity.

A typical photodiode volt-ampere characteristic is indicated in Fig.

6-22. The curves (with the exception of the dark-current curve) do not pass through the origin. The characteristics in the millivolt range of potentials are discussed in the following section. The slope of the curves of Fig. 6-22 (for voltages greater than a few volts) corresponds to a dynamic resistance of the order of a few megohms to hundreds of megohms. These characteristics resemble the volt-ampere curves of a vacuum photocell (Fig. 6-14), but there are several important differences between vacuum and semiconductor photodiodes. The dark current in a vacuum cell is zero, whereas that in a junction diode may be as high as 20 μa. The characteristics of a vacuum photocell are almost independent of temperature, whereas those of a semiconductor diode vary very rapidly with temperature. In Sec. 5-8 it was pointed out that the reverse saturation current in germanium increases about 11 per cent per degree

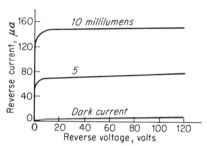

FIG. 6-22. A typical photodiode volt-ampere characteristic.

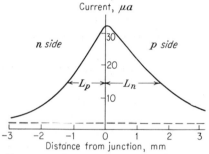

FIG. 6-23. Sensitivity of a semiconductor photodiode as a function of the distance of the light spot from the junction.

increase in temperature. It is found that the light current increases even more rapidly with temperature than does the dark current, resulting in an increased sensitivity at elevated temperatures. This increased sensitivity results from the temperature variations of mobility, diffusion constant, and lifetime of the minority carriers. The sensitivity of the type 020 photocell is 0.045 μa/millilumen (with a tungsten lamp as light source) whereas that of the type 1N188 junction photodiode is about 10 μa/millilumen, which represents an improvement by a factor of 200 for the same total flux on both devices.

The current in a semiconductor photodiode depends upon the diffusion of minority carriers to the junction. If the radiation is focused into a small spot far away from the junction, the injected minority carriers can recombine before diffusing to the junction. Hence, a much smaller current will result than if the minority carriers were injected near the junction. The photocurrent as a function of the distance from the junction at which the light spot is focused is indicated in Fig. 6-23. The curve is somewhat asymmetrical because of the differences in the diffusion lengths of minority carriers in the n and p sides (Prob. 6-15).

The spectral response of a semiconductor photodiode is indicated in Fig. 6-24 and is similar in shape to that of a vacuum photocell. The long-wave-length limit is given by Eq. (6-5) with E_W replaced by V_g, the energy required to break a covalent bond. For germanium, $V_g = 0.75$ volt and hence $\lambda_c = 12,400/0.75 = 16,400$ A, or $1.64~\mu$. It is found that

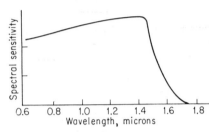

FIG. 6-24. The spectral response of germanium.

some small current exists for wave lengths up to about $1.8~\mu$, probably because of the photoionization of those donor or acceptor atoms which are not already thermally ionized. The peak of the spectral-response curve is broad and occurs over approximately the same wave-length range as that of a tungsten lamp (Fig. 6-12). It is this coincidence of peak spectral responses which accounts for the very high sensitivity of the semiconductor photodiode.

The junction photocell will undoubtedly replace the vacuum phototube in many applications because of the following properties: The semiconductor photodiode has a high sensitivity, is very small in size, is rugged, has a very long life, operates at low voltages, and has low noise. It may even be operated under short-circuited or open-circuited conditions (Sec. 6-9). However, it is found that the semiconductor photodiode characteristics drift with age. Also, the frequency response of such a device is inferior to that of the vacuum phototube, the cutoff frequency being of the order of 2×10^5 cps.

6-9. The Photovoltaic Effect. In Fig. 6-22 we see that an almost constant reverse current due to injected minority carriers is collected for large reverse voltages. If the applied voltage is reduced in magnitude, the barrier at the junction is reduced. This decrease in the potential hill does not affect the minority current (since these particles fall down the barrier), but when the hill is reduced sufficiently then some majority carriers can also cross the junction. These carriers correspond to a forward current, and hence such a flow will reduce the net (reverse) current. It is this increase in majority-carrier flow which accounts for the drop in the reverse current near the zero-voltage axis in Fig. 6-22. An expanded view of the origin in this figure is indicated in Fig. 6-25. (Note that the first quadrant of Fig. 6-22 corresponds to the third quadrant of Fig. 6-25.)

We see from Fig. 6-25 that a definite current (approximately 10 μa/millilumen) is obtained at zero applied voltage. Hence, a junction photocell can be used under short-circuit conditions.   The current is proportional to the light flux and is zero for a darkened cell.

If a forward bias is applied, the potential barrier is lowered and the majority current increases rapidly.   When this majority current equals the minority current the total current is reduced to zero.   The voltage at which zero resultant current is obtained is called the *photovoltaic* potential.   Since certainly no current flows under open-circuited conditions, the photovoltaic emf is obtained across the open terminals of a *p-n* junction.

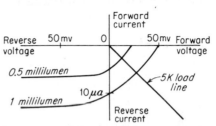

An alternative (but, of course, equivalent) physical explanation of the photovoltaic effect is the following: In Sec. 5-1 we see that the height of the potential barrier at an open-circuited (nonilluminated) *p-n* junction adjusts itself so that

FIG. 6-25. Volt-ampere characteristics of a *p-n* junction photodiode.   (*Approximately those of type X-4, Transistor Products, Inc.*)

the resultant current is zero, the electric field at the junction being in such a direction as to repel the majority carriers.   If light falls on the surface, minority carriers are injected, and since these fall down the barrier, then the minority current increases.   Since under open-circuited conditions the total current must remain zero, the majority current (for example, the hole current in the *p* side) must increase the same amount as does the minority current.   This rise in majority current is possible only if the retarding field at the junction is reduced.   Hence, the barrier height is automatically lowered as a result of the radiation.   Across the diode terminals there appears a voltage just equal to the amount by which the barrier potential is decreased.   This potential is the photovoltaic emf and is of the order of magnitude of 0.15 volt.

If a resistor *R* is placed directly across the diode terminals, the current which flows can be found by drawing the load line corresponding to *R* and passing through the origin, as shown in Fig. 6-25.

The copper–copper oxide rectifier of Fig. 5-13 may be used as a photovoltaic cell, provided that the contact electrode is made semitransparent.   Such a device is available commercially under the name *Photox cell.*[13]   Radiation passes through the semitransparent layer and emits minority carriers in the *p*-type copper oxide, resulting, as explained above, in the generation of an open-circuit voltage.   These devices are called *front wall cells*, since the barrier layer is in the direction of incidence of the light.   A *back wall cell* has also been manufactured in which the barrier layer lies at the boundary between the semiconductor and the back metallic contact (as in Fig. 5-14).   The sensitivity of the front wall cell is greater than that of the back wall type because the light does not have to penetrate the cuprous oxide to get to the rectifying layer.

The iron-selenium *Photronic*[14] *cell* is of the front wall type and consists essentially of a base plate of iron on which is placed a thin layer of iron selenide, which is covered with a semitransparent layer of gold or silver.[15] The variation of the generated emf with the intensity of illumination is illustrated in Fig. 6-26. The chief application of this device is as a photographic exposure meter.

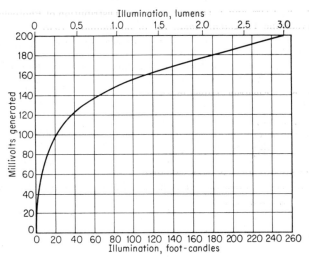

FIG. 6-26. Generated voltage in a Photronic cell as a function of light intensity. (*Courtesy of Weston Electrical Instrument Corp.*)

A silicon photovoltaic cell giving high ($\cong 7$ per cent) photoelectric conversion efficiencies in sunlight has been developed by the Bell Telephone Laboratories and is called a *Bell Solar Battery*.[16] A slab of n-type silicon is exposed to boron trichloride vapor at a high temperature, resulting in the formation of a thin p layer on the surface. When it is exposed to direct noonday sunlight an open-circuited voltage of about 0.6 volt is generated.

REFERENCES

1. HUGHES, A. L., and L. A. DuBRIDGE, "Photoelectric Phenomena," 1st ed., McGraw-Hill Book Company, Inc., New York, 1932.
2. RICHARDSON, O. W., and K. T. COMPTON, "The Photoelectric Effect," *Phil. Mag.*, **24**, 575–594, October, 1912.
3. LAWRENCE, E. O., and J. W. BEAMS, "The Element of Time in the Photoelectric Effect," *Phys. Rev.*, **32**, 478–485, September, 1928.
4. PERKINS, T. B., "An Automatic Spectral-sensitivity Curve Tracer," *JOSA*, **29**(6), 226–234, 1939.

5. EINSTEIN, A., "Über einen du Erzeugung und Verwandlung des Lichtes betreffenden heuristischen Gesichtspunkt," *Ann. Physik*, **17**(4), 132–148, 1905.
6. MILLIKAN, R. A., "A Direct Photoelectric Determination of Planck's *h*," *Phys. Rev.*, **7**, 355–388, March, 1916.
7. FOWLER, R. H., "The Analysis of Photoelectric Sensitivity Curves for Clean Metals at Various Temperatures," *Phys. Rev.*, **38**, 45–56, July, 1931.

   DUBRIDGE, L., and W. W. ROEHR, "Photoelectric and Thermionic Properties of Palladium," *ibid.*, **39**, 99–107, January, 1932.

   DUBRIDGE, L. A., "A Further Experimental Test of Fowler's Theory of Photoelectric Emission," *ibid.*, **39**, 108–118, January, 1932.

   APKER, L., E. TAFT, and J. DICKEY, "Energy Distribution of Photoelectrons from Polycrystalline Tungsten," *ibid.*, **73**, 46–50, January, 1948.
8. SKELLETT, A. M., "The Time Lag in Gas-filled Photoelectric Cells," *J. Appl. Phys.*, **9**, 631–635, October, 1938.
9. GLOVER, A. M., and R. B. JANES, "New High-sensitivity Photosurface," *Electronics*, **13**, 26–27, August, 1940.
10. HENNEY, K., "Electron Tubes in Industry," 2d ed., McGraw-Hill Book Company, Inc., New York, 1937.
11. ZWORYKIN, V. K., G. A. MORTON, and L. MALTER, "The Secondary Emission Multiplier—a New Electronic Device," *Proc. IRE*, **21**, 351–375, March, 1936.
12. HUNTER, L. P., Photoconductivity and Photovoltaic Cells, in L. P. HUNTER (ed.), "Handbook of Semiconductor Electronics," 1st ed., Chap. 5, McGraw-Hill Book Company, Inc., New York, 1956.

    BEVITT, W. D., "Transistors Handbook," Chap. 9, Prentice-Hall, Inc., Englewood Cliffs, N.J., 1956.

    SHIVE, J. N., "Properties of the M-1740 *p-n* Junction Photocell," *Proc. IRE*, **40**, 1410–1413, November, 1952.

    SEED, R. G., "Photosensitive Germanium Devices and Some Device Applications," *Transistor Products, Inc., Bull.*

    SHIVE, J. N., and P. ZUK, "Junction Photocells," *Bell Labs. Record*, **33**, 445–449, December, 1955.
13. GRONDAHL, L. O., "The Copper–Cuprous-oxide Rectifier and Photoelectric Cell," *Revs. Mod. Phys.*, **5**, 141–168, April, 1933.

    GRONDAHL, L. O., and P. H. GEIGER, "A New Electronic Rectifier," *J. AIEE*, **46**, 215–222, March, 1927.
14. WILSON, A. H., "Semi-conductors and Metals," Cambridge University Press, London, 1939.

    MACGREGOR-MORRIS, J. T., and R. M. BILLINGTON, "Selenium Rectifier Photocell: Its Characteristics and Response to Intermittent Illumination," *JIEE*, **79**, 435–438, October, 1936.

    "The Photronic Photoelectric Cell," Monographs B-8 and B-18-A, Weston Electrical Instrument Corp., 1935.
15. BERGMANN, L., "Über eine neue Selen-Sperrschicht-Photozelle," *Physik. Z.*, **32**(7), 286–288, 1931.
16. RAISBECK, G., "The Solar Battery," *Sci. American*, **193**, 102–110, December, 1955.

CHAPTER 7

VACUUM-TRIODE CHARACTERISTICS

In 1906 DeForest introduced a third electrode, called a *grid*, into a vacuum diode. This triode was found to be capable of amplifying small-signal voltages, a discovery of such great practical importance that it made possible the electronics industry.

In this chapter we shall study the volt-ampere characteristics of the triode and define certain parameters which are useful in describing these curves. We shall carry through the analysis of a simple circuit containing a triode and show that such a circuit is indeed an amplifier.

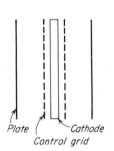

FIG. 7-1. Schematic arrangement of the electrodes in a triode. The tube has cylindrical symmetry.

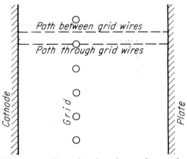

FIG. 7-2. Sketch of a plane-electrode triode, showing the paths for the potential profiles given in Fig. 7-4.

7-1. The Potential Variation in a Triode. Suppose that the mechanical structure of a vacuum diode is altered by inserting an electrode in the form of a wire grid structure between the cathode and the anode, thus converting the tube into a triode. A schematic arrangement of the electrodes in a triode having cylindrical symmetry is shown in Fig. 7-1.

A study of the potential variation within a triode is very instructive. For simplicity, consider a plane cathode and a parallel anode each of infinite extent. The grid is assumed to consist of parallel equidistant wires lying in a plane parallel to the cathode. The diameter of the wires is small compared with the distance between wires. Such an arrangement is shown in Fig. 7-2. If we assume that the cathode is so cold that it emits no electrons, then the potential at any point in the tube can be

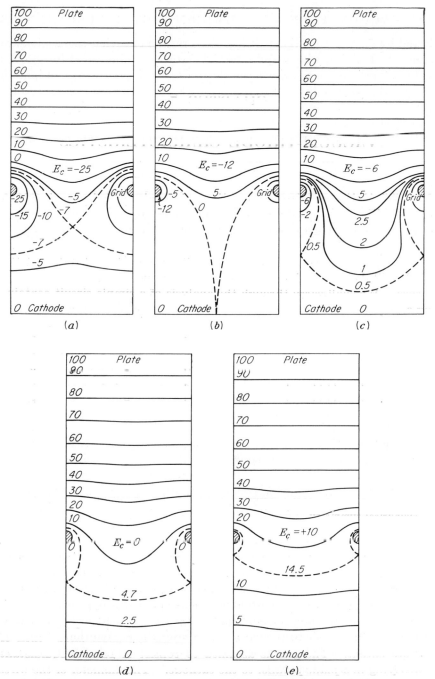

Fig. 7-3. Equipotential contours in the plane-electrode triode. (a) Grid beyond cutoff potential. (b) Grid at cutoff potential; (c) Grid negative at one-half cutoff value. (d) Grid at zero potential. (e) Grid positive. (From K. R. Spangenberg, "Vacuum Tubes," McGraw-Hill Book Company, Inc.)

found by an electrostatic analysis. The results of such a calculation are shown in Fig. 7-3, where equipotential surfaces are indicated for various values of grid voltage. Since the electrodes are assumed to be of infinite extent, then it is only necessary to plot the equipotentials over a distance corresponding to the spacing between grid wires. Each picture is to be imagined repeated indefinitely to the right and left.

It should be noted, in particular, that the grid structure does not produce an equipotential plane at the position of the grid. If it did, there could never be plate current for *any* value of negative grid voltage because the electrons would find themselves in a retarding field as soon as they left the cathode. (This assumes, for the moment, that the cathode is heated but that the electrons leave with zero initial velocity.) Because of the influence of the positive plate potential, it is possible for an electron to find a path between grid wires such that it does not collide with a potential-energy barrier (provided that the grid is not too highly negative). Thus, the potential variation between cathode and anode depends upon the path. The potential vs. distance curves (called "profile presentations") corresponding to Fig. 7-3 are given in Fig. 7-4 for the two extreme conditions, a path midway between grid wires (upper curve) and a path directly through the grid wires (lower curve).

If an electron finds itself in a retarding field regardless of what part of the cathode it comes from, then it certainly cannot reach the anode. This situation is pictured in (a) of Figs. 7-3 and 7-4 and corresponds to conditions beyond cutoff. In (b) are shown the conditions just at cutoff, where the electric-field intensity at the cathode is everywhere zero. Actually, cutoff is obtained at a grid voltage slightly less than this value so that the field at the cathode is somewhat negative and hence repels all the emitted electrons. It should be clear from a study of these figures that the current distribution is not constant along paths at different distances from the grid wires. If the grid is made sufficiently negative, then cutoff will occur throughout the entire region. This condition prevails for all grid voltages more negative than that indicated in (b). If the grid voltage is made more positive than this cutoff value, then, as shown in (c), current will flow only in the region midway between the grid wires, because any electrons starting out toward a grid will be repelled. This situation corresponds to the usual operating conditions of a triode voltage amplifier. In (d) the grid is at cathode potential, and in (e) it is held positive with respect to the cathode. Under these conditions, electrons can reach the anode by all paths unless they collide with a grid wire and are collected as grid current.

It should be emphasized that these diagrams represent space-charge-free conditions. In Chap. 4 it was shown that under space-charge conditions the electric-field intensity at the cathode is reduced to zero.

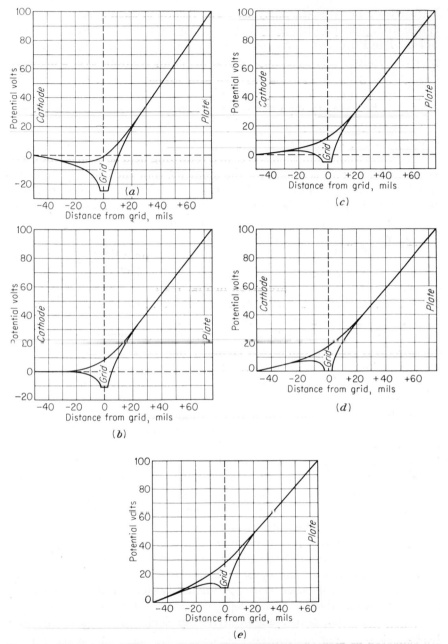

Fig. 7-4. Potential profiles of a plane-electrode triode. (a) Grid at twice the cutoff value of potential; (b) grid at the cutoff value of potential; (c) grid negative at one-half the cutoff value of potential; (d) grid at zero potential; (e) grid positive. (From K. R. Spangenberg, "Vacuum Tubes," McGraw-Hill Book Company, Inc.)

Hence, for a hot cathode, the diagrams (c), (d), and (e) must be modified (lowered) somewhat and must have zero slope at the cathode.

7-2. The Electrode Currents. From the qualitative discussion already given, it follows that the plate current should depend upon the space-charge-free cathode field intensity. This electrostatic field, in turn, is a linear function of the grid and plate potentials. Since the grid is much closer to the cathode than the plate, a given change in potential of the grid has a much greater effect on the field intensity at the cathode than does the same change in potential of the anode. For example, if the plate voltage is changed slightly in Fig. 7-4, then it will affect the slope of the potential curve at the cathode very little. If the grid voltage is altered the same amount, the slope will change by a very much larger amount. In view of this discussion and the known three-halves-power law for diodes, it is anticipated that the plate current may be represented approximately by the equation

$$i_b = G \left(e_c + \frac{e_b}{\mu} \right)^n \qquad (7\text{-}1)$$

where e_b is the plate potential, e_c is the grid potential, and where the factor μ is a measure of the relative effectiveness of the grid and plate potentials. The parameter μ is known as the "amplification factor" and is substantially constant and independent of current. The exponent n is approximately equal to $\frac{3}{2}$. The constant G is called the "perveance."

The validity of Eq. (7-1) has been verified experimentally for many triodes. No rigorous theoretical derivation of this equation exists, even for a triode of relatively simple geometry. In particular, the exact dependence of the constant G upon the dimensions of the tube is not known.[1] However, the value of the amplification factor μ can be calculated with a fair degree of accuracy from equations that are based on certain electrostatic considerations.[2] Semiempirical relationships that are suitable for design calculations are available.[3]

Deviations from Eq. (7-1) exist for the same reasons that deviations from the three-halves-power law exist for diodes, viz., the effects of contact potential, initial velocities, nonuniform structure, etc. (Sec. 4-6). Fortunately, it is seldom necessary to know the exact mathematical relationship that exists among i_b, e_b, and e_c. Hence the principal emphasis in what follows will be on the experimentally determined relationships among these variables.

If the grid potential be made positive, the electron stream will increase because of the combined action of both the grid and the plate. With a positive potential on the grid, some of the electrons will be attracted to it and a current into the grid will result. Unless the grid is designed to dissipate the power represented by the current to it, when maintained at a positive potential, the grid structure may be seriously damaged. The grid is generally maintained negative, although positive-grid triodes for power-amplifier applications are available. Also, in many pulse-forming circuits the grid is driven positive during a portion of the wave form. The positive grid characteristics of a 6SN7 triode are given in Fig. A9-9.

The plate and grid currents as a function of grid voltage are illustrated in Fig. 7-5. In this diagram, the plate potential is assumed to be constant. It is seen that cutoff occurs if the grid potential is sufficiently negative. As the grid potential is made less negative, the plate current follows a smooth curve, this variation being expressed analytically with fair approximation by Eq. (7-1). As the grid potential is made positive with respect to the cathode, an appreciable grid current is obtained.

Once the grid potential is made positive so that a grid current i_c exists, Eq. (7-1) is no longer applicable, since only a portion of the total space-charge current is collected by the anode. Equation (7-1) does give a good representation of the total cathode current $i_k = i_b + i_c$. Hence, as the grid potential is made increasingly positive, the plate current increases rapidly, but not according to Eq. (7-1).

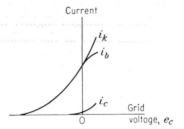

FIG. 7-5. Plate i_b, grid i_c, and total cathode current i_k in a triode as a function of grid voltage for a constant plate voltage.

Because the electrons are emitted with finite initial velocities, some of these will be collected by the grid even when its potential is slightly negative. This grid current may be of the order of a few microamperes when the grid voltage is, say, $\frac{1}{2}$ volt negative, whereas at zero grid voltage i_c may be as large as 0.5 ma. For many triodes the grid current increases in the range of 0.5 to 4.0 ma for each volt increase in positive grid potential. This rate corresponds to an effective *static grid resistance* r_c, defined by $r_c \equiv e_c/i_c$, of 250 to 2,000 ohms.

If the grid voltage is made a few volts negative, it is found that the direction of the grid current reverses.[4] This negative current is due to positive ions which are attracted to the grid. Since the positive-ion current comes from the residual gas in a "vacuum tube," it is very variable from tube to tube, although it is usually a small fraction of a microampere (it is too small to be noticeable in Fig. 7-5). Negative grid current can also result from thermionic and photoelectric emission from the grid.

7-3. Triode Characteristics. The plate current depends upon the plate potential and upon the grid potential and may be expressed mathematically by the functional relationship

$$i_b = f(e_b, e_c) \tag{7-2}$$

This equation is read "i_b is some function f of e_b and e_c." This relationship is sometimes written as $i_b = i_b(e_b, e_c)$, the quantities in the parentheses designating the variables upon which the function f (or i_b) depends. If it is assumed that the grid current is zero, then the approximate explicit form of this function is that expressed by Eq. (7-1). Of course, the plate current also depends upon the heater current; but as this is usually maintained constant at the rated value, and this is such as to provide perhaps five to ten times the normal required space-charge current, this parameter does not enter into the functional relationship.

The important variables that give a complete description of the characteristics of the triode are, as already noted, i_b, e_b, and e_c. By plotting these three variables on a three-dimensional system of axes, a space diagram is obtained. The traces of this surface on the three coordinate

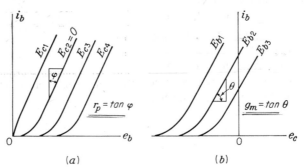

Fig. 7-6. (a) Plate and (b) transfer characteristic curves of a triode.

$$E_{c1} > E_{c2} > E_{c3} > E_{c4} \qquad E_{b1} > E_{b2} > E_{b3}$$

planes (and on planes parallel to these) give three families of characteristic curves. These curves, which are easy to visualize, are given in Figs. 7-6 and 7-7.

Figure 7-6a shows a family of characteristic curves known as the "plate characteristics," since they give the variation of the plate current with the plate potential for various values of grid potential, $e_c = E_{c1}$, E_{c2}, etc. The effect of making the grid more negative is to shift the curves to the right without changing the slopes appreciably. If the grid potential is made the independent variable and if the plate voltage is held constant as a parameter, $e_b = E_{b1}$, E_{b2}, etc., the family of curves known as the "mutual" or "transfer" characteristics, illustrated in Fig. 7-6b, is obtained. The effect of making the plate potential less positive is to shift the curves to the right, the slopes again remaining substantially unchanged. These conditions are readily evident if it is remembered that the sets of curves in these diagrams are plots of Eq. (7-1) with either e_c or e_b maintained constant as a parameter.

The simultaneous variation of both the plate and the grid potentials so that the plate current remains constant, $i_b = I_{b1}, I_{b2}$, etc., gives rise to a third group of curves, known as the "constant-current" characteristics, illustrated in Fig. 7-7.

The most important family of characteristics is the plate family, and these are supplied in convenient form in data books provided by the tube manufacturers.   The plate character- istics for several representative tubes are reproduced in Appendix IX. These curves are average values, and the characteristics for a specific tube may differ appreciably from these published values.   The Joint Army- Navy Specifications, JAN-1A, for Electron Tubes give the limits of variability which may be expected in a given tube type.

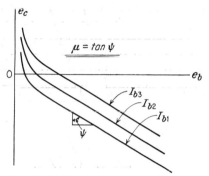

Fig. 7-7. Constant-current character- istic curves of a triode.

$$I_{b3} > I_{b2} > I_{b1}$$

The volt-ampere characteristics vary with heater temperature and with aging of the tube. As with a diode, so for a multielement tube the temperature effect is found experimentally to be equivalent to a 0.1 volt shift in cathode voltage (relative to the other electrodes) for each 10 per cent change in heater voltage.

7-4. Triode Parameters.   In the analysis of networks using triodes as circuit elements (Chap. 8), it is found necessary to make use of the slopes of the characteristic curves of Figs. 7-6 and 7-7.   Hence it is convenient to introduce special symbols and names for these quantities.   This will now be done.

The slope of the constant-current characteristic gives the amplification factor μ introduced in Eq. (7-1).   That is, the amplification factor is defined as the ratio of the change in plate voltage to the change in grid voltage for a constant plate current.   Mathematically, μ is given by the relation

$$\mu = - \left(\frac{\partial e_b}{\partial e_c}\right)_{I_b} \tag{7-3}$$

The subscript I_b denotes that the plate current remains constant in per- forming the indicated partial differentiation.   In order that μ be a posi- tive number, the minus sign is necessary because an increasing plate voltage will require a decreasing grid potential, if the current is to remain unchanged.   The reciprocal of the amplification factor is called the "durchgriff" or the "penetration factor."

The quantity $(\partial e_b/\partial i_b)_{E_c}$, which expresses the ratio of an increment of plate potential to the corresponding increment of plate current when the grid potential is kept constant, has units of resistance and is known as the "plate resistance" of the tube. It is designated by the symbol r_p. We note that the plate resistance is the reciprocal of the slope of the plate characteristics of Fig. 7-6a. It should be recalled that the dynamic plate resistance of a diode was defined in a similar manner. The reciprocal of the plate resistance is called the "plate conductance," $g_p \equiv 1/r_p$.

The quantity $(\partial i_b/\partial e_c)_{E_b}$, which gives the ratio of an increment of plate current to the corresponding increment in grid potential for constant plate potential, has the units of conductance. This quantity is known as the "plate-grid transconductance" and represents the change of current in the plate circuit for unit change in potential of the grid. The plate-grid transconductance is frequently referred to simply as the "mutual conductance" and is designated by the symbol g_m. The quantity g_m is the slope of the mutual characteristic curves of Fig. 7-6b.

To summarize: The triode coefficients, parameters, or "constants," which are characteristic of the tube, are

$$\left.\begin{array}{l} \left(\dfrac{\partial e_b}{\partial i_b}\right)_{E_c} \equiv r_p, \text{ plate resistance} \\[2em] \left(\dfrac{\partial i_b}{\partial e_c}\right)_{E_b} \equiv g_m, \text{ mutual conductance} \\[2em] -\left(\dfrac{\partial e_b}{\partial e_c}\right)_{I_b} \equiv \mu, \text{ amplification factor} \end{array}\right\} \qquad (7\text{-}4)$$

Since there is only one equation (7-2) relating the three quantities i_b, e_b, and e_c, the three partial derivatives cannot be independent. The interrelationship may be shown to be (Sec. 8-4)

$$\mu = r_p g_m \qquad (7\text{-}5)$$

The variations of these parameters for a 6SN7 tube as a function of plate current (for three particular values of plate voltage) are shown in Fig. 7-8. It is noticed that the plate resistance varies over rather wide limits. It is very high at zero plate current and varies approximately inversely as the one-third power of the plate current (Prob. 7-3). The transconductance increases with plate current from zero at zero plate current and varies directly as the one-third power of the plate current. The amplification factor is observed to remain reasonably constant over a wide range of currents, although it falls off rapidly at the low currents.

The usual order of magnitude of the tube parameters for conventional triodes is approximately as follows:

μ: from 2.5 to 100.

r_p: from 0.5 to 100 kilohms.

g_m: from 0.5 to 10 millimhos.

Among the most commonly used triodes are those listed in Table 7-1. These contain two triode units in one envelope, and each section has, at the recommended operating point, the parameters given in the table.

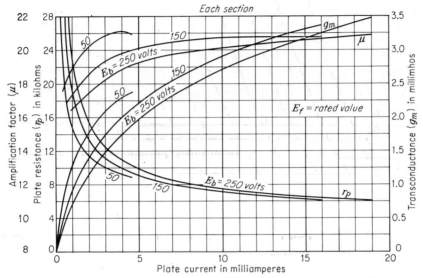

FIG. 7-8. The parameters μ, r_p, and g_m for a 6SN7 triode as a function of plate current for three values of plate voltage.   (*Courtesy of General Electric Co.*)

TABLE 7-1

SOME TRIODE PARAMETERS

Triode type	μ	r_p, kilohms	g_m, millimhos
6SL7............	70	44	1.6
6SN7............	20	7.7	2.6
12AT7..........	55	5.5	10
12AU7..........	17	7.7	2.2
12AX7..........	100	62	1.6
5965............	47	7.2	6.5

Since the plate current is given in milliamperes and the potentials in volts, it is convenient to express the plate resistance in kilohms and the transconductance in millimhos.   Note that the product of milliamperes and kilohms (K) is volts and that the reciprocal of kilohms is millimhos.

Example. Find approximate values of r_p, μ, and g_m directly from the plate characteristics of a 6SN7 at the operating point $E_b = 200$ and $E_c = -6$ volts.

Solution. The plate curves are given in Appendix IX and are reproduced for convenience in Fig. 7-9. The operating point is designated A and is seen to correspond to 7.6 ma. To find the tube parameters, the definitions summarized in Eq. (7-4) are

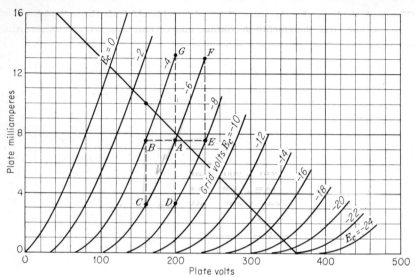

FIG. 7-9. The plate characteristics of a 6SN7 triode. (The straight line passing through the point $i_b = 0$, $e_b = 360$ volts is discussed in Sec. 7-6.)

used. Approximate values of the partial derivatives are obtained by taking finite differences instead of differentials. Thus,

$$r_p \equiv \left(\frac{\text{change in plate voltage}}{\text{change in plate current}}\right)_{\text{grid voltage const}}$$

$$= \left(\frac{\Delta e_b}{\Delta i_b}\right)_{E_c} = \frac{AB}{BC} \quad \} \text{ SEE APROW p 167}$$

The point B is characterized by $E_b = 160$, $I_b = 7.6$, and $E_c = -4$. The point C is specified by $E_b = 160$, $I_b = 3.2$, and $E_c = -6$. Hence $AB = 200 - 160 = 40$ volts, and $BC = 7.6 - 3.2 = 4.4$ ma.

$$r_p = \frac{40}{4.4} = 9.1 \text{ K}$$

Similarly,

$$g_m \equiv \left(\frac{\text{change in plate current}}{\text{change in grid voltage}}\right)_{\text{plate voltage const}}$$

$$= \left(\frac{\Delta i_b}{\Delta e_c}\right)_{E_b} = \frac{AD}{\Delta e_c}$$

The point D is specified by $E_b = 200$, $I_b = 3.4$, and $E_c = -8$. Hence $AD = 7.6 - 3.4 = 4.2$ ma, and $\Delta e_c = -6 - (-8) = 2$ volts.

$$g_m = \frac{4.2}{2} = 2.1 \text{ millimhos}$$

Similarly,

$$\mu \equiv -\left(\frac{\text{change in plate voltage}}{\text{change in grid voltage}}\right)_{\text{plate current const}}$$

$$= -\frac{AB}{\Delta e_c} = -\frac{40}{-6-(-4)} = \frac{40}{2} = 20$$

The product of r_p and g_m is $r_p g_m = 9.1 \times 2.1 = 19$, which checks well with $\mu = 20$, considering the large increments in voltage and current that were taken, whereas, theoretically, infinitesimal changes are indicated.

These parameters were evaluated at the point A for decreasing currents and voltages. If positive increments are taken, a new set of values is obtained. Thus,

MUST BE THROUGH-OUT CONSISTANT THE COMPUTATIONS. for r_p, g_m & μ.

$$r_p = \frac{EA}{FE} \qquad g_m = \frac{GA}{\Delta e_c} \qquad \text{and} \qquad \mu = -\frac{EA}{\Delta e_c}$$

For point E, $E_b = 240$, $I_b = 7.6$, and $E_c = -8$
For point F, $E_b = 240$, $I_b = 13.0$, and $E_c = -6$
For point G, $E_b = 200$, $I_b = 13.2$, and $E_c = -6$

Hence

$$r_p = \frac{240 - 200}{13.0 - 7.6} = \frac{40}{5.4} = 7.4 \text{ K}$$

$$g_m = \frac{13.2 - 7.6}{-4 - (-6)} = \frac{5.6}{2} = 2.8 \text{ millimhos}$$

$$\mu = -\frac{240 - 200}{-8 - (-6)} = \frac{40}{2} = 20$$

$$r_p g_m = 7.4 \times 2.8 = 20.8$$

which checks well with $\mu = 20$.

It should be noted that, for increasing currents, the plate resistance decreased, the transconductance increased, and the amplification remained essentially constant (actually increased slightly). This trend is consistent with Fig. 7-8. The average values of the parameters obtained above are $\mu = 20$, $r_p = 8.3$ kilohms, and $g_m = 2.5$ millimhos. These values are in good agreement with the corresponding quantities read from Fig. 7-8 at $I_b = 7.6$ ma and $E_b = 200$ volts.

If r_p were constant, then the slope of the plate characteristics would everywhere be constant. In other words, these curves would be parallel lines. If μ were constant, then the horizontal spacing of the lines (AB or EA in the above example) would be constant. This statement assumes that the characteristics are drawn with equal increments in grid voltage (as they always are). If r_p and μ are constant, so also is $g_m = \mu/r_p$. Hence, an important conclusion can be drawn: *If over a portion of the i_b-e_b plane the characteristics can be approximated by parallel lines which are equidistant for equal increments in grid voltage, then the parameters μ, r_p, and g_m can be considered constant over this region.* It is shown in the next chapter that if the tube operates under this condition (tube parameters sensibly constant) then the behavior of the tube as a circuit element can be obtained analytically.

7-5. Symbols and Terminology. Even if the tube characteristics are very nonlinear, we can determine the behavior of the triode in a circuit by a graphical method, as will now be demonstrated. This procedure is essentially the same as that which is used (Sec. 4-10) in treating the diode as a circuit element, except that the diode has two active electrodes and one characteristic curve, whereas the triode has three active elements and a family of curves. The three terminals are marked P (plate), K (cathode), and G (grid). A grounded-cathode circuit in which the triode acts as an amplifier is shown in Fig. 7-10. Before proceeding with an analysis of this circuit, it is necessary to explain the meanings of the symbols and the terminology to be used in this and subsequent analyses.

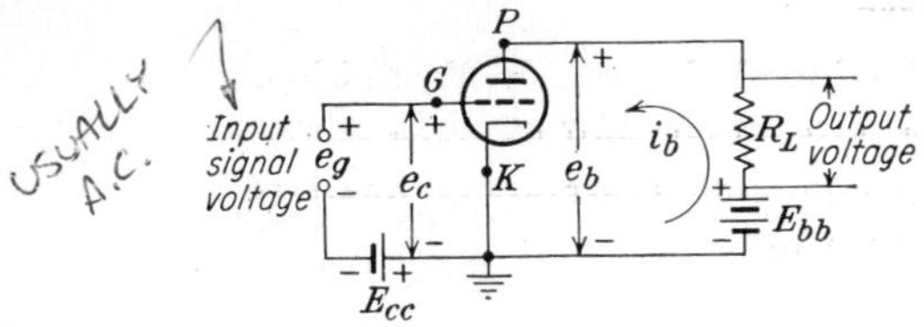

USUALLY A.C.

FIG. 7-10. The basic circuit of a triode used as an amplifier.

The input circuit of this amplifier refers to all elements of the circuit that are connected between the grid and cathode terminals of the tube. Similarly, the output or plate circuit usually refers to the elements that are connected between the plate and cathode terminals. In the circuit illustrated the output circuit contains a d-c supply voltage which is in series with a load resistor R_L. The input circuit consists of a d-c supply voltage in series with the input voltage. The input signal may have any wave shape whatsoever, but it is usually chosen, for convenience in analysis, to be a sinusoidally varying voltage.

Because a variety of potentials and currents, both d-c and a-c, are involved simultaneously in a vacuum-tube circuit, it is necessary that a precise method of labeling be established, if confusion is to be avoided. We shall adhere to the IRE Standards[b] for vacuum-tube symbols, which may be summarized as follows:

1. Instantaneous values of quantities which vary with time are represented by lower-case letters (i for current, e for voltage, and p for power).

2. Maximum, average (d-c), and effective, or root-mean-square (rms), values are represented by the upper-case letter of the proper symbol (I, E, or P).

3. D-c values and instantaneous total values are indicated by the subscript b in the plate circuit and c in the grid circuit.

4. Varying component values are indicated by the subscript p in the plate circuit and g in the grid circuit.

5. If necessary to distinguish between maximum, average, or rms values, then maximum and average values may be distinguished by the additional subscript m and av, respectively.

6. Conventional current flow into the plate (or grid) from the external circuit is positive.

7. A single subscript is used if the reference electrode is clearly understood. If there is any possibility of ambiguity, the conventional double-subscript notation should be used. For example, e_{pk} = instantaneous value of varying component of voltage drop from plate to cathode and is positive if the plate is positive with respect

to the cathode.   If the circuit of Fig. 7-10 is under consideration, then the symbol e_{pk} may be shortened to e_p.

8. The *magnitude* of the supply voltage is indicated by repeating the electrode subscript.   The plate supply voltage E_{bb} is called the *B supply*, and the grid supply voltage is called the *C supply* or the *grid bias* voltage.

Table 7-2 summarizes the notation introduced above.   In the table are also listed some symbols not yet defined, but which will be used in later sections.   This table should serve as a convenient reference until the reader is thoroughly familiar with the notation.

TABLE 7-2

TRIODE SYMBOLS

	Grid voltage with respect to cathode	Plate voltage with respect to cathode	Current in direction toward plate through the load
Instantaneous total value.......	e_c	e_b	i_b
Quiescent value...............	E_c	E_b	I_b
Instantaneous value of varying component.................	e_g	e_p	i_p
Effective value of varying component....................	E_g	E_p	I_p
Amplitude of varying component	E_{gm}	E_{pm}	I_{pm}
Supply voltage...............	E_{cc}*	E_{bb}*	

* These are positive numbers giving the *magnitude* of the voltages.

For example, if the input signal voltage is sinusoidal and of the form

$$e_g = E_{gm} \sin \omega t = \sqrt{2}\, E_g \sin \omega t$$

then the net instantaneous grid voltage in Fig. 7-10 is

$$e_c = -E_{cc} + e_g = -E_{cc} + E_{gm} \sin \omega t \qquad (7\text{-}6)$$

7-6. Graphical Analysis of the Grounded-cathode Circuit.   Suppose for the moment that no grid signal is applied in Fig. 7-10, so that $e_g = 0$ It must not be supposed that there will be no plate current, although this might be true if the bias were very negative.   In general, a definite direct current will exist when the input signal is zero.   The value of this current may be found graphically in the same way as that used to determine the instantaneous plate current in the diode circuit of Fig. 4-9 for a given instantaneous input voltage.

Because of the presence of the load resistor R_L, the potential that exists between the plate and the cathode will depend upon both the magnitude of the battery supply and the magnitude of the current in the load resistor. It follows from Fig. 7-10 that

$$e_b = E_{bb} - i_b R_L \qquad (7\text{-}7)$$

This one equation is not sufficient to determine the current corresponding to any voltage E_{bb} because there are two unknown quantities in this expression, e_b and i_b. A second relation between these two variables is given by the plate characteristics of the triode. The straight line represented by Eq. (7-7) is plotted on the plate curves of Fig. 7-11. This line is obviously independent of the tube characteristics, for it depends only upon elements external to the tube itself. The intersection of this *load line* with the curve for $e_c = -E_{cc}$ is called the "operating point" or the "quiescent point" Q. The quiescent current in the external circuit is I_b, and the corresponding quiescent plate potential is E_b.

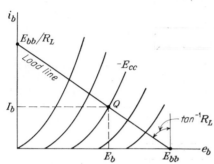

The simplest method of drawing the load line is to locate two points of this line and to connect these with a straightedge. One such point is the intersection with the horizontal axis, namely, $i_b = 0$

FIG. 7-11. The operating point Q is located at the intersection of the load line and the plate characteristic for the bias $e_c = -E_{cc}$.

and $e_b = E_{bb}$. Another is the intersection with the vertical axis, namely, $e_b = 0$ and $i_b = E_{bb}/R_L$. These are illustrated in Fig. 7-11.

Sometimes this latter point falls off the printed plate characteristics supplied by the manufacturer, the current E_{bb}/R_L being considerably greater than the rated tube current. In such a situation any value of current, say i_0, that is given on the plate characteristics is chosen and the corresponding plate voltage is found from Eq. (7-7), namely, $E_{bb} - i_0R_L$.

Example. One section of a 6SN7 triode is operated at a bias of -8 volts and a plate supply of 360 volts. If the load resistance is 20 K, what are the quiescent current and voltage values?

Solution. The plate characteristics of the 6SN7 are given in Fig. 7-9. One point on the load line is $i_b = 0$ and $e_b = 360$. Corresponding to $e_b = 0$ the value of i_b is $E_{bb}/R_L = 360/20 = 18$ ma, whereas the largest current in Fig. 7-9 is 16 ma. Hence a second point on the load line is found by choosing $i_b = 10 = i_0$, and then

$$e_b = E_{bb} - i_0R_L = 360 - 10 \times 20 = 360 - 200 = 160$$

The load line is now drawn through the pair (i_b, e_b) of points (0, 360) and (10, 160) on Fig. 7-9. This line is found to intersect the plate curve corresponding to $E_c = -8$ at a plate current of 6.4 ma $= I_b$ and a plate voltage of 233 volts $= E_b$.

If the voltage of the grid with respect to the cathode in the above example is changed to -14 volts, then the plate current is found to be approximately 2.6 ma (this is the intersection of the load line with $E_c = -14$ volts). If the grid voltage is changed to -2 volts, then the plate current is found to be 10.9 ma (the reader should check these values). A change in input voltage of $-2 - (-14) = 12$ volts has resulted in a change of plate current of $10.9 - 2.6 = 8.3$ ma and a corresponding change in output voltage across the 20-kilohm load of $20 \times 8.3 = 166$ volts. Hence the varying component of the output voltage is $\frac{166}{12} = 13.8$ times as great as the input signal. This example illustrates that a triode can be an amplifier.

The above method of finding the output current corresponding to a given input voltage will now be discussed in more detail. Suppose that

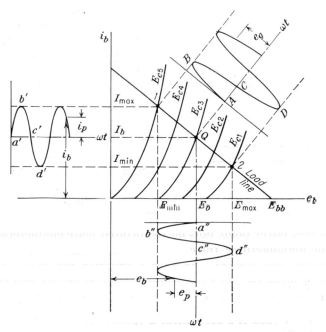

Fig. 7-12. The output current and voltage wave forms for a given input grid signal are determined from the plate characteristics and the load line.

the grid potential is given by Eq. (7-6) The maximum and minimum values of e_c will be $-E_{cc} \pm E_{gm}$, which indicates that the grid swings about the point $-E_{cc}$. Consequently, the plate current and the plate voltage will then swing about the values I_b and E_b, respectively. The graphical construction showing these conditions is illustrated in Fig. 7-12. *For any given value of e_c, the corresponding values of i_b and e_b are located at the intersection of the load line and the i_b-e_b curve corresponding to this value of e_c.* This construction is valid *for any input wave form* and is not restricted to sinusoidal voltages. The points a', b', c', etc., of the output current, and the points a'', b'', c'', etc., of the output-voltage wave correspond, respectively, to the points A, B, C, etc., of the input grid-voltage wave form.

A word is in order about the manner in which the grid voltage is drawn on the diagram. The time axis is shown normal to the load line. This representation has no real significance but is used to indicate that the signal voltage e_g causes the grid voltage to vary about the Q point ($e_c = E_{c3}$) from E_{c5} at one extreme of the signal-voltage swing to E_{c1} at the other extreme of this swing.

7-7. The Dynamic Transfer Characteristic. The static transfer characteristic of Fig. 7-6b gives the relationship between i_b and e_c with the

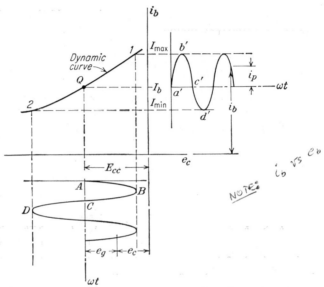

FIG. 7-13. The dynamic transfer characteristic is used to determine the output wave shape for a given input signal.

plate voltage held constant. The dynamic transfer characteristic gives the relationship between i_b and e_c for a given plate supply voltage E_{bb} and a given load resistance R_L. This functional relationship is obtained from the plate characteristics and the load line by the graphical construction described in the preceding section. Thus the values of i_b and e_c at points 1, Q, and 2 in Fig. 7-13 are the same as those obtained at the corresponding points 1, Q, and 2 in Fig. 7-12. The dynamic characteristic will, in general, be curved although often it may be approximated by a straight line.

The utility of the dynamic characteristic is that it allows the output wave form to be determined for any given input wave form. The construction should be clear from Fig. 7-13, where points a', b', c', etc., of the output current correspond to points A, B, C, etc., respectively, of the input grid-voltage signal e_g.

← MACKEY CALLS THIS "AC LOAD LINE."

7-8. Load Curve. Dynamic Load Line. A graphical method of obtaining the operating characteristics of a triode with a resistance load is given in Sec. 7-6.   It is there shown that the operating region in the i_b-e_b plane is a straight line, which is called the "load line."   However, if the load is reactive, then the work curve is no longer a straight line but attains the form of an ellipse.   This result follows from the fact that the plate current and the plate voltage are given by

$$e_p = E_{pm} \sin \omega t \qquad \text{and} \qquad i_p = -I_{pm} \sin (\omega t + \theta) \qquad (7\text{-}8)$$

which are the parametric equations of an ellipse.   If the angle θ is zero, the ratio of these equations yields

$$\frac{e_p}{i_p} = -\frac{E_{pm}}{I_{pm}} = -R_L$$

which represents the load line for a resistance load.   This load line and also the elliptical work curve for a reactive load are shown on the volt-ampere characteristics of Fig. 7-14.

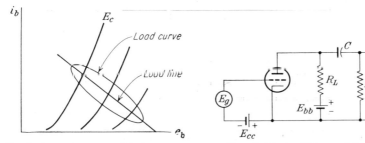

FIG. 7-14. The load line for a resistive load becomes a load curve (an ellipse, under linear operation) for a reactive load.

FIG. 7-15. An RC-coupled circuit.

The above analysis depends upon the tube parameters μ, r_p, and g_m being constant over the range of operation in the i_b-e_b plane.   If these parameters are not constant, the operating curve will no longer be an ellipse.   No simple analysis of the output of an amplifier with a reactive load exists under these conditions.

An important special case of a reactive load is indicated in Fig. 7-15. Here the output is taken not across R_L but rather across R_g, which is isolated from the plate of the tube by means of a capacitor C.   Since a capacitor cannot pass direct current, no d-c voltage appears across R_g. The a-c signal voltage developed across R_g may then be applied to the input of another amplifier without affecting its bias voltage.   This method of connection between amplifier stages is called *RC coupling* and is discussed in detail in Chap. 15.

Under d-c conditions the capacitor C acts as an open circuit. Hence the quiescent tube current and voltage are obtained as in Fig. 7-11 by drawing a *static* load line corresponding to the resistance R_L through the point $e_b = E_{bb}$, $i_b = 0$. If we assume, as is often the case, that at the signal frequency the reactance of C is negligible compared with R_g, then

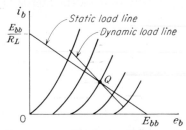

FIG. 7-16. Static and dynamic load lines for the RC-coupled circuit.

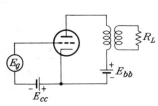

FIG. 7-17. A transformer-coupled load.

under signal conditions the effective load is again resistive. This *dynamic* load represents the parallel resistance of R_L and R_g and has a value given by

$$R_L' = \frac{R_L R_g}{R_L + R_g}$$

The dynamic load line must be drawn with a slope equal to $-1/R_L'$ through the quiescent point Q, as indicated in Fig. 7-16.

For the RC-coupled circuit the a-c load resistance is always smaller than the d-c resistance. If the load is transformer-coupled to the plate,

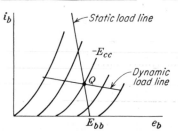

FIG. 7-18. Static and dynamic load lines for a transformer-coupled load.

as indicated in Fig. 7-17, then the converse is true. The static load line corresponds to the very small d-c resistance of the transformer primary and hence is almost a vertical line, as indicated in Fig. 7-18. The dynamic load line corresponds to the much larger resistance R_L reflected into the plate circuit.

If the dynamic load resistance were infinite, then the dynamic load line would be horizontal. Under these circumstances the output voltage would vary with signal voltage but the output current would remain constant. Hence, a circuit with a very large effective load acts as a constant-current device.

7-9. Graphical Analysis of a Circuit with a Cathode Resistor. Many practical circuits have a resistor R_k in series with the cathode in addition to (or in place of) the load resistor R_L in series with the plate. The resistor R_k is returned either to ground or to a negative supply $-E_{cc}$, as indicated in Fig. 7-19.

We consider now how to use the characteristic curves of a vacuum tube to determine such matters as range of output-voltage swing, proper bias voltage, and operating point for any arbitrary input voltage. In Fig. 7-19, e, e_c, e_b, and i_b are, respectively, the *total* instantaneous input

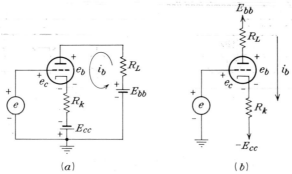

(a) (b)

FIG. 7-19. (a) A tube with both a cathode and a load resistor. (b) An alternative representation of the same circuit.

voltage, grid-to-cathode voltage, plate-to-cathode voltage, and plate current. Kirchhoff's law applied to the plate circuit yields

$$E_{bb} + E_{cc} = e_b + i_b(R_L + R_k) \qquad (7\text{-}9)$$

Similarly, from the grid circuit we obtain

$$e = e_c + i_bR_k - E_{cc} \qquad (7\text{-}10)$$

Equation (7-9) is the equation of the load line corresponding to an effective voltage $E_{bb} + E_{cc}$ and a total resistance $R_L + R_k$. The procedure for constructing the dynamic characteristic (plate current vs. external input voltage) is, then, the following:

1. On the plate characteristics draw the load line corresponding to the given values of $E_{bb} + E_{cc}$ and $R_L + R_k$.

2. Note the current value corresponding to each point of intersection of the load line with the characteristic curves. In each case relabel the individual plate characteristics with an input voltage e equal to $e_c + i_bR_k - E_{cc}$ in accordance with Eq. (7-10). The procedure is illustrated in Fig. 7-20.

3. The required curve is now a plot of the plate current vs. the input voltage. For example, i_{b2} and e_2 are corresponding values on the graph.

When cutoff occurs, there is, of course, no drop across the cathode resistor. Consequently, the externally applied voltage required to attain cutoff is independent of the size of the cathode resistor. As long as the tube operates within its grid base, the potential of the cathode will be slightly (perhaps a few volts) positive with respect to the grid. Hence, *if the grid is grounded ($e = 0$), then the cathode voltage is slightly positive with respect to ground, independent of the magnitudes of the supply voltages or the resistances.* As the input voltage e increases positively, the grid-to-cathode voltage must decrease slightly in magnitude in order to supply the increased tube current demanded by this increased e. Hence, the cathode tries to follow the grid in potential. If $R_L = 0$, it turns out (Sec. 7-10) that the change in cathode voltage is almost exactly equal to the change in grid voltage. Hence, such a circuit is called a *cathode follower.* The grid voltage is sometimes driven highly (perhaps several

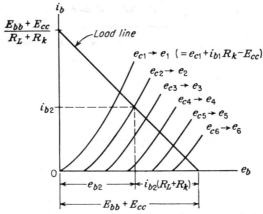

FIG. 7-20. Construction for obtaining the dynamic characteristic of a circuit with both a cathode and a load resistor, as in Fig. 7-19. The symbolism $e_{c1} \rightarrow e_1$ means that e_{c1} is replaced by $e_1 = e_{c1} + i_{b1}R_k - E_{cc}$.

hundreds of volts) positive *with respect to ground.* The maximum input voltage is limited by grid current which takes place approximately where the grid-to-cathode voltage is zero.

It is often desirable to find the current corresponding to a specified input voltage without drawing the entire dynamic characteristic as outlined above. A very simple procedure is as follows:

1. On the plate characteristics draw the load line as in Fig. 7-20.
2. Corresponding to each value of e_c for which there is a plotted plate characteristic, calculate the current for the specified value of input voltage E. In accordance with Eq. (7-10), this current is given by

$$i_b = \frac{E + E_{cc} - e_c}{R_k}$$

The corresponding values of i_b and e_c are plotted on the plate characteristics, as indicated by the dots in Fig. 7-21. The locus of these points is called the *bias curve.*

3. The intersection of the bias curve and the load line gives the plate current I_b corresponding to the given input voltage E.

The procedure outlined above is very easy to carry out. It is not really necessary to use all values of e_c but only two adjacent values which give currents above and below the load line, as indicated by points A and

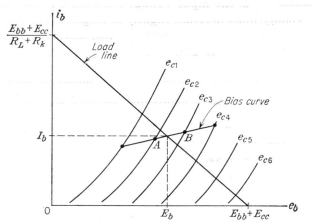

FIG. 7-21. The intersection of the load line and the bias curve gives the quiescent point.

B in Fig. 7-21. The intersection of the straight line connecting A and B with the load line gives the desired current. In particular, it should be noted that, if $E + E_{cc}$ is large compared with the range of values of e_c, then i_b will be almost constant and hence the curve connecting the dots in Fig. 7-21 will be approximately a horizontal straight line.

Often no negative supply is available, and _self-bias_ is obtained from the quiescent voltage drop across R_k. For example, if the plate current and the grid-to-cathode voltage at the quiescent point are I_b and E_c, respectively, the proper bias is obtained by choosing $R_k = -E_c/I_b$. On the other hand, if a circuit with a definite R_k is specified, then the quiescent point is obtained from the construction in Fig. 7-21. For the special case under consideration, $E = E_{cc} = 0$, and the bias curve is obtained from $i_b = -e_c/R_k$.

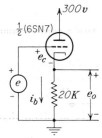

FIG. 7-22. An example of a cathode-follower circuit.

7-10. Practical Cathode-follower Circuits. In order to see why it is sometimes advantageous to use a negative supply, consider the cathode-follower configuration of Fig. 7-22.

Example. Find the maximum positive and negative input voltages and the corresponding output voltages. Calculate the voltage amplification.

Solution. From the plate characteristics and the load line it is found that the current corresponding to $e_c = 0$ is $i_b \cong 10$ ma. Hence, the maximum output voltage is $i_b R_k = 200$ volts, and since $e_c = 0$, the maximum input voltage is also 200 volts.

The cutoff voltage for the 6SN7 corresponding to 300 volts is found to be -18 volts. Hence, the cathode follower may swing from $+200$ volts to -18 volts without drawing grid current or driving the tube beyond cutoff. The corresponding output swing is from $+200$ volts to zero. Hence, the amplification is $200/218 = 0.92$. (A more general proof that the voltage gain of a cathode follower is approximately unity is given in Sec. 8-6.)

In passing we note that the corresponding input range for an amplifier using the same tube and the same supply voltage is only 0 to -18 volts, which is far narrower than that of the cathode follower.

In the above illustration the input could swing 200 volts in the positive direction before drawing grid current but could go only 18 volts in the negative direction before driving the tube to cutoff. If a more symmetrical operation is desired, the tube must be properly biased. One configuration is that indicated in Fig. 7-19, where the bottom of R_k is

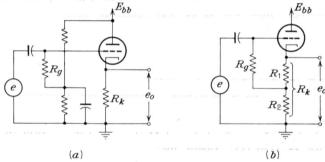

(a)   (b)

Fig. 7-23. Two biasing arrangements for a cathode-follower circuit.

made negative with respect to ground, $R_L = 0$, and the output is taken from the cathode. Two other biasing arrangements, indicated in Fig. 7-23a and b, do not require the use of a negative supply. In (a) the grid is maintained positive with respect to ground by the use of a voltage divider across the plate supply. In (b) self-bias is used, the self-biasing voltage appearing across R_1. That is, with no input signal the grid-to-cathode voltage is the drop across R_1. This resistor is chosen so that the quiescent voltage across R_k is approximately one-half the peak-to-peak output swing. In the above example, where the total output swing was 200 volts, the quiescent value is chosen as 100 volts across the 20-K resistor. This corresponds to a quiescent plate current of 5 ma. From the plate characteristics of the 6SN7 and the 20-K load line, the grid-to-cathode voltage corresponding to 5 ma is -7 volts. Hence, R_1 must be chosen equal to $\frac{7}{5}$ K $= 1.4$ K.

REFERENCES

1. Dow, W. G., "Equivalent Electrostatic Circuits for Vacuum Tubes," *Proc. IRE*, **28**, 548–556, December, 1940.

FREMLIN, J. H., "Calculation of Triode Constants," *Phil. Mag.*, **27**, 709–741, June, 1939.

RODDA, S., Note on Paper on "Calculation of Triode Constants," *ibid.*, **29**, 601–603, June, 1940.

SPANGENBERG, K. R., "Vacuum Tubes," 1st ed., McGraw-Hill Book Company, Inc., New York, 1948.

2. OLLENDORFF, F., "Berechnung des Durchgrippes durch enge Steggitter," *Elektrotech. u. Maschinenbau*, **52**, 585–591, Dec. 16, 1934.

DOW, W. G., "Fundamentals of Engineering Electronics," John Wiley & Sons, Inc., New York, 1937.

SPANGENBERG, K. R., "Vacuum Tubes," 1st ed., McGraw-Hill Book Company, Inc., New York, 1948.

MILLER, J. M., "The Dependence of the Amplification Constant and Internal Plate Circuit Resistance of a Three-electrode Vacuum Tube upon the Structural Dimensions," *Proc. IRE*, **8**, 64–72, February, 1920.

VOGDES, F. B., and F. R. ELDER, "Formulas for the Amplification Constant for Three-element Tubes in Which the Diameter of Grid Wires Is Large Compared to the Spacing," *Phys. Rev.*, **24**, 683–689, December, 1924.

VOGDES, F. B., and F. R. ELDER, *ibid.*, **25**, 255, January, 1925.

KING, R. W., "Calculation of the Constants of the Three-electrode Thermionic Vacuum Tube," *ibid.*, **15**, 256–268, April, 1920.

3. KUSUNOSE, Y., "Calculations on Vacuum Tubes and the Design of Triodes," *Proc. IRE*, **17**, 1706–1749, October, 1929.

4. VALLEY, G. E., Jr., and H. WALLMAN, "Vacuum Tube Amplifiers," Radiation Laboratory Series, Vol. 18, pp. 418–419, McGraw-Hill Book Company, Inc., New York, 1948.

5. IRE Standards on Letter Symbols and Mathematical Signs, 1948 (Reprinted), *Proc. IRE*, **45**, 1140–1147, August, 1957.

CHAPTER 8

TRIODE LINEAR EQUIVALENT CIRCUITS

IF THE triode parameters r_p, g_m, and μ are reasonably constant in some region of operation, the tube behaves linearly over this range. Two linear equivalent circuits, one involving a voltage source and the other a current source, will be derived in this chapter. Networks involving triodes will be replaced by these linear representations and solved analytically (rather than graphically, as was done in the preceding chapter). Also, the input impedance of a triode amplifier will be obtained.

8-1. Variations from Quiescent Values. Suppose that in Fig. 7-10 e_g represents the output from a microphone and that R_L is the effective resistance of a loud-speaker. There is no particular interest in the quiescent current, which is the current to the speaker when no one talks into the microphone. (Actually, the speaker would be transformer-coupled into the plate circuit, and the current in the secondary under quiescent conditions would be zero.) The principal interest is in the speaker output for a given microphone output. Thus the variations in current and voltage with respect to the quiescent values are most important.

If the load is a resistor and not a speaker and if the output from this resistor is taken through a coupling capacitor (as in Fig. 7-15), then under zero input conditions the capacitor will charge up to the quiescent voltage E_b. The voltage across R_g is zero under these conditions. If a varying grid voltage is now added to the bias, the output will again represent voltage variations about the quiescent value.

It is evident that the significant quantities are the currents and voltages with respect to their quiescent values. To examine this matter in some detail, refer to Figs. 7-12 and 7-13. For convenience the latter is repeated in Fig. 8-1. We see that the output current, defined by the equation

$$i_p \equiv i_b - I_b \tag{8-1}$$

is simply the current variation about the quiescent-point current I_b. The output voltage e_p, which is similarly defined, represents the potential variations about the Q point. Consequently, if the input signal is a pure sinusoidal wave and if the tube characteristics are equidistant lines for equal intervals of e_c, i_p will also be a sinusoidal wave. If the characteristic curves are not equidistant lines over the range 1-2 for equal intervals of e_c, the wave form of i_p will differ from that of the input-signal wave form. The latter condition will give rise to harmonics, since a nonsinusoidal wave may be expressed as a Fourier series in which some of the higher harmonic terms are appreciable. These considerations should be clear if reference is made to Figs. 7-12 and 8-1.

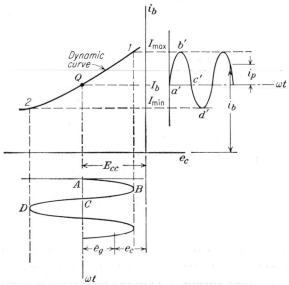

FIG. 8-1. The dynamic transfer characteristic is used to determine the output wave shape for a given input signal.

Corresponding to Eq. (8-1) the variables e_p and e_g are defined by the equations

$$e_p \equiv e_b - E_b \qquad e_g \equiv e_c + E_{cc} \tag{8-2}$$

If the symbol Δ is used to denote a change from the quiescent value, then

$$\Delta e_b \equiv e_p \qquad \Delta e_c \equiv e_g \qquad \Delta i_b \equiv i_p \tag{8-3}$$

An inspection of Fig. 7-12 reveals the following extremely significant result: If i_p is a sine wave, then i_p and e_p are exactly 180 deg out of phase with each other. This result follows from the fact that i_p is a maximum, whereas e_p is a minimum at the point 1. The reverse is true at the point 2.

8-2. Equivalent Voltage-source Representation of a Triode. As discussed in the preceding section, we are ordinarily interested only in the variation in voltage and current about the Q point, rather than in the total values of these quantities. That is, the primary interest is in determining the values of e_p and i_p for a given value of e_g. This solution is referred to as the "a-c response" of the tube, since e_g is often a periodically varying voltage.

The graphical methods of the previous chapter are tedious to apply and often are very inaccurate. Certainly if the input signal is very small, say 0.1 volt or less, then values cannot be read from the plate characteristic curves with any degree of accuracy. But for such small input signals, the parameters μ, r_p, and g_m will remain substantially constant over the small operating range. Under these conditions it is possible to replace the graphical method by an analytical one. This is often called the *small-signal method*, but it is applicable even for large signals provided only that the tube parameters are constant over the range of operation. The constancy of the parameters is judged by an inspection of the plate characteristics. If these are straight lines, equally spaced for equal intervals of grid bias over the operating range, then the parameters are constant. Under these conditions it will be found that the tube may be replaced by a simple linear system. The resulting circuit may then be analyzed by the general methods of a-c circuit analysis.

Thevenin's theorem may be used to find the small-signal equivalent circuit between the plate and cathode terminals. This theorem states that any *two-terminal linear network may be replaced by a generator equal to the open-circuit voltage between the terminals in series with the equivalent output impedance*. The *output impedance* is that impedance which appears between the output terminals when all independent energy sources are replaced by their internal impedances. From the definition of r_p given in Eqs. (7-4) as

$$r_p \equiv \left(\frac{\Delta e_b}{\Delta i_b}\right)_{E_c}$$

this dynamic plate resistance is the output impedance between the terminals P and K. The open-circuit voltage e_{pk} between P and K is $-\mu e_{gk}$. This result follows from the definition of μ given in Eqs. (7-4) as

$$\mu \equiv -\left(\frac{\Delta e_b}{\Delta e_c}\right)_{I_b} = -\left.\frac{e_p}{e_g}\right|_{I_b} = -\left.\frac{e_{pk}}{e_{gk}}\right|_{I_b} \tag{8-4}$$

where use has been made of the definitions in Eqs. (8-3) and, for the sake of clarity, $e_p(e_g)$ has been replaced by $e_{pk}(e_{gk})$ to represent the voltage drop from plate (grid) to cathode. The subscript I_b in Eq. (8-4) means that the plate current is constant, a condition which certainly is satisfied if the plate is open-circuited so that I_b remains at zero. From Thévenin's theorem it follows that the tube may be replaced, viewed from its output terminals, by a generator $-\mu e_{gk}$ in series with a resistor r_p. This linear equivalent circuit is indicated in Fig. 8-2 for instantaneous voltages and currents.   This diagram also includes a schematic of the tube itself in order to stress the correspondence between it and its equivalent representation.

A point of the utmost importance is that no d-c quantities are indicated in Fig. 8-2 because the equivalent circuit of the tube applies only for

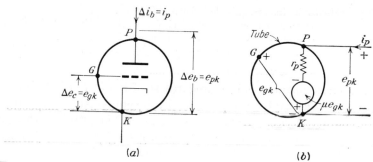

(a)   (b)

Fig. 8-2. A triode (a) and its equivalent voltage-source representation (b).   The brace from G to K indicates that the quantity e_{gk} is to be evaluated by traversing the circuit from G to K and adding all the voltage drops on the way.
— e_{gk} MUST BE PERIODIC.

changes about the Q point.   Moreover, the equivalent-tube-circuit representation is valid for any type of load whether it be a pure resistance, an impedance, or another tube.   This statement is true because the above derivation was accomplished without any regard to the external circuit in which the tube is incorporated.   The only restriction is that the parameters μ, r_p, and g_m must remain substantially constant over the operating range.

If sinusoidally varying quantities are involved in the circuit, and this is usually assumed to be the case, the analysis proceeds most easily if the phasors (sinors) of elementary a-c circuit theory are introduced. The circuit notation used in this text is discussed in Appendix VIII, and the reader is urged to read this very carefully before proceeding further.   For the case of sinusoi-

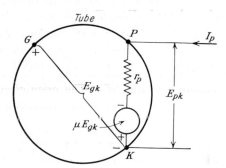

Fig. 8-3. For sinusoidally varying quantities the tube is replaced by this simple network, where $\mathbf{I}_p$, $\mathbf{E}_{pk}$, and $\mathbf{E}_{gk}$ are sinors. (PHASORS)

dally varying quantities, the tube is replaced by the equivalent network shown in Fig. 8-3.

8-3. Linear Analysis of a Triode Circuit.   Based on the foregoing discussion, a triode circuit may be replaced by an equivalent form which permits an analytic determination of its a-c operation.   The following simple rules should be adhered to in drawing the equivalent form of even relatively complicated amplifier circuits.

1. Draw the actual wiring diagram of the circuit neatly.
2. Mark the points G, P, and K on this circuit diagram. Locate these points as the start of the equivalent circuit. Maintain the same relative positions as in the original circuit.
3. Replace the tube by its linear equivalent form (Fig. 8-3).
4. Transfer all circuit elements from the actual circuit to the equivalent circuit of the amplifier. Keep the relative positions of these elements intact.
5. Replace each d-c source by its internal resistance, or by a short circuit, if its resistance is negligible.

A point of special importance is that, regardless of the form of the input circuit, the fictitious generator that appears in the equivalent representation of the tube is *always* μE_{gk}, where E_{gk} is the drop from grid to cathode. The positive reference terminal of the generator is *always* at the cathode.

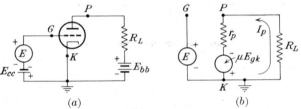

(a)   (b)

FIG. 8-4. The schematic and equivalent circuits of a simple amplifier.

To illustrate the application of these rules, four examples will be given. The first is a single-mesh circuit involving resistors only, the results being given in terms of symbols rather than numerical values. The second illustration is a simple circuit which includes reactive elements and which requires a numerical result. The third is a two-mesh circuit. The fourth network contains two tubes.

Example 1. Find the a-c output current and voltage of the basic triode amplifier circuit illustrated in Fig. 8-4a.

Solution. According to the foregoing rules, the equivalent circuit is that of Fig. 8-4b. Kirchhoff's voltage law, which requires that the sum of the voltage drops around the circuit equal zero, yields

$$I_p R_L + I_p r_p - \mu E_{gk} = 0$$

A glance at this circuit shows that the voltage drop from grid to cathode is **E**. Hence $E_{gk} = E$, and the output current I_p is

$$I_p = \frac{\mu E}{R_L + r_p}$$

The corresponding output-voltage drop from plate to cathode is

$$E_{pk} = -I_p R_L$$

The minus sign arises because the direction from P to K is opposite to the positive reference direction of the current $\mathbf{I}_p$.

$$\mathbf{E}_{pk} = \frac{-\mu \mathbf{E} R_L}{R_L + r_p}$$

The *voltage gain*, or *voltage amplification* **A**, of the tube circuit is defined as the ratio of the output- to input-voltage drops. For the simple amplifier of Fig. 8-4,

$$\mathbf{A} \equiv \frac{\mathbf{E}_{\text{out}}}{\mathbf{E}_{\text{in}}} = \frac{\mathbf{E}_{pk}}{\mathbf{E}_{gk}} = \frac{\mathbf{E}_{pk}}{\mathbf{E}} = -\mu \frac{R_L}{R_L + r_p} = -\mu \frac{1}{1 + r_p/R_L} \qquad (8\text{-}5)$$

The minus sign signifies a phase shift of 180 deg between the output and the input voltages, in agreement with the result obtained from the graphical analysis of the problem in Sec. 8-1.

The magnitude of the gain increases with the load resistance and approaches a maximum value as R_L becomes much greater than r_p. The general form of this variation is illustrated in Fig. 8-5. We note that *the maximum possible gain is μ*, although this can be obtained only if $R_L = \infty$. Too large a value of R_L cannot be used, however, since for a given quies- cent current this would require an im-

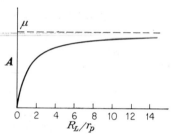

Fig. 8-5. The gain of the amplifier of Fig. 8-4 as a function of the load resistance. μ and r_p are assumed to be constant.

practically high power supply voltage. Nevertheless, since A increases rapidly at first and then approaches μ asymptotically, a gain approaching μ may be realized with a reasonable value of R_L. For $R_L = r_p$ then $A = \mu/2$.

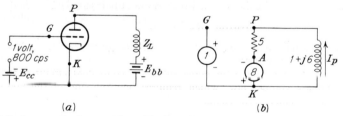

(a)   (b)

Fig. 8-6. A numerical example. (a) Actual circuit and (b) equivalent circuit.

Example 2. A 1-volt rms potential at 800 cps is impressed on the grid of a tube for which $\mu = 8$, $r_p = 5$ K, and the load impedance is $\mathbf{Z}_L = 1 + j6 = 6.08/\underline{80.5°}$ K. Calculate the voltage amplification of the circuit, and draw the complete phasor dia- gram of the system.

Solution. The actual and equivalent circuits are shown in Fig. 8-6. In numerical problems we shall express currents in milliamperes and impedances in kilohms. (Note that the product of milliamperes and kilohms is volts.) Evidently $E_{gk} = 1$, and the fictitious-generator voltage is $\mu E_{gk} = 8$ volts rms. Employing the customary analysis using complex numbers, the voltage drop from G to K is $1 + j0$. This voltage is chosen along the axis of reals, for convenience. The Thévenin's generator $\mathbf{E}_{ka}$ is in phase with this voltage and equals $8 + j0$. Therefore,

$$\mathbf{I}_p = \frac{8 + j0}{5 + (1 + j6)} = 0.943\underline{/-45°}\text{ ma}$$

The output-voltage drop is

$$\mathbf{E}_{pk} = -\mathbf{I}_p\mathbf{Z}_L = -0.943\underline{/-45°} \times 6.08\underline{/80.5°} = -5.73\underline{/35.5°}$$
$$= 5.73\underline{/-144.5°}\text{ volts}$$

The voltage gain of the system is

$$\mathbf{A} = \frac{\text{output-voltage drop}}{\text{input-voltage drop}} = \frac{5.73\underline{/-144.5°}}{1\underline{/0°}} = 5.73\underline{/-144.5°}$$

The amplification $\mathbf{A}$ is a complex number. Its magnitude gives the ratio of output to input voltages. Its phase angle gives the number of degrees by which the output

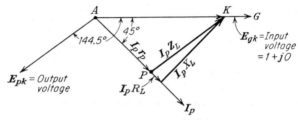

Fig. 8-7. The phasor diagram for the circuit of Fig. 8-6.

leads the input. In this illustration the input leads the output by 144.5 deg. The complete phasor diagram of the circuit is shown in Fig. 8-7.

Example 3. In the circuit sketched in Fig. 8-8a the input signal E is 0.5 volt rms at 2,000 cps. If the 12-K resistor represents the resistance of an a-c voltmeter, what will this meter read?

Solution. The quiescent values will first be found. Since the capacitor cannot pass direct current, then the branch of the circuit containing the capacitor is effectively open as far as the quiescent point is concerned. The grid bias is -6 volts since the d-c drop through the 800 ohms is zero (assuming zero grid current). A load line corresponding to a load of $6 + 4 = 10$ kilohms and a plate supply of 300 volts drawn on Fig. A9-8 give $I_b = 9.0$ ma and $E_b = 210$ volts at $E_c = -6$ volts. From Fig. 7-8 we find that at this quiescent point $\mu = 20$ and $r_p = 7.5$ K.

The equivalent circuit is shown in Fig. 8-8b. The magnitude of the reactance of the capacitor is

$$X_c = \frac{1}{2\pi fC} = \frac{10^6}{(2\pi)(2,000)(0.0025)}\text{ ohms} = 31.8\text{ K}$$

The reference directions for the mesh currents are completely arbitrary and have been chosen clockwise. It is most important to note that $\mathbf{E}_{gk}$ is *not* equal to the input voltage. It can be found by traversing the network from the grid to the cathode and adding all the voltage *drops* encountered. Any path from G to K may be chosen but the most direct one is usually taken since it involves the least amount of labor. Thus

$$\mathbf{E}_{gk} = 0.5 + 0.8\mathbf{I}_1 \tag{8-6}$$

Adding the voltage drops in the direction of the current $\mathbf{I}_1$ and equating the result to zero yields

$$(12 + 0.8 + 4 - j31.8)\mathbf{I}_1 - 4\mathbf{I}_2 = 0$$

or

$$\mathbf{I}_2 = (4.2 - j7.95)\mathbf{I}_1 \tag{8-7}$$

Similarly, Kirchhoff's voltage law around mesh 2 gives

$$-4\mathbf{I}_1 + (7.5 + 6 + 4)\mathbf{I}_2 + 20\mathbf{E}_{gk} = 0 \tag{8-8}$$

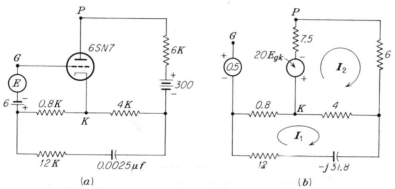

(a)   (b)

Fig. 8-8. A network with two meshes. (a) Actual circuit and (b) equivalent circuit.

Equations (8-6), (8-7), and (8-8) determine the solution. Thus, putting Eqs. (8-6) and (8-7) into (8-8) yields

$$-4\mathbf{I}_1 + (17.5)(4.2 - j7.95)\mathbf{I}_1 + (20)(0.5 + 0.8\mathbf{I}_1) = 0$$

or

$$\mathbf{I}_1 = -0.032 - j0.052 \text{ ma}$$

Since the capacitor blocks the quiescent current from getting to the meter, it will read only the product of its resistance and the alternating current through it. It is this alternating current which we have just calculated from the equivalent circuit (which is valid only for variations from the quiescent value). The rms voltage is therefore

$$(12)[(0.032)^2 + (0.052)^2]^{\frac{1}{2}} = 0.73 \text{ volt}$$

Example 4. Draw the equivalent circuit for the network of Fig. 8-9a, and set up the equations from which the alternating currents and voltages may be found. Since there are two generators shown in the network, the problem is not uniquely specified unless the phase between these two is given. Assume, therefore, that with the reference polarities indicated, $\mathbf{E}_2$ leads $\mathbf{E}_1$ by 30 deg and that the rms value of $\mathbf{E}_1$ is 1.50 volts and that of $\mathbf{E}_2$ is 2.00 volts.

Solution. The phasor $\mathbf{E}_1$ is arbitrarily chosen along the horizontal axis, so that

$$\mathbf{E}_1 = 1.50 + j0$$

and

$$\mathbf{E}_2 = (2.00)\underline{/30^\circ} = (2.00)(\cos 30^\circ + j \sin 30^\circ) = 1.73 + j1.00$$

The points K, P, and G are indicated for each tube. The subscript 1 or 2 is used to designate which tube is under consideration. For example, P_2 is the plate of the second tube; $\mathbf{E}_{gk1}$ represents the voltage drop from grid to cathode of tube 1. The rules given at the beginning of this section are followed for each tube separately, and the resultant equivalent circuit is shown in Fig. 8-9b.

The positive reference directions for the mesh currents are arbitrarily taken clockwise. For any network the fictitious generators μE_{gk} of each tube *must* have the positive reference polarity at its respective cathode independent of any other voltage or current polarities in the circuit.

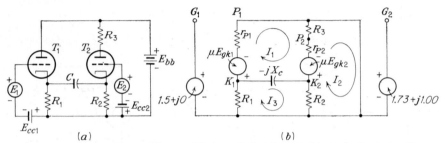

FIG. 8-9. A two-tube problem. (*a*) Actual circuit and (*b*) equivalent circuit.

It should be noted that the battery E_{bb} has been replaced on the equivalent network by a short circuit from the plate of P_1 to the junction of R_1 and R_2. (This assumes that the battery has zero internal resistance.)

The most systematic way of setting up the equations is as follows:

1. Traverse each mesh in the current reference direction.

2. Find the voltage drops due to $\mathbf{I}_1$ flowing through all the passive impedances in this mesh. Use a plus sign for the voltage drops if traversing the circuit in the current reference direction and a minus sign if traveling in the opposite direction.

3. Repeat for $\mathbf{I}_2$ and all other currents.

4. Find the voltage drops of all the generators (in the chosen traversing direction).

5. Set the sum of all these equal to zero.

Applying these rules to mesh 1 yields

$$+ (r_{p1} + R_3 + r_{p2} - jX_C)\mathbf{I}_1 - (R_3 + r_{p2})\mathbf{I}_2 - (-jX_C)\mathbf{I}_3 + \mu\mathbf{E}_{gk1} - \mu\mathbf{E}_{gk2} = 0 \quad (8\text{-}9)$$

Similarly for mesh 2, there is obtained

$$-(R_3 + r_{p2})\mathbf{I}_1 + (R_2 + r_{p2} + R_3)\mathbf{I}_2 - R_2\mathbf{I}_3 + \mu\mathbf{E}_{gk2} = 0 \quad (8\text{-}10)$$

and, for mesh 3, there results

$$-(-jX_C)\mathbf{I}_1 - R_2\mathbf{I}_2 + (R_1 - jX_C + R_2)\mathbf{I}_3 = 0 \quad (8\text{-}11)$$

Before it is possible to solve for the currents, $\mathbf{E}_{gk1}$ and $\mathbf{E}_{gk2}$ must be found. Adding drops from G_1 to K_1 gives

$$\mathbf{E}_{gk1} = 1.50 + j0 + R_1\mathbf{I}_3 \quad (8\text{-}12)$$

Adding drops from G_2 to K_2 yields

$$\mathbf{E}_{gk2} = 1.73 + j1.00 + R_2\mathbf{I}_2 - R_2\mathbf{I}_3 \quad (8\text{-}13)$$

Substitute from Eqs. (8-12) and (8-13) into Eqs. (8-9) and (8-10). The resulting equations and Eq. (8-11) will then be a set of three for the three unknowns $\mathbf{I}_1$, $\mathbf{I}_2$, and $\mathbf{I}_3$ in terms of the circuit constants.

8-4. Taylor's Series Derivation of the Equivalent Circuit. It is instructive to obtain the equivalent circuit of a triode from a Taylor's series expansion of the current i_b about the quiescent point Q. This derivation will show the limitations of this equivalent circuit and will also supply the proof that $\mu = r_p g_m$.

If the grid voltage remains constant but the plate voltage changes by an amount Δe_b, then the change in current equals the rate of change of current with plate voltage times the change in plate voltage, or

$$\Delta i_b = \left(\frac{\partial i_b}{\partial e_b}\right)_{E_c} \Delta e_b$$

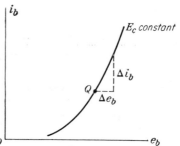

The subscript indicates the variable held constant in performing the partial differentiation. This relationship is illustrated in Fig. 8-10 and is seen to be strictly true only if the slope of the plate characteristic is constant for the assumed change in voltage. Similarly, if the plate voltage remains constant but the grid voltage changes by Δe_c, then the change in current is given by

FIG. 8-10. If the grid voltage is constant, then $\Delta i_b = (\text{slope})(\Delta e_b)$ $= (\partial i_b/\partial e_b)_{E_c} \Delta e_b$.

$$\Delta i_b = \left(\frac{\partial i_b}{\partial e_c}\right)_{E_b} \Delta e_c$$

If both the grid and plate voltages are varied, then the plate-current change is the sum of the two changes indicated above, or

$$\Delta i_b = \left(\frac{\partial i_b}{\partial e_b}\right)_{E_c} \Delta e_b + \left(\frac{\partial i_b}{\partial e_c}\right)_{E_b} \Delta e_c \tag{8-14}$$

As mentioned above, this expression is only approximate. It is, in fact, just the first two terms of the Taylor's series expansion of the function $i_b(e_b, e_c)$. In the general case,

$$\Delta i_b = \left(\frac{\partial i_b}{\partial e_b}\right)_{E_c} \Delta e_b + \left(\frac{\partial i_b}{\partial e_c}\right)_{E_b} \Delta e_c + \frac{1}{2}\left(\frac{\partial^2 i_b}{\partial e_b^2}\right)_{E_c} (\Delta e_b)^2 + \frac{1}{2}\left(\frac{\partial^2 i_b}{\partial e_c^2}\right)_{E_b} (\Delta e_c)^2$$
$$+ \frac{\partial^2 i_b}{\partial e_b \, \partial e_c} \Delta e_b \, \Delta e_c + \cdots \tag{8-15}$$

Consider the third term in this expansion. Since from Eqs. (7-4) the plate resistance is given by $1/r_p = (\partial i_b/\partial e_b)_{E_c}$, this term equals

$$\frac{1}{2}\left[\frac{\partial(1/r_p)}{\partial e_b}\right]_{E_c} (\Delta e_b)^2$$

Similarly, the fourth-, fifth-, and higher-order terms in Eq. (8-15) represent derivatives of r_p and g_m with respect to plate and grid voltages.

The present method of analysis is based on the assumption that the tube parameters are sensibly constant over the operating range Δe_b and Δe_c. Under these conditions a satisfactory representation of the variations in plate current about the quiescent point is given by Eq. (8-14). This expression may be written in the following form, by virtue of Eqs. (7-4):

$$\Delta i_b = \frac{1}{r_p} \Delta e_b + g_m \, \Delta e_c \qquad (8\text{-}16)$$

We shall digress a moment and show that

$$\mu = r_p g_m \qquad (8\text{-}17)$$

It follows from Eq. (8-16) that, if the plate current is constant so that $\Delta i_b = 0$, then

$$0 = \frac{\Delta e_b}{r_p} + g_m \, \Delta e_c$$

or

$$-\frac{\Delta e_b}{\Delta e_c} = g_m r_p$$

But since the plate current has been taken to be constant, then $-\Delta e_b/\Delta e_c$ is by definition [Eq. (7-3)] the amplification factor. Hence, $\mu = g_m r_p$.

Since $g_m = \mu/r_p$, Eq. (8-16) becomes

$$r_p \, \Delta i_b = \Delta e_b + \mu \, \Delta e_c \qquad (8\text{-}18)$$

where, as before, the Δ's denote changes about the quiescent point. Using the notation of Eqs. (8-3), this becomes

$$i_p r_p = e_p + \mu e_g$$

or

$$e_p = -\mu e_g + i_p r_p \qquad (8\text{-}19)$$

This expression shows that the varying voltage e_p with respect to the Q point is made up of two components: One is a generated emf which is μ times as large as the grid-to-cathode voltage variation e_g; the second is a varying voltage across the tube resistor r_p that results from the varying load current i_p through it.

The result of this discussion is the equivalent shown in Fig. 8-2. It is seen from the diagram that the voltage drop e_{pk} from plate to cathode is equal to the voltage drop in the plate resistor less the generator voltage, or

$$e_{pk} = i_p r_p - \mu e_{gk}$$

This is exactly Eq. (8-19), which verifies that Fig. 8-2 is the correct equivalent-circuit representation of the tube.

8-5. Equivalent Current-source Representation of a Triode. Thévenin's equivalent circuit is used if a network is analyzed by the mesh method. However, if a nodal analysis is made, then Norton's equivalent circuit is more useful. Norton's theorem states that *the equivalent circuit between two points in a network consists of the impedance* **Z**, *seen looking back between these two terminals, in parallel with a current generator whose value is the current* **I** *which flows when the terminals are short-circuited.* In other words, *a voltage source* **E** *in series with an impedance* **Z** *is equivalent to a current source* **E**/**Z** *in parallel with an impedance* **Z**. These equivalent circuits are indicated in Fig. 8-11a and b.

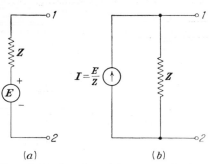

(a)   (b)

Fig. 8-11. As viewed from terminals 1 and 2, the Thévenin's circuit in (a) is equivalent to the Norton's circuit in (b).

An alternative form of Norton's theorem which is evident from Fig. 8-11b is the following: *The voltage between two points in a linear network equals the product of the current* **I** *which flows in a short circuit placed between these terminals by the impedance* **Z** *between these points.* This form is very useful in solving for a nodal voltage in a network, as we shall demonstrate later.

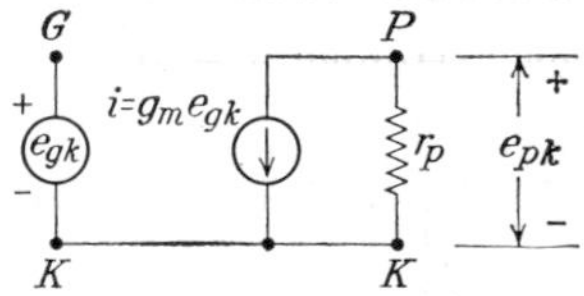

From the voltage-source representation of a triode given in Fig. 8-2b we see that the short-circuit current has a magnitude $\mu e_{gk}/r_p = g_m e_{gk}$, where use is made of Eq. (8-17). The direction of the current is such that it will flow *through an external load* in the direction from cathode to plate. Hence, the current-source equivalent circuit is as indicated in Fig. 8-12.

Fig. 8-12. The current-source equivalent circuit of a triode.

We shall now again solve Example 1 in Sec. 8-3 using the Norton's equivalent representation. For convenience, the circuit of Fig. 8-4 is repeated in Fig. 8-13a. Its current-source equivalent is given in Fig. 8-13b and is the same as that indicated in Fig. 8-12 but with the addition of the load resistor R_L in parallel with r_p. If $R' \equiv r_p R_L/(r_p + R_L) =$ the parallel combination of r_p and R_L, then the output voltage is

$$\mathbf{E}_o = \mathbf{E}_{pk} = -\mathbf{I}R' = -g_m \mathbf{E}_{gk} R'$$

The voltage amplification **A** is

$$\mathbf{A} = \frac{\mathbf{E}_{pk}}{\mathbf{E}_{gk}} = -g_m R' \tag{8-20}$$

which is equivalent to Eq. (8-5) because $\mu = r_p g_m$. The circuit just considered has its cathode common to the input and output circuits and hence is called the *common-cathode* (or *grounded-cathode*) *amplifier*. The important result, that *the voltage gain of a common-cathode amplifier is the product of the transconductance and the total impedance between plate and cathode*, is well worth remembering. If the load $\mathbf{Z}_L$ is reactive, then

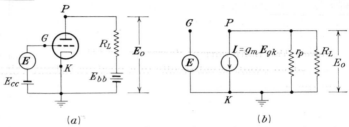

FIG. 8-13. (*a*) The common-cathode amplifier configuration and (*b*) its current-source equivalent circuit.

R' in Eq. (8-20) must be replaced by $\mathbf{Z}'$, where $\mathbf{Z}'$ represents the parallel impedance of r_p and $\mathbf{Z}_L$.

8-6. The Vacuum Triode as a Small-signal Amplifier. The grounded-cathode amplifier is the one most frequently used, but two other configurations, the *grounded-grid* and the *grounded-plate amplifiers*, are possible. We shall now study and compare the characteristics of these three amplifier circuits.

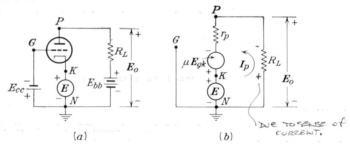

FIG. 8-14. (*a*) The grounded-grid amplifier and (*b*) its equivalent circuit.

The grounded-grid amplifier is shown in Fig. 8-14. As far as a-c voltages are concerned, the grid is at ground potential, which accounts for the name "grounded-grid amplifier." The input signal $\mathbf{E}$ is applied between cathode and ground, and, for the moment, we shall neglect the impedance R_s of the signal source. The output $\mathbf{E}_o$ is taken across the load resistor R_L. Since the grid is common to the input and the output circuits, this configuration is also called the *common-grid amplifier*. The voltage equivalent circuit is given in Fig. 8-14b. We see that

$$\mathbf{I}_p(r_p + R_L) - \mu\mathbf{E}_{gk} + \mathbf{E} = 0 \qquad \mathbf{E}_{gk} = -\mathbf{E} \qquad (8\text{-}21)$$

$$\therefore \quad \underline{I}_p = \frac{-E(\mu+1)}{(r_p + R_L)}$$

and the voltage gain **A** is given by

DUE TO SENSE of I_P

$$\mathbf{A} \equiv \frac{\mathbf{E}_o}{\mathbf{E}} = \frac{-\mathbf{I}_p R_L}{\mathbf{E}} = \frac{+(\mu + 1) R_L}{R_L + r_p} \qquad (8\text{-}22)$$

The magnitude of the amplification is almost the same (since $\mu \gg 1$) as that obtained from the grounded-cathode amplifier [Eq. (8-5)] but the output is now in phase with the input. This result could have been anticipated from an inspection of Fig. 8-14a. As the input voltage is made more positive, the grid voltage decreases with respect to the cathode. Hence, the plate current decreases, and the plate voltage rises. Therefore, a positive input signal results in a positive output voltage, as indicated by the + sign of Eq. (8-22).

AS INDICATED BY POSITIVE VALUE OF A

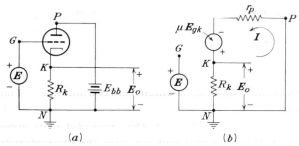

FIG. 8-15. (a) The grounded-plate (cathode-follower) amplifier and (b) its equivalent circuit.

SEE CLASS NOTES 12-13-60

The source impedance R_s has been neglected in the above discussion. If this impedance is taken into account, we find that

$$\mathbf{A} = \frac{\mathbf{E}_o}{\mathbf{E}} = \frac{+(\mu + 1) R_L}{R_L + r_p + (\mu + 1) R_s} \qquad (8\text{-}23)$$

Hence, the voltage gain is greatly reduced unless R_s is kept small compared with $(R_L + r_p)/(\mu + 1)$, which usually is of the order of 1,000 ohms or less. The physical reason for this loss of amplification, called *degeneration*, is that the plate current passes through the source impedance. With the grounded-cathode amplifier the source impedance adds no degeneration because it is in series with the grid which (ideally) draws no current. The grounded-grid circuit is employed only in special applications. For example, it finds use as a tuned voltage amplifier at ultrahigh frequencies[1] because the grounded grid acts as a grounded electrostatic shield which prevents coupling between input and output circuits.

The grounded-plate amplifier is indicated in Fig. 8-15a. The signal **E** is applied between grid and ground, and the output voltage $\mathbf{E}_o$ is taken across a resistor R_k between cathode and ground. As far as a-c voltages are concerned, the plate is at ground potential, which accounts for the name "grounded-plate amplifier." This important circuit is more popularly known as the *cathode follower* for reasons which will appear presently. The vacuum tube has been replaced by its equivalent circuit in Fig. 8-15b. The current $\mathbf{I}$ must satisfy Kirchhoff's voltage equation

$$\mathbf{I}(r_p + R_k) - \mu\mathbf{E}_{gk} = 0$$

The voltage drop from G to K is *not* the input voltage but now equals

$$\mathbf{E}_{gk} = \mathbf{E} - \mathbf{I}R_k$$

Eliminating $\mathbf{E}_{gk}$ and solving for $\mathbf{E}_o = \mathbf{I}R_k$, we have for the amplification

$$\mathbf{A} = \frac{\mathbf{E}_o}{\mathbf{E}} = \frac{+\mu R_k}{(\mu + 1)R_k + r_p} \tag{8-24}$$

If $(\mu + 1)R_k \gg r_p$, then the gain is $\mu/(\mu + 1)$, or approximately unity if $\mu \gg 1$. A gain of 0.95 or larger is not difficult to achieve. The

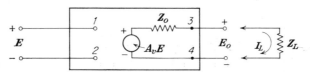

FIG. 8-16. The Thévenin equivalent circuit of an amplifier.

polarity of the output signal, the voltage at the cathode, is the same as the input signal, the voltage at the grid. The cathode voltage therefore *follows* the grid voltage very closely, and this feature accounts for the name *cathode follower* given to the circuit.

The Thévenin equivalent of any amplifier circuit is indicated in Fig. 8-16. The input terminals are marked 1 and 2, and the input voltage is $\mathbf{E}$. The output terminals are marked 3 and 4. The external load is marked $\mathbf{Z}_L$ and the output impedance is $\mathbf{Z}_o$. Since the open-circuit voltage is the amplifier voltage gain $\mathbf{A}_v$ times the externally applied voltage, the Thévenin's generator is $\mathbf{A}_v\mathbf{E}$, as indicated. Note that $\mathbf{A}_v$ is the unloaded voltage gain, *i.e.*, the gain with no external load placed across the amplifier and hence zero load current, $\mathbf{I}_L = 0$. The loaded gain (the amplification with the load $\mathbf{Z}_L$ in place) is called $\mathbf{A}$. We have already made use of this notation in Eqs. (8-5), (8-20), (8-22), etc. Capital letters are used for phasor (sinor) quantities. If instantaneous rather than phasor voltages are under consideration, then lower-case letters should be used for current and voltage and an impedance $\mathbf{Z}_o$ should be replaced by a resistance R_o.

The output voltage is given by

$$\mathbf{E}_o = \mathbf{A}_v\mathbf{E} - \mathbf{I}_L\mathbf{Z}_o \tag{8-25}$$

This equation may be used to define $\mathbf{A}_v$ and $\mathbf{Z}_o$ for a particular circuit. For example, if we find that the output voltage of an amplifier varies linearly with load current, as indicated in Eq. (8-25), then the factor multiplying the applied voltage $\mathbf{E}$ is the unloaded gain $\mathbf{A}_v$, and the factor multiplying the load current $\mathbf{I}_L$ is the output impedance $\mathbf{Z}_o$, *provided that these factors $\mathbf{A}_v$ and $\mathbf{Z}_o$ are independent of the load $\mathbf{Z}_L$.*

An alternative expression for the output voltage, obtained from inspection of Fig. 8-16, is

$$\mathbf{E}_o = \mathbf{A}_v \mathbf{E}\, \frac{\mathbf{Z}_L}{\mathbf{Z}_L + \mathbf{Z}_o} \qquad (8\text{-}26)$$

This equation may also be used to define $\mathbf{A}_v$ and $\mathbf{Z}_o$. We note that the output voltage is given by the product of three factors, one of which is the externally applied voltage $\mathbf{E}$ and another is of the form of the load impedance divided by the sum of the load impedance and some other

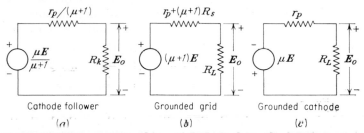

FIG. 8-17. The Thévenin equivalent circuits of the three basic amplifier configurations.

impedance $\mathbf{Z}_o$. This $\mathbf{Z}_o$ is interpreted as the output impedance, and the third factor as the unloaded gain $\mathbf{A}_v$, *provided that these factors $\mathbf{A}_v$ and $\mathbf{Z}_o$ are independent of the load $\mathbf{Z}_L$.* For example, from Eq. (8-24) we find for the output voltage of the cathode follower

$$\mathbf{E}_o = \frac{\mu \mathbf{E}}{\mu + 1} \frac{R_k}{R_k + r_p/(\mu + 1)} \qquad (8\text{-}27)$$

This expression has been put into the form of Eq. (8-26) provided that R_k is considered as an external load. Hence, *for the cathode follower*

$$\mathbf{A}_v = \frac{\mu}{\mu + 1} \qquad \mathbf{Z}_o = \frac{r_p}{\mu + 1} \qquad (8\text{-}28)$$

Equation (8-23) is already the form of Eq. (8-26) and hence, if R_L is considered as an external load, we conclude that *for a grounded-grid amplifier*

$$\mathbf{A}_v = \mu + 1 \qquad \mathbf{Z}_o = r_p + (\mu + 1)R_s \qquad (8\text{-}29)$$

Similarly, from Eq. (8-5), we find that for a *grounded-cathode amplifier*

$$\mathbf{A}_v = -\mu \qquad \mathbf{Z}_o = r_p \qquad (8\text{-}30)$$

These results are indicated in the equivalent circuits of Fig. 8-17. We note that the output impedance of the cathode follower is much smaller than the plate resistance. For example, if $\mu \gg 1$, then

$$Z_o = \frac{r_p}{\mu + 1} \cong \frac{r_p}{\mu} = \frac{1}{g_m}$$

For a g_m of 2 millimhos the output impedance is only 500 ohms, and for a higher value of transconductance Z_o is even less. On the other hand, since the input signal is applied to the grid, the input impedance (for negative grid voltages where the grid current is negligible) is very high (ideally infinite). A cathode follower is usually employed when a high input impedance and a low output impedance are desired. Many more of the characteristics and applications of the cathode follower are given in Sec. 8-10 and in Chap. 17.

The output impedance of the grounded-grid amplifier will be much higher than the plate resistance if the source has appreciable resistance R_s or if an additional resistance is intentionally added in series with the cathode. On the other hand, we have already mentioned that the input impedance is quite low (Prob. 8-23). Hence, a grounded-grid amplifier may be employed when a low input impedance and a high output impedance are desired. Such applications are infrequent.

The grounded-cathode amplifier has a high input impedance, an output impedance equal to the plate resistance, and a voltage gain which may approach the μ of the tube (although an amplification of the order of $\mu/2$ is more common). This circuit is employed more often than the other two configurations. Cascaded common-cathode amplifiers are discussed in Chap. 15.

8-7. Measurement of Triode Coefficients.[2] The values of μ, r_p, and g_m illustrated in Fig. 7-8 may be determined graphically from the static characteristic curves given in Figs. 7-6a, 7-6b, and 7-7 by drawing tangents to these curves and determining the slopes at the points in question. The accuracy with which these determinations may be made is generally low, and it is usually more desirable to measure these quantities dynamically by means of suitable a-c bridge networks.

The amplification factor μ is readily determined by means of the circuit shown in Fig. 8-18a. The equivalent circuit of this network is given in Fig. 8-18b. The operations involved in balancing this bridge consist simply in varying R_1 and R_2 until no a-c signal from the oscillator is heard in the earphones. This requires, of course, that the current I_1 be zero. When this condition is satisfied, $\mu = R_2/R_1$. This equation can be proved as follows:

By applying Kirchhoff's law to the plate circuit and remembering that I_1 must be zero under the conditions of balance,

$$+\mu E_{gk} - I R_2 = 0$$

From Fig. 8-18b we see that $\mathbf{E}_{gk} = \mathbf{I}R_1$.   Hence,

$$\mu\mathbf{E}_{gk} = \mathbf{I}R_2 = \mu\mathbf{I}R_1$$

from which it follows that

$$\mu = \frac{R_2}{R_1} \qquad\qquad (8\text{-}31)$$

This extremely convenient method may be used for measuring the amplification factor for any desired value of d-c plate current I_b in the tube simply by adjusting the grid bias E_{cc}.   The telephone is preferably

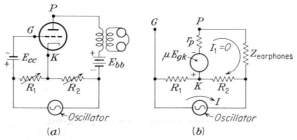

FIG. 8-18. The Miller bridge circuit for determining the amplification factor of a triode under operating conditions.   (a) Actual circuit and (b) equivalent circuit.

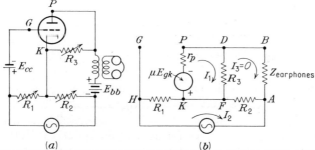

FIG. 8-19. The Miller bridge circuit for determining the transconductance of a triode under operating conditions.   (a) Actual circuit and (b) equivalent circuit.

connected to the secondary of a small transformer so that the direct current does not pass through the telephone and thereby polarize it.

In order to measure the transconductance g_m, the foregoing circuit is modified slightly.   This modification consists in inserting the resistor R_3 between the cathode and the plate.   The schematic and equivalent circuits of this modified network are shown in Fig. 8-19.   To make this measurement, the resistances are varied until no sound is heard in the telephone.   The current in mesh 3 is zero, since this is the current in the telephone at balance.   Kirchhoff's law is applied to mesh 1.   The sum of the voltage drops is

$$(R_3 + r_p)\mathbf{I}_1 + \mu\mathbf{E}_{gk} = 0$$

The voltage drop from grid to cathode is

$$\mathbf{E}_{gk} = \mathbf{I}_2 R_1$$

Then,

$$\mathbf{I}_1(R_3 + r_p) = -\mu \mathbf{E}_{gk} = -\mu \mathbf{I}_2 R_1 \tag{8-32}$$

Kirchhoff's law applied to mesh 3 yields

$$-\mathbf{I}_2 R_2 - \mathbf{I}_1 R_3 = 0$$

or

$$\mathbf{I}_1 R_3 = -\mathbf{I}_2 R_2 \tag{8-33}$$

The ratio of Eq. (8-32) to Eq. (8-33) is

$$\frac{R_3 + r_p}{R_3} = \mu \frac{R_1}{R_2}$$

from which

$$r_p = R_3 \left(\mu \frac{R_1}{R_2} - 1 \right) \tag{8-34}$$

If μ is first measured, this circuit permits r_p to be calculated. However, the value of r_p is then dependent upon the measurement of μ.

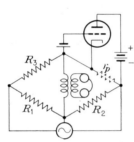

Hence this bridge network is used, not to measure r_p, but to measure g_m instead. The transconductance is calculated by choosing R_1 much greater than R_2, so that $\mu R_1/R_2 \gg 1$. Then, approximately, from Eq. (8-34)

$$r_p = \mu \frac{R_3 R_1}{R_2}$$

or

$$g_m = \frac{\mu}{r_p} = \frac{R_2}{R_3 R_1} \tag{8-35}$$

FIG. 8-20. A Wheatstone bridge arrangement for determining the plate resistance of a triode under operating conditions.

A transformer should be used with the telephone receiver, as in the measurement of μ.

The plate resistance r_p of the tube can be directly measured by incorporating the plate circuit of the tube as the fourth arm of a Wheatstone bridge, as shown in Fig. 8-20. When the bridge is balanced,

$$r_p = \frac{R_2 R_3}{R_1} \tag{8-36}$$

In order to obtain perfect balance in the bridge circuits of Figs. 8-20, 8-19, and 8-18, it is sometimes necessary to provide means for balancing the capacitive effects of the tube. Basically, however, the circuits are those given above.

8-8. Interelectrode Capacitances in a Triode. We assumed in the foregoing discussions that with a negative bias the input current was negligible and that changes in the plate circuit were not reflected into the grid circuit. These assumptions are not strictly true, as will now be shown.

The grid, plate, and cathode elements are conductors separated by a dielectric (a vacuum), and hence, by elementary electrostatics, there exist capacitances between pairs of electrodes. Clearly, the input current in a grounded-cathode amplifier cannot be zero because the source must supply current to the grid-cathode capacitance and to the grid-plate capacitance. Furthermore, the input and output circuits are no longer isolated, but there is coupling between them through the grid-plate capacitance. Although these capacitances are small, usually less than 10 $\mu\mu$f, yet at the upper audio frequencies and above they produce appreciable loading of the input source and they also cause output-to-input feedback. They must therefore be taken into account.

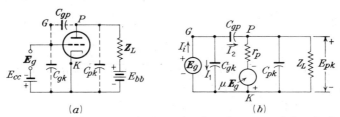

(a)   (b)

FIG. 8-21. The schematic and equivalent circuits of a grounded-cathode amplifier taking into account the interelectrode capacitances.

A more complete circuit and its equivalent circuit, which includes the interelectrode capacitances, are given in Fig. 8-21. In this circuit, C_{gp} represents the capacitance between the grid and the plate; C_{gk} is the capacitance between the grid and the cathode; and C_{pk} is the capacitance between the plate and the cathode. The inclusion of these tube capacitances [shown dashed in the schematic diagram and shown explicitly in the equivalent amplifier circuit of (b)] yields results that are more precise than those resulting from the analysis of the simple circuit of Fig. 8-4. It will be noted that the same procedure outlined in Sec. 8-3 has been followed in order to obtain the equivalent circuit of the amplifier. It is evident that $E_{gk} = E_g$, and so μE_g has been written for the emf of the Thévenin's generator in the equivalent circuit (b).

The output voltage between terminals P and K is easily found with the aid of the theorem of Sec. 8-5, viz., $E_{pk} = IZ$, where I is the short-circuit current and Z is the impedance seen between the terminals. To find Z, the generators E_g and μE_g in Fig. 8-21b are (imagined) short-circuited, and we note that Z is the parallel combination of the impedances corresponding to Z_L, C_{pk}, r_p, and C_{gp}. Hence,

$$Y \equiv \frac{1}{Z} = Y_L + Y_{pk} + Y_p + Y_{gp} \tag{8-37}$$

where $\mathbf{Y}_L = 1/\mathbf{Z}_L$ is the admittance corresponding to $\mathbf{Z}_L$

$\mathbf{Y}_{pk} = j\omega C_{pk}$ is the admittance corresponding to C_{pk}

$\mathbf{Y}_p = 1/r_p$ is the admittance corresponding to r_p

$\mathbf{Y}_{gp} = j\omega C_{gp}$ is the admittance corresponding to C_{gp}

The current in the direction from P to K in a zero-resistance wire connecting the output terminals is $-\mu\mathbf{E}_g/r_p = -g_m\mathbf{E}_g$ due to the generator $\mu\mathbf{E}_g$ and is $\mathbf{E}_g\mathbf{Y}_{gp}$ due to the signal $\mathbf{E}_g$. Hence the total short-circuit current is

$$I = -g_m\mathbf{E}_g + \mathbf{E}_g\mathbf{Y}_{gp} \tag{8-38}$$

The amplification $\mathbf{A}$ with the load $\mathbf{Z}_L$ in place is given by

$$\mathbf{A} = \frac{\mathbf{E}_{pk}}{\mathbf{E}_g} = \frac{I\mathbf{Z}}{\mathbf{E}_g} = \frac{I}{\mathbf{E}_g\mathbf{Y}}$$

or, from Eqs. (8-37) and (8-38),

$$\mathbf{A} = \frac{-g_m + \mathbf{Y}_{gp}}{\mathbf{Y}_L + \mathbf{Y}_{pk} + \mathbf{Y}_p + \mathbf{Y}_{gp}} \tag{8-39}$$

It is interesting to see that Eq. (8-39) reduces to the expression already developed for the case where the interelectrode capacitances are neglected. Under these conditions, $\mathbf{Y}_{pk} = \mathbf{Y}_{gp} = 0$, and Eq. (8-39) reduces to

$$\mathbf{A} = \frac{-g_m}{\mathbf{Y}_p + \mathbf{Y}_L} = \frac{-g_m}{1/r_p + 1/\mathbf{Z}_L} = -\mu\frac{1}{1 + r_p/\mathbf{Z}_L} \tag{8-40}$$

This is a generalization of Eq. (8-5), which is valid for the case where the load is $\mathbf{Z}_L$. Of course, if $\mathbf{Z}_L = R_L$, this reduces to Eq. (8-5).

It is a simple matter to show that the error made in the calculation of the gain is very small when the interelectrode capacitances are neglected for frequencies covering the entire audio-frequency range. These interelectrode capacitances are seldom as large as 15 $\mu\mu$f, which corresponds to an admittance of only about 2 micromhos at 20,000 cps. Since the transconductance g_m of a triode is generally several millimhos, $\mathbf{Y}_{gp}$ may be neglected in comparison with g_m. Furthermore, if $\mathbf{Y}_p$ is greater than 20 micromhos ($r_p < 50$ kilohms), the terms $\mathbf{Y}_{gp} + \mathbf{Y}_{pk}$ may be neglected in comparison with $\mathbf{Y}_p + \mathbf{Y}_L$. Under these conditions the gain is that given by the simple expression (8-40).

Since the interelectrode capacitances have a relatively minor effect on the audio gain of an amplifier, why is it important to make note of them? The answer is to be found in the input impedance of the tube (the loading of the tube on the input circuit) and in the feedback between output and input circuits. Also, if the amplifier is to be used beyond the audio range, say as a video (television or radar) amplifier, then the capacitances may seriously affect the gain and the exact expression, Eq. (8-39), must be used. These effects will be examined.

[handwritten margin note: GROUND TO CATHODE AMPLIFIER. ∴ EQUATIONS BELOW ARE FOR THAT TYPE OF AMPLIFIER. ONLY!]

8-9. Input Admittance of a Triode. An inspection of Fig. 8-21 reveals that the grid circuit is no longer isolated from the plate circuit. The input signal must supply a current I_i. In order to calculate this current, it is observed from the diagram that

$$I_1 = E_g Y_{gk}$$

and

$$I_2 = E_{gp} Y_{gp} = (E_g + E_{kp}) Y_{gp}$$

Since $E_{kp} = -E_{pk} = -AE_g$, then the total input current is

$$I_i = I_1 + I_2 = [Y_{gk} + (1 - A)Y_{gp}]E_g \qquad (8\text{-}41)$$

By definition, the admittance of any circuit element is the ratio of the current through the element to the voltage drop across it in the direction of the current. Consequently, the input admittance is given by

$$Y_i = \frac{I_i}{E_g} = Y_{gk} + (1 - A)Y_{gp} \qquad (8\text{-}42)$$

This explicit expression for the input admittance of the triode clearly indicates that, for the system to possess a negligible input admittance over a wide range of frequencies, the grid-cathode and the grid-plate capacitances must be negligible.

Consider a triode with a pure resistance load. Within the audio-frequency range, the gain is given by the simple expression

$$A = -\frac{\mu R_L}{r_p + R_L}$$

for the reasons outlined. In this case Eq. (8-42) becomes

$$Y_i = j\omega \left[C_{gk} + \left(1 + \frac{\mu R_L}{r_p + R_L} \right) C_{gp} \right] \qquad (8\text{-}43)$$

Thus the input admittance is that arising from the presence of a capacitance from the grid to the cathode of magnitude C_i, where

$$C_i = C_{gk} + \left(1 + \frac{\mu R_L}{r_p + R_L} \right) C_{gp} \qquad (8\text{-}44)$$

This increase in input capacitance C_i over the capacitance from grid to cathode C_{gk} is known as the *Miller effect*. The maximum possible value of this expression is $C_{gk} + (1 + \mu)C_{gp}$, which, for large values of μ, may be considerably larger than any of the interelectrode capacitances. The presence of this input capacitance may prove detrimental in certain circuits.

This input capacitance is important in the operation of cascaded amplifiers. In such a system the output from one tube is used as the input to a second tube. Hence, the input impedance of the second stage acts as a shunt across the load of the first stage. In those cases for which the foregoing is valid, the load is being shunted by the capacitance C_i. Since the reactance of a capacitor decreases with increasing frequencies, the resultant output impedance of the first stage will be correspondingly low for the high frequencies. This will result in a decreasing gain at the higher frequencies.

Example. A 6SL7 has a load resistance of 100,000 ohms and operates at 20,000 cps at the quiescent point recommended by the manufacturers. Calculate the gain of this tube as a single stage and then as the first tube in a cascaded amplifier consisting of two identical stages.

Solution. The pertinent information for the 6SL7 is obtained from a tube data book.

$$g_m = 1.6 \text{ millimhos} \qquad r_p = 44 \text{ kilohms} \qquad \mu = 70$$
$$C_{gk} = 3.0 \qquad C_{pk} = 3.8 \qquad C_{gp} = 2.8 \ \mu\mu\text{f}$$

Then, at 20,000 cps,

$$\mathbf{Y}_{gk} = j\omega C_{gk} = j2\pi \times 2 \times 10^4 \times 3.0 \times 10^{-12} = j3.76 \times 10^{-7} \text{ mho}$$
$$\mathbf{Y}_{pk} = j\omega C_{pk} = j4.77 \times 10^{-7} \text{ mho}$$
$$\mathbf{Y}_{gp} = j\omega C_{gp} = j3.52 \times 10^{-7} \text{ mho}$$
$$\mathbf{Y}_p = \frac{1}{r_p} = 2.27 \times 10^{-5} \text{ mho}$$
$$\mathbf{Y}_L = \frac{1}{\mathbf{R}_L} = 10^{-5} \text{ mho}$$
$$g_m = 1.60 \times 10^{-3} \text{ mho}$$

The gain of a one-stage amplifier is given by Eq. (8-39):

$$\mathbf{A} = \frac{-g_m + \mathbf{Y}_{gp}}{\mathbf{Y}_p + \mathbf{Y}_L + \mathbf{Y}_{pk} + \mathbf{Y}_{gp}} = \frac{-1.60 \times 10^{-3} + j3.52 \times 10^{-7}}{3.27 \times 10^{-5} + j8.29 \times 10^{-7}}$$

It is seen that the j terms (arising from the interelectrode capacitances) are negligible in comparison with the real terms. If these are neglected, then $\mathbf{A} = -49.0$. This value can be checked by using Eq. (8-40), which neglects interelectrode capacities. Thus

$$\mathbf{A} = \frac{-\mu}{1 + r_p/R_L} = \frac{-70}{1 + 0.44} = -48.7$$

Since the gain is a real number, then the input impedance consists of a capacitor whose value is given by Eq. (8-44),

$$C_i = C_{gk} + \left(1 + \frac{\mu R_L}{r_p + R_L}\right) C_{gp} = 3.0 + (1 + 49)(2.8) = 143 \ \mu\mu\text{f}$$

Consider now a two-stage amplifier, each stage consisting of a 6SL7 operating as above. The gain of the second stage is that just calculated. However, in calculating the gain of the first stage it must be remembered that *the input impedance of the second stage acts as a shunt on the load resistance of the first stage.* Thus the plate load now consists of 100,000 ohms resistance in parallel with 143 $\mu\mu$f. To this must be added the capacitance from plate to cathode of the first stage since this is also in shunt with the plate load. Furthermore, any stray capacitances due to wiring should be taken into account. For example, for every 1 $\mu\mu f$ capacitance between the leads going to the plate and grid of the second stage there is 50 $\mu\mu f$ effectively added across the load resistor of the first tube! This clearly indicates the importance of making connections with very short direct leads in high-frequency amplifiers. Let it be assumed that the input capacitance taking into account the various factors just discussed is 200 $\mu\mu f$ (probably a conservative figure). Then the load admittance is

$$\mathbf{Y}_L = \frac{1}{R_L} + j\omega C_i = 10^{-5} + j2\pi \times 2 \times 10^4 \times 200 \times 10^{-12}$$
$$= 10^{-5} + j2.52 \times 10^{-5} \text{ mho}$$

The gain is given by Eq. (8-40):

$$\mathbf{A} = \frac{-g_m}{\mathbf{Y}_p + \mathbf{Y}_L} = \frac{-1.6 \times 10^{-3}}{2.27 \times 10^{-5} + 10^{-5} + j2.52 \times 10^{-5}}$$
$$= -30.7 + j23.7 = 38.8\underline{/143.3^\circ}$$

Thus, the effect of the capacitances has been to reduce the magnitude of the amplification from 49.0 to 38.8 and to change the phase angle between the output and input from 180 to 143.3 deg.

If the frequency were higher, the gain would be reduced still further. For example, this circuit would be useless as a video amplifier, say to a few megacycles per second, since the gain would then be less than unity. This variation of gain with frequency is called *frequency distortion.* Cascaded amplifiers and frequency distortion are discussed in detail in Chap. 15.

If the load circuit of the amplifier is an impedance instead of a pure resistance, then **A** is a complex number in general and the input admittance will consist of two terms, a resistive and a reactive term. Let **A** be written in the general form

$$\mathbf{A} = A_1 + jA_2 \qquad (8\text{-}45)$$

Then Eq. (8-42) becomes

$$\mathbf{Y}_i = \omega C_{gp} A_2 + j\omega[C_{gk} + (1 - A_1)C_{gp}] \qquad (8\text{-}46)$$

The expression indicates that the equivalent grid input circuit comprises a resistance R_i in parallel with a capacitance C_i as shown in Fig. 8-22.

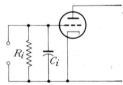

Fig. 8-22. The equivalent grid input circuit may be represented as a resistance R_i in parallel with a capacitance C_i.

$$\mathbf{Y}_i = \frac{1}{R_i} + j\omega C_i \qquad (8\text{-}47)$$

It follows from this that the input admittance consists of a resistance

$$R_i = \frac{1}{\omega C_{gp} A_2}$$

in parallel with a capacitance

$$C_i = C_{gk} + (1 - A_1)C_{gp}$$

$$(8\text{-}48)$$

Since no restrictions have been placed on the system, it is possible for the term A_2 to be negative and the effective input resistance to be negative. It is interesting to note that an effective negative input resistance is possible only when the load is inductive, with the inductance in a definite range.[3]

The presence of a negative resistance in a circuit can mean only that some power is being generated, rather than being absorbed. Physically, this means that power is being fed back from the output circuit into the grid circuit through the coupling provided by the grid-plate capacitance. If this feedback feature reaches an extreme stage, the system will lose its entire utility as an amplifier, becoming in fact a self-excited amplifier, or oscillator.

Example. Calculate the input admittance of a 6J5 triode working into a load consisting of a 25-millihenry coil whose resistance is 2,000 ohms. Assume that the tube is operated under recommended conditions and at a frequency of 10,000 cps.

Solution. The pertinent information for the 6J5 triode is obtained from a tube data book.

$$g_m = 2.6 \text{ millimhos} \qquad r_p = 7.7 \text{ kilohms} \qquad \mu = 20$$
$$C_{gk} = 3.4 \qquad C_{pk} = 3.6 \qquad C_{gp} = 3.4 \ \mu\mu\text{f}$$

At 10,000 cps,

$$\mathbf{Y}_{gk} = \mathbf{Y}_{gp} = j\omega C_{gk} = j2.13 \times 10^{-7} \text{ mho}$$
$$\mathbf{Y}_{pk} = j\omega C_{pk} = j2.26 \times 10^{-7} \text{ mho}$$
$$\mathbf{Y}_p = \frac{1}{r_p} = 1.3 \times 10^{-4} \text{ mho}$$
$$\mathbf{Z}_L = 2,000 + j1,570 \text{ ohms}$$
$$\mathbf{Y}_L = \frac{1}{\mathbf{Z}_L} = (3.08 - j2.42) \times 10^{-4} \text{ mho}$$

All wiring capacitances are neglected in this example. The gain of the amplifier is

$$\mathbf{A} = -\frac{g_m}{\mathbf{Y}_p + \mathbf{Y}_L} = \frac{-26 \times 10^{-4}}{1.3 \times 10^{-4} + (3.08 - j2.42)10^{-4}} = -4.55 - j2.51$$

whence the input admittance becomes

$$\mathbf{Y}_i = \mathbf{Y}_{gk} + (1 - \mathbf{A})\mathbf{Y}_{gp} = (-5.35 + j13.9) \times 10^{-7}$$

If the input circuit is supposed to consist of a resistance and capacitance in parallel, the constants are, according to Eq. (8-48),

$$R_i = \frac{1}{-5.35 \times 10^{-7}} \text{ ohms} = -1.87 \text{ megohms}$$
$$C_i = \frac{13.9 \times 10^{-7}}{2\pi \times 10^4} \text{ farads} = 22.2 \ \mu\mu\text{f}$$

8-10. The Cathode Follower at High Frequencies.

Our previous discussion of cathode followers (Sec. 8-6) neglected the influence of the tube capacitances. These capacitances will now be taken into account. The grounded-plate configuration including all capacitances is given in Fig.

8-23a, and its linear equivalent circuit in Fig. 8-23b. The capacitance from cathode to ground is C_{kn} and includes the capacitance from cathode to heater if, as usual, the heater is grounded. The output voltage $\mathbf{E}_o$ can be found as in Sec. 8-8 from the product of the short-circuit current and the impedance between terminals K and N. We now find for the voltage gain $\mathbf{A} \equiv \mathbf{E}_o/\mathbf{E}_i$

$$\mathbf{A} = \frac{g_m + \mathbf{Y}_{gk}}{\mathbf{Y}_k + \mathbf{Y}_p + g_m + \mathbf{Y}_T} \tag{8-49}$$

where $\mathbf{Y}_k \equiv 1/R_k$
$\mathbf{Y}_T \equiv j\omega C_T$
$C_T \equiv C_{gk} + C_{pk} + C_{kn}$

Equation (8-49) may be written in the form

$$\mathbf{A} = \frac{(g_m + j\omega C_{gk})R_k}{1 + [(\mu + 1)/r_p + j\omega C_T]R_k} \tag{8-50}$$

Assuming $\mu + 1 \cong \mu$ and $g_m R_k \gg 1$,

$$\mathbf{A} \cong \frac{g_m + j\omega C_{gk}}{g_m + j\omega C_T} \tag{8-51}$$

The term $j\omega C_{gk}$ in the numerator represents the effect of the coupling from input to output through C_{gk}. If the cathode follower is driving a capacitive load C_L, the expression for $\mathbf{A}$ need but be modified by adding C_L to C_T.

Usually C_T is much larger than C_{gk} and hence the decrease in gain with frequency is due principally to $C_T + C_L$. The frequency f_2 at which the magnitude of the amplification has dropped to 0.707 of its low-frequency value is, under these circumstances, given by the condition $\omega(C_T + C_L) = y_m$. Typically, if the total capacitance is, say, 50 $\mu\mu$f and $g_m = 3$ millimhos, as for a half section of a 12AU7, then $f_2 \cong 9.5$ megacycles. This calculation shows that a cathode follower may be useful well into the video range.

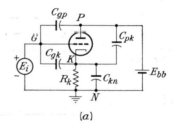

(a)

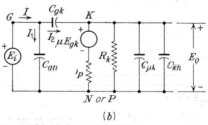

(b)

FIG. 8-23. (a) The cathode follower, with interelectrode capacitances taken into account, and (b) its equivalent circuit.

An important advantage of the cathode follower over a conventional triode amplifier is that the capacitive impedance seen looking into the grid of the cathode follower is appreciably larger than the capacitive impedance looking into the amplifier. We shall now calculate the input admittance from Fig. 8-23b. The current $I_1 = E_i(j\omega C_{gp})$ and $I_2 = (E_i - E_o)j\omega C_{gk} = E_i(1 - A)(j\omega C_{gk})$, where A is the amplifier gain. Hence, the input admittance

$$Y_i \equiv \frac{I}{E_i} = \frac{I_1 + I_2}{E_i}$$

is given by

$$Y_i = j\omega C_{gp} + j\omega C_{gk}(1 - A) \tag{8-52}$$

In general, Y_i contains a resistive as well as a capacitive component. If the frequency is low enough so that A may be considered a real number, then the input impedance consists of a capacitance C_i, and hence $Y_i = j\omega C_i$. From Eq. (8-52) the input capacitance is given by

$$C_i(\text{cathode follower}) = C_{gp} + C_{gk}(1 - A) \tag{8-53}$$

On the other hand, for a grounded-cathode amplifier we have, from Eq. (8-44),

$$C_i(\text{amplifier}) = C_{gk} + C_{gp}(1 + A) \tag{8-54}$$

where A is the magnitude of the gain.

A numerical comparison is interesting. Consider a half section of a 12AU7, first as a cathode follower of nominal gain, say equal to 0.8, and then as an amplifier of nominal gain, say $A = 10$. The capacitances are $C_{gp} = 1.5$ $\mu\mu$f, $C_{gk} = 1.6$ $\mu\mu$f. At a frequency at which the capacitances do not yet have a marked effect on the gain, we have

$$C_i(\text{cathode follower}) = 1.5 + 0.2 \times 1.6 = 1.8 \ \mu\mu\text{f}$$

and

$$C_i(\text{amplifier}) = 1.6 + 11 \times 1.5 = 18 \ \mu\mu\text{f}$$

The input capacitance of the amplifier is ten times that of the cathode follower.

A fairer comparison may be made by comparing the cathode follower with a conventional amplifier of equivalent gain. In this case

$$C_i(\text{amplifier}) = 1.6 + 1.8 \times 1.5 = 4.3 \ \mu\mu\text{f}$$

which is still more than twice that for the cathode follower.

The output impedance or, more conveniently, the output admittance Y_o of a cathode follower, taking interelectrode capacitances into account, is obtained by adding to the low-frequency admittance $g_m + Y_p$ [Eq. (8-28)] the admittance of the total shunting capacitance C_T. Thus

$$Y_o = g_m + Y_p + Y_T \tag{8-55}$$

This result may be justified directly by applying a signal E_a to the output terminals and computing the current which flows through E_a with the grid grounded (and R_k considered as an external load). Since $g_m = \mu Y_p$ and assuming $\mu \gg 1$, we may neglect Y_p compared with g_m and consider that the output admittance is unaffected by the capacitance until Y_T becomes large enough to be comparable to g_m. The calculation made above in connection with the frequency response of the cathode follower indicates that the output impedance does not acquire an appreciable reactive component until the frequency exceeds several megacycles.

The high input impedance of a cathode follower makes it ideal for applications where the loading on a signal source must be kept at a minimum. The low output impedance permits it to support a heavy capacitive load. These features, together with its stability and linearity, account for the many applications which are found for cathode followers. For example, the cathode follower is almost universally used as the input tube in oscilloscope amplifiers. It is also used where a signal must be transmitted through a short section of coaxial cable or shielded wire with its attendant high shunt capacitance.

If the output from one circuit acts as the input to another circuit and the second circuit reacts back onto the first, a cathode follower may be used as a buffer stage to eliminate this reaction.

Because the cathode follower is a feedback amplifier (Sec. 17-5) it possesses great stability and linearity. The characteristics and applications of this circuit are summarized in Sec. 17-6.

REFERENCES

1. TERMAN, F. E., "Electronic and Radio Engineering," 4th ed., pp. 430–432, McGraw-Hill Book Company, Inc., New York, 1955.
2. "Standards Report on Electronics," Institute of Radio Engineers, New York, 1938.
3. MILLMAN, J., and S. SEELY, "Electronics," 1st ed., p. 536, McGraw-Hill Book Company, Inc., New York, 1941.

CHAPTER 9

TRANSISTOR CHARACTERISTICS

THE volt-ampere characteristics of a semiconductor triode, called a _transistor,_ are first described qualitatively and, later in the chapter, are derived theoretically. Simple circuits are studied, and it is demonstrated that the transistor is capable of giving amplification. A quantitative study of the transistor as an amplifier is left for the next chapter.

9-1. The Junction Transistor.[1] A _junction transistor_ consists of a germanium (or silicon) crystal in which a layer of n-type germanium is sandwiched between two layers of p-type germanium. Alternatively, a

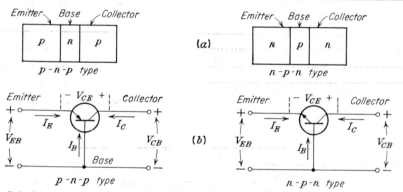

FIG. 9-1. (a) A p-n-p and an n-p-n transistor. (b) Circuit representation of the two transistor types.

transistor may consist of a layer of p-type between two layers of n-type material. In the former case the transistor is referred to as a p-n-p transistor and in the latter case as an n-p-n transistor. The semiconductor sandwich (about 1 by 1 mm in cross section and 3 mm long) is hermetically sealed against moisture inside a metal or plastic case. The entire unit is extremely small, typical dimensions being 0.5 by 0.4 by 0.2 in.

The transistor can perform many of the functions of a vacuum tube, as we shall presently demonstrate. The transistor has the following advantages over the tube: The former requires no vacuum; it has no filament and hence uses no standby power; it is smaller, lighter, and mechanically more rugged than a tube; it is able to operate from a B battery of low voltage; its dissipation is low; and it has appreciably longer life than a tube. Vacuum tubes are superior to transistors in their larger power-handling capabilities, their higher frequency response, and their lower noise (except for microphonics, a transistor being completely non-microphonic). Also, vacuum tubes are less likely to be damaged by electrical overloads, and their characteristics are almost independent of ambient temperature. On the other hand, transistor characteristics may be very sensitive to changes in temperature.

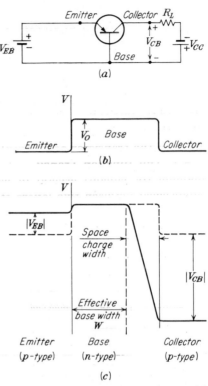

The two types of transistors are represented in Fig. 9-1a. The representations employed when the transistors are used as circuit elements are shown in Fig. 9-1b. The three portions of the transistors are known as *emitter*, *base*, and *collector*, respectively. The arrow on the emitter lead specifies the direction of current flow when the emitter-base junction is biased in the forward direction. In both cases, however, the emitter, base, and collector currents, I_E, I_B, and I_C, respectively, are assumed positive when the currents flow into the transistor. The symbols V_{EB}, V_{CB}, and V_{CE} are the emitter-base, collector-base, and collector-emitter voltages, respectively. (More specifically, V_{EB} represents the voltage drop from emitter to base.)

Fig. 9-2. (a) A p-n-p transistor with biasing voltages. (b) The potential barriers at the junction of the unbiased transistor. (c) The potential variation through the transistor under biased conditions. As the reverse-bias collector voltage is increased, the effective base width W decreases.

We may now begin to appreciate the essential features of a transistor as an active circuit element by considering the situation depicted in Fig. 9-2a. Here a p-n-p transistor is shown with voltage sources which serve to bias the emitter-base junction in the *forward* direction and the base-collector junction in the *reverse* direction. The variation of potential through the unbiased transistor is shown in Fig. 9-2b. The potential variation through the biased transistor is indicated in Fig. 9-2c. The dashed curve applies in the case before the application of external biasing voltages, and the solid curve to the case where the biasing voltages are applied. In the absence of applied voltages the potential barriers at the junctions adjust themselves to the height V_0 (a few tenths of a volt) required so that no current flows across each junction. (Since the transistor may be looked upon as a p-n junction diode in series with an n-p diode, much of the theory developed in Chap. 5 for the junction diode will be made use of in order to explain the characteristics of a transistor.) If, now, external potentials are applied, these voltages appear essentially across the junctions. Hence, the forward biasing of the emitter-base junction lowers the emitter-base potential barrier by $|V_{EB}|$ volts, while the reverse biasing of the base-collector junction increases the base-collector potential barrier by $|V_{CB}|$ volts. The lowering of the emitter-base barrier permits the emitter current to increase, and holes are injected into the base region. The potential is constant across the base region (except for the small ohmic drop), and the injected holes diffuse across the n-type material to the base-collector junction. The holes which reach this junction fall down the potential barrier and are therefore *collected* by the collector.

We now can explain why a transistor may act as an amplifier. A load resistor R_L is in series with the applied potential V_{CC} of Fig. 9-2a. A small voltage change between emitter and base causes a relatively large emitter current change ΔI_E. We shall define by the symbol α that fraction of this current which is collected and passes through R_L. The change in output voltage across the load resistor $\Delta V_L = \alpha \, \Delta I_E \, R_L$ may be many times the change in input voltage ΔV_i. Under these circumstances, the voltage amplification $A \equiv \Delta V_L / \Delta V_i$ will be greater than unity, and the transistor acts as an amplifier. If the dynamic resistance of the emitter junction is r_e', then $\Delta V_i = r_e' \, \Delta I_E$ and

$$A \equiv \frac{\alpha R_L \, \Delta I_E}{r_e' \, \Delta I_E} = \frac{\alpha R_L}{r_e'} \tag{9-1}$$

From Eq. (5-6), $r_e' = 26/I_E$ ohms, where I_E is the quiescent emitter current in milliamperes. For example, if $r_e' = 40$ ohms, $\alpha = 1$, and $R_L = 3,000$ ohms, $A = 75$. This calculation is oversimplified somewhat (Sec. 10-5) but in essence it is correct and gives a physical explanation of why the transistor acts as an amplifier. The transistor gives power gain as well as voltage amplification.

From the above explanation it is clear that current in the low-resistance input circuit is transferred to the high-resistance output circuit. The word "transistor" which originated as a contraction of "transfer resistor," is based upon the above physical picture of the device. Thus the amplification is really due to an impedance transformation.

The parameter α introduced above is one of the most important in transistor theory.   It is defined as the ratio of the change in the collector current to the change in the emitter current at constant collector-to-base voltage and is called the *forward short-circuit current-transfer ratio* or *gain*.   More specifically,

$$\alpha \equiv - \left.\frac{\Delta I_C}{\Delta I_E}\right|_{V_{CB}} \equiv \alpha_B \qquad (9\text{-}2)$$

Since we shall later introduce several other α's, then if there is the possibility of confusion the α defined by Eq. (9-2) is designated by α_B, the *common-base alpha*.   (Some authors also use α_{CE} but this symbol is not recommended in the IRE Standards.)   Since ΔI_C and ΔI_E are of opposite sign, then α, as defined in Eq. (9-2), is a positive number.   It is advantageous to have α as close to unity as possible.   Several features of construction are normally incorporated into a transistor in order to achieve this end.   The ratio of hole to electron current crossing the emitter junction is proportional to the ratio of the conductivity of the p material to that of the n material (Prob. 5-14).   Hence the doping of the emitter is made much larger than the doping of the base.   This feature ensures (in a p-n-p transistor) that the current across the emitter junction consists almost entirely of the flow of holes.   Such a situation is desired since the current which results from electrons crossing the emitter junction from base to emitter does not contribute holes which may be collected by the collector.   Second, the width of the base region is made small so that the holes diffuse across the base in a short time and hence little opportunity is afforded for a loss of holes due to recombination with electrons.   The base width is of the order of 1 mil (0.001 in.).   These two factors which determine α are studied quantitatively in Sec. 9-7.

One type of transistor construction is indicated in Fig. 9-3a.   This type of transistor is known as an *alloyed-junction* or *fused* type of transistor.   The center section is a thin wafer of n-type germanium.   Two small dots of indium are attached to opposite sides of the wafer, and the whole structure is raised for a short time to a high temperature.   At the junction between the indium and the wafer enough indium dissolves into the germanium to change the germanium from n-type to p-type.   The collector is made larger than the emitter so that the collector subtends a large angle as viewed from the emitter.   Because of this geometrical arrangement, very little emitter current follows a diffusion path which carries it to the base rather than to the collector.

A second type of construction gives rise to a type of transistor which is called a *grown-junction* transistor.   This type of construction is illustrated in Fig. 9-3b.   It is made by drawing a single crystal from a melt of germanium whose type is changed during the crystal-drawing operation by adding n- or p-type impurities as required.

Transistors are normally not symmetrical; *i.e.*, emitter and collector may not be interchanged without changing the electrical properties of the transistor. In the alloyed-junction transistor this lack of symmetry results from the larger mechanical dimensions of the collector. In the grown-junction transistor lack of symmetry results from the fact that the conductivity of the collector is usually much less than the conductivity of the emitter.

Another type of transistor (which is a natural extension of the point-contact diode) consists of two sharply pointed tungsten wires pressed against a semiconductor wafer. These point-contact transistors are

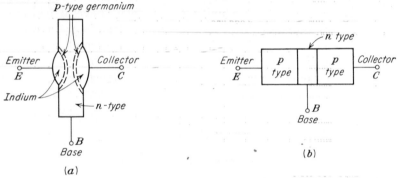

FIG. 9-3. Cross section of (*a*) an alloyed-junction transistor and (*b*) a grown-junction transistor.

capable of operating at a higher speed than junction transistors. Also, in some applications a single point-contact transistor replaces two junction transistors. However, at the present state of the art (1958) the reproducibility and reliability of point-contact transistors is very poor, and nearly all manufacturers have discontinued production of point-contact transistors in favor of junction transistors. For this reason our discussion is confined entirely to the junction transistor.

9-2. Characteristics of Transistors. If the voltages across the two junctions are known, the three transistor currents can be uniquely determined. The analytical relationships between these voltages and currents are given in Sec. 9-5. Many different families of characteristic curves can be drawn, depending upon which two parameters are chosen as the independent variables. Two such families are supplied by most transistor manufacturers because of their practical importance. The first of these is given in Fig. 9-4 for an n-p-n transistor and is a plot of collector current I_C vs. collector-to-base voltage drop V_{CB}, with emitter current I_E as a parameter. A typical application in which such characteristics are useful is indicated in Fig. 9-5, where an *n-p-n* transistor is shown in a *grounded-base* configuration. This circuit is also referred to as a *common-base* configuration, since the base is common to the input

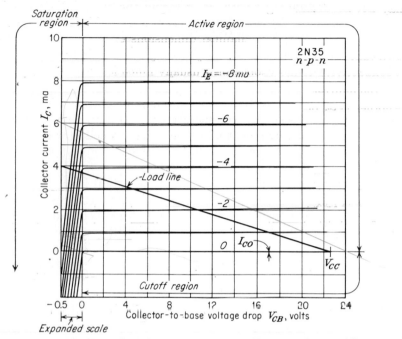

FIG. 9-4. Common-base characteristics of the type 2N35 transistor. (*Courtesy of Sylvania Electric Products, Inc.*)

and output circuits. For an *n-p-n* transistor the current is due to electrons flowing from emitter to collector and down toward ground out of the base terminal. Hence, referring to the polarity conventions of Fig. 9-1, we see that I_E is negative, I_C is positive, and I_B is positive.

For a forward-biased emitter, V_{EB} is negative, and for a reverse-biased collector, V_{CB} is positive. For a *p-n-p* transistor all current and voltage polarities are the negative of those for an *n-p-n* transistor.

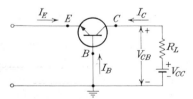

FIG. 9-5. The grounded-base transistor configuration.

The characteristics of Fig. 9-4 may be divided into three regions which are particularly worthy of note.

Active Region. In this region *the collector is biased in the reverse direction and the emitter in the forward direction*. Consider first that the emitter current is zero. Then the collector current is small and equals the *reverse saturation current* I_{CO} ($\cong$2 μa for the 2N35) of the collector junction considered as a diode. Suppose now that a forward emitter current I_E is caused to flow in the emitter circuit. Then, from Eq. (9-2) the magnitude of the change in collector current is αI_E. The collector current is therefore

$$I_C = I_{CO} - \alpha I_E \tag{9-3}$$

In this active region, the collector current is essentially independent of collector voltage and depends only upon the emitter current.

Because $\alpha < 1$, the collector current is (slightly) smaller than the emitter current. An average value of α may be obtained by noting that when the collector-to-base voltage drop V_{CB} is, say, about 5 volts then an emitter-current increment of -4 ma yields a collector-current increment of 3.9 ma. Hence $\alpha = 3.9/4.0 = 0.98$. Typically, values of α lie in the range 0.90 to 0.999.

From Fig. 9-4 we see that α is not strictly constant because I_C increases slightly with increasing values of V_{CB}. To explain this result physically we must recall that the space-charge width at a junction diode increases with an increase in reverse voltage [Eq. (5-12)]. Hence, as seen in Fig. 9-2c, the effective base width W decreases with increasing values of V_{CB}. This decrease in W has two consequences. First, there is less chance of recombination within the base width. Second, the charge gradient is increased within the base and hence the current of minority carriers injected across the emitter junction is increased. Clearly, then, the effect of the decrease in W is an increase in collector current with increased reverse collector bias.

Saturation Region. The region to the left of the ordinate $V_{CB} = 0$ and above the $I_E = 0$ characteristics in which *both emitter and collector junctions are forward-biased* is called the *saturation* region. From the load line drawn in Fig. 9-4, we see that, for a given value of V_{CC} and R_L, the collector current is approximately independent of the emitter current. We say that *bottoming* has taken place because the voltage has fallen near the bottom of the characteristic where $V_{CB} \cong 0$. Actually, V_{CB} is slightly negative in this region, and this forward biasing of the collector accounts for the large change in collector current with small changes in collector voltage. For a forward bias, I_C increases exponentially with voltage according to the diode relationship [Eq. (5-2)]. A forward bias means that the collector n material is made negative with respect to the base p side and hence that an electron current flows from the n side across the collector junction to the p material. This electron flow corresponds to a negative change in collector current. Hence, the collector current decreases rapidly, and, as indicated in Fig. 9-4, I_C may even become negative if the forward bias is sufficiently large.

The magnitude of the emitter current required to bias the transistor in Fig. 9-4 to the point of saturation ($V_{CB} \cong 0$) may be estimated in the following way: Since I_{CO} is small compared with the value of I_E necessary to drive the transistor into saturation, then $|I_C| \cong \alpha |I_E|$. Also, assuming that the collector-to-base voltage is zero, $|I_C| = |V_{CC}/R_L|$. Hence an emitter current equal to or larger than

$$|I_E|_{sat} = \left| \frac{V_{CC}}{\alpha R_L} \right| \qquad (9\text{-}4)$$

will bias the transistor into the saturation region.

Cutoff Region. The characteristic for $I_E = 0$ passes through the origin but is otherwise similar to the other characteristics. This characteristic is not coincident with the voltage axis, though the separation is difficult to show because I_{CO} is only a few microamperes. The region below and to the right of the $I_E = 0$ characteristic, for which the *emitter and collector junction are both reverse-biased*, is referred to as the *cutoff region*.

With increased temperature the current I_{CO} increases while the relative spacing of the individual curves of Fig. 9-4 remains essentially the same. Hence, with an increase in temperature the curves shift in the upward direction. As noted in Sec. 5-8, the reverse saturation current in germanium increases 11 per cent per degree rise in temperature and in silicon the increase is 15 per cent. However, the value of I_{CO} for silicon is so much smaller than that for germanium that actually the operation of a silicon transistor is appreciably less sensitive to temperature changes.

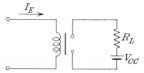

Fig. 9-6. A current-controlled switch.

In some applications it is desired that the transistor act as a switch or a relay which is current-operated, as indicated in Fig. 9-6. To see how effective the circuit of Fig. 9-5 is when used as such a switch, let us consider an example in which $R_L = 5.6$ kilohms and $V_{CC} = 22.5$ volts. The load line for these values of R_L and V_{CC} has been superimposed on the transistor curves in Fig. 9-4. If the emitter current is zero or if the emitter junction is slightly reverse-biased, the collector voltage V_{CB} will be very close to V_{CC} so that the switch is *open* or *off*. At the other extreme, if the emitter current is about 4.0 ma, the voltage drop at the collector will be zero and the full voltage V_{CC} will appear across the load so that the switch is *closed* or *on*. Larger emitter currents will actually reverse the voltage at the collector so that a voltage change slightly larger than V_{CC} may appear across the load.

9-3. The Grounded-emitter Configuration. Most transistor circuits have the emitter, rather than the base, as the terminal common to both input and output. Such a *common-emitter*, or *grounded-emitter*, configuration is indicated in Fig. 9-7. Because of the practical importance of this circuit, most manufacturers publish common-emitter characteristics such as those given in Fig. 9-8 for the type 2N35 (n-p-n) transistor. Here

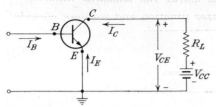

the abscissa is the collector-to-emitter voltage V_{CE}, the ordinate is the collector current I_C, and the curves are given for various values of base current I_B. For a fixed value of I_B, the collector current is not a very sensitive value of V_{CE}. However, the slopes of the curves in Fig. 9-8 are larger than in the common-base characteristics of Fig. 9-4. Observe that the base current is much smaller than the emitter current.

FIG. 9-7. A grounded-emitter transistor configuration.

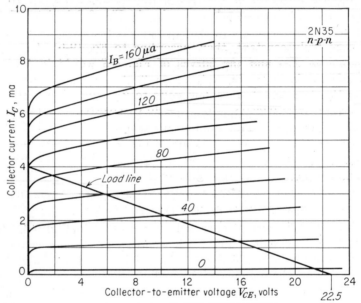

FIG. 9-8. Common-emitter characteristics for the type 2N35 transistor. (*Courtesy of Sylvania Electric Products, Inc.*)

The common-emitter characteristics are readily understood qualitatively on the basis of our earlier discussion of the grounded-base configuration. The base current is

$$I_B = -(I_C + I_E) \qquad (9\text{-}5)$$

Combining this equation with Eq. (9-3), we find

$$I_C = \frac{I_{CO}}{1 - \alpha} + \frac{\alpha I_B}{1 - \alpha} \qquad (9\text{-}6)$$

Equation (9-3) is based upon the assumption that the transistor is operating in the active region and that V_{CB} is fixed. However, if V_{CB} is larger than several volts, the voltage across the collector junction is much larger than that across the emitter junction and we may consider $V_{CE} \cong V_{CB}$. Hence, Eq. (9-6) is valid for values of V_{CE} in excess of a few volts. At a fixed value of V_{CE} in Fig. 9-8, the ratio of the change in collector current ΔI_C to the change in base current ΔI_B is

$$\frac{\Delta I_C}{\Delta I_B}\bigg|_{V_{CE}} = \frac{\alpha}{1 - \alpha} \equiv \alpha_E \qquad (9\text{-}7)$$

where α_E is the *common-emitter forward short-circuit current transfer ratio or gain.* (Some authors have used the symbols β or α_{CB} for α_E, but these are not recommended in the IRE Standards.[2]) While the spacing in the vertical direction in Fig. 9-4 is determined by α, we see from Eq. (9-7) that the corresponding spacing in Fig. 9-8 is determined by $\alpha/(1 - \alpha)$.

If α were truly constant, then, according to Eq. (9-6), I_C would be independent of V_{CE} and the curves of Fig. 9-8 would be horizontal. Assume that α increases by only one-half of 1 per cent from 0.98 to 0.985 as V_{CE} increases from a few volts to 24 volts. Then the value of α_E increases from $0.98/(1 - 0.98) = 40$ to $0.985/(1 - 0.985) = 66$ or by about 34 per cent. This numerical example illustrates that a very small slope (0.5 per cent) in the curves of Fig. 9-4 is reflected into a very large slope (34 per cent) in the curves of Fig. 9-8. It should also be clear that a slight change in α has a large effect on the common-emitter curves and hence that *common-emitter characteristics are normally subject to a wide variation even among transistors of a given type.* This variability is caused by the fact that I_B is the difference between large and nearly equal currents I_E and I_C.

A load line has been superimposed on Fig. 9-8 corresponding to a load resistor $R_L = 5.6$ kilohms and a supply voltage of 22.5 volts. The saturation region may be defined as the one in which *bottoming* occurs and hence as the region where the collector current is approximately independent of base current, for given values of V_{CC} and R_L. Hence we may consider that the onset of saturation takes place at the knee of the transistor curves in Fig. 9-8. Saturation occurs for the given load line at a base current of 100 μa, and at this point the collector voltage is too small to be read in Fig. 9-8.

9-4. The Grounded-collector Configuration. Another transistor-circuit configuration, shown in Fig. 9-9, is known as the *grounded-collector* configuration. The circuit is basically the same as the circuit of Fig. 9-7 with the exception that the load resistor is in the emitter circuit rather than in the collector circuit. If we continue to specify the operation of the circuit in terms of the currents which flow, the operation of the grounded collector is much the same as for the grounded emitter. When the base current is $I_{CO} = 2$ μa, the emitter current will be zero and no

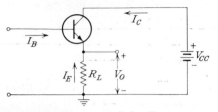

current will flow in the load. As the transistor is brought out of this back-biased condition by increasing the base current, the transistor will pass through the active region and eventually reach the region of saturation. This saturation region will again occur at a base current of about 100 μa, and in this condition

Fig. 9-9. The grounded-collector transistor configuration.

all the supply voltage except for a very small drop across the transistor will appear across the load.

9-5. Analytical Expressions for Transistor Characteristics.[3] There are a number of problems which arise in practice which cannot be solved by using the transistor characteristic curves. One such problem is the following: The base is short-circuited to the emitter whereas the collector junction is reverse-biased. What are the transistor currents? This query can be answered only if the theoretical functional relationships between currents and voltages are used. A second problem which is of importance in many pulse-circuit applications is the following: A transistor in the common-emitter configuration is driven into saturation by a base current I_B. What is the voltage drop V_{CE}? In principle, this voltage can be read from Fig. 9-8. However, the magnitude of V_{CE} under saturation conditions is in the millivolt range and can *not* be obtained with the desired accuracy from the common-emitter curves.

Because of problems of the type enumerated in the preceding paragraph, we shall now make a study of the interdependence of currents and voltages in a transistor. Furthermore, such an analysis will lead to a better understanding of the behavior of this semiconductor device. Also, expressions for α and the other transistor parameters will be obtained in terms of the physical constants of the transistor from such a quantitative study. The emitter current I_E and the collector current I_C are given by the expressions

$$I_E = a_{11}(\epsilon^{V_E/V_T} - 1) + a_{12}(\epsilon^{V_C/V_T} - 1) \tag{9-8}$$

and

$$I_C = a_{21}(\epsilon^{V_E/V_T} - 1) + a_{22}(\epsilon^{V_C/V_T} - 1) \tag{9-9}$$

where V_E and V_C are the potentials across the emitter and collector junctions, respectively (Fig. 9-10). The electron-volt equivalent of temperature V_T is defined in Eq. (5-1). *The symbol V_C (or V_E) is posi-*

$$V_T = \frac{T (°K)}{11,600}$$

tive for a forward-bias condition, i.e., for the p side positive with respect to the n side. This convention is used regardless of whether an n-p-n or a p-n-p transistor is under consideration. These expressions should appear reasonable in view of the fact that a transistor is a combination of two diodes and that the volt-ampere crystal-rectifier characteristic is of the form $I_0(\epsilon^{V/V_T} - 1)$. Equations (9-8) and (9-9) are derived in the next section, where the constants a_{11}, a_{12}, a_{21}, and a_{22} are found in terms of the physical parameters of the transistor.

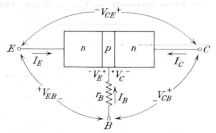

FIG. 9-10. The voltage polarity conventions in a transistor. The base-spreading resistance is r_B.

If V_E is eliminated from these equations, the common-base characteristic, I_C as a function of V_C and I_E, is obtained. The result is

$$I_C = \frac{a_{21}}{a_{11}} I_E + \left(a_{22} - \frac{a_{21}a_{12}}{a_{11}} \right)(\epsilon^{V_C/V_T} - 1) \qquad (9\text{-}10)$$

In the active region where the collector is reverse-biased (V_C is negative) by more than a few tenths of a volt, ϵ^{V_C/V_T} is negligible compared with unity, and Eq. (9-10) has the same form as Eq. (9-3). Hence, let us write Eq. (9-10) in the notation of Eq. (9-3), namely,

$$I_C = I_{CO}(1 - \epsilon^{V_C/V_T}) - \alpha_F I_E \qquad (9\text{-}11)$$

where

$$I_{CO} \equiv \frac{a_{21}a_{12}}{a_{11}} - a_{22} \qquad \alpha_F \equiv -\frac{a_{21}}{a_{11}} \qquad (9\text{-}12)$$

The symbol α_F is called the _common-base short-circuit forward current transfer ratio_ or _gain_, or simply the _normal alpha_. The symbol α_N, α_B, or α (without a subscript) is often used in place of α_F. The symbol I_{CO} is the _reverse saturation collector current_ and is the collector current when the emitter current is zero and the collector is reverse-biased. _Since currents entering the transistor terminals are considered positive (Fig. 9-1), then for an n-p-n transistor a positive number must be substituted for I_{CO}. On the other hand, if a p-n-p transistor is under consideration, then I_{CO} is a negative number._

The common-base characteristics (Fig. 9-4) are represented analytically in all three regions (active, saturation, and cutoff) by Eq. (9-11). Note that for a given value of I_E this equation is the volt-ampere diode characteristic of the collector junction. The constant emitter current I_E serves to bias this diode with a fixed current.

We must remember that the abscissa in Fig. 9-4 is V_{CB}, the voltage drop from collector to base terminals, whereas V_C is the voltage drop across the collector-base junction. Hence V_{CB} differs from V_C by the ohmic drops in the base and the collector materials. Recalling that the base region is very thin (of the order of 1 mil), we see that the current which enters the base region across the junction area must flow through a long narrow path to reach the base terminal. The cross-sectional area for current flow in the collector (or emitter) is very much larger than in the base. Hence, usually the ohmic drop in the base alone is of importance. This d-c ohmic base resistance r_B is called the *base-spreading resistance* and is indicated in Fig. 9-10. From this figure we see that *for an n-p-n transistor*

$$V_{CB} = -V_C - I_B r_B \qquad (9\text{-}13)$$

and I_B is positive.

By eliminating V_C from Eqs. (9-8) and (9-9) we obtain an equation in the form of Eq. (9-11), namely,

$$I_E = I_{EO}(1 - \epsilon^{V_E/V_T}) - \alpha_R I_C \qquad (9\text{-}14)$$

where

$$I_{EO} \equiv \frac{a_{12}a_{21}}{a_{22}} - a_{11} \qquad \alpha_R \equiv -\frac{a_{12}}{a_{22}} \qquad (9\text{-}15)$$

I_{EO} is called the *reverse saturation emitter current.* It must be emphasized that I_{EO} *is a positive quantity for an n-p-n transistor but is a negative number for a p-n-p transistor.* The parameter α_R is called the *short-circuit reverse current transfer ratio*, the *reverse current gain*, or the *inverted alpha* (sometimes written α_I). The reason for this terminology can be found by imagining that the transistor is connected into the circuit in the *reverse* or *inverted* direction so that the emitter and collector terminals are interchanged. Under these circumstances the subscripts C and E must be interchanged and F must be replaced by R in Eq. (9-11), with the result that Eq. (9-14) is obtained. Similarly, if the subscripts 1 and 2 are interchanged in Eqs. (9-12), the result is Eqs. (9-15).

The relationships among a_{11}, a_{12}, a_{21}, a_{22} and I_{CO}, I_{EO}, α_F, and α_R are found from Eqs. (9-12) and (9-15) to be

$$\begin{array}{ll} a_{11} = \dfrac{-I_{EO}}{1 - \alpha_F \alpha_R} & a_{12} = \dfrac{\alpha_R I_{CO}}{1 - \alpha_F \alpha_R} \\[3mm] a_{21} = \dfrac{\alpha_F I_{EO}}{1 - \alpha_F \alpha_R} & a_{22} = \dfrac{-I_{CO}}{1 - \alpha_F \alpha_R} \end{array} \qquad (9\text{-}16)$$

In the next section we prove that $a_{12} = a_{21}$. Hence, the parameters I_{CO}, I_{EO}, α_F, and α_R are not independent but are related by

$$\alpha_F I_{EO} = \alpha_R I_{CO} \qquad (9\text{-}17)$$

For many commercial transistors I_{EO} lies in the range $0.5I_{CO}$ to I_{CO}. For the 2N35 transistor $I_{EO} \cong 0.8I_{CO} \cong 1.6$ μa and hence $\alpha_R \cong 0.8\alpha_F \cong 0.78$.

Equations (9-11) and (9-14) may be solved for the junction voltages with the result

$$V_E = V_T \ln\left(1 - \frac{I_E + \alpha_R I_C}{I_{EO}}\right) \qquad (9\text{-}18)$$

$$V_C = V_T \ln\left(1 - \frac{I_C + \alpha_F I_E}{I_{CO}}\right) \qquad (9\text{-}19)$$

Given two of the three junction currents, the third can be found from the equation

$$\boxed{I_B + I_E + I_C = 0} \qquad (9\text{-}20)$$

and the junction voltages can be found from Eqs. (9-18) and (9-19). Conversely, if V_C and V_E are given, the currents can be found from Eqs. (9-11), (9-14), and (9-20).

We shall now derive the analytic expression for the common-emitter characteristics of Fig. 9-8. The abscissa in this figure is the collector-to-emitter voltage $V_{CE} = V_E - V_C$ for an n-p-n transistor (Fig. 9-10) and is $V_{CE} = V_C - V_E$ for a p-n-p transistor (remember that V_C and V_E are positive at the p side of the junction). Hence, the common-emitter characteristics are found by subtracting Eqs. (9-18) and (9-19) and by eliminating I_E by the use of Eq. (9-20). The resulting equation can be simplified provided that the following inequalities are valid: $I_B \gg I_{EO}$ and $I_B \gg I_{CO}/\alpha_F$. After some algebraic manipulation we obtain (except for very small values of I_B)

$$V_{CE} \cong \pm V_T\left[\ln\frac{1}{\alpha_R} + \ln\frac{1 + (1 - \alpha_R)\dfrac{I_C}{I_B}}{1 - \dfrac{1 - \alpha_F}{\alpha_F}\dfrac{I_C}{I_B}}\right] \qquad (9\text{-}21)$$

where the $+$ sign is used for an n-p-n transistor and the $-$ sign for a p-n-p device. For the former type, at $I_C = 0$, $V_{CE} = V_T \ln(1/\alpha_R)$ so that the common-emitter characteristics do not pass through the origin. For $\alpha_R = 0.78$, $V_{CE} = 6$ mv at room temperature. This voltage is so small that the curves of Fig. 9-8 look as if they do pass through the origin but they are actually displaced to the right by 6 mv.

If I_C is increased, then V_{CE} rises only slightly until I_C/I_B approaches $\alpha_F/(1 - \alpha_F)$. For example, even for $I_C/I_B = 0.9\alpha_F/(1 - \alpha_F) = 45$ (for $\alpha_F = 0.98$), then $V_{CE} = 0.006 + 0.026 \ln[(1 + 0.22 \times 45)/(1 - 0.9)] = 0.12$ volt. This voltage can barely be detected at the scale to which Fig.

9-8 is drawn and hence near the origin it appears as if the curves rise vertically.

The maximum value of I_C/I_B is $\alpha_F/(1 - \alpha_F)$, and as this value of I_C/I_B is approached, $V_{CE} \to \infty$. Hence, as I_C/I_B increases from $0.9\alpha_F/(1 - \alpha_F)$ to $\alpha_F/(1 - \alpha_F)$, V_{CE} increases from 0.12 volt to infinity. A plot of the theoretical common-emitter characteristic is indicated in Fig. 9-11 (the numerical values apply to the 2N35). Because the ordinate has been taken as I_C/I_B, this one curve is equivalent to the family of curves in Fig. 9-8. We see that at a fixed value of V_{CE} the ratio I_C/I_B is a constant. Hence, for equal increments in I_B we should obtain equal increments in I_C at a given V_{CE}. This conclusion is fairly well satisfied by the curves in Fig. 9-8. However, the $I_B = 0$ curve seems to be inconsistent since for a constant I_C/I_B this curve should coincide with the $I_C = 0$ axis. This discrepancy is due to the approximations made in deriving Eq. (9-21). If the unity in Eq. (9-19) is not neglected, we come to the conclusion that, for $I_B = 0$ and $V_{CE} \to \infty$, $I_C = I_{CO}/(1 - \alpha_F) \cong 0.1$ ma for the 2N35, in fair agreement with Fig. 9-8.

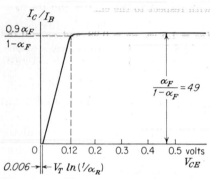

Fig. 9-11. The common-emitter characteristic as obtained analytically.

The theoretical curve of Fig. 9-11 is much flatter than the curves of Fig. 9-8 because we have implicitly assumed that α_F is truly constant. As already pointed out in Sec. 9-3, a very slight increase of α_F with V_{CE} can account for the slopes of the common-emitter characteristic.

Let us now find the solutions of the problems posed at the beginning of this section.

Example 1. *a.* A common-emitter configuration has the base short-circuited to the emitter, and the collector is reverse-biased by an amount V_{CC}. Find the currents.

b. If the base is open-circuited, instead of short-circuited, find the currents. Calculate the emitter-junction voltage.

Solution. *a.* Since $V_E = 0$ and $V_C = -V_{CC}$, then Eqs. (9-11) and (9-14) become

$$I_C = I_{CO}(1 - \epsilon^{-V_{CC}/V_T}) - \alpha_F I_E$$

and

$$I_E = -\alpha_R I_C$$

or

$$I_C = \frac{I_{CO}(1 - \epsilon^{-V_{CC}/V_T})}{1 - \alpha_F \alpha_R}$$

If, as is usually the case, the reverse bias is greater than a few tenths of a volt, $\epsilon^{-V_{CC}/V_T} = 0$, and to an excellent approximation

$$I_C = \frac{I_{CO}}{1 - \alpha_F \alpha_R} \qquad I_E = \frac{-\alpha_R I_{CO}}{1 - \alpha_F \alpha_R}$$

and from Eq. (9-20),

$$I_B = -(I_C + I_E) = \frac{-(1 - \alpha_R)I_{CO}}{1 - \alpha_F\alpha_R}$$

In this particular case the solution can be obtained even more simply from Eq. (9-9) which, for $V_E = 0$ and $|V_C/V_T| \gg 1$, reduces to $I_C = -a_{22}$. Using the last of Eqs. (9-16), we have

$$I_C = \frac{I_{CO}}{1 - \alpha_F\alpha_R} \equiv I_{CS} \qquad (9\text{-}22)$$

in agreement with the above analysis. The current I_{CS} is defined as the collector current when the collector is reverse-biased with respect to the emitter and the base is d-c short-circuited to the emitter.

For a 2N35 n-p-n transistor, $I_{CO} = 2$ μa, $I_{EO} = 1.6$ μa, $\alpha_F = 0.98$, and $\alpha_R = 0.78$. For these numerical values, I_{CS} is calculated to be 8.3 μa. A transistor power amplifier is often operated at zero d-c input bias, and the above solution indicates that under these circumstances the collector current is very small although it may be several times the reverse saturation current.

b. Since $I_B = 0$, $I_E = -I_C$, and if $|V_C/V_T| \gg 1$, then Eq. (9-11) becomes

$$I_C = I_{CO} - \alpha_F I_E = I_{CO} + \alpha_F I_C$$

or

$$I_C = \frac{I_{CO}}{1 - \alpha_F} = -I_E$$

For the 2N35 transistor, $I_C = 2/(1 - 0.98) = 100$ μa. The emitter-junction voltage is calculated from Eq. (9-18), namely,

$$V_E = V_T \ln\left(1 - \frac{I_E + \alpha_R I_C}{I_{EO}}\right)$$

At room temperature $V_T = 0.026$ volt and

$$V_E = 0.026 \ln\left(1 - \frac{-100 + 78}{1.6}\right) = 0.070 \text{ volt}$$
$$= 70 \text{ mv}$$

Since V_E is a positive number, we see that, even if the base terminal is open-circuited and the collector junction is reverse-biased, the emitter junction is forward-biased

Example 2. Consider the 2N35 transistor in a common-emitter configuration with $V_{CC} = 22.5$ volts, $R_L = 5.6$ kilohms, and $I_B = 200$ μa. Find the collector-to-emitter voltage V_{CE}.

Solution. The load line is drawn in Fig. 9-8, and we see that the transistor is driven into saturation with $I_C = 4.0$ ma. The value of V_{CE} is too small to be read from Fig. 9-8. However, it may be calculated from $V_{CE} = V_E - V_C$ (for an n-p-n transistor), where V_E and V_C are obtained from Eqs. (9-18) and (9-19), respectively. Since $I_B = 0.2$ ma, then $I_E = -(I_C + I_B) = -4.2$ ma, and we easily calculate

$$V_E = 0.17 \qquad V_C = 0.11 \qquad V_{CE} = 0.06 \text{ volt}$$

It is interesting to note that in this saturation condition the collector-to-emitter voltage is only 60 mv and is smaller than the base-to-emitter voltage.

9-6. Detailed Study of the Currents Which Flow in a Transistor.   This analysis follows in many respects that given in Secs. 5-6 to 5-8 for the current components in a junction diode, and these sections should be

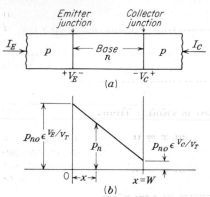

FIG. 9-12. The minority-carrier density in the base region.

reread.   From Fig. 5-11 or Eq. (5-19) we see that the net current crossing a junction equals the sum of the electron current I_{np} in the p side and the hole current I_{pn} in the n side, evaluated at the junction $(x = 0)$.   For a p-n-p transistor (Fig. 9-12a) electrons are injected from the base region across the emitter junction into a p region which is large compared with the diffusion length.   This is precisely the condition which exists in a junction diode, and hence the expression for I_{np} calculated previously is also valid for the transistor.   From Eqs. (5-23) and (5-33) we find that at the junction

$$I_{np}(0) = \frac{AeD_n n_{EO}}{L_E} (\epsilon^{V_E/V_T} - 1) \tag{9-23}$$

where in Eq. (5-33) we have replaced V by V_E; we have changed n_{po} to n_{EO} because there are now two p regions and the emitter (E) is under consideration; and we have changed L_n to L_E in order to refer to the diffusion length of the minority carriers in the emitter.

A summary of the symbols used follows:

A = cross section of transistor, m²
e = electronic charge, coulombs
D_n (D_p) = diffusion constant for electrons (holes), m²/sec
n_{EO} (n_{CO}) = thermal-equilibrium electron concentration in the p-type material of the emitter (collector), m⁻³
L_E (L_C) (L_B) = diffusion length for *minority carriers* in the emitter (collector) (base), m
V_E (V_C) = voltage drop across emitter (collector) junction; positive for a positive bias (p side positive with respect to n side)
V_T = electron-volt equivalent of temperature [Eq. (5-1)]
p_n = hole concentration in the n-type material, m⁻³
p_{no} = thermal-equilibrium value of p_n
W = base width, m
I_{pn} (I_{np}) = hole (electron) current in n (p) material

The value of I_{pn} is not that found in Sec. 5-6 for a diode because in the transistor the hole current exists in a base region of finite width whereas in a diode the n region extends over a distance large compared with L_n.   The diffusion current is given, as usual, by Eq. (3-38); namely,

$$I_{pn} = -AeD_p \frac{dp_n}{dx} \tag{9-24}$$

— SEE PG. 534

where p_n is found from the continuity equation. From Eq. (A6-11),

$$p_n - p_{no} = K_1 \epsilon^{-x/L_B} + K_2 \epsilon^{+x/L_B} \tag{9-25}$$

where K_1 and K_2 are constants to be determined by the boundary conditions. The situation at each junction is exactly as for the diode junction, and the boundary condition (5-28) is valid. Hence,

$$p_n = p_{no}\epsilon^{V_E/V_T} \qquad \text{at } x = 0$$

and $\tag{9-26}$

$$p_n = p_{no}\epsilon^{V_C/V_T} \qquad \text{at } x = W$$

These junction concentrations are pictured in Fig. 9-12.

The exact solution is not difficult to find (Prob. 9-7). However, usually the base width W is small compared with L_B, and we can simplify the solution by introducing this inequality. Since $0 \leq x \leq W$, we shall assume $x/L_B \ll 1$, and then the exponentials in Eq. (9-25) can be expanded into a power series. If only the first two terms are retained, this equation has the form

$$p_n - p_{no} = K_3 + K_4 x \tag{9-27}$$

where K_3 and K_4 are new (and, as yet, undetermined) constants. To this approximation p_n is a linear function of distance in the base and it has so been plotted in Fig. 9-12. Then, from Eq. (9-24),

$$I_{pn} = -AeD_p K_4 = \text{const}$$

This result, that the minority current is a constant throughout the base region, is readily understood because we have assumed that $W \ll L_B$. Under these circumstances, little recombination can take place within the base and hence the hole current entering the base at the emitter junction leaves the base at the collector junction unattenuated. Substituting the boundary conditions (9-26) into (9-27), we easily solve for K_4 and then find

$$I_{pn}(0) = -\frac{AeD_p p_{no}}{W} [(\epsilon^{V_C/V_T} - 1) - (\epsilon^{V_E/V_T} - 1)] \tag{9-28}$$

Since $I_E = I_{pn}(0) + I_{np}(0)$, then from Eqs. (9-23) and (9-28) we find

$$I_E = a_{11}(\epsilon^{V_E/V_T} - 1) + a_{12}(\epsilon^{V_C/V_T} - 1) \tag{9-29}$$

where

$$a_{11} = Ae\left(\frac{D_p p_{no}}{W} + \frac{D_n n_{EO}}{L_E}\right) \qquad a_{12} = -\frac{AeD_p p_{no}}{W} \tag{9-30}$$

We see that Eq. (9-29) verifies Eq. (9-8) of the preceding section.   In a similar manner we can obtain Eq. (9-9), namely,

$$I_C = a_{21}(\epsilon^{V_E/V_T} - 1) + a_{22}(\epsilon^{V_C/V_T} - 1) \tag{9-31}$$

where we can show that

$$a_{21} = -\frac{AeD_p p_{no}}{W} \qquad a_{22} = Ae\left(\frac{D_p p_{no}}{W} + \frac{D_n n_{CO}}{L_C}\right) \tag{9-32}$$

We note that $a_{12} = a_{21}$.   This result may be shown[4] to be valid for a transistor possessing any geometry.

9-7. The Forward Transistor Alpha.   From Eqs. (9-12) $\alpha_F = -a_{21}/a_{11}$. Using Eqs. (9-30) and (9-32), we obtain

$$\alpha_F = \frac{1}{1 + D_n n_{EO}W/L_E D_p p_{no}} \tag{9-33}$$

Making use of Eq. (3-30) for the conductivity, Eq. (3-39) for the diffusion constant, and Eq. (3-32) for the concentration, the above equation reduces to

$$\alpha_F = \frac{1}{1 + W\sigma_B/L_E\sigma_E} \tag{9-34}$$

where σ_B (σ_E) is the conductivity of the base (emitter).   We see that in order to keep α_F close to unity σ_E/σ_B should be made large and W should be kept small.

The analysis of the preceding section is based upon the assumption that $W/L_B \ll 1$.   If this restriction is removed, the solution given in Prob. 9-7 is obtained.   Then $\alpha_F = -(a_{21}/a_{11})$ is found to be given by the product of two factors

$$\alpha_F = \beta\gamma \tag{9-35}$$

where

$$\beta \equiv \text{sech} \frac{W}{L_B} \tag{9-36}$$

and

$$\gamma \equiv \frac{1}{1 + \dfrac{D_n}{D_p}\dfrac{L_B}{L_E}\dfrac{n_{EO}}{p_{no}} \tanh \dfrac{W}{L_B}} \tag{9-37}$$

If $W \ll L_B$, the hyperbolic secant and the hyperbolic tangent can be expanded in powers of W/L_B, and the first approximations are

$$\beta \cong 1 - \frac{1}{2}\left(\frac{W}{L_B}\right)^2 \tag{9-38}$$

$$\gamma \cong \frac{1}{1 + W\sigma_B/L_E\sigma_E} \cong 1 - \frac{W\sigma_B}{L_E\sigma_E} \tag{9-39}$$

and

$$\alpha_F \cong 1 - \frac{1}{2}\left(\frac{W}{L_B}\right)^2 - \frac{W\sigma_B}{L_E\sigma_E} \tag{9-40}$$

As the reverse-bias collector voltage is increased, the space-charge layer at the collector increases and the effective base width W decreases (Fig. 9-2). Hence, Eq. (9-40) indicates that α_F increases with the collector bias voltage.

Consider a *p-n-p* transistor with the collector terminal a-c short-circuited. The change in collector current for a unit change in emitter current is the short-circuited forward current gain α_F, or

$$\alpha_F = -\left.\frac{\partial I_C}{\partial I_E}\right|_{V_C} \tag{9-41}$$

The parameter α_F is not unity for several reasons. First, the emitter current does not consist entirely of holes crossing from emitter to base because there is also a small electron current in the reverse direction across the emitter junction. The *emitter efficiency* γ is defined as the ratio of hole emitter current to total emitter current, or, more specifically,

$$\gamma \equiv \left.\frac{\partial I_{pn}(0)}{\partial I_E}\right|_{V_C} \tag{9-42}$$

Second, because of recombination not all the minority-carrier current entering the base can reach the collector junction. The fraction of the hole current from the emitter which reaches the collector is called the *base transport factor* β, or, more specifically,

$$\beta \equiv -\left.\frac{\partial I_C}{\partial I_{pn}(0)}\right|_{V_C} \tag{9-43}$$

We note that

$$\beta\gamma = \left[-\left.\frac{\partial I_C}{\partial I_{pn}(0)}\right|_{V_C}\right]\left[\left.\frac{\partial I_{pn}(0)}{\partial I_E}\right|_{V_C}\right] = -\left.\frac{\partial I_C}{\partial I_E}\right|_{V_C}$$

or, using Eq. (9-2),

$$\alpha_F = \beta\gamma \tag{9-44}$$

which proves that the *forward alpha* is the product of the *transport factor* by the *emitter efficiency*.

If the partial derivatives indicated in the definitions for β and γ are carried out, the results indicated in Eqs. (9-36) and (9-37) are obtained.

9-8. Minority-carrier Storage. The density of minority carriers in the base region decreases linearly from $p_{no}\epsilon^{V_E/V_T}$ at $x = 0$ to $p_{no}\epsilon^{V_C/V_T}$ at $x = W$, as indicated in Fig. 9-12b. In the cutoff region, both V_E and V_C are negative and p_n is almost zero everywhere. In the active region,

V_E is positive and V_C negative so that p_n is large at $x = 0$ and almost zero at $x = W$. Finally, in the saturation region, where V_E and V_C are both positive, p_n is large everywhere. These conclusions are pictured in Fig. 9-13.

If the transistor is used as a switch, then the minority-carrier density stored in the base plays an important part in its operation. Consider that an input current step has turned the transistor on (put it into its saturation region) and that now an input current step of the reverse polarity is used to turn the transistor off. Since the turn-off process cannot really begin until this abnormal carrier density has been removed, a relatively long delay (called the *storage-time delay*) may elapse before the transistor responds to a turn-off signal at the input. In an extreme case this storage-time delay may be two or three times the rise or fall time through the active region. In any event, it is clear that, when transistor switches are to be used in an application where speed is at a premium, it is advantageous to restrain the transistor from entering the saturation region.

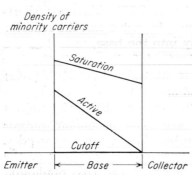

FIG. 9-13. Minority-carrier concentration in the base for cutoff, active, and saturation conditions of operation.

9-9. Maximum Voltage Rating. Even if the rated dissipation of a transistor is not exceeded, there is an upper limit to the maximum allowable collector-junction voltage since at high voltages there is the possibility of voltage breakdown in the transistor. Two types of breakdown which are possible are the avalanche breakdown and the Zener breakdown which were discussed earlier in Sec. 5-2. Even if the reverse voltage is not large enough to produce breakdown, a large reverse voltage may still cause difficulty. Suppose that there is some ionization by collision. Then the carriers may increase in number sufficiently to produce a value of α in excess of unity. In this case the emitter input circuit of the transistor may exhibit a negative resistance characteristic over some range of operation, and regeneration is possible.

A third type of voltage breakdown may occur in transistors and is known as *punch-through* breakdown. At the junction between n-type and p-type semiconductors there exists an electric field. This field results from the uncovered charges which exist in the neighborhood of the junction. These uncovered charges are the ions of the impurity atoms. There are equal numbers of charges on the two sides of the junction, since there are no fields within the body of the semiconductor and all

See pg. 214.

electric lines originating on positive charges on one side of the junction must terminate on negative charges on the other side of the junction. At the junction between two semiconductors, one of which is doped more heavily than the other, the field extends farther into the less heavily doped semiconductor. This is so because the less heavily doped (higher-resistivity) semiconductor has fewer impurity atoms per unit volume. In a p-n-p diffused-junction transistor, for example, the resistivity of the p-type collector and emitter may be as low as 0.001 ohm-cm while the n-type base has a resistivity of 1.5 ohm-cm. In such a case the collector-junction field will extend almost entirely into the base, as in Fig. 9-2. With increasing collector voltage the field extends farther and farther into the base until finally it reaches the emitter junction. Beyond this point the collector-emitter impedance is low and normal transistor action is not possible. Commercial transistors usually carry a maximum collector-voltage rating in the range 15 to 30 volts. This maximum collector voltage is determined by Zener, avalanche, or punch-through breakdown, whichever occurs first.

9-10. Transistor Symbols. We shall adhere to the IRE Standards[2] for semiconductor symbols. These are summarized as follows:

1. Instantaneous values of *quantities* which vary with time are represented by lower-case letters (i for current, v for voltage, and p for power).

2. Maximum, average (d-c), and effective, or root-mean-square (rms), values are represented by the upper-case letter of the proper symbol (I, V, or P).

3. D-c values and instantaneous total values are indicated by the upper-case *subscript* (B for base, E for emitter, and C for collector).

4. Varying component values are indicated by the lower-case *subscript*. Examples of this notation are:

$$i_E = \text{total instantaneous emitter current}$$
$$i_e = \text{instantaneous value of varying component of emitter current}$$
$$I_B = \text{average, or d-c, value of base current}$$
$$I_b = \text{rms value of varying component of base current}$$

5. If necessary to distinguish between maximum, average, or rms values, then maximum or average values may be represented by the additional subscript m and av, respectively. For example,

$$I_{bm} = \text{maximum value of the varying component of the base current}$$

6. Conventional current flow into an electrode from the external circuit is positive.

7. A single subscript is used if the reference electrode is clearly understood. If there is any possibility of ambiguity, the conventional double-subscript notation should be used. For example, v_{eb} = instantaneous value of varying component of voltage drop from emitter to base and is positive if the emitter is positive with respect to the base. If a common-base circuit is under consideration, then the symbol v_{eb} may be shortened to v_e.

8. The magnitude of the supply voltage is indicated by repeating the electrode subscript. example: V_{cc}

These conventions differ from those introduced for vacuum tubes in only two respects. First, <u>the symbol for voltage is E for a vacuum tube and V for a transistor.</u> Second, for a vacuum tube, two different subscripts (c and g for the grid; b and p for the plate) are used to distinguish between total values and varying component values, respectively. For a transistor the same subscript symbol is used but a capital or lower-case letter differentiates between the above two functions.

9-11. Graphical Analysis. A simple n-p-n grounded-base transistor circuit is shown in Fig. 9-14. The total instantaneous currents are i_E, i_B, and i_C. The total instantaneous voltages are v_E and v_C. The instantaneous input signal generator voltage is v_g and the generator output impedance (or an impedance added in series with the generator) is R_g.

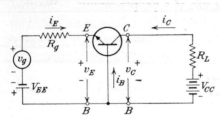

FIG. 9-14. A common-base circuit.

If $v_g = 0$, the quiescent emitter current I_E flows. Since the emitter is forward-biased, then the drop across the emitter junction is usually small compared with V_{EE} and hence $I_E \cong -V_{EE}/R_g$. A load line corresponding to V_{CC} and R_L is drawn on the common-base characteristics furnished by the manufacturer (Fig. 9-4). Then the quiescent collector current I_C is found at the intersection of the load line and the characteristic for the quiescent emitter current I_E. The corresponding collector-to-base voltage is V_C. $V_{CB} = V_C$

The above graphical method of analysis may be used to find the instantaneous collector current i_C and voltage v_C when an external signal v_g is applied (corresponding to the construction in Fig. 7-12 for a vacuum triode). <u>The collector and emitter currents and voltage variations from the quiescent point are, respectively,</u>

$$i_c = i_C - I_C \qquad v_c = v_C - V_C \qquad (9\text{-}45)$$

and

$$i_e = i_E - I_E \qquad v_e = v_E - V_E \qquad (9\text{-}46)$$

<u>A similar method of analysis can be made for the common-emitter circuit.</u>

9-12. D-c Bias and Stability.[5] We have seen (Sec. 5-8) that <u>the reverse saturation current I_{CO} is a very rapidly varying function (an exponential) of temperature.</u> This fact may cause considerable practical difficulty in using a transistor as a circuit element. For example, the collector current I_C causes the collector-junction temperature to rise, which in turn increases I_{CO}. As a result of this growth of I_{CO}, I_C will increase, which may further increase the junction temperature and consequently I_{CO}. It is possible for this succession of events to become cumulative so that the ratings of the transistor are exceeded and the device burns out. Even if such a drastic state of affairs does not take place, it is possible for the transistor (which was biased in the active region) to find itself in the saturation region as a result of the "thermal runaway" just mentioned. And such a bias would render the circuit useless as a linear amplifier.

One obvious way of avoiding the cumulative events described above is to provide adequate cooling of the collector junction. Such provisions are usually made with power transistors but are uneconomical for transistors operating in the milliwatt range. A second method of avoiding thermal runaway is to compensate for the drift in the quiescent point by the proper use of thermistors.[6] However, the most common method of avoiding d-c instability is through the use of a proper circuit. We shall now describe several ways to bias a transistor. In order to compare these configurations we shall define a stability factor S as the rate of change of collector current with respect to the reverse saturation current, or

$$S \equiv \frac{dI_C}{dI_{CO}} \qquad (9\text{-}47)$$

The smaller the value of S, the less likely the circuit is to exhibit thermal runaway. We shall confine our attention to the common-emitter stage since this configuration is used most often.

Fixed-current Bias. The circuit of Fig. 9-15 is one in which the quiescent collector and base currents are supplied by a single battery V_{CC}. For a forward-biased emitter the voltage across this junction is in the millivolt

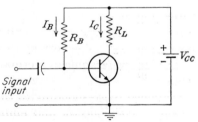

FIG. 9-15. A fixed-current-bias common-emitter circuit.

range, and little error is made if this voltage is neglected compared with V_{CC}. Then the quiescent base current I_B is given approximately by

$$I_B = \frac{V_{CC}}{R_B} \qquad (9\text{-}48)$$

This current is constant, independent of the quiescent collector current I_C, and the circuit of Fig. 9-15 is called the *fixed-bias circuit*.

We shall assume that the quiescent point is in the active region and that α is a constant independent of collector voltage so that Eq. (9-6) is applicable; namely,

$$I_C = \frac{I_{CO}}{1 - \alpha} + \frac{\alpha}{1 - \alpha} I_B \qquad (9\text{-}49)$$

Since I_B is independent of I_C, then the stability factor S defined by Eq. (9-47) is

$$S = \frac{1}{1 - \alpha} \tag{9-50}$$

For $\alpha = 0.98$, $S = 1/0.02 = 50$, which means that I_C increases fifty times as fast as I_{CO}. Such a large value of S makes thermal runaway a definite possibility with this circuit.

Another difficulty with the simple configuration of Fig. 9-15 is that the quiescent currents and voltages may differ greatly among transistors of the same type. We have already mentioned (Sec. 9-3) that the common-emitter characteristics are subject to a wide variation because α may differ slightly from transistor to transistor. Since the base current used in the circuit of Fig. 9-15 is fixed at the value given by Eq. (9-48), the collector current (determined from the load line corresponding to V_{CC} and R_L) will depend upon the particular transistor used. This current may differ appreciably from that calculated from the published collector characteristics.

Collector-to-base Bias. An improvement in stability is obtained if the resistor R_B in Fig. 9-15 is returned to the collector junction rather than to the battery terminal. Such a con-

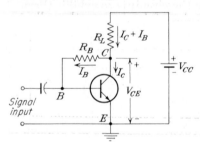

FIG. 9-16. A collector-to-base-bias circuit.

nection is indicated in Fig. 9-16. The physical reason that this circuit is an improvement over that in Fig. 9-15 is not difficult to find. If I_C tends to increase (either because of a rise in temperature or because the transistor has been replaced by another), then V_{CE} decreases. Hence I_B also decreases, and as a consequence of this lowered bias current the collector current is not allowed to increase as much as it would have if fixed bias had been used.

We shall now calculate the stability factor S. Again neglecting the emitter-junction voltage, we have, from Kirchhoff's law,

$$-V_{CC} + (I_B + I_C)R_L + I_B R_B = 0$$

or

$$I_B = \frac{V_{CC} - I_C R_L}{R_L + R_B} \tag{9-51}$$

Combining this equation with Eq. (9-49) yields

$$I_C \left(1 - \alpha + \frac{\alpha R_L}{R_L + R_B}\right) = I_{CO} + \frac{\alpha V_{CC}}{R_L + R_B} \tag{9-52}$$

$I_b = \dfrac{V_{CE}}{R_B}$; $V_{CE} = V_{CC} - I_c R_L$

Hence, S, defined by Eq. (9-47), is given by

$$S = \frac{1}{1 - \alpha + \alpha R_L/(R_L + R_B)} \tag{9-53}$$

This value is smaller than $1/(1 - \alpha)$ which is obtained for the fixed-bias circuit.

Example. The transistor in Fig. 9-16 is a 2N35 with $V_{CC} = 22.5$ volts and $R_L = 5.6$ kilohms. It is desired that the quiescent point be approximately at the middle of the load line. Find R_B and calculate S.

Solution. Since we may neglect I_B compared with I_C in R_L, then we may draw a load line corresponding to 22.5 volts and 5.6 kilohms. From this load line, which is drawn in Fig. 9-8, we choose the quiescent point at $I_B = 40$ μa, $I_C = 2.2$ ma, and $V_{CE} = 10.5$ volts. From Eq. (9-51) we find

$$R_B + R_L = \frac{V_{CC} - I_C R_L}{I_B} = \frac{22.5 - (2.2)(5.6)}{0.040} = 255 \text{ K}$$

or

$$R_B = 250 \text{ K}$$

From Eq. (9-53),

$$S = \frac{1}{1 - 0.98 + (0.98)(5.6)/255} = 24$$

which is about one-half the value found for the circuit of Fig. 9-15.

If the circuit component values are specified, the quiescent point is found as follows: Corresponding to each value of I_B given on the collector curves, the collector voltage $V_{CE} = I_B R_B$ is calculated. The locus of these corresponding points plotted on the common-emitter characteristics is called the *bias curve*. The intersection of the load line and the bias curve gives the quiescent point.

The increased stability of the circuit in Fig. 9-16 over that in Fig. 9-15 is due to the "feedback" from the output or collector terminal to the input or base terminal via R_B. Such feedback amplifiers are studied in detail in Chap. 17. The a-c gain of such an amplifier is less than it would be if there were no feedback. Thus, if the signal voltage causes an increase in the base current, then i_C tends to increase, v_{CE} decreases, and the component of base current coming from R_B decreases. Hence, the net change in base current is less than it would have been if R_B were connected to a fixed potential rather than to the collector terminal. This degeneration may be avoided by splitting R_B into two parts and connecting the junction of these resistors to ground through a capacitor C, as indicated in Fig. 9-17. At the frequencies under consideration the reactance of C must be an effective short circuit.

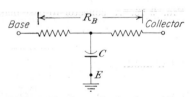

FIG. 9-17. A method of avoiding a-c degeneration in the collector-to-base-biasing circuit.

Emitter Bias or Self-bias. If the load resistance R_L is very small, as, for example, in a transformer-coupled circuit, then from Eq. (9-53) we see that there is no improvement in stabilization in the collector-to-base-bias circuit over the fixed-bias circuit. A circuit which can be used even if there is zero d-c resistance in series with the collector terminal is the self-biasing configuration of Fig. 9-18. The current in the resistance R_1 in the emitter lead causes a voltage drop which is in the direction to reverse-bias the emitter junction. Since this junction must be forward-biased, then the bleeder $R_2 - R_3$ has been added to the circuit.

The physical reason for the improvement in stability is the following: If I_C tends to increase, say because I_{CO} has risen as a result of an elevated temperature, the current in R_1 increases. As a consequence of the

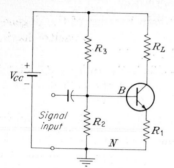

FIG. 9-18. A self-biasing circuit.

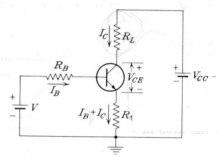

FIG. 9-19. Simplification of the circuit of Fig. 9-18 by the use of Thévenin's theorem.

increase in voltage drop across R_1, the base current is decreased. Hence I_C will increase less than it would have had there been no self-biasing resistor R_1.

We shall now find the analytical expression for the stabilization factor S. If the network to the left between the base B and ground N terminals in Fig. 9-18 is replaced by its Thévenin's equivalent, the circuit of Fig. 9-19 is obtained, where

$$V = \frac{R_2 V_{CC}}{R_2 + R_3} \qquad R_B = \frac{R_2 R_3}{R_2 + R_3} \qquad (9\text{-}54)$$

Obviously R_B is the effective resistance seen looking back from the base terminal. If, as usual, the voltage across the emitter junction is neglected, then Kirchhoff's voltage law around the base circuit yields

$$-V + I_B R_B + (I_B + I_C)R_1 = 0 \qquad (9\text{-}55)$$

Eliminating I_B from this equation with the aid of Eq. (9-49) and taking the derivative dI_C/dI_{CO} results in

$$S = \frac{1}{1 - \alpha + \alpha[R_1/(R_1 + R_B)]} \qquad (9\text{-}56)$$

The smaller the value of R_B, the better the stabilization. It is interesting to note that even if R_B approaches zero the value of S cannot be reduced below unity. Hence, I_C always increases faster than I_{CO}. As R_B is reduced while the Q point is held fixed, the current drawn in the bleeder $R_2 - R_3$ from the supply V_{CC} increases. Also, if R_1 is increased while R_B is held constant, then to operate at the same quiescent currents the magnitude of V_{CC} must be increased. In either case a loss of power (decreased efficiency) is the disadvantage which accompanies the improvement in stability.

In order to avoid the loss of a-c (signal) gain because of the degeneration caused by R_1, this resistor is often bypassed by a capacitor having negligible reactance at the frequencies under consideration.

If the circuit component values are specified, the quiescent point is found as follows. Kirchhoff's voltage law around the collector circuit yields

$$-V_{CC} + I_C(R_L + R_1) + I_B R_1 + V_{CE} = 0 \qquad (9\text{-}57)$$

If the drop in R_1 due to I_B is neglected compared with that due to I_C, then this relationship between I_C and V_{CE} is a straight line whose slope corresponds to $R_L + R_1$ and whose intercept at $I_C = 0$ is $V_{CE} = V_{CC}$. This *load line* is drawn on the collector characteristics. If I_C from Eq. (9-57) is substituted into Eq. (9-55) a relationship between I_B and V_{CE} results. Corresponding to each value of I_B given on the collector curves, V_{CE} is calculated and the *bias curve* is plotted. The intersection of the load line and the bias curve gives the quiescent point.

Example. A 2N35 transistor is used in the circuit of Fig. 9-18 with $V_{CC} = 22.5$ volts, $R_L = 5.6$ K, $R_1 = 1$ K, $R_2 = 10$ K, and $R_3 = 90$ K. (a) Find the Q point. (b) Calculate S.

Solution. a. From Eqs. (9-54),

$$V = \frac{10 \times 22.5}{100} = 2.25 \text{ volts} \qquad \text{and} \qquad R_B = \frac{(10)(90)}{100} = 9.0 \text{ K}$$

The equivalent circuit is indicated in Fig. 9-20. The load line corresponding to a total resistance of 6.6 kilohms and a supply of 22.5 volts is drawn on the collector characteristics of Fig. 9-21. Kirchhoff's voltage law applied to the collector and base circuits, respectively, yields

$$-22.5 + 6.6 I_C + I_B + V_{CE} = 0$$
$$-2.25 + I_C + 10.0 I_B = 0$$

Eliminating I_C from these two equations, we find

$$V_{CE} = 65.0 I_B + 7.65$$

Values of V_{CE} corresponding to $I_B = 20$, 40, and 60 μa are obtained from this equation and are plotted in Fig. 9-21. We see that the intersection of this bias curve and the load line occurs at $V_{CE} = 10.0$ volts, $I_C = 1.9$ ma, and, from the bias-curve equation, $I_B = 35$ μa.

b. From Eq. (9-56),

$$S = \frac{1}{1 - 0.98 + (0.98)[1.0/(1.0 + 9.0)]} = 8.5$$

This value is about one-sixth of the stabilization factor for the fixed-bias circuit, which indicates that a great improvement in stability results if self-bias is used.

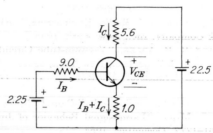

FIG. 9-20. An illustrative example. (Currents are in milliamperes, resistances in kilohms, and voltages in volts.)

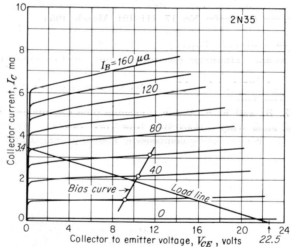

FIG. 9-21. The intersection of the load line and the bias curve determines the Q point.

In the collector-to-base-bias circuit the value of R_B is determined from the desired quiescent base current, and no control is exercised over the stabilization factor S. However, in the self-bias circuit I_B and S may be specified independently because these requirements can be satisfied by the proper choice of R_1 and R_2. For this reason and because generally lower values of S are obtained with the self-bias arrangement, this circuit is more popular than that of Fig. 9-16.

For the sake of simplicity the resistor R_2 is sometimes omitted from Fig. 9-18. In such a circuit R_3 is determined by I_B but S cannot be specified as a design parameter. The value of S is calculated from Eq. (9-56) with R_B replaced by R_3.

REFERENCES

1. Shockley, W., "The Theory of p-n Junctions in Semiconductors and p-n Junction Transistors," *Bell System Tech. J.*, **28**, 435–489, July, 1949.

   Middlebrook, R. D., "An Introduction to Junction Transistor Theory," pp. 115–130, John Wiley & Sons, Inc., New York, 1957.

   Terman, F. E., "Electronic and Radio Engineering," 4th ed., pp. 747–760, McGraw-Hill Book Company, Inc., New York, 1955.

   Arguimbau, L. B., and R. B. Adler, "Vacuum-tube Circuits and Transistors," pp. 110–125, John Wiley & Sons, Inc., New York, 1956.

   Moll, J. L., "Junction Transistor Electronics," *Proc. IRE*, **43**, 1807–1819, December, 1955.
2. "IRE Standards on Semiconductor Symbols," *Proc. IRE*, **44**, 935–937, July, 1956.
3. Ebers, J. J., and J. L. Moll, "Large-signal Behavior of Junction Transistors," *Proc. IRE*, **42**, 1761–1772, December, 1954.

   Ebers, J. J., and S. L. Miller, "Design of Alloyed Junction Germanium Transistors for High-speed Switching," *Bell System Tech. J.*, **34**, 761–781, July, 1955.

   Bright, R. L., "Junction Transistors Used as Switches," *Trans. AIEE, Communications and Electronics*, No. 17, 111–121, March, 1955.
4. Ebers, J. J., and J. L. Moll, "Large-signal Behavior of Junction Transistors," *Proc. IRE*, **42**, 1761–1772, December, 1954.
5. Low, A. W., et al., "Transistor Electronics," pp. 131–153, Prentice-Hall, Inc., Englewood Cliffs, N.J., 1956.

   Shea, R. F., et al., "Principles of Transistor Circuits," pp. 97–131, John Wiley & Sons, Inc., New York, 1953.

   Arguimbau, L. B., and R. B. Adler, "Vacuum-tube Circuits and Transistors," pp. 174–181, John Wiley & Sons, Inc., New York, 1956.
6. Wheeler, A. J., "Thermistors Compensate Transistor Amplifiers," *Electronics*, **30**, 169–171, January, 1956.

CHAPTER 10

TRANSISTOR LINEAR EQUIVALENT CIRCUITS

In the preceding chapter we were primarily interested in the static characteristics of a transistor. In the active region the transistor operates with reasonable linearity, and we shall now inquire into small-signal equivalent circuits which represent the operation of the transistor in this active region. The parameters introduced in these equivalent circuits will be interpreted in the light of the physics of the semiconductor sandwich and, alternatively, in terms of circuit theory. Methods for measuring these parameters will also be given. Finally, a detailed study of the transistor amplifier in its various configurations will be made.

10-1. A Linear Equivalent Circuit. We are interested now only in variations from the quiescent value. Hence, we seek a circuit which gives us the relationships between the signal currents and voltages (i_c, i_e, v_c, and v_e) introduced in Sec. 9-10. We shall set up this circuit more or less intuitively so that it represents the characteristics which we know the transistor possesses. To be specific, consider the grounded-base configuration. Looking into the emitter, we see a forward-biased diode. Hence, between input terminals E and B there is a dynamic resistance r_e', obtained as the slope of the (forward-biased) emitter-junction volt-ampere characteristic. Looking back into the output terminals C and B, we see a back-biased diode. Hence, between these terminals there is a dynamic resistance r_c' obtained as the slope of the (reverse-biased) collector-junction volt-ampere characteristic. From the physical behavior of a transistor as discussed in Chap. 9, we know that the collector current is proportional to the emitter current. Hence, a current generator αi_e is added across r_c', resulting in the equivalent circuit of Fig. 10-1. The parameter α is called the forward *current gain for an a-c short-circuited* output and is the same constant for which the symbol α_F or α_B was used in Chap. 9.

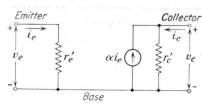

Fig. 10-1. An oversimplified equivalent circuit for a transistor.

The equivalent circuit of Fig. 10-1 is unrealistic because it indicates a

238

lack of dependence of emitter current on collector voltage.   Actually, there is some such small dependence, and the physical reason for this relationship is not hard to find.   As was noted in Sec. 9-7, an increase in the magnitude of the collector voltage effectively narrows the base width W, a phenomenon known as the *Early effect*.[1]   The minority-carrier current in the base is proportional to the slope of the injected minority-carrier density curve.   From Fig. 9-12 we see that this slope increases as W decreases.   Hence, the emitter current injected into the base increases

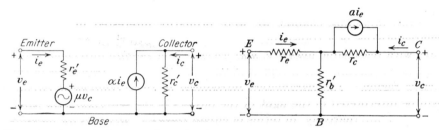

FIG. 10-2. An equivalent transistor circuit which contains a current generator and also a voltage generator.

FIG. 10-3. A T-equivalent circuit with only one (current) generator.

with reverse collector voltage.   This effect of collector voltage v_c on emitter current may be taken into account by including a voltage source μv_c in series with r_e', as indicated in Fig. 10-2.   A little thought should convince the reader that the polarity shown for generator μv_c is consistent with the physical explanation just given.

The equivalent circuit of Fig. 10-2 contains two generators, one a current source and the other a voltage source.   It is possible to make a transformation of this circuit into another one in which the generator μv_c does not appear explicitly.   This new circuit is shown in Fig. 10-3 and should be considered in conjunction with Table 10-1.   This table gives the transformation equations and in addition specifies typical values of the parameters in each of the circuits.   The derivation of the equations

TABLE 10-1

TYPICAL PARAMETER VALUES AND THE EQUATION OF
TRANSFORMATION BETWEEN THE CIRCUITS OF
FIGS. 10-2 AND 10-3

Parameter in Fig. 10-2	Transformation equations	Parameter in Fig. 10-3
$r_e' = 40$ ohms $\mu = 5 \times 10^{-4}$ $r_c' = 2 \times 10^6$ ohms $\alpha = 0.98$	$r_e = r_e' - (1 - \alpha)\mu r_c'$ $r_b' = \mu r_c'$ $r_c = (1 - \mu)r_c'$ $a = \dfrac{\alpha - \mu}{1 - \mu}$	$r_e = 20$ ohms $r_b' = 1{,}000$ ohms $r_c = 2 \times 10^6$ ohms $a = 0.98$

of transformation is an entirely straightforward matter. It is necessary only to find v_e as a function of i_e and i_c (and also v_c as a function of i_e and i_c) for both circuits and to require that the corresponding equations be identical. The transformed circuit, we observe, accounts for the effect of the collector circuit on the emitter circuit essentially through the resistor r_b' rather than through the generator $\mu v_c'$. We observe that $r_c \cong r_c'$, $a \cong \alpha$, and that $r_e = r_e'/2$. This last equation is a consequence of the Early theory, provided that the emitter efficiency can be taken as unity (Sec. 10-9).

From Eq. (5-5) for a forward-biased diode we have* that

$$r_e' = \frac{T}{11{,}600|I_E|} \qquad \text{ABSOLUTE VALUE of } I_E \qquad (10\text{-}1)$$

where I_E is the d-c (quiescent) emitter current. At room temperature (25°C) and with I_E expressed in milliamperes, Eq. (10-1) reduces to

$$r_e' = \frac{26}{|I_E|} \qquad \text{ohms} \qquad (10\text{-}2)$$

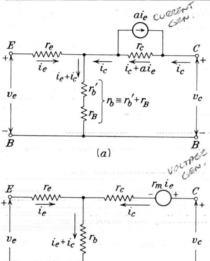

To complete the equivalent circuit the effect of the finite resistivity of the base region must be taken into account by including the d-c ohmic resistance r_B of the order of magnitude of 100 or 200 ohms in series with the base lead. The reason that this base-spreading resistance is included but no account is taken of the emitter or collector ohmic resistances is explained in Sec. 9-5. The complete *low-frequency* T-equivalent circuit is indicated in Fig. 10-4a. The resistance r_e is called *the resistance of the emitter branch*, r_c *the resistance of the collector branch*, $r_b \equiv r_b' + r_B$ *the base resistance, and a the internal short-circuit forward current gain.* The

Fig. 10-4. The T-equivalent circuit taking the base-spreading resistance r_B into account. Kirchhoff's current law has been used to find the currents in r_b and r_c. Circuit containing (a) current generator, (b) voltage generator, with $r_m \equiv ar_c$.

external short-circuit forward gain α equals the ratio $-i_c/i_e$ for $v_c = 0$. We see from Fig. 10-4a that the voltage drop in r_b is $(i_e + i_c)r_b$ and the drop in r_c is $-(i_c + ai_e)r_c$. If $v_c = 0$, then these two voltages must be

---

* For a more rigorous proof see Sec. 10-9.

equal, or

$$(i_e + i_c)r_b = -(i_c + ai_e)r_c \qquad (10\text{-}3)$$

From this equation we find that $\alpha = -i_c/i_e$ is given by

$$\alpha = \frac{ar_c + r_b}{r_c + r_b} \qquad (10\text{-}4)$$

Since $r_c \gg r_b$ and $a \cong 1$, then $\alpha \cong a$ and sometimes α is used in place of a in the equivalent circuit of Fig. 10-4a.

It is possible to replace the current generator in parallel with r_c in Fig. 10-4a with a voltage generator (whose value is the open-circuit voltage, namely $r_m i_e$, where $r_m = ar_c$) in series with r_c. The equivalent circuit containing a voltage generator is indicated in Fig. 10-4b.

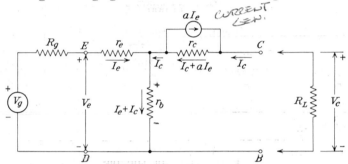

FIG. 10-5. The grounded-base T-equivalent amplifier circuit.

One other effect in a transistor, which we may note for the sake of completeness, is the modification[1] of the base-spreading resistance with current. As the collector voltage varies, the effective base width changes and hence the base-spreading resistance is actually not constant. This effect may be taken into account by including still another generator in series with r_B. Ordinarily, however, this effect is small and may be neglected.

10-2. The Grounded-base Transistor as a Small-signal Amplifier.[2] In Sec. 8-6 we dealt with the small signal equivalent circuit of vacuum-tube amplifier configurations. In that section we noted that an amplifier stage could be completely specified by stating a Thévenin-theorem equivalent circuit with respect to the amplifier-stage output terminals. We shall follow the same procedure now for the transistor circuit.

Consider the grounded-base configuration of Fig. 9-14 excited by a generator V_g of internal impedance R_g. The T-equivalent circuit is indicated in Fig. 10-5. The symbols V_g, V_e, V_c, I_e, and I_c are phasor* quantities representing variations from the quiescent values. Kirch-

---

* Because the circuits under consideration in this chapter are resistive, we shall, for simplicity, use italic instead of boldfaced type for phasor quantities.

hoff's voltage law applied to the input and output loops, respectively, yields the following equations:

$$V_g = I_e(R_g + r_e + r_b) + I_c r_b \qquad (10\text{-}5)$$
$$V_c = 0 = I_e(ar_c + r_b) + I_c(R_L + r_c + r_b) \qquad (10\text{-}6)$$

We desire the equivalent circuit looking back into the collector-base output terminals of the amplifier.   The load resistor R_L is to be considered external to and therefore not part of the amplifier.   The Thévenin's equivalent circuit is shown in Fig. 10-6, where the voltage gain is A_v and

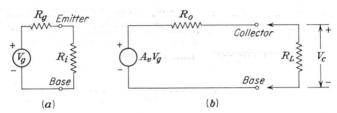

FIG. 10-6. The Thévenin's equivalent circuits between (a) input terminals and (b) output terminals.

the output impedance is R_o.   The output voltage V_c in the presence of a load is given by

$$V_c = V_g A_v \frac{R_L}{R_L + R_o} \qquad (10\text{-}7)$$

Hence, A_v and R_o may be found by expressing $V_c = -I_c R_L$ in the form indicated in Eq. (10-7), this being the same procedure that was used in Sec. 8-6.   Solving for I_c from Eqs. (10-5) and (10-6), we compute A_v and R_o to be

$$A_v = \frac{ar_c + r_b}{R_g + r_b + r_e} \qquad (10\text{-}8)$$

$$R_o = r_c - r_b \frac{ar_c - R_g - r_e}{R_g + r_b + r_e}$$
$$= \frac{r_c r_b(1 - a) + (r_e + R_g)(r_c + r_b)}{R_g + r_b + r_e} \qquad (10\text{-}9)$$

Example.   Calculate A_v directly as the ratio of output to input voltages with $R_L = \infty$.

Solution.   If the load is open-circuited, then $I_c = 0$.   From the input loop in Fig. 10-5 we find

$$I_e = \frac{V_g}{R_g + r_e + r_b}$$

The output voltage is

$$V_c = ar_c I_e + r_b I_e$$

Hence,

$$A_v = \frac{V_c}{V_g} = \frac{ar_c + r_b}{R_g + r_e + r_b}$$

in agreement with Eq. (10-8).

The expressions in Eqs. (10-8) and (10-9) may be simplified if we take account of the relative order of magnitude of the values of the parameters normally encountered in a transistor. We note from Table 10-1 that $r_c \gg r_b \gg r_e$ and that $a \cong 1$. Hence

$$A_v \cong \frac{ar_c}{R_g + r_b} \tag{10-10}$$

$$R_o \cong \frac{r_c[r_b(1 - a) + r_e + R_g]}{R_g + r_b} \tag{10-11}$$

We observe that A_v and R_o depend on R_g. This feature results, of course, from the fact that the input impedance of the transistor is not infinite. The open-circuit gain is a maximum $(A_v)_{max}$ when $R_g = 0$. In this case Eqs. (10-10) and (10-11) reduce to

$$(A_v)_{max} = \frac{ar_c}{r_b} \quad \text{and} \quad (R_o)_{R_g=0} = r_c\left[(1 - a) + \frac{r_e}{r_b}\right] \tag{10-12}$$

The gain A in the presence of a load is defined by $A \equiv V_c/V_g$ and is found from Eq. (10-7), using the appropriate values of A_v and R_o given above. The input resistance R_i to a transistor is defined as the voltage V_e applied to the input terminals divided by the input current I_e or

$$R_i = \frac{V_e}{I_e} = \frac{V_g - I_e R_g}{I_e} = \frac{V_g}{I_e} - R_g \tag{10-13}$$

Solving Eqs. (10-5) and (10-6) for I_e, we find that

$$R_i = r_e + r_b \frac{r_c(1 - a) + R_L}{r_b + r_c + R_L} \tag{10-14}$$

The range of R_i may be seen by computing R for $R_L = 0$ and $R_L = \infty$. Assuming again that $r_c \gg r_b \gg r_e$, we have approximately

$$\begin{cases} R_i = r_e + r_b(1 - a) & \text{for } R_L = 0 \tag{10-15a} \\ R_i = r_b & \text{for } R_L = \infty \tag{10-15b} \end{cases}$$

Example. By direct computation, verify Eqs. (10-15a) and (10-15b).

Solution. If $R_L = \infty$, $I_c = 0$ and the impedance seen looking into the input terminals E and B is $r_e + r_b$. Since $r_b \gg r_e$, then $R_i \cong r_b$, which agrees with Eq. (10-15b).

If $R_L = 0$, then $V_c = 0$, and it follows from the definition of α that $I_c = -\alpha I_e$. From the input mesh of Fig. 10-5 we have

$$V_e = I_e r_e + (I_e + I_c)r_b = I_e(r_e + r_b - \alpha r_b)$$

Hence,

$$R_i = \frac{V_e}{I_e} = r_e + r_b(1 - \alpha)$$

Since $\alpha \cong a$, this result is in agreement with Eq. (10-15a).

10-3. The Short-circuit Current Gain. The dual of Thévenin's theorem is Norton's theorem which states that a voltage source V in series with a resistor R is equivalent to a current source V/R in parallel with a resistor R. Hence the Norton-theorem equivalent circuit for the transistor consists of a current generator $A_v V_g / R_o$ shunted by a resistor R_o.

We have

$$\frac{A_v V_g}{R_o} = \frac{R_g A_v}{R_o} \frac{V_g}{R_g} = A_i I_g \tag{10-16}$$

where

$$A_i \equiv \frac{R_g A_v}{R_o} \quad \text{and} \quad I_g \equiv \frac{V_g}{R_g} \tag{10-17}$$

Hence, the Norton equivalent circuit with respect to the output terminals of the transistor is as shown in Fig. 10-7b. The physical meaning of the symbols A_i and I_g will appear in the following considerations.

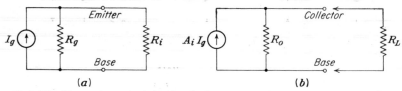

FIG. 10-7. The Norton's equivalent circuits between (a) input terminals and (b) output terminals.

We note that the Thévenin-theorem circuit becomes particularly simple [Eq. (10-12)] in the case where R_g is very small. We shall now see that the Norton-theorem circuit becomes particularly simple when R_g is very large.

If the input source which is represented in Fig. 10-5 by V_g and R_g is itself replaced by a Norton equivalent, V_g/R_g is the current furnished by the equivalent current generator source, as indicated in Fig. 10-7a. If R_g is much greater than the input resistance R_i, then I_g may be considered the input current to the transistor. If $R_L \ll R_o$, $A_i I_g$ is the load current and hence A_i represents the *short-circuit current gain*. This gain A_i goes to a maximum as R_g becomes infinite and is given by

$$(A_i)_{\max} = \frac{a r_c + r_b}{r_c + r_b} = \alpha \tag{10-18}$$

where use was made of Eqs. (10-8), (10-9), and (10-4). We also find

$$(R_o)_{R_g=\infty} = r_c + r_b \cong r_c \tag{10-19}$$

When R_g is small in comparison with the transistor input impedance, the equivalent circuit of Fig. 10-6 will be more convenient to use. If R_g

is large in comparison with the input resistance, the equivalent circuit of Fig. 10-7 will be more convenient.

10-4. The Grounded-emitter T-equivalent Circuit. Consider a transistor circuit in which the emitter terminal is common to the input and output circuits and the signal voltage V_g is applied in series with a resistance R_g to the base terminal. The equivalent circuit based upon the considerations in Sec. 10-1 is given in Fig. 10-8. This circuit may be used to find the voltage and current gains and also the input and output impedances. We note, however, that the generator in Fig. 10-8 is proportional to the emitter current whereas the input current is I_b. Hence,

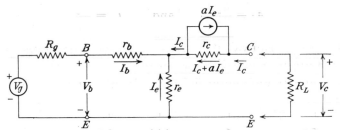

FIG. 10-8. A possible common-emitter equivalent circuit.

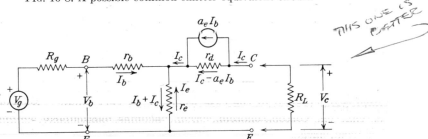

THIS ONE IS BETTER

FIG. 10-9. A common-emitter T-equivalent circuit with a current generator proportional to the input (base) current.

it is more convenient to look for another equivalent circuit containing a current generator which is proportional to I_b. For example, let us see if it is possible to specify the values a_e and r_d in Fig. 10-9 so that this circuit will be equivalent to that of Fig. 10-8. If the corresponding currents in these two circuits are equal, then the voltage across r_b is the same in Fig. 10-8 as in Fig. 10-9. A similar statement is valid with respect to the voltage across r_e. Hence, it is only necessary for the voltage across r_d in Fig. 10-9 to be equal to that across r_c in Fig. 10-8 in order that these circuits be equivalent to one another. Thus

$$(I_c - a_e I_b)r_d = (I_c + aI_e)r_c \qquad (10\text{-}20)$$

If use is made of the fact that the sum of the three transistor currents is always zero, then we have that

$$(I_c - a_e I_b)r_d = [I_c - a(I_b + I_c)]r_c \tag{10-21}$$

The coefficients of I_c and I_b, respectively, on both sides of this equation must be equal because these two circuits are to be identical, independent of the values of the currents.   Hence

$$r_d = (1 - a)r_c \tag{10-22}$$

and

$$r_m = a_e r_d = a r_c = a_e(1 - a)r_c \tag{10-23}$$

or

$$a_e = \frac{a}{1 - a} \tag{10-24}$$

Equations (10-22) and (10-24) are the necessary relationships so that the circuits of Figs. 10-8 and 10-9 are identical.

Kirchhoff's voltage law applied to the input and output loops of Fig. 10-9 yields

$$V_g = I_b(R_g + r_b + r_e) + I_c r_e \tag{10-25}$$
$$0 = I_b(r_e - a_e r_d) + I_c(r_e + r_d + R_L) \tag{10-26}$$

REPLACE $a_e I_b$ by $r_m I_b = a_e r_d I_b$

These equations are solved for I_b and I_c.   Then the input resistance R_i is found from $R_i = V_b/I_b$:

$$R_i = \frac{V_b}{I_b} = \frac{V_g - I_b R_g}{I_b} = \frac{V_g}{I_b} - R_g \tag{10-27}$$

If $V_c = -I_c R_L$ is put in the form indicated in Eq. (10-7), then the open-circuit voltage gain A_v and the output impedance R_o can be evaluated.   Finally, the short-circuit current gain A_i can be found from $A_i = A_v R_g/R_o$.   The common-collector configuration may be analyzed in a similar manner using the common-emitter equivalent circuit.

10-5. Comparison of Transistor Amplifier Configurations.   Table 10-2 gives exact expressions for A_v, A_i, R_o, and R_i for the various configurations.   The maximum voltage gain $(A_v)_{max}$ may be obtained from the table simply by letting $R_g = 0$ in the expressions for A_v.   Similarly, the expressions for $(A_i)_{max}$ may be obtained from A_i by letting $R_g \to \infty$. Note that the quantities A_v, A_i, R_i, and R_o in Table 10-2 are the parameters in the equivalent circuits of Figs. 10-6 and 10-7.   To compute the voltage or current gain in a particular case, it is still necessary to take account of the loading effect of R_L.   The formulas of Table 10-2 are useful for general-reference purposes but are too complicated to yield any easy insight into transistor performance.

An easier comparison may be made from Table 10-3.   Here we have computed for the various configurations the voltage gain $(A_v)_{max}$ when the

TABLE 10-2

EXACT FORMULAS FOR THE
VARIOUS TRANSISTOR CONFIGURATIONS

A_v = open-circuit voltage gain
A_i = short-circuit current gain
R_o = output impedance
R_i = input impedance
$r_m = ar_c = a_e r_d$
$r_d = r_c(1 - a) = r_c - r_m$

Grounded base

$$A_v = \frac{r_m + r_b}{R_g + r_b + r_e}$$

$$A_i = \frac{R_g(r_m + r_b)}{r_c(R_g + r_b + r_e) - r_b(r_m - R_g - r_e)}$$

$$R_o = r_c - r_b \frac{r_m - R_g - r_e}{R_g + r_b + r_e}$$

$$R_i = r_e + r_b \frac{r_d + R_L}{r_b + r_c + R_L}$$

Grounded emitter

$$A_v = - \frac{r_m - r_e}{R_g + r_b + r_e}$$

$$A_i = \frac{-R_g(r_m - r_e)}{r_e(R_g + r_b + r_c) + r_d(R_g + r_b)}$$

$$R_o = r_d + r_e \frac{R_g + r_b + r_m}{R_g + r_b + r_e}$$

$$R_i = r_b + r_e \frac{r_c + R_L}{r_d + r_e + R_L}$$

Grounded collector

$$A_v = \frac{r_c}{R_g + r_b + r_c}$$

$$A_i = \frac{R_g r_c}{r_e(R_g + r_b + r_c) + r_d(R_g + r_b)}$$

$$R_o = r_e + r_d \frac{R_g + r_b}{R_g + r_b + r_c}$$

$$R_i = r_b + r_c \frac{r_e + R_L}{r_d + r_e + R_L}$$

---

input is a zero-impedance voltage source and the current gain $(A_i)_{max}$ when the input is a perfect current source. In addition, the output impedance for both cases and the total range over which the input impedance may vary have also been tabulated. In this table we have taken account of the approximations which may be allowed because of the fact that $r_c \gg r_b \gg r_e$. In computing numerical-value parameters, we have used $r_c = 2$ megohms, $r_b = 1$ kilohm, $r_e = 20$ ohms, and $a \; (= \alpha) = 0.98$.

TABLE 10-3

APPROXIMATE FORMULAS ($r_c \gg r_b \gg r_e$) FOR THE
VARIOUS TRANSISTOR CONFIGURATIONS

Numerical values calculated for $r_c = 2$ megohms, $r_b = 1$ kilohm, $r_e = 20$ ohms, $a\ (\cong \alpha) = 0.98$.

Parameter	Grounded base	Grounded emitter	Grounded collector
$(A_v)_{max}$ $R_g = 0$	$\dfrac{ar_c}{r_b} = 1{,}960$	$-\dfrac{ar_c}{r_b} = -1{,}960$	$1 \approx \dfrac{r_c}{r_c}$ SEE TABLE 10-2
$(A_i)_{max}$ $R_g = \infty$	$a = 0.98$	$-\dfrac{a}{1-a} = -49$	$\dfrac{1}{1-a} = 50$
R_o $R_g = 0$	$r_c\left[(1-a) + \dfrac{r_e}{r_b}\right]$ $= 80$ kilohms	$r_c\left[(1-a) + \dfrac{ar_e}{r_b}\right]$ $= 80$ kilohms	$r_e + r_b(1-a) = 40$ ohms
R_o $R_g = \infty$	$r_c = 2$ megohms	$r_c(1-a) = 40$ kilohms	$r_c(1-a) = 40$ kilohms
R_i $R_L = 0$	$r_e + r_b(1-a)$ $= 40$ ohms	$r_b + \dfrac{r_e}{1-a} = 2$ kilohms	$r_b + \dfrac{r_e}{1-a} = 2$ kilohms
R_i $R_L = \infty$	$r_b = 1$ kilohm	$r_b = 1$ kilohm	$r_c = 2$ megohms

The table brings out the relative versatility of the grounded-emitter configuration. This configuration is capable of both a voltage gain and a current gain, features not shared by the other configurations. To realize a gain nominally equal to $(A_v)_{max}$ would require not only that a zero-impedance voltage source be used but also that R_L be many times larger than the output impedance. Normally, however, so large a value of R_L is not feasible. Suppose, for example, that a manufacturer specifies a maximum collector voltage of, say, 30 volts. Then we should not be inclined to use a collector supply voltage in excess of this maximum voltage since in such a case the collector voltage would be exceeded if the transistor were driven to cutoff. Suppose further that the transistor is designed to carry a collector current of, say, 5 ma when biased in the middle of its active region. Then the load resistor should be selected to have a resistance of about 15 volts/5 ma = 3 kilohms. Using the values in Table 10-3, we compute for the grounded emitter a voltage gain under load of

$$A = -1{,}960 \times \tfrac{3}{83} = -71$$

Of course the load resistor may be smaller than 3 kilohms, as, for example, when a transistor is used to drive another transistor. Or in some applications a much higher load resistor may be acceptable.

When used as a voltage amplifier, the grounded-base configuration is capable roughly of the same gain as the grounded emitter. The grounded-collector circuit has a maximum voltage gain $(A_v)_{max}$ which is, at most, unity. To achieve this gain, the load resistor must be very large in comparison with the output impedance.

The grounded emitter and grounded collector are both capable of providing current gain which is nominally the same in both cases. It is to be noted, however, that in both cases the current gain is not a very stable characteristic. We can compute, for the grounded-emitter case, that

$$\frac{d(A_i)_{max}}{(A_i)_{max}} = \frac{1}{1-a}\frac{da}{a} \tag{10-28}$$

If $a = 0.98$, then $1/(1 - a) = 50$, and Eq. (10-28) indicates that a 1 per cent change in a will result in a 50 per cent change in $(A_i)_{max}$. An approximately similar relationship applies in the grounded-collector case. For this reason, too, we may expect that transistor characteristic curves of collector current vs. collector voltage for various values of base current (Fig. 9-8) will be subject to a great deal of variation.

The output impedance is least for the grounded-collector and greatest for the grounded-base configuration for a given value of R_g. The output impedance for the common collector may be less than 100 ohms whereas R_o for the common-base circuit may exceed 100 kilohms. The common-emitter configuration shows the least variation of output impedance with R_g, and for this circuit $R_o \cong 60$ kilohms.

The input impedance is least for the common-base and greatest for the common-collector configuration. The input impedance for the grounded-base circuit may be less than 100 ohms. The common-collector configuration shows the greatest variation of R_i with load resistance and, as indicated in Table 10-3, 2 kilohms $< R_i < 2$ megohms. The least variation of R_i with R_L is exhibited by the common-emitter circuit, and for this circuit, $R_i \cong 1.5$ kilohms.

Example. Consider the two-stage transistor amplifier of Fig. 10-10. The biasing arrangements and the coupling capacitors have been omitted for simplicity. The parameters of each transistor are

$$r_e = 26 \text{ ohms} \qquad r_b = 1,320 \text{ ohms}$$
$$r_c = 1 \text{ megohm} \qquad \text{and} \qquad \alpha = 0.975$$

Evaluate (*a*) the input impedance, (*b*) the current gain, and (*c*) the voltage amplification.

Solution. *a.* The input impedance of a stage depends upon its load. The effective load impedance R_{L1}' of the first stage is R_{L1} in parallel with the input impedance R_{i2}

of the second stage. Hence, we must first find R_{i2}. From Table 10-2,

$$R_{i2} = r_b + r_e \frac{r_c + R_{L2}}{r_d + r_e + R_{L2}} \tag{10-29}$$

Since

$$r_d = r_c(1 - a) = (10^6)(1 - 0.975) = 25 \times 10^3$$

then

$$R_{i2} = 1{,}320 + 26 \frac{10^6 + 25 \times 10^3}{(25 \times 10^3 + 26 + 25 \times 10^3)}$$
$$= 1{,}850 \text{ ohms} = 1.85 \text{ K}$$

Hence,

$$R_{L1}' = \frac{R_{L1} R_{i2}}{R_{L1} + R_{i2}} = \frac{(25)(1.85)}{25 + 1.85} = 1.73 \text{ K}$$

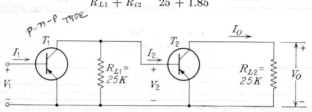

Fig. 10-10. A two-stage amplifier.

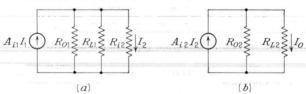

(a)　　　　(b)

Fig. 10-11. The Norton's equivalent circuit between output terminals of (a) the first stage and (b) the second stage in Fig. 10-10.

Using Eq. (10-29) with R_{i2} replaced by R_{i1} and R_{L2} replaced by R_{L1}', we find

$$R_{i1} = 1{,}320 + 26 \frac{10^6 + 1.73 \times 10^3}{(25 \times 10^3 + 26 + 1.73 \times 10^3)}$$
$$= 2{,}290 \text{ ohms} = 2.29 \text{ K}$$

b. The Norton's equivalent circuits between the output terminals of the first stage and of the second stage, respectively, are indicated in Fig. 10-11a and b. The *short-circuit* current gains of the two stages are A_{i1} and A_{i2}, respectively. The current gains A_{i1}' of the first stage, A_{i2}' of the second stage, and the over-all current gain A_i' *under load* are defined, respectively, by

$$A_{i1}' \equiv \frac{I_2}{I_1} \qquad A_{i2}' \equiv \frac{I_o}{I_2} \qquad A_i' \equiv \frac{I_o}{I_1} \tag{10-30}$$

From Eqs. (10-30) it follows that

$$A_i' = A_{i1}' A_{i2}' \tag{10-31}$$

In a multistage amplifier the over-all current gain equals the product of the current gains of the individual stages. In general, the loaded current gain is *not* equal to the short-circuit current gain.   If R' is the parallel combination of R_{o1} and R_{L1},

$$R' \equiv \frac{R_{o1}R_{L1}}{R_{o1} + R_{L1}} \tag{10-32}$$

then it follows from Fig. 10-11a that

$$I_2 = A_{i1}I_1 \frac{R'}{R' + R_{i2}} \tag{10-33}$$

or

$$A_{i1}' = \frac{A_{i1}}{1 + R_{i2}/R'} \tag{10-34}$$

We see that the loaded current gain A_{i1}' equals the short-circuit current gain A_{i1} only if R_{i2} is negligible compared with R'.   Similarly, we find from Fig. 10-11b that

$$A_{i2}' = \frac{A_{i2}}{1 + R_{L2}/R_{o2}} \tag{10-35}$$

In order to evaluate the current gains we must first find the output impedance of each stage.   A comparison of Fig. 10-11 with Fig. 10-7 (which defines the short-circuit current A_i) shows that since I_1 (and also I_2) is the current directly into the input terminals then, effectively, $R_g = \infty$.   For this value of R_g we find from Table 10-3 that $R_{o1} = R_{o2} \cong r_d = 25$ K and

[handwritten: PLUGGING IN VALUES GIVEN FOR THIS EXAMPLE —]

$$A_{i1} = A_{i2} = -\frac{a}{1-a} = \frac{-0.975}{1 - 0.975} = -39.0$$

From Eq. (10-32), $R' = 12.5$ K, and from Eqs. (10-34) and (10-35)

$$A_{i1}' = \frac{-39.0}{1 + 1.85/12.5} = -34.0 \qquad A_{i2}' = \frac{-39.0}{1 + 25.0/25.0} = -19.5$$

The over-all current gain is

$$A_i' = A_{i1}'A_{i2}' = (-34.0)(-19.5) = 663$$

c.   The voltage amplification A is given by

$$A = \frac{V_o}{V_1} = \frac{I_oR_{L2}}{I_1R_{i1}} = A_i'\frac{R_{L2}}{R_{i1}} = (663)\left(\frac{25.0}{2.29}\right) = 7,250 \tag{10-36}$$

The voltage gain may also be calculated directly without first finding the current gains.   In order to do so, the Thévenin's equivalent circuits of the two stages are drawn in Fig. 10-12.   Under load the voltage gains A_1 of the first stage, A_2 of the second stage, and the over-all voltage amplification A are defined by

$$A_1 \equiv \frac{V_2}{V_1} \qquad A_2 \equiv \frac{V_o}{V_2} \qquad A \equiv \frac{V_o}{V_1} \tag{10-37}$$

From Eqs. (10-37) it follows that

$$A = A_1A_2 \tag{10-38}$$

In a multistage amplifier the over-all voltage amplification equals the product of the voltage gains of the individual stages.   From Fig. 10-12,

$$A_1 = \frac{A_{v1}}{1 + R_{o1}/R_{L1}'} \qquad A_2 = \frac{A_{v2}}{1 + R_{o2}/R_{L2}} \tag{10-39}$$

where R_{L1}' is the parallel combination of R_{L1} and R_{i2} and equals 1.73 kilohms. A comparison of Fig. 10-12 with Fig. 10-6 (which defines the open-circuit gain $\overline{A_v}$)

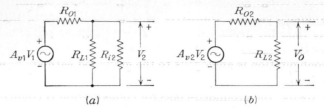

(a)   (b)

FIG. 10-12. The Thévenin's equivalent circuit between output terminals of (a) the first stage and (b) the second stage in Fig. 10-10.

shows that since the voltage V_1 (and also V_2) is taken directly at the input terminals then, effectively, $R_g = 0$. For this value of R_g we find from Table 10-3 that

$$R_{o1} = R_{o2} = r_c \left[(1 - a) + \frac{ar_e}{r_b} \right] = 10^6 \left(1 - 0.975 + \frac{0.975 \times 26}{1,320} \right) = 44.2 \text{ K}$$

and

$$A_{v1} = A_{v2} = \frac{-ar_c}{r_b} = \frac{-0.975 \times 10^6}{1,320} = -738$$

From Eqs. (10-39),

$$A_1 = \frac{-738}{1 + 44.2/1.73} = -27.6 \qquad A_2 = \frac{-738}{1 + 44.2/25.0} = -266$$

and, from Eq. (10-38),

$$A = A_1 A_2 = (-27.6)(-266) = 7,350$$

which agrees with the value found above based upon the current-gain calculation.

Note that R_{o2} in Fig. 10-11b is not numerically equal to R_{o2} in Fig. 10-12b. Furthermore, in neither of these circuits does R_{o2} represent the true output impedance of the over-all two-stage amplifier. It must be emphasized that the only significance which should be attached to the Norton's equivalent circuits of Fig. 10-11 is that they are useful for calculating the current gains of each stage as defined by Eq. (10-30). Similarly the Thévenin's equivalent circuits of Fig. 10-12 are to be used only for the purpose of calculating the voltage gains as defined by Eq. (10-37).

10-6. A Vacuum-tube–Transistor Analogy.[3]

It is possible to draw a very rough analogy between a transistor and a vacuum tube. In this analogy the base, emitter, and collector of a transistor are identified, respectively, with the grid, cathode, and plate of a vacuum tube. Correspondingly, the grounded-base, grounded-emitter, and grounded-collector configurations are identified, respectively, with the grounded-grid, grounded-cathode, and grounded-plate (cathode-follower) vacuum-tube circuits, as in Fig. 10-13.

Consider, for example, the circuits of Fig. 10-13a. For the tube circuit, we find that in the normal amplifier region $|I_k| = |I_p|$. In the transistor circuit, in the active region, we find that $|I_e| \cong |I_c|$, the difference between I_e and I_c being of the order of 2 per cent. In both the transistor and tube circuits of Fig. 10-13a, we find that the input impedance is low because of the large current at low voltage which must be furnished by the driving generator.   Also, both circuits are capable of considerable voltage gain without inverting the input signal.

The grounded-emitter transistor of Fig. 10-13b has a higher input impedance than the grounded-base.   As a voltage amplifier a large gain with polarity inversion is possible.   In all these respects the grounded-emitter configuration is analogous to the grounded-cathode vacuum-tube amplifier stage.

In Fig. 10-13c, the grounded-collector configuration is compared to the grounded-plate (cathode-follower) circuit.   As a matter of fact, the

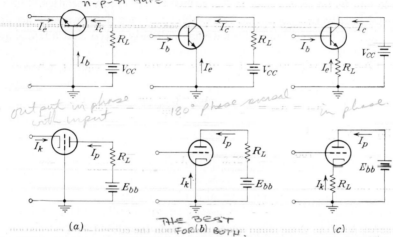

n-p-n TYPE

output in phase with input   *180° phase reversal*   *in phase*

(a)   *THE BEST FOR BOTH*   (b)   (c)

Fig. 10-13. Analogous transistor and vacuum-tube circuits.   (a) Grounded base and grounded grid.   (b) Common emitter and common cathode.   (c) Emitter follower and cathode follower.

grounded-collector configuration is often referred to as the *emitter-follower* circuit.   In the emitter-follower circuit the input current is relatively small, and the voltage difference between base and emitter is essentially the small voltage drop across the forward biased emitter junction when operating in the active region.   Hence, we may expect the input voltage and the output voltage, as in a cathode follower, to be nominally the same.   The emitter follower, as the cathode follower, provides a gain of the order of unity without polarity inversion when used as a voltage amplifier.   The emitter follower may also be expected to handle an input signal comparable in size with the collector supply voltage.   The input current swing from cutoff to saturation is the same for grounded-emitter and grounded-collector operation, but in the grounded-collector operation the input voltage swing is larger.

The cutoff region of the transistor corresponds to the region in the vacuum tube where the tube grid bias is larger than the cutoff bias. The active region of the transistor corresponds to the region in which the tube operates as a linear amplifier. This region covers not only the region within the grid base but also the region of positive grid voltages where the tube operates linearly. The saturation region of the transistor corresponds to the tube region where the grid is so positive and the plate voltage is so low that the plate current is almost independent of grid voltage (see Fig. A9-9). In the transistor the base takes current at all points in its active region, while in the tube the grid draws appreciable current only when it is positive. The analogy may be improved by assuming that cutoff occurs in the tube at zero grid bias; *i.e.*, the grid base is zero. Also, the volt-ampere transistor characteristics are shaped more like pentode curves (see Chap. 11) rather than triode characteristics.

It need hardly be emphasized that the analogies drawn above are far from exact. On several occasions we have already noted that a transistor is a more complicated device than a vacuum tube. In the former the current is due to charge carriers of both signs moving in a solid, whereas in the latter the current is carried by electrons in a vacuum. There is nothing in a vacuum tube corresponding to minority-carrier storage in a transistor. The low-frequency input impedance of a grounded-cathode or cathode-follower circuit is infinite whereas a transistor has a relatively low input impedance in all three configurations. The low-frequency equivalent circuit of a tube contains only two parameters, μ and r_p (or g_m and r_p), whereas four parameters, r_e, r_c, r_b, and a, are required in the corresponding transistor small-signal equivalent circuit.

The analogies are principally useful as mnemonic aids and for the purpose of providing an appreciation of the approximate operation of a transistor circuit to one who is more familiar with vacuum-tube circuits. For example, we may note that the most generally useful tube circuit is the grounded-cathode circuit. We may then expect from our analogy that the grounded-emitter configuration will occupy the same preferred position in the transistor configurations. This anticipated result is borne out in practice.

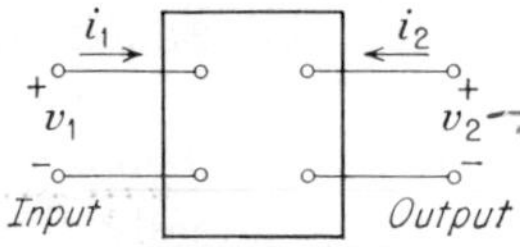

10-7. The Small-signal Parameters. We obtained the circuit of Fig. 10-2 by considering the physical behavior of the transistor. However, it must be emphasized that this circuit represents one form of the most general linear, lumped, active, resistive, four-terminal network. That such is the case may be seen by considering the box in Fig. 10-14 which is to represent an arbitrary linear four-terminal network. The small-signal (incremental) input voltage v_1 and the output current i_2 are linear combinations of the input current i_1 and output voltage v_2 so that we may write

FIG. 10-14. An arbitrary four-terminal network.

$$v_1 = h_{11}i_1 + h_{12}v_2 \qquad i_2 = h_{21}i_1 + h_{22}v_2 \qquad (10\text{-}40)$$

$$v_1 = h_i i_1 + \mu_r v_2 \qquad i_2 = \alpha_f i_1 + h_o v_2$$

[annotations: i_b, v_{ce} over first equation; i_b, v_{ee} over second equation]

The quantities h_{11}, h_{12}, h_{21}, and h_{22} are called the H or *hybrid parameters* and may be obtained easily experimentally. It follows from Eqs. (10-40) that these parameters are defined as follows:

$$h_{11} = \frac{v_1}{i_1}\bigg|_{v_2=0} = \text{input resistance with output short-circuited} \quad = h_i$$

$$h_{12} = \frac{v_1}{v_2}\bigg|_{i_1=0} = \text{fraction of output voltage at input with input open-circuited, or more}$$
$$\text{simply, reverse open-circuit voltage amplification} \quad = \mu_r$$

$$h_{21} = \frac{i_2}{i_1}\bigg|_{v_2=0} = \text{current gain with output short-circuited} \quad = \alpha_f$$

$$h_{22} = \frac{i_2}{v_2}\bigg|_{i_1=0} = \text{output conductance with input open-circuited} \quad = h_o$$

The following convenient alternative subscript notation is recommended by the IRE Standards:[4] THESE ARE THE ONES TO USE.

$$i = 11 = \text{input} \qquad o = 22 = \text{output}$$
$$f = 21 = \text{forward transfer} \qquad r = 12 = \text{reverse transfer}$$

Another subscript (b, e, or c) is added to designate the type of configuration. For example,

$$h_{ib} = h_{11b} = \text{input impedance in common-base configuration}$$
$$\alpha_{fe} = h_{fe} = h_{21e} = \text{short-circuit forward current gain in common-emitter circuit}$$

Another notation which is found in the literature but is *not* recommended by the Standards is to replace the numbers 1 and 2 by the letters b, e, or c which represent the input and output terminals. For example, in the common-emitter configuration, 1 is replaced by b and 2 is replaced by c so that $h_{cb} = \text{short-circuit current gain}$.

From the definitions given above and from the T-equivalent circuit of Fig. 10-5 for the grounded-base configuration the following approximate relationships are found to be valid:

$$h_{ib} = r_e + r_b(1 - a) \quad \mu_{rb} = h_{rb} = \frac{r_b}{r_c} \quad \alpha_{fb} = h_{fb} = -a \quad h_{ob} = \frac{1}{r_c} \quad (10\text{-}41)$$

As an example of how to verify these relationships, consider the equation for h_{ib}. From Fig. 10-5,

$$v_e = i_e(r_e + r_b) + i_c r_b \qquad (10\text{-}42)$$

If the output is short-circuited, then $i_c = -\alpha i_e \cong -a i_e$, and Eq. (10-42) becomes

$$\frac{v_e}{i_e} = r_e + (1 - a)r_b \qquad (10\text{-}43)$$

Since, by definition,

$$h_{ib} = \frac{v_e}{i_e}\bigg|_{v_c=0}$$

then Eq. (10-43) verifies the first of Eqs. (10-41).

If the hybrid parameters are measured (Sec. 10-8) or are supplied by the transistor manufacturer, the parameters in the common-base T-equivalent circuit are calculated from the following relationships obtained from Eqs. (10-41):

$$a = -h_{fb} \qquad r_c = \frac{1}{h_{ob}} \qquad r_b = \frac{h_{rb}}{h_{ob}} \qquad r_e = h_{ib} - \frac{h_{rb}(1 + h_{fb})}{h_{ob}}$$

$$\text{(10-44)}$$

The equivalent circuit of the common-emitter configuration using hybrid parameters is given in Fig. 10-15. The corresponding T-equivalent circuit is indicated in Fig. 10-9. Proceeding as above, we can derive the following approximate relationships:

$$h_{ie} = r_b + (1 + a_e)r_e \qquad h_{re} = \frac{r_e}{r_d} \qquad h_{fe} = a_e \qquad h_{oe} = \frac{1}{r_d} \quad \text{(10-45)}$$

and

$$a_e = h_{fe} = \frac{a}{1 - a} \qquad r_d = \frac{1}{h_{oe}} \qquad r_e = \frac{h_{re}}{h_{oe}} \qquad r_b = h_{ie} - \frac{h_{re}(1 + h_{fe})}{h_{oe}}$$

$$\text{(10-46)}$$

for common emitter

Often a manufacturer will supply three sets of curves of hybrid parameters. In one of these the independent variable is quiescent emitter current, in the second it is quiescent collector voltage, and in the third it is junction temperature.

The hybrid parameters are so called because they do not all have the same dimensions; h_i represents a resistance and h_o a conductance, whereas h_r and h_f are dimensionless. This situation arises because in the arbitrary four-terminal network of Fig. 10-14 we have chosen input *current* and output *voltage* as independent variables. If, instead, we select both currents as independent variables and express the voltages as linear combinations of the currents, then each of the four coefficients z_{11}, z_{12}, z_{21}, and z_{22} has the dimension of ohms. These factors are called the *impedance* (z) or *resistance* (r) parameters. Similarly, the two voltages may be chosen as the independent variables and the currents expressed as linear combinations of these voltages. The four coefficients y_{11}, y_{12}, y_{21}, and y_{22} each has the dimension of mhos, and these are called the *admittance* (y) or *conductance* (g) *parameters*.

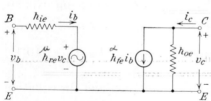

FIG. 10-15. The common-emitter configuration described by hybrid parameters.

10-8. Measurement of H Parameters.[5] Based upon the definitions given in the preceding section, simple experiments may be carried out for the direct measurement of the hybrid parameters.   Consider the circuit of Fig. 10-16.   The desired quiescent collector voltage is obtained from the variable supply V_{CC}.   The desired quiescent emitter current is obtained by adjusting the supply V_{EE} and/or the resistor R_2.   The impedance of the inductor L (250 henrys) and the resistor R_2 at the audio frequency (270 cps) at which the measurements are made is large compared with the transistor input impedance R_i.   The value of R_1 (10 kilohms) is large compared with R_i and also compared with the reactance of C.   The drop across R_3 (1 kilohm) due to the small base current is negligible compared with the drop across R_1 or the voltage V_{CC}.   Because of these inequalities, we may consider the signal input current to be $i_1 = v_s/R_1$ and the signal

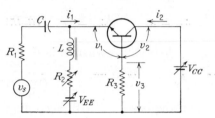

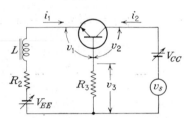

FIG. 10-16. Circuit for measuring h_{ib} and h_{fb}.

FIG. 10-17. Circuit for measuring h_{rb} and h_{ob}.

output voltage v_2 to be zero.   If we short out R_3, the value of h_{ib} is given by

$$h_{ib} = \frac{v_1}{i_1}\bigg|_{v_2=0} = \frac{v_1 R_1}{v_s} \qquad (10\text{-}47)$$

Hence, the input resistance may be calculated from the two measured voltages v_1 and v_s.

Since $h_{fb} = -a$ has a magnitude which is close to unity, it is customary to measure $1 + h_{fb}$ rather than h_{fb} directly.   By definition,

$$1 + h_{fb} = 1 + \frac{i_2}{i_1}\bigg|_{v_2=0} = \frac{i_1 + i_2}{i_1}\bigg|_{v_2=0} = \frac{v_3}{R_3}\frac{R_1}{v_s} \qquad (10\text{-}48)$$

because the current through R_3 is $i_1 + i_2 = v_3/R_3$.   Hence, the short-circuit current gain may be calculated from the measured voltage v_3 and v_s.

The circuit of Fig. 10-17 may be used to measure h_{rb} and h_{ob}.   The signal is now applied to the collector circuit.   Because the impedance of L and R_2 is large compared with R_i, the emitter circuit may be considered effectively open-circuited as far as the signal is concerned, so that $i_1 = 0$. If we short out R_3, then

$$h_{rb} = \frac{v_1}{v_2}\bigg|_{i_1=0} \qquad (10\text{-}49)$$

and hence the reverse amplification factor is obtained from the two measured voltages v_1 and v_2. The output conductance is defined by

$$h_{ob} = \frac{i_2}{v_2}\bigg|_{i_1=0} = \frac{v_3}{R_3 v_2}\bigg|_{i_1=0} \tag{10-50}$$

because with $i_1 = 0$ the current in R_3 is $i_2 = v_3/R_3$. Hence h_{ob} is obtained from the measured voltages v_2 and v_3.

OMIT

10-9. The Hybrid Parameters in Terms of the Physical Constants of the Transistor. In this section we shall return to the intrinsic transistor of Fig. 10-2 and shall neglect the base-spreading resistance r_B. From the definitions of the hybrid parameters in Sec. 10-7 and from Fig. 10-2, it should be clear that

$$h_{ib} = r_e' \qquad h_{rb} = \mu \qquad h_{fb} = -\alpha \qquad h_{ob} = \frac{1}{r_c'} \tag{10-51}$$

common-base configuration

The theory of the transistor alpha is given in Sec. 9-7, where it is shown that

$$-h_{fb} = \alpha = \beta\gamma \tag{10-52}$$

where the transport factor β depends upon the base width W according to Eq. (9-38) and the emitter efficiency γ as a function of W is given by Eq. (9-39).

In order to find the input impedance h_{ib}, note that

$$\frac{1}{h_{ib}} = \frac{i_e}{v_e}\bigg|_{v_c=0} = \frac{\partial I_E}{\partial V_E}\bigg|_{V_c \text{ const}} \tag{10-53}$$

and that I_E and V_E are related by Eq. (9-29), namely,

$$I_E = a_{11}(\epsilon^{V_E/V_T} - 1) + a_{12}(\epsilon^{V_C/V_T} - 1) \tag{10-54}$$

Hence,

$$\frac{1}{h_{ib}} = \frac{a_{11}\epsilon^{V_E/V_T}}{V_T} \tag{10-55}$$

In the active region where the emitter is forward-biased and the collector is reverse-biased,

$$I_E = a_{11}\epsilon^{V_E/V_T} - (a_{11} + a_{12})$$

In the cutoff region where both the emitter and the collector are reverse-biased the emitter current equals $-(a_{11} + a_{12})$. Since this cutoff current is very small, then

$$I_E \cong a_{11}\epsilon^{V_E/V_T}$$

and from Eq. (10-55)

$$h_{ib} = r_e' = \frac{V_T}{I_E} \tag{10-56}$$

This expression is in agreement with Eq. (10-1), which was derived somewhat intuitively.

In order to evaluate the output conductance h_{ob} we recall that in the active region where the collector is reverse-biased the collector current may be approximated by

$$I_C = -\alpha I_E + I_{CO}$$

and hence that

$$h_{ob} = \frac{i_c}{v_c}\bigg|_{i_e=0} = \frac{\partial I_C}{\partial V_C}\bigg|_{I_E \text{ const}} = -I_E \frac{\partial \alpha}{\partial V_C} \qquad (10\text{-}57)$$

Now according to the Early theory[1] the reason that α varies with V_C is that α depends upon the base width W and the effective space-charge layer varies with collector voltage. Hence,

$$h_{ob} = \frac{1}{r_c'} = -I_E \frac{\partial \alpha}{\partial W} \frac{\partial W}{\partial V_C} \qquad (10\text{-}58)$$

The dependence of W upon V_C is determined by the type of junction under consideration. For a grown junction the relationship is given by Prob. 5-10 whereas for an alloy junction it is given in Eq. (5-12).

In order to evaluate the reverse feedback factor h_{rb} defined by

$$h_{rb} = \frac{v_e}{v_c}\bigg|_{i_e=0} = \frac{\partial V_E}{\partial V_C}\bigg|_{I_E \text{ const}} \qquad (10\text{-}59)$$

we differentiate Eq. (10-54) with respect to V_C. We must remember that a_{11} and a_{12} are functions of W and hence are not independent of V_C. The result of the differentiation is

$$0 = \frac{a_{11}\epsilon^{V_E/V_T}}{V_T} \frac{\partial V_E}{\partial V_C}\bigg|_{I_E} + \frac{\partial a_{11}}{\partial V_C}(\epsilon^{V_E/V_T} - 1) + \frac{a_{12}\epsilon^{V_C/V_T}}{V_T}$$
$$+ \frac{\partial a_{12}}{\partial V_C}(\epsilon^{V_C/V_T} - 1) \qquad (10\text{-}60)$$

In the active region where the collector is reverse-biased we may neglect the terms containing ϵ^{V_C/V_T}, and Eq. (10-60) becomes

$$-\frac{a_{11}\epsilon^{V_E/V_T}}{V_T} h_{rb} = \frac{\partial a_{11}\epsilon^{V_E/V_T}}{\partial V_C} - \frac{\partial a_{11}}{\partial V_C} - \frac{\partial a_{12}}{\partial V_C} \qquad (10\text{-}61)$$

From Eq. (9-30) it follows that

$$\frac{\partial a_{11}}{\partial V_C} = -\frac{\partial a_{12}}{\partial V_C}$$

and Eq. (10-61) reduces to

$$h_{rb} = -\frac{V_T}{a_{11}} \frac{\partial a_{11}}{\partial V_C} = \frac{V_T}{a_{21}} \frac{\partial a_{11}}{\partial V_C} \qquad (10\text{-}62)$$

because, from Eq. (9-12), $a_{11} = -a_{21}/\alpha$ and $\alpha \cong 1$. If use is made of

Eqs. (9-30) and (9-32), we finally obtain

$$h_{rb} = \mu = \frac{V_T}{W} \frac{\partial W}{\partial V_C} \tag{10-63}$$

The hybrid parameters can be evaluated in terms of the physical constants of the transistor by means of the above equations. Since $\alpha = \beta\gamma$, then $\partial\alpha/\partial W$ needed in Eq. (10-58) is given as

$$\frac{\partial\alpha}{\partial W} = \beta \frac{\partial\gamma}{\partial W} + \gamma \frac{\partial\beta}{\partial W} \tag{10-64}$$

From Eqs. (9-38) and (9-39) we find that

$$\frac{\partial\gamma}{\partial W} = -\frac{1-\gamma}{W} \qquad \frac{\partial\beta}{\partial W} = \frac{-2(1-\beta)}{W} \tag{10-65}$$

Remembering that $\beta \cong 1$ and $\gamma \cong 1$, Eq. (10-64) reduces to

$$\frac{\partial\alpha}{\partial W} = -\frac{1}{W}[2(1-\beta) + (1-\gamma)] \tag{10-66}$$

Based upon the above theory an interesting expression can be obtained for the product $\mu r_c'$ which appears in the transformation equations in Table 10-1. From Eqs. (10-63) and (10-58) we find

$$\mu r_c' = -\frac{V_T}{I_E W(\partial\alpha/\partial W)} \tag{10-67}$$

Using Eqs. (10-56) and (10-66),

$$\mu r_c' = \frac{r_e'}{2(1-\beta) + (1-\gamma)} \tag{10-68}$$

From Table 10-1,

$$r_e = r_e' - (1-\alpha)\mu r_c' = r_e'\left[1 - \frac{1-\alpha}{2(1-\beta) + (1-\gamma)}\right] \tag{10-69}$$

The emitter efficiency is often much closer to unity than is the transport factor. Under these circumstances we may assume that $\gamma \cong 1$ and $\alpha \cong \beta$ so that Eq. (10-69) reduces to

$$r_e = \frac{r_e'}{2} = \frac{V_T}{2I_E} \tag{10-70}$$

From Table 10-1 we have that $r_b' = \mu r_c'$. Subject to the condition that γ is very close to unity, Eq. (10-68) reduces to

$$r_b' = \frac{r_e'}{2(1-\alpha)} = \frac{r_e}{1-\alpha} \tag{10-71}$$

Example.   The 2N34 transistor has a total base resistance r_b of 800 ohms and $\alpha =$ 0.975 at a quiescent emitter current of 1.0 ma.   Find the value of r_b at $I_E = 0.5$ ma.

Solution.   From Eq. (10-70), at room temperature and a quiescent current of 1.0 ma,

$$r_e = \frac{0.026}{(2)(10^{-3})} = 13 \text{ ohms}$$

From Eq. (10-71),

$$r_b' = \frac{13}{0.025} = 520 \text{ ohms}$$

If the base-spreading resistance is designated by r_B, then

$$r_b = r_B + r_b'$$

or

$$r_B = 800 - 520 = 280 \text{ ohms}$$

Now for $I_E = 0.5$ ma, r_e and hence r_b' is twice the value found at 1.0 ma.   Hence,

$$r_b' = (2)(520) = 1,040 \text{ ohms}$$

and

$$r_b = 280 + 1,040 = 1,320 \text{ ohms}$$

REFERENCES

1. EARLY, J. M., "Effects of Space-change Layer Widening in Junction Transistors," *Proc. IRE*, **40**, 1401–1406, November, 1952.
2. LO, A. W., R. O. ENDRES, I. ZAWELS, F. D. WALDHAUER, and C. C. CHENG, "Transistor Electronics," Chaps. 2 and 3, Prentice-Hall, Inc., Englewood Cliffs, N.J., 1955.
   SHEA, R. F., "Transistor Circuits," Chaps. 2, 3, and 4, John Wiley & Sons, Inc., New York, 1953.
3. GIALCOLETTO, L. J. "Junction Transistor Equivalent Circuits and Vacuum-tube Analogy," *Proc. IRE*, **40**, 1490–1493, November, 1952.
4. "IRE Standards on Semiconductor Symbols," *Proc. IRE*, **44**, 935–937, July, 1956.
5. KNIGHT, G., R. A. JOHNSON, and R. B. HOLT, "Measurement of Small Signal Parameters in Transistors," *Proc. IRE*, **41**, 983, August, 1953.
   HUNTER, L. P., "Handbook of Semiconductor Electronics," pp. 19-5 to 19-7, McGraw-Hill Book Company, Inc., New York, 1956.
   TERMAN, F. E., "Electronic and Radio Engineering," 4th ed., pp. 781–783, McGraw-Hill Book Company, Inc., New York, 1955.

CHAPTER 11

MULTIELECTRODE VACUUM TUBES AND HIGH-FREQUENCY TRANSISTORS

The basic vacuum tube employing a control element is the triode. In Sec. 8-9 it is shown that the input admittance of a triode is principally capacitive and that the major portion of this capacitance is contributed by the grid-to-plate interelectrode capacitance. As the frequency is increased the input impedance decreases and the tube may act as a heavy load on the circuit which feeds it. Furthermore, the coupling between the plate and the grid may be large enough to cause the circuit to oscillate. In this chapter we shall show that the addition of one or two electrodes reduces the capacitance between input and output circuits to a negligible amount. The characteristics of these new tubes will be studied.

The equivalent circuit of the transistor at high frequencies will be given.

11-1. Screen-grid Tubes or Tetrodes. The screen-grid tube was introduced commercially about 1928. In these tubes a fourth electrode is interposed between the grid and the plate. This new electrode is known as the *screen grid*, the *shield grid*, or *grid* 2, in order to distinguish it from the "control" grid of the three-electrode tube. It may entirely enclose the plate, as shown schematically in Fig. 11-1.[1] Because of its design and disposition, the screen grid affords very complete electrostatic shielding between the plate and the grid. This shielding is such that the grid-plate capacitance is divided by a factor of about 1,000 or more. However, the screen mesh is sufficiently coarse so that it does not interfere appreciably with the flow of electrons.

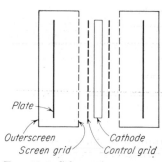

Plate

Outerscreen
Screen grid
Cathode
Control grid

FIG. 11-1. Schematic arrangement of the electrodes in a screen-grid tetrode. The tube has cylindrical symmetry.

Because of the shielding action of the plate by the screen grid, the electric field produced in the neighborhood of the cathode by the anode potential is practically zero. Since the total space current is determined almost wholly by the field near the cathode surface, the plate exerts little or no effect on the total space charge drawn from the cathode. The plate in a triode performs two distinct functions, that of controlling the total space current and that of collecting the plate current. In a tetrode, the plate serves only to collect those electrons which succeed in passing through the screen.

This passive character of the plate makes the tetrode a much better voltage amplifier than the triode. Physically, this follows from the fact that in a three-element tube an increase in signal voltage causes an increase in load current. This increased current causes a decreased plate-cathode potential, because of the increased $i_b R_L$ drop. The decreased potential reduces the space current below its value were there no such reduction in the plate-cathode voltage. Although the $i_b R_L$ drop still exists in the tetrode, no consequent decrease in space current occurs because the plate is effectively isolated by the screen. Hence the input signal must necessarily have a much greater effect on the output voltage in a tetrode than in a triode.

This reasoning is valid, of course, only if the change in plate current for a given change in control-grid voltage in both tubes is the same. That is, this discussion presumes that the plate-grid transconductance is the same for the two tubes. In most cases, the disposition of the cathode and grid is almost the same in the three- and four-element tubes, and the control of the electron stream by the grid is nearly alike for both types of tube.

Since changes in plate voltage have very little effect upon the plate current, it follows that the plate resistance of tetrodes must be very high. Correspondingly, the amplification factor of the tube must also be high. This follows from the definition of the amplification factor, which measures the relative effectiveness of changes of plate and grid voltage in producing equal plate-current increments. Quantitative definitions of the tube parameters of the tetrode will be given in Sec. 11-3. It can be concluded from the qualitative discussion given that the tetrode is characterized by the following features: a plate-grid capacitance which is only a few thousandths of that of a triode, a plate-grid transconductance which is roughly the same as that of a triode, and an amplification factor and plate resistance which are about ten or one hundred times that of a triode.

11-2. Tetrode Characteristics. As already discussed, the main purpose of the plate is to collect those electrons which succeed in passing through the screen. Also, the total space current is practically constant for given control-grid and screen-grid potentials. Hence, that portion of the space current which is not collected by the plate must be collected by the screen; *i.e.*, the two currents are complementary. Where the plate current is large, the screen current must be small, and vice versa. These features can be noted from Fig. 11-2 obtained with a 6J7 tube connected as a tetrode.

Although the plate voltage does not affect the total space current very markedly (a slight dip does occur in the curve of total space current at the lower plate potentials), it does determine the division of the space current between the plate and the screen.   At zero plate potential, none of the electrons has sufficient energy to reach the anode, if it is assumed that the electrons are liberated with zero initial velocities.   Hence, the plate current should be zero.   As the plate voltage is increased, one should expect a rapid rise in plate current and a corresponding fall in the screen current. When the plate potential is very much larger than the screen potential, the plate current should approach the space current and the screen current should approach zero.   This asymptotic behavior is noted in Fig. 11-2.

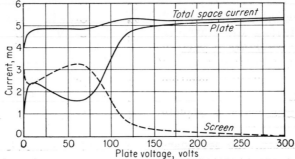

FIG. 11-2. The currents in a 6J7 tube connected as a tetrode.   The screen potential is 100 volts and the grid potential is −2 volts (the suppressor is tied to the screen).

An inspection of Fig. 11-2 indicates that the plate current rises very rapidly for the first few volts, but it is then followed by a rather anomalous behavior in the region of plate potentials from a few volts to potentials somewhat lower than the screen voltage.   The plate current is seen to decrease with increasing values of plate potential.   That is, the tube possesses a negative plate resistance in this region.

The general character of the curves of Fig. 11-2 may be described on the basis of the approximate potential distribution diagram of Fig. 11-3. This diagram should be compared with Fig. 7-4, which shows the potential profiles in a triode.   In this diagram it is supposed that the control-grid and the screen-grid voltages are at fixed values and that the plate voltage E_b may be adjusted from zero to a value considerably in excess of the screen voltage.

It is seen that, for a given grid and screen voltage, the curves for different plate voltages merge into one near the cathode.   This means that the field intensity near the cathode is sensibly independent of the plate voltage and depends only on the grid and screen voltages.   As a result, the space current does not depend on the plate voltage. The division of the space current between the screen and the plate does depend on their relative potentials.

Now consider the kinks, or folds, that appear in the curves of Fig. 11-2 in the region where the plate potential is lower than the screen potential. These are caused by the liberation of secondary electrons from the plate by the impact of the primary electrons with the plate. These secondary electrons are attracted to the screen. The screen current is increased, whereas the plate current is decreased. The number of secondary electrons liberated by this electron bombardment depends upon many factors and may even exceed the total number of primary electrons that strike the plate and thus result in an effective negative plate current.

In the region where the plate potential is higher than the potential of the screen, the secondary electrons that are liberated from the plate by the impact of the primary electrons are drawn back to the plate. In addition, some secondary electrons may also be liberated from the screen by the impact of the primary electrons on it. These secondary electrons from the screen are attracted to the plate, with the result that the plate current is slightly higher than it would be in the absence of secondary emission from the screen. Further-

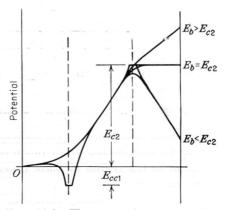

Fig. 11-3. The approximate potential profiles in an idealized tetrode for several values of plate voltage. Two curves are shown for each plate voltage. One is for a path between grid and screen wires, and the other is for a path through the wires.

more, the plate current continues to increase with increasing plate potentials because the collection of these secondary electrons is more complete. At the same time, the screen current tends toward zero.

Although the total space current should be a constant, in accordance with the previous discussion, Fig. 11-2 indicates that it is somewhat less than the ultimate value in the region of low plate potentials. This apparent inconsistency is readily explained in terms of the electrostatic deflection of the electrons by the screen wires at plate potentials that are less than the screen potential. The electrons that pass close to the screen wires are deflected from their path toward the plate and return toward the screen as a result of the electrostatic attraction. As they again approach the screen, they may once more suffer a deflection that will direct them toward the plate. This process may continue, the electrons oscillating back and forth between the screen wires until they are ultimately collected by this electrode. Because of the electrons that may exist in the neighborhood of the screen, a partial space charge will develop. This will reduce the effective screen potential, with a consequent reduction in the total space-charge current in the tube.

11-3. Tube Parameters. It has already been shown that the plate current of a triode is a function of the potentials on the grid and the plate. Similarly, for multielectrode tubes, variations in potential of the various electrodes influence the current to these electrodes. The plate current may be expressed as a function of the potential of the various electrodes by the expression

$$i_b = f(e_{c1}, e_{c2}, e_b) \tag{11-1}$$

where the symbol e_{c1} denotes the voltage of the first, or control, grid; e_{c2} denotes the voltage of the second, or screen, grid; and e_b is the potential of the plate.

An approximate explicit form of the dependence is possible. This form, which is an extension of Eq. (7-1), may be written as

$$i_b = G\left(e_{c1} + \frac{e_b}{\mu_1} + \frac{e_{c2}}{\mu_2}\right)^{\frac{3}{2}} \tag{11-2}$$

where μ_1 and μ_2 are the control-grid and screen amplification factors, respectively, and G is called the "perveance."

The variation in the plate current, second and higher-order terms in the expansion being neglected, is given by

$$\Delta i_b = \left(\frac{\partial i_b}{\partial e_{c1}}\right)\Delta e_{c1} + \left(\frac{\partial i_b}{\partial e_{c2}}\right)\Delta e_{c2} + \left(\frac{\partial i_b}{\partial e_b}\right)\Delta e_b \tag{11-3}$$

Generally, the screen potential is maintained constant at some appropriate value. Under these conditions, $\Delta e_{c2} = 0$, and the second term can be omitted from the equation. Note, however, that the screen grid may be used to exercise a control function in much the same way as the control grid. Owing to its disposition relative to the cathode, the amplification factor of the screen grid is less than that of the control grid. With $\Delta e_{c2} = 0$, and proceeding as for the case of triodes, the partial-differential coefficients appearing in this expression are used in order to define the tube parameters. These are

$$\left(\frac{\partial e_b}{\partial i_b}\right)_{E_{c1}, E_{c2}} \equiv r_p, \text{ plate resistance}$$

$$\left(\frac{\partial i_b}{\partial e_{c1}}\right)_{E_b, E_{c2}} \equiv g_m, \text{ plate-grid transconductance}$$

$$-\left(\frac{\partial e_b}{\partial e_{c1}}\right)_{I_b, E_{c2}} \equiv \mu, \text{ plate-grid amplification factor}$$

(11-4)

The two subscripts outside the parentheses indicate the parameters that are maintained constant during the partial differentiation. These should likewise appear in Eq. (11-3) but have been omitted for the sake of simplicity.

It is easy to show that the relation $\mu = r_p g_m$ applies in the present case as well as for the triodes. Nominal values for the various parameters that appear in this relationship are $r_p = 0.1$ to 2 megohms, $g_m = 0.5$ to 3 millimhos, and $\mu = 100$ to 1,200 in the ordinary screen-grid tubes.

By employing the same system of notation in this case as for the triode, viz.,

$$\Delta i_b = i_p \qquad \Delta e_b = e_p \qquad \Delta e_{c1} = e_g$$

and if the screen voltage is maintained constant, so that $\Delta e_{c2} = 0$, as is customary, then Eq. (11-3) becomes

$$i_p = g_m e_g + \frac{e_p}{r_p}$$

(11-5)

This equation is equivalent to Eq. (8-19) for the triode.

11-4. Equivalent Circuit of a Tetrode. The basic equivalent-circuit representation of the tetrode is essentially that of the triode, even though

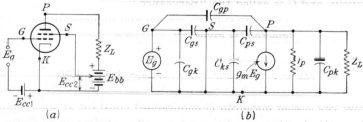

(a) (b)

Fig. 11-4. The schematic and equivalent circuits of a tetrode connected as an amplifier.

a screen grid exists in the tetrode. The screen is connected to the cathode through a source of d-c potential which is usually less than, or at most equal to, the plate potential. A schematic diagram of a simple amplifier circuit employing a tetrode is given in Fig. 11-4a. The equivalent circuit is shown in Fig. 11-4b.

In drawing the equivalent circuit, the rules given in Sec. 8-3 have been appropriately extended and employed. Thus, in addition to the points K, G, and P, the screen terminal S is also marked. The circuit elements of the original circuit are included in their appropriate positions between these four points, except that all d-c potentials are omitted and the tube itself is replaced by an equivalent current generator $g_m\mathbf{E}_{gk}$ having an internal resistance r_p, between the points K and P. The capacitances between all pairs of the four electrodes are included, the double subscript denoting the pair of electrodes under consideration.

Since the screen battery must be short-circuited in the equivalent circuit, this puts the screen at ground potential in so far as a-c (signal) variations about the Q point are concerned. Usually, the screen potential is obtained from the plate supply through a screen dropping resistor. In this case a capacitor is connected from the screen to cathode. This capacitor is chosen sufficiently large so that the screen potential remains constant even though the screen current may vary. In this case, too, the screen is at a-c ground potential. Thus, as indicated in the figure, this effectively shorts out C_{ks} and puts C_{gk} and C_{gs} in parallel. Let this parallel combination be denoted C_1. The capacity C_{ps} now appears from plate to ground and is effectively in parallel with C_{pk}. Let this parallel combination be denoted C_2. From the discussion of the shielding action of the screen grid, the capacitance between the plate and the control grid C_{gp} has been reduced to a very small value. If this capacitance is assumed to be negligible, then Fig. 11-4b may be redrawn more simply as shown in Fig. 11-5, where

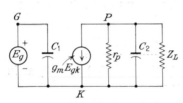

FIG. 11-5. The ideal equivalent circuit of a tetrode. The grid-plate capacitance has been assumed equal to zero.

$$C_1 = C_{gk} + C_{gs} \qquad C_2 = C_{ps} + C_{pk} \qquad (11\text{-}6)$$

Owing to the shielding action of the screen, little error will be made if C_{pk} is neglected in comparison with C_{ps}, so that $C_2 = C_{ps}$, to a good approximation. This capacitance acts as a shunt across the load. The input admittance of the tube is seen to be simply

$$\mathbf{Y}_i = j\omega C_1 \qquad (11\text{-}7)$$

A significant difference is seen to exist between the ideal equivalent circuit of the tetrode and the complete equivalent circuit of the triode, given in Fig. 8-21. The idealization made here consists in the assumption that the grid-plate capacitance is zero rather than a very small fraction of a micromicrofarad.   The circuit of Fig. 11-5 clearly shows that under this condition the plate circuit has been isolated from the grid circuit.

It should be pointed out, however, that the mere substitution of a tetrode for a triode will not, in general, effect any marked difference in the amplifier response.   This follows because the wiring and stray capacitances between circuit elements external to the tube may provide the capacitances that the tube itself seeks to eliminate.   It is necessary, therefore, that the elements of the circuit should be carefully arranged in order to permit short interconnecting leads and generally neat wiring so as to reduce wiring capacitances.   It is only if the capacitance between the grid and anode circuits external to the tube is small that the inherent possibilities of the tetrode can be utilized.

In order to calculate the approximate performance of circuits equipped with tetrodes, either the static curves of the tube or an analytical method based upon the equivalent circuit may be used.   Since the equivalent circuit of the tetrode is that which was found to be valid approximately for triodes, all of the previous discussion and analysis actually apply more exactly for the present case than they did for triodes.   It must be kept in mind that the results in both cases are based upon the existence of an approximately linear dynamic curve.

11-5. Pentodes.   Although the insertion of the screen grid between the control grid and the plate serves to isolate the plate circuit from the grid circuit, nevertheless the folds in the plate characteristic arising from the effects of secondary emission limit the range of operation of the tube. This limitation results from the fact that if the plate-voltage swing is made too large the instantaneous plate potential may extend into the region of rapidly falling plate current, which will cause a marked distortion in the output.

The kinks, or folds, that appear in the plate characteristic curves and that limit the range of operation of the tetrode may be removed or suppressed by inserting a coarse grid structure between the screen grid and the plate of Fig. 11-1.   Tubes equipped with this extra suppressor grid are known as "pentodes" and were first introduced commercially in 1929. The suppressor grid must be maintained at a lower potential than the instantaneous potential reached by the plate.   It is usually connected directly to the cathode, either internally in the tube or externally. Because the potential of the screen is considerably above that of the suppressor grid, a retarding force prevents the secondary electrons liberated from the screen from flowing to the plate.   On the other hand, the secondary electrons emitted from the plate are constrained, by the retarding field between the suppressor grid and the plate, to return to the plate.   However, the electrons from the cathode that pass through the screen are not kept from reaching the plate by the presence of the suppressor grid, although their velocities may be affected thereby.

The plate, screen, and total current curves as a function of the plate voltage are shown in Fig. 11-6 for the 6J7 tube. These should be compared with the corresponding tetrode curves of Fig. 11-2. It is noticed that the kinks resulting from the effects of secondary emission are entirely missing in the pentode. Furthermore, the screen current no longer falls asymptotically to zero but approaches a constant value for large plate voltages. This value is determined principally by the amount of space current that is intercepted by the screen-grid wires. An examination of the characteristics of a number of the more important voltage pentodes indicates that the screen current is ordinarily from 0.2 to 0.4, of the plate current

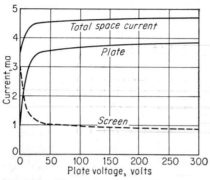

FIG. 11-6. The currents in a 6J7 pentode. The suppressor is at zero voltage, the screen at 100 volts, and the grid at −2 volts.

at the recommended operating point. The total space current is seen to remain practically constant over the entire range of plate voltage, except for the very low values of potential.

The pentode has displaced the tetrode (except the beam power tube discussed in Sec. 11-7) in all applications. The tetrode was discussed above for historical reasons and because an understanding of this tube is necessary before the pentode can be appreciated. The pentode rather than the triode is used in radio-frequency voltage amplifiers because the former virtually eliminates feedback from the plate to the grid. The pentode is used as a video amplifier because a triode at these high frequencies has a very large input admittance which acts as a heavy load on the preceding stage. The pentode has also found extensive application as an audio-frequency power-output tube (Chap. 16). Finally, the pentode has been used as a constant-current device because the plate current is essentially constant independent of the plate potential.

The plate characteristics of a typical pentode are illustrated in Fig. 11-7. The static transfer characteristics, plate current and screen current vs. grid voltage, are reproduced in Fig. 11-8. The most important pentode parameter is the grid-plate transconductance g_m. Since this parameter is not a constant but depends sensitively upon the quiescent operating point, g_m is plotted in Fig. 11-9 as a function of grid voltage with screen voltage as a parameter.

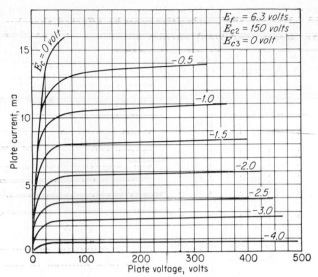

FIG. 11-7. The plate characteristics of a 6AU6 pentode with $E_{c2} = 150$ volts and $E_{c3} = 0$ volt.   (*Courtesy of the General Electric Co.*)

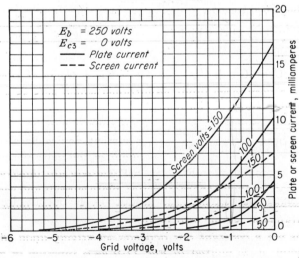

FIG. 11-8. The static transfer characteristics of the 6AU6 pentode.   (*Courtesy of the General Electric Co.*)

The plate resistance r_p, plate-grid transconductance g_m, and amplification factor μ of a pentode are defined exactly as for a tetrode (but with the suppressor at zero voltage) by Eqs. (11-4). Typical values lie in the ranges from $r_p = 0.1$ to 2 megohms, $g_m = 0.5$ to 10 millimhos, and $\mu = 100$ to $10,000$. Since the shape and disposition of the control grid and cathode are the same for triode and pentode, these tubes have comparable values of g_m. However, the values of r_p and μ may be 100 times as great in the pentode as in the triode.

When used in a circuit as a voltage amplifier, the pentode is connected in the circuit exactly like a tetrode

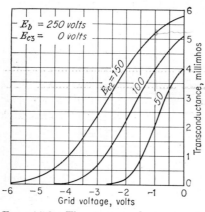

Fig. 11-9. The transconductance of the 6AU6 pentode as a function of grid and screen voltages. (*Courtesy of the General Electric Co.*)

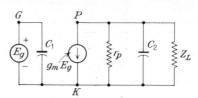

Fig. 11-10. The equivalent circuit of a pentode.

(see Fig. 11-4), with the addition that the suppressor grid is connected to the cathode. Then, subject to the same considerations as for tetrodes (Secs. 11-3 and 11-4), it follows that the equivalent circuit of a pentode is also given by Fig. 11-5, which is repeated in Fig. 11-10 for convenience. In this diagram

$$C_1 = C_{gk} + C_{gs} \qquad C_2 = C_{pk} + C_{ps} + C_{p3} \qquad (11\text{-}8)$$

where C_{p3} is the capacitance between the plate and grid 3 (the suppressor). When the input and output capacitances of a tube are listed by the manufacturer, reference is being made to C_1 and C_2, respectively.

In Fig. 11-10 the output-voltage drop is

$$\mathbf{E}_{pk} = -g_m \mathbf{E}_g \mathbf{Z} \qquad (11\text{-}9)$$

where $\mathbf{Z}$ is the combined parallel impedance in the output circuit. Since

$$\mathbf{A} = \frac{\mathbf{E}_{pk}}{\mathbf{E}_{gk}} = -g_m \mathbf{Z} \qquad (11\text{-}10)$$

then the gain equals the product of g_m and the output impedance. If, as is usually the case, the plate resistance and the reactance of the output capacitor are each large compared with the load impedance, then $Z \cong Z_L$ and the gain is given by

$$A \cong -g_m Z_L$$ (11-11)

This most important result is well worth remembering.

11-6. Remote-cutoff Tubes.[2] If the grid-cathode spacing, the spacing between grid wires, or the diameter of the grid wires is not uniform along the entire length of the control-grid structure, the various portions of the grid will possess different degrees of electrostatic control over the plate current. It is possible for one portion of the grid to cut off the flow of electrons for a given grid voltage, whereas a more open section might allow a considerable number of electrons to pass unimpeded to the plate. The result is that the plate current will decrease rather slowly as the grid voltage is made more and more negative. This asymptotic approach of the transfer characteristic to the zero-current axis is exhibited by the type 6BA6 tube. This characteristic is to be compared with the fairly sharp cutoff of the characteristic of the 6AU6 pentode, which is provided with a uniformly wound grid.

Owing to its construction, a given grid-voltage increment results in a plate-current change that is a function of the grid bias. This means, of course, that the mutual conductance is a function of the bias. For this reason, these tubes are called "variable-mu," "remote-cutoff," or "supercontrol" tubes.

11-7. Beam Power Tubes. The suppressor grid is introduced into the pentode in order to remove the kinks due to secondary emission in the tetrode. Although the pentode permits a greater range of operation than is possible with the tetrode, nevertheless the curvature of the i_b-e_b characteristic limits the extent of operation of the pentode. The broad knee of the plate characteristic in the region of small plate voltage arises from the overeffectiveness of the suppressor grid at these low plate voltages. That is, the suppressor grid may prevent some of the primary electrons that pass through the screen from reaching the plate when the plate voltage is low This effect arises from the deflections that may be given to some of the primary electrons if they approach close to a screen wire. Thus, if an electron is deflected by this action, its velocity in the plate direction will be reduced and the field of the suppressor grid may repel it back toward the screen.

Because of this, the shape of the suppressor grid in some pentodes has been so dimensioned[3] that the effects of secondary emission are just suppressed or are only admitted to a slight extent at the low anode voltages. This results in an improved plate characteristic.

If the complete overeffectiveness of the suppressor grid could be avoided, the ideal power-tube characteristic, *viz.*, constant current for all plate voltages, would be achieved. This is approached in the beam power tube,[4] a sketch of which is given in Fig. 11-11.

One feature of the design of this tube is that each spiral turn of the screen is aligned with a spiral turn of the control grid. This serves to

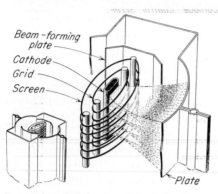

Beam-forming plate

Cathode

Grid

Screen

Plate

FIG. 11-11. Schematic view of the shapes and arrangements of the electrodes in a beam power tube. (*Courtesy of Radio Corporation of America.*)

keep the screen current small. The screen current in such tubes ranges from 0.05 to 0.08 of the plate current, which is considerably below the range 0.2 to 0.4 for voltage pentodes. Other features are the flattened cathode, the beam-forming side plates (maintained at zero potential), and a relatively large spacing between the screen and the plate. As a result of these design characteristics, the electrons flow between the grid wires toward the plate in dense sheets or beams, as indicated schematically in Fig. 11-11.

The region between the screen and the plate possesses features which are somewhat analogous to those which exist in the space-charge-limited diode. That is, a flow of electrons exists between two electrodes between which a difference of potential exists. There is one significant difference, however. Whereas the electrons leave the cathode of a diode with almost zero initial velocities, the electrons that pass through the screen wires in the beam tube do so with a velocity corresponding essentially to the screen potential. As described in Sec. 4-6 in connection with the effects of initial velocities on the space-charge equation, the effect of the initial velocities of the electrons in the screen-plate region will appear as a potential minimum in this region (see Fig. 4-5). This is shown in the approximate potential profile in Fig. 11-12 and is to be compared with the corresponding figure for the tetrode (see Fig. 11-3).

The production of the potential minimum also receives contributions from a suppressor grid, if one is present. Since the predominant effect in the beam tube is the space charge, the suppressor grid is sometimes reduced to a pair of plates (the beam-forming side plates of Fig. 11-11).[5] However, other beam tubes are provided with a mechanical suppressor grid. The potential minimum that is produced acts as a virtual suppressor grid, since any secondary electrons emitted from either the plate or the screen will encounter a potential-energy barrier. They will be compelled to return to the electrode (which is at a positive potential with respect to the potential minimum) from which they originate.

The actual potential distribution[6] in the screen-plate region will depend upon the instantaneous plate potential and the plate current (a constant screen potential being assumed) and so is not constant.   This results in variable suppressor action.   This is quite different from the action that arises in a simple pentode provided only with a mechanical grid structure for supplying the retarding field.

Thus, because of the beam formation, which serves to keep the screen current small, and because of the variable suppressor action, which serves to suppress secondary emission from the screen and from the plate, the ideal power-tube characteristic is closely approximated.   A family of plate characteristics for the 6L6 is shown in Fig. 11-13.   It should be noted that this tube is a tetrode when considered in terms of the number of active electrodes.   At low currents, where the suppressor action of the beam is too small, the characteristic "kinks" of a tetrode are noticeable.

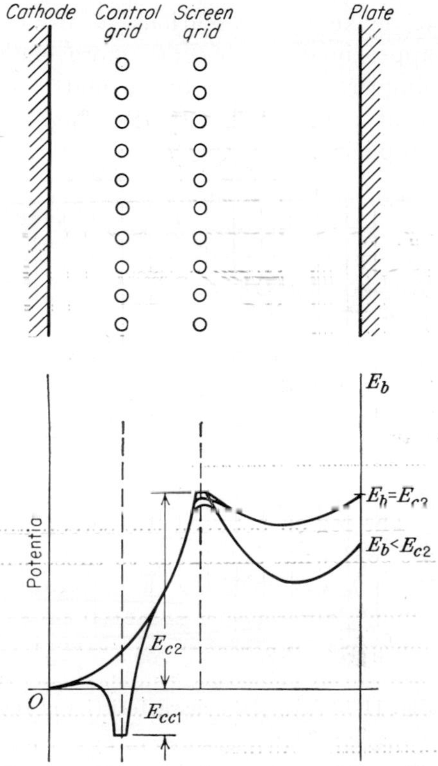

11-8. Equivalent Circuit of a Transistor at High Frequencies.[7] So far we have assumed that the transistor responds instantly to changes of input voltage or current.   Actually, of course, such is not the case because the mechanism of the transport of current carriers from emitter to collector

FIG. 11-12. Approximate potential profile in an idealized beam power tube for two values of plate voltage.   Two curves are shown for each plate voltage.   One is for a path between grid and screen wires, and the other is for a path through the wires. Note the potential minimum in the region between the screen grid and the plate.

junction is essentially one of diffusion.   Hence, to find out how the transistor behaves at high frequencies, it is necessary to examine this diffusion mechanism in more detail.   Unfortunately such an analysis is involved and shows that all the transistor parameters are functions of frequency.   The equations which specify this frequency dependence are suggestive of the equations which are encountered in connection with a lossy transmission line.   Some such result is to have been anticipated in view of the fact that some time delay must be involved in the transport of carriers across the base region by the process of diffusion. Even having these transmission-line equations available does not put us in a much improved position because the equations are quite complicated. Hence, if we use them, we should have an equivalent circuit which is quite accurate but, unfortunately, not manageable. It is therefore necessary to make approximations in using the equations. Of course, as the approximations become more rough, the equivalent circuit becomes simpler. It is therefore a matter of engineering judgment to decide at what point we have a reasonable compromise between accuracy and simplicity.

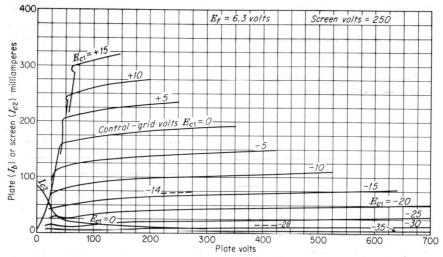

Fig. 11-13. The plate characteristics of a 6L6 beam tube with $E_{c2} = 250$ volts. (See also Fig. A9-11.)

Experience shows that as a first reasonable approximation the diffusion phenomenon can be taken into account by assuming a relatively simple frequency dependence for α and by shunting the transistor junctions by diffusion capacitances at the emitter and collector. In addition to the diffusion capacitances, there are also space-charge or transition capacitances across the junctions. From the discussions in Secs. 5-3 and 5-4 we know that for a forward-biased junction the diffusion capacitance greatly exceeds the space-charge capacitance and that for a reverse-biased diode the converse is true. Hence, across the emitter junction in Fig. 11-14 C_e represents the diffusion capacitance (Sec. 11-10) whereas across the collector junction C_c is the space-charge capacitance (Sec. 5-3). Figure 11-14 is obtained from Fig. 10-2 by adding the junction capacitances, by writing the currents and voltages as phasor quantities, and by considering $\alpha(\omega)$ to be a function of frequency.

In the next section we shall show that (in complex notation) the frequency dependence of α is given approximately by

$$\alpha = \frac{\alpha_0}{1 + j\omega/\omega_\alpha} \tag{11-12}$$

In this equation, α_0 is the low-frequency value of α. The form of the equation indicates a frequency response which is identical with that of a simple resistance-capacitance network. The angular frequency ω_α ($= 2\pi f_\alpha$) is the frequency at which the magnitude of α is $0.707\alpha_0$. The frequency f_α is termed the *alpha cutoff frequency*. At frequencies which are appreciably less than f_α Eq. (11-12) is reasonably accurate. The approximation is progressively poorer as f approaches and exceeds f_α. General-purpose transistors have frequencies f_α in the range of hundreds

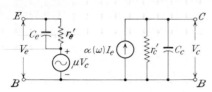

FIG. 11-14. Approximate high-frequency equivalent circuit of a transistor, including frequency dependence of α.

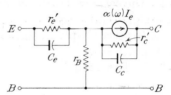

FIG. 11-15. A simple high-frequency equivalent circuit.

of kilocycles. Special-purpose high-frequency transistors may have f_α in the range of tens of megacycles.

In many video applications the load impedance is quite small. Hence we shall assume that we are working essentially into a short circuit so that $V_c \rightarrow 0$. Under these circumstances (and because μ is extremely small), we may neglect the feedback generator μV_c. Omitting this generator and at the same time adding the base-spreading resistance r_B lead to the equivalent circuit of Fig. 11-15. It must be emphasized that the resistances included in this circuit are not the same as those in the low-frequency circuit of Fig. 10-4. The resistance $r_e' = V_T/I_E$ is approximately twice that of the low-frequency emitter branch resistance r_e [Eq. (10-70)]. The low-frequency resistance r_b is several times larger than r_B, the difference between these two quantities being $r_b' = r_e/(1 - a)$ [Eq. (10-71)]. The low- and high-frequency collector resistances are approximately equal to one another, $r_c \cong r_c'$.

If in Fig. 11-15 the emitter is grounded and the short-circuit current gain

$$\mathbf{A}_i \equiv -\frac{\mathbf{I}_c}{\mathbf{I}_b}\bigg|_{V_{CE}=0} \tag{11-13}$$

is calculated, we find approximately that

$$\mathbf{A}_i = \frac{\alpha(\omega)}{1 - \alpha(\omega)} \tag{11-14}$$

Using Eq. (11-12), the common-emitter short-circuit current gain becomes

$$\mathbf{A}_i = \frac{A_{i0}}{1 + jf/f_{ae}} \tag{11-15}$$

where

$$f_{ae} = f_\alpha(1 - \alpha_0) \qquad \text{and} \qquad A_{i0} = \frac{\alpha_0}{1 - \alpha_0} \tag{11-16}$$

At zero frequency this expression for the current gain reduces to A_{i0}, agreeing with Eq. (10-24). The frequency at which the magnitude of the current gain A_i is reduced to 0.707 of its zero frequency value is called the *common-emitter alpha cutoff frequency* and is f_{ae}. The common-base alpha cutoff frequency is designated by f_{ab} (or, if no ambiguity is likely to arise, simply by f_α). The relationship between f_{ae} and f_{ab} is given by Eq. (11-16).

11-9. The Frequency Dependence of Alpha. The emitter efficiency γ is usually quite close to unity and is essentially independent of frequency[7] up to frequencies of the order of f_α. Hence, we shall assume that $\alpha = \beta$, the transport factor, and shall investigate the frequency behavior of β. The zero frequency value of β is given in Eq. (9-36) as

$$\beta = \operatorname{sech} \frac{W}{L_B} \tag{11-17}$$

where W is the base width and L_B is the diffusion length of the minority carriers in the base. From the third example in Appendix VI, the value of β and hence α at a frequency ω is given by

$$\alpha = \operatorname{sech} \frac{W}{L_B} (1 + j\omega\tau_B)^{\frac{1}{2}} \tag{11-18}$$

where τ_B is the mean lifetime of the minority carriers in the base.

Since $W/L_B \ll 1$, then for frequencies which are not too high the hyperbolic secant may be expanded into a power series. Thus

$$\operatorname{sech} x = (\cosh x)^{-1} = \left(\frac{\epsilon^x + \epsilon^{-x}}{2}\right)^{-1} = \left(1 + \frac{x^2}{2} + \frac{x^4}{24} + \cdots\right)^{-1} \tag{11-19}$$

If the first two terms in this expansion are used, then

$$\alpha = \frac{1}{1 + \frac{1}{2}(W^2/L_B^2)(1 + j\omega\tau_B)} = \frac{1}{\left(1 + \frac{1}{2}\frac{W^2}{L_B^2}\right)\left[1 + \dfrac{j\omega\tau_B W^2/2L_B^2}{1 + \frac{1}{2}(W^2/L_B^2)}\right]}$$

or

$$\alpha = \frac{\alpha_0}{1 + j\omega/\omega_\alpha} \tag{11-20}$$

where $\alpha_0 = 1/[1 + \frac{1}{2}(W^2/L_B^2)]$ is the first-order approximation of sech W/L_B and represents the value of α at zero frequency.   The alpha cutoff frequency is given by

$$\omega_\alpha = \frac{2L_B^2}{W^2 \tau_B \alpha_0} \tag{11-21}$$

From Eq. (A6-12) $L_B^2 = D_B \tau_B$, where D_B is the diffusion constant for minority carriers in the base, and hence

$$\omega_\alpha = \frac{2D_B}{W^2 \alpha_0} \tag{11-22}$$

At the cutoff frequency we have from Eqs. (11-18) and (11-21) that

$$\alpha(\omega_\alpha) = \text{sech} \frac{W}{L_B} \left(1 + j \frac{2L_B^2}{W^2 \alpha_0}\right)^{\frac{1}{2}} \cong \text{sech} \left(\frac{j2}{\alpha_0}\right)^{\frac{1}{2}} \tag{11-23}$$

because $W/L_B \ll 1$.   For $\alpha_0 = 1$ the magnitude of $\alpha(\omega_\alpha)$ is 0.775, and its phase angle is 50 deg.   These same quantities calculated from Eq. (11-20) are obviously 0.707 and 45 deg.   This comparison gives some idea of the errors made in using the approximate formula (11-20) rather than the exact but formidable expression (11-18).

It is possible to retain the simple frequency dependence for α as given in Eq. (11-20) and at the same time obtain excellent agreement with the exact expression (11-18) as far as the magnitude of α is concerned up to frequencies beyond ω_α, provided that for ω_α we use the formula[8]

$$\omega_\alpha = \frac{2.43 D_B}{W^2} \tag{11-24}$$

The factor 2.43 which replaces $2/\alpha_0$ in Eq. (11-22) and Eq. (11-23) has been chosen so that the magnitude of α at the cutoff frequency is 0.707, as it should be.   The agreement in phase angle between Eqs. (11-18) and (11-20) has now, however, been worsened.   At the cutoff frequency a value of 58 deg is calculated from Eq. (11-18), whereas 45 deg is obtained from Eq. (11-20).   Other more complicated but more accurate approximations for α as a function of frequency are found in the literature.[9]

From the above formulas it follows that the alpha cutoff frequency will increase as the base thickness is decreased.   However, the smaller that W is made, the larger the base-spreading resistance r_B becomes.   In order to decrease r_B, the conductivity σ_B of the base is increased.   This increase in σ_B reduces the emitter efficiency, lowers the breakdown voltage at the collector junction, and increases the collector capacitance C_c. Hence, the manufacturer must make a compromise among these various design parameters.

For a p-n-p germanium transistor with a base thickness of 1 mil (2.54×10^{-3} cm) Eq. (11-24) predicts an $f_\alpha = 2.7$ megacycles.   In order to obtain an even thinner base section and hence higher frequency, the Philco Corporation has developed the *surface barrier transistor.*[10]   A wafer which is a few mils thick is mounted between two coaxial jets of etching solution which reduces the thickness to about 0.2 mil with good control.   The emitter and collector are then deposited electrolytically with the same jets.   A value of f_α of the order of 50 megacycles is obtained with such surface barrier transistors.

Another fabrication process used to obtain a high-frequency transistor is the following.   A wafer of germanium with an impurity on its surface is placed in an oven and heated.   A very thin layer of the impurity is allowed to diffuse into the germanium forming the base.   The emitter is then alloyed onto the base, and the original wafer is used as the collector.   Such a device is called a *diffused base transistor.*

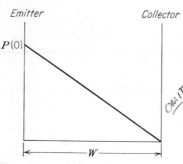

Emitter   Collector

$P(0)$

W

FIG. 11-16. Injected-hole concentration vs. distance in the base region, if $W/L_p \ll 1$.

11-10. The Diffusion Capacitance. Let us consider a *p-n-p* transistor operating in the active region.   Since the collector is reverse-biased, the hole concentration at the collector junction is essentially zero.   If $W \ll L_p$, then the injected-hole concentration P varies almost linearly from the value $P(0)$ at the emitter to zero at the collector, as indicated in Fig. 11-16.   This figure should be compared with Fig. 9-12.   For simplicity we have dropped the subscript n and are now considering only the injected holes.   The total stored charge Q is proportional to the area in Fig. 11-16, or

$$Q = \tfrac{1}{2}AeP(0)W \qquad (11\text{-}25)$$

The diffusion current due to holes is

$$I = -AeD_p\frac{dp}{dx} = AeD_p\frac{P(0)}{W} \qquad (11\text{-}26)$$

The diffusion capacitance is

$$C_D \equiv \frac{dQ}{dV} = \frac{dQ}{dP(0)}\frac{dP(0)}{dI}\frac{dI}{dV} \qquad (11\text{-}27)$$

Differentiating Eqs. (11-25) and (11-26), we obtain

$$C_D = \left(\frac{1}{2}AeW\right)\left(\frac{W}{AeD_p}\right)g_e = \frac{W^2}{2D_p}g_e \qquad (11\text{-}28)$$

where $g_e \equiv dI/dV = 1/r_e'$ is the conductance of the emitter junction. This expression for C_D should be compared with Eq. (5-42) obtained for the *p-n* junction diode.

If Eq. (11-24) is used $(D_B \equiv D_p)$, then

$$C_D = \frac{1.22 g_e}{\omega_\alpha} \tag{11-29}$$

REFERENCES

1. PIDGEON, H. A., "Theory of Multi-electrode Vacuum Tubes," *Bell System Tech. J.*, **14**, 44–84, January, 1935.
2. BALLANTINE, S., and H. A. SNOW, "Reduction of Distortion and Cross-talk in Radio Receivers by Means of Variable-mu Tetrodes," *Proc. IRE*, **18**, 2102–2127, December, 1930.
3. VAN DER VEN, A. J. H., "Output Stage Distortion: Some Measurements on Different Types of Receivers," *Wireless Eng.*, **16**, 444–452, September, 1939.
4. SCHADE, O. H., "Beam Power Tubes," *Proc. IRE*, **26**, 137–181, February, 1938.
5. JONKER, J. L. H., "Pentode and Tetrode Output Valves," *Wireless Eng.*, **16**, 279–286, June, 1939.
6. FAY, C. E., A. L. SAMUEL, and W. SHOCKLEY, "On the Theory of Space Charge between Parallel Plane Electrodes," *Bell System Tech. J.*, **17**, 49–79, January, 1938.

   SALZBERG, B., and A. V. HAEFF, "Effects of Space Charge in the Grid-anode Region of Vacuum Tubes," *RCA Rev.*, **2**, 336–374, January, 1938.
7. PRITCHARD, R. L., "Frequency Variations of Junction Transistor Parameters," *Proc. IRE*, **42**, 786–799, May, 1954.

   EARLY, J. M., "Design Theory of Junction Transistors," *Bell System Tech. J.*, **32**, 1271–1312, November, 1953.

   LO, A. W., et al., "Transistor Electronics," Chap. 8, Prentice-Hall, Inc., Englewood Cliffs, N.J., 1955.
8. HANEMAN, D., "Expression for the Alpha Cutoff Frequency in Junction Transistors," *Proc. IRE*, **42**, 1808–1809, December, 1954.
9. MIDDLEBROOK, R. D., and R. M. SCARLETT, "An Approximation to Alpha of a Junction Transistor," *IRE, PGED*, **ED-3**, 25–29, January, 1956.
10. BRADLEY, W. E., et al., "The Surface-barrier Transistor," *Proc. IRE*, **41**, 1702–1720, December, 1953.

CHAPTER 12

ELECTRICAL DISCHARGES IN GASES

An ELECTRICAL discharge is a very complicated phenomenon involving neutral molecules, excited molecules, positive ions, and electrons. In order to understand what goes on inside a discharge tube, we must first study the fundamental processes that can take place in a gas. The first part of this chapter is devoted to such a study. Then the characteristics of the non-self-maintained discharge, the glow, and the arc will be explained. In the following chapter commercial tubes based upon these discharge phenomena are described.

12-1. Kinetic Theory of Gases. According to the classical concept of a gas, an atom is considered as a simple spherical particle that possesses a size and a mass which are characteristic of the gas under survey. This theory postulates that the molecules are in continual motion, the direction of flight of any particle constantly undergoing changes because of the collisions with other molecules or with the walls of the container.

On the basis of the physical picture just described, the perfect-gas law can be derived. By definition, the term *pressure* means the *force per unit area*. In a gaseous system, the force is that resulting from the bombardment of the walls of the container by the molecules. Since, by Newton's second law, the force is the rate of change of momentum, then the pressure is the change in momentum of all particles that strike unit area of the container in unit time. The result of such a calculation is

$$p = NkT \qquad (12\text{-}1)$$

where p is the pressure in newtons per square meter, N is the concentration in molecules per cubic meter, k is called the *Boltzmann constant* in joules per degree Kelvin (see Appendix I), and T is the temperature in degrees Kelvin.

An extremely important conclusion can be reached from Eq. (12-1): *At a given temperature and pressure all gases must contain the same number of molecules per cubic meter.* This is called *Avogadro's principle.*

Consider two containers occupying the same volume, one filled with gas A and the other with gas B. If these are at the same temperature and pressure, then, by the above principle, the two containers enclose equal numbers of molecules. Hence, the weight of the gas in the first container is to that in the second as the weight of gas molecule A is to the weight of molecule B. This leads to the concept of *molecular weight*.

The molecular weight of any substance is the ratio of the mass of one molecule of that substance to that of another which has been chosen as a standard. The molecular weight of diatomic oxygen is arbitrarily taken as 32.0000 (actually, the atomic weight of monatomic oxygen is taken as 16.0000). Hence the molecular weight of any substance is simply a numeric. Also, the term *gram-molecular weight* denotes a quantity of substance equal to this numeric, in grams. It thus follows that a gram-molecular weight, or *mole*, of any substance must contain the same number of molecules as the gram-molecular weight of any other substance. This number, known as *Avogadro's number*, is 6.02×10^{23} molecules per mole. Furthermore, from the foregoing, a mole of any gas must occupy the same volume. This volume (the gram-molecular volume) has been found by experiment to be 0.0224 m³, or 22.4 liters, under standard conditions of 0°C and 760 mm Hg pressure. Hence, there are $6.02 \times 10^{23}/0.0224 = 2.69 \times 10^{25}$ molecules per cubic meter of any gas at these standard conditions. This quantity is known as *Loschmidt's number*.

This is a large concentration, and yet it is only about one one-thousandth the density of electrons in a metal, which in Chap. 3 is found to be approximately 10^{28} electrons per cubic meter. Furthermore, the volume occupied by these molecules is (under standard conditions) only about one one-hundredth of 1 per cent of the container volume. This follows from the fact that the radius of a molecule is approximately 1 A $(10^{-10}$ m), and hence the volume occupied by all the molecules in 1 m³ is $(\frac{4}{3}\pi)(10^{-10})^3 \times 2.69 \times 10^{25} = 10^{-4}$ m³. Most of the gas container is empty!

According to Eq. (12-1), the concentration varies directly as the pressure and inversely as the temperature. Thus, at any temperature $T°K$ and pressure p mm Hg the concentration is

$$N = 2.69 \times 10^{25} \frac{p}{760} \frac{273}{T}$$

$$= 9.68 \times 10^{24} \frac{p}{T} \qquad \text{molecules/m}^3 \qquad (12\text{-}2)$$

Equation (12-1) is one form of the equation of state of an ideal gas. The form that is more familiar in elementary physics and chemistry may be obtained as follows: Each member of Eq. (12-1) is multiplied by V, the volume of the gas in cubic meters. Then

$$pV = NVkT \qquad (12\text{-}3)$$

Since N is the number of molecules per cubic meter, then NV gives the total number of molecules in the container of volume V. The total number of molecules NV remains unchanged as p, T, and V are varied. Hence, a still more elementary form of the perfect-gas law is obtained from Eq. (12-3), namely,

$$\frac{pV}{T} = \text{const} \tag{12-4}$$

In the next section it is shown that the average speed of a nitrogen molecule at room temperature is 475 m/sec or more than 1,000 mph. If the molecule travels at such tremendous speeds, we might expect that all the gas in a container would escape in a small fraction of a second after the cover was removed. However, the diffusion rate is actually very slow because of the very large number of collisions which the molecules make with themselves and with the walls of the container.

The average distance that a molecule travels between successive collisions with other molecules is called the *molecular mean free path*. In electronic devices in which both molecules and electrons exist, the *electronic mean free path* is defined as the average distance that an electron travels between collisions with gas molecules. The electronic and molecular mean free paths will be denoted, respectively, by l_e and l_m. From the kinetic theory of gases it is found that

$$l_m = \frac{1}{4 \sqrt{2}\, \sigma N} \qquad \text{meters} \tag{12-5}$$

where $\sigma = \pi r^2$ is the molecular cross section (r is the molecular radius in meters) and N is the concentration per cubic meter. This expression shows that the mean free path varies inversely with the number of molecules present per cubic meter. The electronic mean free path is given by the following expression:

$$l_e = \frac{1}{\sigma N} = 4 \sqrt{2}\, l_m \tag{12-6}$$

Since the mean free path varies inversely as the concentration, then if the pressure is reduced sufficiently the mean free path can be made very large. For example, in a "vacuum" tube in which the pressure is about 10^{-6} mm Hg, the mean free path may be calculated to be approximately 4×10^2 m. This distance is so very much larger than the distance between the electrodes in a tube that very few of the electrons leaving the cathode will collide with gas molecules in the interelectrode space. Because of the lack of collisions, little ionization by collision can take place, and the tube will act as a vacuum tube and not as a gaseous-discharge device.

12-2. The Energy Distribution Function. By using probability theory and the laws of conservation of energy and momentum and by making the basic assumption that the average kinetic energy of the molecules is proportional to the temperature, the distribution in energy among the molecules can be derived.   This relationship is known as the *Maxwell-Boltzmann distribution function*.   If the energy is expressed in units of E_T electron volts, this distribution has a form which is valid for any gas at any temperature.   If e is the electronic charge, then E_T is defined by

$$E_T \equiv \frac{kT}{e} = \frac{T}{11{,}600} \tag{12-7}$$

Introducing $\eta \equiv E/E_T$, the Maxwell-Boltzmann distribution is given by

$$\rho_\eta = \frac{2N}{\sqrt{\pi}} \eta^{\frac{1}{2}} \epsilon^{-\eta} \tag{12-8}$$

This function is plotted in Fig. 12-1. ρ_η represents the energy density, and so the number of molecules having (dimensionless) energies between η and $\eta + d\eta$ is $\rho_\eta\, d\eta$.   It is seen that the molecules possess all energies from zero to infinity.   Since the curve approaches the axis exponentially, there are very few molecules having very large energies.   The energy at which the maximum of the distribution occurs is the *most probable energy*, since more particles have energies in this neighborhood than any other.   This is given by

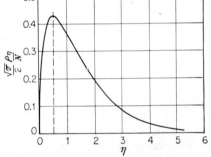

FIG. 12-1. The Maxwell-Boltzmann energy distribution function, plotted in terms of the variable $\eta \equiv E/E_T$.

$$\eta = \tfrac{1}{2} = \frac{E}{E_T}$$

or at an energy of $E_T/2$.   At room temperature (say, 300°K) this most probable energy is only 0.013 ev.   At absolute zero, the most probable energy is zero, which indicates that all the gas molecules have zero energy.

This distribution should be compared with Fig. 3-10 for electrons in a metal.   Even at absolute zero, the electrons are much more energetic than the gas molecules at room temperature.   The most probable electronic energy is E_M, which is of the order of a few electron volts, or about 500 times the most probable molecular energy at room temperature.

The average energy of the gas molecules is found to be $\tfrac{3}{2}E_T$ electron volts, or $\tfrac{3}{2}kT$ joules.

The average speed of the gas molecules is given by

$$\bar{v} = \sqrt{\frac{8kT}{m\pi}} \tag{12-9}$$

The random current density J_r is the charge per second crossing 1 m² in the gas and is given by

$$J_r = \frac{1}{4} Ne\bar{v} = Ne \sqrt{\frac{kT}{2\pi m}} \tag{12-10}$$

Example. Calculate the number of collisions per second made by a nitrogen molecule at room temperature and atmospheric pressure. The molecular radius of nitrogen is 1.58×10^{-10} m.

Solution. If the temperature is taken as 300°K, then the concentration is, according to Eq. (12-2),

$$N = (9.68 \times 10^{24}) \tfrac{760}{300} = 2.45 \times 10^{25} \text{ molecules/m}^3$$

From Eq. (12-5),

$$l_m = \frac{1}{(4\sqrt{2})(\pi)(1.58)^2(10^{-20})(2.45)(10^{25})} = 9.18 \times 10^{-8} \text{ m}$$

Since l_m represents the distance (in meters) traveled per collision, then the reciprocal of l_m gives the number of collisions per meter. Hence

$$\frac{1}{l_m} = \frac{1}{9.18 \times 10^{-8}} = 1.09 \times 10^7 \text{ collisions/m}$$

The average molecular speed is, according to Eq. (12-9),

$$\bar{v} = \left(\frac{8 \times 1.38 \times 10^{-23} \times 300}{28 \times 1.66 \times 10^{-27} \times \pi}\right)^{\frac{1}{2}} = 4.75 \times 10^2 \text{ m/sec}$$

Hence there are

$$\left(1.09 \times 10^7 \frac{\text{collisions}}{\text{m}}\right)\left(4.75 \times 10^2 \frac{\text{m}}{\text{sec}}\right) = 5.18 \times 10^9 \text{ collisions/sec}$$

This example is not intended as a rigorous quantitative calculation. It does give some idea, however, of the incessant activity that is taking place in a gas.

12-3. The Bohr-Rutherford Theory of the Atom. In order to explain gaseous-discharge phenomena it is necessary to abandon the simple model of a neutral solid atom and to introduce the concept of ionization. We must assume that the atom has loosely bound electrons which can be torn away from it. In this way, charge carriers will be created which can account for the electrical nature of the discharge.

Rutherford[1] found that the atom consists of a nucleus of positive charge that contains nearly all the mass of the atom. Surrounding this central positive core are negatively charged electrons. As a specific illustration of this atomic model, consider the hydrogen atom. This atom consists of a positively charged nucleus (a proton) and a single electron. The charge on the proton is positive and is equal in magnitude to the charge on the electron. Therefore the atom as a whole is electrically neutral. Because the proton carries practically all the mass of the atom, it will remain substantially immobile, whereas the electron will move about it in a closed orbit. The force of attraction between the electron and the proton follows Coulomb's law. It can be shown from classical mechanics that the resultant closed path will be a circle or an ellipse under the action of such a force. This motion is exactly analogous to that of the planets about the sun, because in both cases the force varies inversely as the square of the distance between the particles.

Assume, therefore, that the orbit of the electron in this planetary model of the atom is a circle, the nucleus being supposed fixed in space. It is a simple matter to calculate its radius in terms of the total energy, W joules, of the electron. The force of attraction between the nucleus and the electron is $e^2/4\pi\epsilon_0 r^2$ newtons, where the electronic charge e is in coulombs, the separation r between the two particles is in meters, and ϵ_0 is the permittivity of free space. By Newton's second law of motion, this must be set equal to the product of the electronic mass m in kilograms and the acceleration v^2/r toward the nucleus, where v is the speed of the electron in its circular path, in meters per second. Then

$$\frac{e^2}{4\pi\epsilon_0 r^2} = \frac{mv^2}{r} \tag{12-11}$$

Furthermore, the potential energy of the electron at a distance r from the nucleus is $-e^2/4\pi\epsilon_0 r$ joules, and its kinetic energy is $\frac{1}{2}mv^2$ joules. Then, according to the conservation of energy,

$$W = \frac{1}{2} mv^2 - \frac{e^2}{4\pi\epsilon_0 r} \quad \text{joules} \tag{12-12}$$

Combining this expression with (12-11) produces

$$W = - \frac{e^2}{8\pi\epsilon_0 r} \quad \text{joules} \tag{12-13}$$

which gives the desired relationship between the radius and the energy of the electron. This equation shows that the total energy of the electron is always negative. The negative sign arises because the potential energy has been chosen to be zero when r is infinite. This expression also shows that the energy of the electron becomes smaller (*i.e.*, more negative) as it approaches closer to the nucleus.

The foregoing discussion of the planetary atom has been considered only from the point of view of classical mechanics. However, an accelerated charge must radiate energy, in accordance with the classical laws of electromagnetism. If the charge is performing oscillations of a frequency f, then the radiated energy will also be of this frequency. Hence, classically, it must be concluded that the frequency of the emitted radiation equals the frequency with which the electron is rotating in its circular orbit.

There is one feature of this picture that cannot be reconciled with experiment.   If the electron is radiating energy, then its total energy must decrease by the amount of this emitted energy.   As a result the radius r of the orbit must decrease, in accordance with Eq. (12-13). Consequently, as the atom radiates energy, the electron must move in smaller and smaller orbits, eventually falling into the nucleus.   Since the frequency of oscillation depends upon the size of the circular orbit, the energy radiated would be of a gradually changing frequency.   Such a conclusion, however, is incompatible with the sharply defined frequencies of spectral lines.

This difficulty was resolved by Bohr in 1913.[2]   He postulated the following two fundamental laws:

1. Not all energies as given by classical mechanics are possible, but the atom can possess only certain discrete energies.   While in states corresponding to these discrete energies, the electron does *not* emit radiation, and the electron is said to be in a "stationary," or nonradiating, state.

2. In a transition from one stationary state corresponding to a definite energy W_2 to another stationary state, with an associated energy W_1, radiation will be emitted. The frequency of this radiant energy is given by

$$f = \frac{W_2 - W_1}{h} \qquad \text{cps} \qquad (12\text{-}14)$$

where h is Planck's constant in joule-seconds and where the W's are expressed in joules.

Bohr gave the quantitative rule (Prob. 12-10) whereby the energies of the stationary states could be calculated.   Then, upon making use of Eq. (12-14), the exact frequencies found in the hydrogen spectrum were obtained, a remarkable achievement.

12-4. Atomic Energy Levels.   Though it is theoretically possible to calculate the various energy states of the atoms of the simpler elements, these levels must be determined indirectly from spectroscopic and other data for the more complicated atoms.   The experimentally determined *energy-level diagram* for mercury is shown in Fig. 12-2.

The numbers to the left of the horizontal lines give the energy of these levels in electron volts.   The arrows represent some of the transitions that have been found to exist in actual spectra, the attached numbers giving the wave length of the emitted radiation, expressed in angstrom units $(10^{-10}$ m).   The light emitted in these transitions gives rise to the luminous character of the gaseous discharge.   However, all the emitted radiation need not appear in the form of visible light but may exist in the ultraviolet or infrared regions.   The meaning of the broken lines will be explained in Sec. 12-10.

It is customary to express the energy value of the stationary states in electron volts E rather than in joules W. Also, it is more common to specify the emitted radiation by its wave length λ angstroms rather than

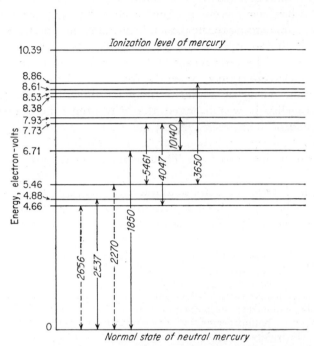

FIG. 12-2. The lower energy levels of atomic mercury.

by its frequency f cycles per second. In these units, Eq. (12-14) may be rewritten in the form

$$\lambda = \frac{12,400}{E_2 - E_1} \quad A \qquad (12\text{-}15)$$

Since only differences of energy enter into this expression, the zero state may be chosen at will. It is convenient and customary to choose the lowest energy state as the zero level. This was done in Fig. 12-2. The lowest energy state is called the "normal" level, and the other stationary states of the atom are called "excited," "radiating," "critical," or "resonance" levels.

The most intense line in the mercury spectrum is that resulting from the transition from the 4.88-ev level to the zero state. The emitted radiation, as calculated from Eq. (12-15), is $12,400/4.88 = 2,537$ A, as indicated in the diagram. It is primarily this line that is responsible for the ultraviolet burns which arise from mercury discharges.

12-5. The Photon Nature of Light. The mean life of an excited state ranges from 10^{-7} to 10^{-10} sec, the excited electron returning to its previous state after the lapse of this time.[3] In this transition, the atom must lose an amount of energy equal to the difference in energy between the two states that it has successively occupied, this energy appearing in the form of radiation. According to the principle of Bohr, this energy is emitted in the form of a photon of light, the frequency of this radiation being given by Eq. (12-14). The term *photon* denotes an amount of radiant energy equal to Planck's constant h times the frequency.

The photon concept of radiation may be difficult to comprehend at first. Classically, it was believed that the atoms were systems that emitted radiation *continuously* in all directions. According to the foregoing theory, however, this is not true, the emission of light by an atom being a discontinuous process. That is, the atom radiates only when it makes a transition from one energy level to a lower energy state. In this transition, it emits a definite amount of energy of one particular frequency, namely, one photon hf of light. Of course, when a luminous discharge is observed, this discontinuous nature of radiation is not suspected because of the enormous number of atoms that are radiating energy and, correspondingly, because of the immense number of photons that are emitted in unit time.

Example. Given a 50-watt mercury-vapor lamp. Assume that 0.1 per cent of the electrical energy supplied to the lamp appears in the ultraviolet line, 2,537 A. Calculate the number of photons per second of this wave length emitted by the lamp.

Solution. The energy per photon is, according to Eq. (12-15),

$$E = \frac{12,400}{2,537} = 4.88 \text{ ev/photon}$$

The total power being transformed to the 2,537-A line is 0.05 watt, or 0.05 volt $\times$ coulomb/sec. Since the charge per electron is 1.60×10^{-19} coulomb, then the power radiated is

$$\frac{0.05 \text{ volt} \times \text{coulomb/sec}}{1.60 \times 10^{-19} \text{ coulomb/electron}} = 3.12 \times 10^{17} \text{ ev/sec}$$

Hence, the number of photons per second is

$$\frac{3.12 \times 10^{17} \text{ ev/sec}}{4.88 \text{ ev/photon}} = 6.40 \times 10^{16} \text{ photons/sec}$$

This is an extremely large number.

12-6. Ionization. It is now possible to obtain a better insight into the process of ionization, mention of which has been made on several occasions. As the most loosely bound electron of an atom is given more and more energy, it moves into stationary states which are farther and farther away from the nucleus. When its energy is large enough to move completely out of the field of influence of the ion, it becomes "detached" from it. The energy required for this process to occur is called the *ionization potential* and is represented as the highest state in the energy-level diagram. From an inspection of Fig. 12-2, this is seen to be 10.39 volts for mercury. The alkali metals have the lowest ionization potentials, whereas the inert gases have the highest values, the ionizing potentials ranging from approximately 4 to 25 ev.

Table 12-1 gives the values of the ionization potential, the first excitation potential, and the corresponding first resonance wave length of some of the elements that play important roles in discharge tubes.

TABLE 12-1

Gas or vapor	Ionizing potential, ev	First radiative excitation potential, ev	First resonance wave length, A	First metastable excitation potential, ev	Discharge color
A	15.7	11.6	1,065	. . . . .	Blue
Cd	8.96	3.78	3,260	. . . . .	Red
He	24.5	20.6	600	19.8	Yellow
Hg	10.4	4.88	2,537	4.66	Purple
Na	5.12	2.09	5,896	. . . . .	Yellow
Ne	21.5	16.7	743	16.6	Orange

12-7. Collisions of Electrons with Atoms. The foregoing discussion has shown that in order to excite or ionize an atom, energy must be supplied to it. This energy may be supplied to the atom in various ways. The most important method by which an energy interchange occurs in a gaseous discharge is through the medium of electron impact. Other methods of ionization or excitation of atoms will be considered below.

Suppose that an electron is accelerated by the potential field applied to a discharge tube. When this electron collides with an atom, one of several effects may occur. A slowly moving electron suffers an "elastic" collision, i.e., one that entails an energy loss only as required by the laws of conservation of energy and momentum. The direction of travel of the electron will be altered by the collision although its energy remains substantially unchanged. This follows from the fact that the mass of the gas molecule is large compared with that of the electron.

If the electron possesses sufficient energy, the amount depending upon the particular gas present, it may transfer enough of its energy to the atom to elevate it to one of the higher quantum states. The amount of energy necessary for this process is the excitation, or radiation, potential of the atom. If the impinging electron possesses a higher energy, say an amount at least equal to the ionization potential of the gas, it may deliver this energy to an electron of the atom and completely remove it from the parent atom. Three charged particles result from such an ionizing collision, two electrons and a positive ion.

It must not be presumed that the incident electron must possess an energy corresponding exactly to the energy of a stationary state in an atom in order to raise the atom into this level. If the bombarding electron has gained more than the requisite energy from the electric field to raise an atom into a particular energy state, then the amount of energy in excess of that required for excitation will be retained by the incident electron as kinetic energy after the collision. Or if the process of ionization has taken place, the excess energy divides between the two electrons.

12-8. Collisions of Photons with Atoms. Another important method by which an atom may be elevated into an excited energy state is to have radiation fall on the gas. An atom may absorb a photon of frequency f and thereby move from the level of energy W_1 to the higher energy level W_2, where $W_2 = W_1 + hf$ joules.

An extremely important feature of excitation by photon capture is that *the photon will not be absorbed unless its energy corresponds exactly to the energy difference between two stationary levels of the atom with which it collides.* Consider, for example, the following experiment: The 2,537-A mercury radiation falls on sodium vapor in the normal state. What is the result of this irradiation? The impinging photons have an energy of $12,400/2,537 = 4.88$ ev, whereas the first excitation potential of sodium is only 2.09 ev. It is conceivable that the sodium atom might be excited and that the excess energy $4.88 - 2.09 = 2.79$ ev would appear as another photon of wave length $12,400/2.79 = 4,440$ A. Actually, however, the 2,537-A line is transmitted without absorption through the sodium vapor, neither of the two lines appearing. It must be concluded, therefore, that the probability of excitation of a gas by photon absorption is negligible unless the energy of the photon corresponds exactly to the energy difference between two stationary states of the atoms of the gas.

When a photon is absorbed by an atom, the excited atom may return to its normal state in one jump, or it may do so in several steps. If the atom falls into one or more excitation levels before finally reaching the normal state, then it will emit several photons. These will correspond to energy differences between the successive excited levels into which the atom falls. None of the emitted photons will have the frequency of the absorbed radiation! This *fluorescence* cannot be explained by classical theory but is readily understood once Bohr's postulates are accepted.

It is possible for the photons that induce the excitation of certain atoms to originate within the discharge itself. For example, the following chain process has been observed to occur in mercury vapor: An atom near the center of a discharge tube emits the ultraviolet 2,537-A line. This photon is captured by a neighboring atom, thereby exciting it to the first resonance potential. About 10^{-7} sec later, this excited atom returns to its normal state with the emission of a 2,537-A photon. This new photon in turn excites another atom, with the subsequent reemission of a 2,537-A photon. This absorption and emission process may occur several thousand times before an atom near the boundary of the discharge emits a photon that escapes from the discharge. This process has been called the "imprisonment of radiation" in a discharge tube.[4]

If the frequency of the impinging photon is sufficiently high, it may have enough energy to ionize the gas. The photon vanishes, with the appearance of an electron and a positive ion. Unlike the case of photoexcitation, the photon need not possess an energy corresponding exactly to the ionizing energy of the atom. It need merely possess at least this much energy. If it possesses more than ionizing energy, the excess will appear as the kinetic energy of the emitted electron and positive ion. However, it is found by experiment that the maximum probability of photoionization occurs when the energy of the photon is equal to the ionization potential, the probability decreasing rapidly for higher photon energies.

12-9. Other Ionizing Agents. Minute traces of radioactive contamination are always present in all materials. These emit particles and radiations that are capable of producing ionization. Ultraviolet rays, X rays, and cosmic rays can also produce ionization. Because one or more of these ionizing agents are always present, then a (very small) percentage of any gas is ionized. These few free electrons play a most important role in some types of discharge, as will be seen in Sec. 12-13.

One might expect that a certain amount of excitation and ionization will result from collisions between positive ions and neutral gas atoms with which they may collide. Actually, however, the probability of ionization by such a collision is very much smaller than that for an electron collision,[5] so that this process plays a minor role in the formation of additional ions.

12-10. Metastable States. Stationary states may exist which can be excited by electron bombardment but not by photoexcitation. Such levels are called *metastable states*. A transition from a metastable level to the normal state *with the emission of radiation* does not take place. The 4.66- and 5.46-ev levels in Fig. 12-2 are metastable states. The forbidden transitions are indicated by dashed arrows on the energy-level diagram. Transitions from a higher level to a metastable state are permitted, and several of these are shown in Fig. 12-2.

The mean life of a metastable state is found to be very much longer than the mean life of a radiating level. Representative times are 10^{-2} to 10^{-4}

sec for metastable states and 10^{-7} to 10^{-10} sec for radiating levels. The long lifetime of the metastable states arises from the fact that a transition to the normal state with the emission of a photon is forbidden. How then can the energy of a metastable state be expended so that the atom may return to its normal state? One method is for the metastable atom to collide with another molecule and give up its energy to the other molecule as kinetic energy of translation, or potential energy of excitation. Another method is that by which the electron in the metastable state receives additional energy by any of the processes enumerated in the preceding sections. The metastable atom may thereby be elevated to a higher energy state from which a transition to the normal level can take place, or else it may be ionized. If the metastable atom diffuses to the walls of the discharge tube or to any of the electrodes therein, either it may expend its energy in the form of heat or the metastable atoms might induce secondary emission.

Owing to the relatively long lifetime of a metastable state, the probability of cumulative ionization is greatly increased. It is very common in an arc discharge to have ionization take place at a voltage that is appreciably lower than the ionization potential of the gas. For example, the drop across a mercury-arc tube may be considerably less than 10.4 volts. Thus any electron that has fallen through a potential greater than only 5.73 volts and collides with an atom in the 4.66-ev metastable state can ionize the atom (since $5.73 + 4.66 = 10.39$).

Another illustration of the practical importance of metastable states is the *Penning effect*.[6] Penning found that neon, to which a little argon has been added, has a lower sparking potential than pure neon. The explanation is that neon has a metastable level at 16.6 ev, which is higher than the ionization level of 15.7 ev of argon. Hence a metastable neon atom may ionize an argon atom with which it collides.

As a check on the above explanation, Penning illuminated the discharge with strong light from a glow discharge in neon. The emitted photons can be absorbed by the metastable neon atoms, which are thus removed from their metastable states. Hence ionizing collisions with argon become less frequent, and it is found that the breakdown voltage is increased.

12-11. Recombination. If an electron and an ion were to combine in the body of a discharge, an amount of energy equal to the ionization potential would be released. If an attempt is made to satisfy the principles of conservation of energy and conservation of momentum in this two-body problem it is found impossible to do so. Consequently, in the body of the discharge simple electron and ion recombination does not take place. However, deionization may occur if a third body is involved in the process.

The third body might be another electron, an ion, or a molecule that is present in the gas. Such a triple encounter has a low probability of occurrence, and it must be concluded that *very little deionization takes place in the body of the gas.*

Recombination takes place principally at the surface of the container. Thus, when the excitation is removed from a gaseous discharge, the ions diffuse to the walls or to any surfaces in the gas. They also drift to the electrodes if any field is present. The presence of the ion, the electron, and the surface permits satisfying both conservation of energy and momentum, with the consequent neutralization of the ion.

12-12. Electrical Character of Discharges. The most convenient way of distinguishing among the various possible electrical discharges in gases is to study the volt-ampere characteristics of these discharges. Con-
sider a tube containing two cold
plane-parallel electrodes between
which is contained a fixed quantity
of gas at a low pressure (say, a few
millimeters Hg). An adjustable
source of potential in series with a
resistor is connected across the tube.
The current through the tube is ob-

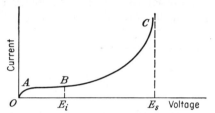

Fig. 12-3 Volt-ampere characteristics of a non-self-maintained discharge.

served as a function of the voltage across it, as either the magnitude of the voltage or the magnitude of the resistance is varied. The general form of the characteristic so obtained is given in Fig. 12-3.

The current is found to vary gradually with variations in potential from the point O to the point A. Further increases in potential in the region from A to B results in no further increase in current through the tube, and the horizontal portion of the curve from A to B is obtained. As the voltage is increased beyond the value corresponding to B, the current is found to increase rapidly to the point C, somewhat as shown. For rea sons which will appear in the next section, this discharge is called a *non-self-maintained, a field-intensified, or a Townsend discharge*. If an attempt is made to obtain the characteristic beyond point C, the entire character of the discharge changes suddenly. The voltage is found to decrease rapidly. The gas in the tube suddenly begins to glow, the color of the luminous region being a function of the gas or gases contained in the tube. Also, the current through the tube rises very rapidly, the magnitude of the current that flows through the tube being determined by the magnitude of the potential and by the size of the current-limiting resistor in the external circuit. The gas in the tube is said to have *broken down*, and the voltage at C is the *sparking potential*. The discharge becomes a glow or an arc. The theory of the Townsend discharge will now be given. Conditions after breakdown are studied in later sections.

12-13. Non-self-maintained Discharge. A gas is always in a state of partial ionization because of the action of a number of natural ionizing sources, as explained in Sec. 12-9. If, therefore, a voltage is applied to two electrodes sealed in a tube containing a gas, a few ions will drift to the cathode and some electrons will be transported to the anode. This will result in the flow of a minute current. If it is assumed, as is generally true, that the rate of production of the ions by the ionizing agent is a constant, then the current is independent of voltage over a range of voltages. This is the region AB of Fig. 12-3. The external radiating agents produce saturation current densities of the order of 10^{-22} amp/m².

In order to explain the rapidly rising portion of the characteristic, the region BC of the figure, suppose that the potential E_i at the point B represents the ionization potential of the gas. Then in the region beyond B the potential through which the electron falls from the time of its liberation by the external ionizing agent until it collides with a gas molecule in its path a short distance away may be sufficient to give it an energy adequate to cause ionization of the molecule. That is, the potential per mean free path of the electron is sufficient to cause ionization. If it ionizes the molecule, it will liberate,

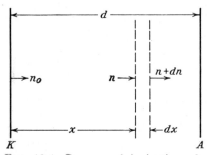

FIG. 12-4. Because of ionization, dn new electrons are formed in the distance dx.

say, one electron. Now two electrons exist to cause further ionization. It is then evident that this process, which is cumulative, may result in very large currents in the tube. An analytical representation of this process is possible.

Suppose that n_0 electrons are ejected from the cathode per second (see Fig. 12-4). If n denotes the number of electrons per second at any distance x from the cathode, then dn new electrons per second will be formed in the distance dx owing to the ionization that occurs. If α *represents the number of new electrons (or ions) formed by one electron in traveling a distance of 1 m through the gas,* then

$$dn = \alpha n \, dx$$

The parameter α is frequently called the *first Townsend coefficient*. This leads, upon integration, to

$$n = n_0 \epsilon^{\alpha x} \tag{12-16}$$

provided that α is independent of x. Thus, for every electron produced at the cathode, ϵ^{ad} electrons reach the anode a distance d away.   The progeny of ϵ^{ad} electrons produced by one electron is called an *electron avalanche.*

By multiplying both sides of Eq. (12-16) by the electronic charge, the expression is transformed into an equation for the current.   It is

$$I_b = I_0 \epsilon^{ad} \qquad (12\text{-}17)$$

where I_b is the current to the collector and I_0 represents the current at the cathode resulting from the effects of the external ionizing agents.   If I_0 drops to zero, so also does I_b.   In other words, if the external excitation is removed the discharge stops.   This is why the discharge is termed *non-self-maintained.*

In a discharge the current is made up of electrons traveling toward the anode and positive ions moving toward the cathode.   The *net* current at any plane must be a constant because otherwise there would be a continuous piling up (or perhaps a depletion) of charge with time, which is not possible if a steady-state condition has been reached.   In Fig. 12-5 a positive superscript is used for positive ions and a negative superscript for electrons.   The arrows indicate the direction of travel of the particles.   The current *everywhere* is I_b.   Note, in particular, that this current at the anode is due entirely to electrons which have entered the collector from the discharge.   These electrons flow in the external circuit to

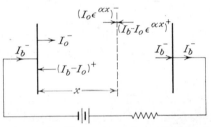

FIG. 12-5. The current in a discharge tube consists of electrons traveling toward the anode and positive ions traveling toward the cathode.

the junction of the cathode and the gas.   Here a certain number of them per second neutralize the positive-ion current $(I_b - I_0)$.   The remainder, I_0, is the electron current entering the discharge under the influence of the external excitation.

Because of the small values of I_0 resulting from the natural ionizing agents, it is difficult to obtain accurate measurements of the currents in the region BC of Fig. 12-3.   It is possible, however, to investigate this theory and that of the next section by using a tube that is provided with a photosensitive cathode, as the current in such a device (of the order of microamperes) may readily be measured.   Except for the fact that the initial electrons are produced photoelectrically instead of by natural ionizing agents, the conditions of gas amplification are the same.   The volt-ampere curve of an argon-filled phototube (General Electric PJ 23) is given in Fig. 6-7.   Its shape is exactly that of the curve of Fig. 12-3.

12-14. Breakdown.   If the potential across the phototube is made too high, the gas in the tube will "break down" and will begin to glow.   The current in the tube will rise to a high value and will be limited principally by the resistance in the external circuit. If, following breakdown, the light source is removed so that the photocathode is no longer illuminated, the current nevertheless continues. Such discharges are called *self-sustained* or *self-maintained discharges*. Although external agencies may assist in starting the discharge, once it has been initiated it will maintain itself without any external source.

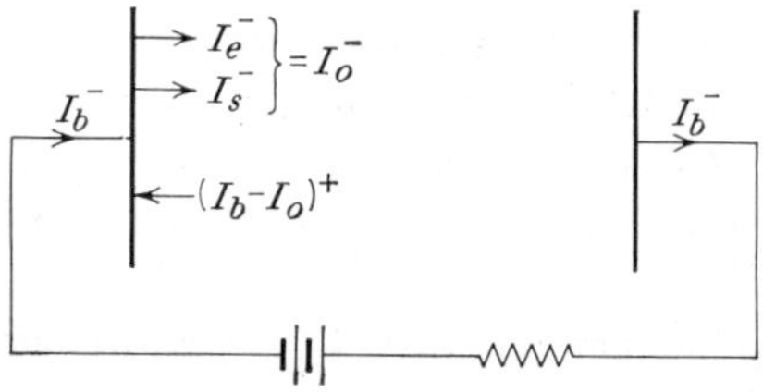

FIG. 12-6. When positive ions strike the cathode, they liberate secondary electrons I_s (in addition to those electrons I_e liberated from the cathode by the external source).

For breakdown to take place there must be some mechanism of electron production in the tube which has not yet been mentioned. The most likely process is that of electron emission at the cathode due to the positive-ion bombardment (often called *secondary emission* by positive ions). This electron current is designated by I_s, the electron current due to the external excitation by I_e, and the total electron current at the cathode by I_0. Thus

$$I_0 = I_e + I_s \qquad (12\text{-}18)$$

If I_b is the plate current, then by the principle outlined in the preceding section, the total current anywhere in the tube is I_b. Since the total electron current at the cathode is I_0, then the ion current at this electrode must be $I_b - I_0$. The situation is as pictured in Fig. 12-6, which is identical with Fig. 12-5 except that the total electron current I_0 at the cathode now consists of two terms. Hence, Eq. (12-17) is still valid provided only that I_0 is given by Eq. (12-18).

If, on the average, γ electrons are liberated from the cathode by one positive ion, then

$$I_s = \gamma(I_b - I_0) \qquad (12\text{-}19)$$

By combining Eqs. (12-17), (12-18), and (12-19) there results

$$I_b = \frac{I_e \epsilon^{\alpha d}}{1 + \gamma - \gamma \epsilon^{\alpha d}} \qquad (12\text{-}20)$$

Since the production of electrons by positive-ion bombardment of the cathode is a rather inefficient process, then the secondary-emission ratio γ is a small quantity. Representative values[7] range from 0.20 to 0.001, meaning that on an average somewhere between 5 and 1,000 positive ions must strike the cathode before a single electron is liberated.

Mathematically, it follows that the current will increase without limit when the denominator of Eq. (12-20) becomes zero. That is, breakdown occurs when

$$\gamma \epsilon^{\alpha d} = 1 + \gamma \qquad (12\text{-}21)$$

Physically, of course, the current can never increase without limit; but rather, as the left-hand term of this expression approaches $1 + \gamma$, an enormous increase in the current will occur, and the transition from the non-self-maintained to the self-maintained discharge takes place.

The existence of a self-maintained discharge requires that the number of ions which are produced by an electron in moving from the cathode to the anode must regenerate one electron when they strike the cathode. This criterion is actually expressed by Eq. (12-21). To verify this, it is noted that if n_0 electrons per second leave the cathode, then these produce $(n_0 \epsilon^{\alpha d} - n_0)$ positive ions per second in their passage to the anode. Therefore, when one electron leaves the cathode, it produces $(\epsilon^{\alpha d} - 1)$ positive ions in the body of the gas. These positive ions eject, in turn, by the γ process at the cathode, $\gamma(\epsilon^{\alpha d} - 1)$ electrons. Evidently, if this quantity just equals unity, then the one electron originally emitted from the cathode has caused another electron to leave the cathode. This new electron will likewise cause the production of a third electron, and so on indefinitely. In other words, the discharge will no longer require an external agent for its maintenance. The criterion for this condition is

$$\gamma(\epsilon^{\alpha d} - 1) = 1$$

which is seen to be equivalent to Eq. (12-21).

12-15. Paschen's Law. Many terms are used synonymously with the term "breakdown voltage." Some of them are "sparking," "ignition," "starting," and "striking" potential. The factors which determine the sparking potential will now be investigated.

The number of electrons formed per electron per meter (the value of α) depends upon the number of collisions that the incident electron makes in traversing this unit path and also upon the energy that the incident electron possesses when it collides with the gas molecules. The number of collisions made by an electron per meter of its path, which is the inverse of the electronic mean free path, is directly proportional to the pressure of the gas. Also, the energy that an impinging electron possesses at the time of collision with a molecule depends upon both the product of the electric-field intensity $\mathcal{E}$ and the mean free path l_e. Since the mean free path varies inversely with the pressure, the energy per mean free path $\mathcal{E}l_e$ may be written proportional to $\mathcal{E}/p$. Thus α is proportional to p and also to some function of $\mathcal{E}/p$. Mathematically, these results may be expressed in the form

$$\alpha = pf\left(\frac{\mathcal{E}}{p}\right) \qquad (12\text{-}22)$$

where $f(\mathcal{E}/p)$ is some undetermined function which remains constant when the ratio $\mathcal{E}/p$ is constant.

The number of secondary electrons emitted from the cathode per incident positive ion (the value of γ) depends upon the energy of the impinging ions. Hence γ is a function of the energy gained by the ion in its last free path before striking the cathode, or γ is a function of $\mathcal{E}l_m$. Therefore γ depends only upon the ratio $\mathcal{E}/p$ and not upon $\mathcal{E}$ or p individually.

If E_s is the sparking potential, then at breakdown the electric-field intensity is given by $\mathcal{E} = E_s/d$, where d is the electrode separation. Since $\mathcal{E}/p = E_s/pd$, both αd and γ are functions of E_s and the product pd. Hence the condition for breakdown, Eq. (12-21), which involves only α and γ, is a relationship between E_s and pd. We are thus led to the conclusion that the breakdown voltage is a function only of the *product* of the pressure and the interelectrode spacing and does not depend upon these two parameters separately. This conclusion is verified experimentally. Thus, if the pressure is doubled while the interelectrode spacing is halved, the breakdown voltage remains unchanged. This relationship is known as *Paschen's law.*

Clearly, from the above discussion, *the sparking voltage also depends upon the cathode material and the type of gas.* These conclusions are verified by experiment. Figure 12-7 shows breakdown in air for a very wide range of pd.

For electrodes of a given area, the volume of gas contained between them is proportional to the separation d. Also, since the concentration is proportional to the pressure, then the product pd is proportional to the number of molecules between the electrodes. Hence, Paschen's law states that the ignition voltage depends only upon the total number of molecules of gas between the cathode and the anode, for a given cathode material and a given gas.

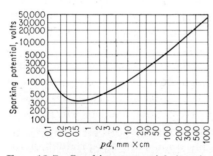

FIG. 12-7. Sparking potential in air between parallel electrodes with a brass cathode. (*After M. J. Druyvesteyn and F. M. Penning, Revs. Mod. Phys.,* **12**, 87–174, 1940.)

The experimentally determined curves of sparking potential vs. the product pd show a minimum, the voltage being high for very low and very high values of pd. Refer to Fig. 12-7, which is for plane-parallel electrodes in air. The minimum value of the product pd is 0.6 mm $\times$ cm. Note that regardless of the pressure or spacing, it is impossible to cause breakdown to occur between parallel electrodes in air at voltages less than 350 volts.

The reason for the existence of a minimum in the sparking-potential curve is easy to discover. Consider, for example, that the spacing is fixed and that p is varied. At very low pressures, there are so few molecules present that enough secondary electrons can be produced only if the energies of the impinging electrons are high. This means that a high voltage must be applied. On the other hand, if the pressure is high, then the number of collisions is so large that the energy gained by each electron per mean free path is small unless the applied potential is high. For ionization to take place, the energy per mean free path must exceed a certain minimum amount (the ionization potential of the gas), and so a high potential will be necessary. Between these two extremes of pressure will be a pressure at which a minimum sparking potential will be necessary.

12-16. Glow Discharge. A low-pressure discharge *after* breakdown, known as the *glow discharge*, is visually characterized by brightly colored luminous regions in the gas. Electrically, it is characterized both by a *low current density* and by a *high voltage drop*. This maintaining voltage is considerably higher than the ionizing potential of the gas present, but lower than the sparking potential. The volt-ampere characteristic of this portion of the discharge is given in Fig. 12-8. Visual inspection of the tube while under operation shows that only a small part of the cathode is covered with glow for low values of total current. In fact, as the current through the tube increases, the portion of the cathode surface that is covered with glow increases linearly with the current. This indicates that the current density remains constant. This constant value is known as the *normal current*

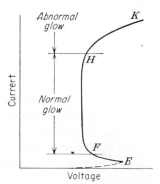

Fig. 12-8. Volt-ampere characteristic of a glow discharge.

density. Normal current densities are of the order of 1 amp/m² at a pressure of 1 mm Hg. The region FH, which is characterized by a fairly high though more or less constant potential and by a constant current density, is known as the *normal glow* discharge.

The variation of potential from cathode to anode has the general form shown in Fig. 12-9. The region adjacent to the anode and extending over the major portion of the tube is called the *plasma*, because it contains approximately equal concentrations of positive and negative charge. The formation of the plasma is discussed in detail in Sec. 12-20. It is sufficient for the present to point out that since the net charge density is zero, the potential must vary linearly with distance (according to Poisson's equation). Actually the variation is often found to be very small, and in what follows the plasma will be taken as an equipotential region at the anode voltage. Almost all the voltage across the tube appears in the small distance between the cathode and the boundary of the plasma, called the *cathode-fall* region.

12-17. Conditions at the Cathode. The cathode fall, which represents the potential through which the positive ions "fall" in passing to the cathode, is the most important part of the discharge. It is found experimentally that the magnitude of this voltage is of the order of (but somewhat less than) the *minimum* value of the breakdown voltage for the given gas and the given cathode material.[8] There appears to be no theoretical explanation for this coincidence. Another important experimentally determined feature is that the cathode fall is substantially independent of the pressure. Hence, the distance d_k covered by the cathode fall adjusts itself so as to yield the correct value of pd_k at which the minimum breakdown voltage occurs. That is to say, Paschen's law applies here, with d replaced by d_k. This is verified by observing that as the pressure is varied the cathode-fall potential remains constant, and d_k varies inversely as the pressure.

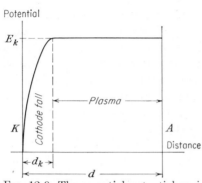

Fig. 12-9. The essential potential variation in a glow.

Normal values for cathode-fall voltages range between about 59 volts (a potassium surface and helium gas) and 350 volts. The presence of a low-work-function coating on the cathode tends to give a low cathode fall with any gas.[9] Also, the use of one of the inert gases (He, Ne, A, etc.) results in a low cathode fall with any cathode material. Of course, the presence of small amounts of impurities in either the gas or the cathode will result in a considerably modified value of cathode fall. It is the characteristic of a substantially constant cathode fall over a rather wide range in currents that accounts for the use of glow-discharge tubes as ballast tubes (Sec. 13-12).

It has been noted that the discharge is maintained by electron emission by positive-ion bombardment at the cathode. Since it takes a large number of positive ions to produce one electron by this γ process, the cathode fall must be a region containing many positive ions. If the small electron current at the cathode is neglected, then only a positive-ion current exists in this region. The conditions in this region are then precisely analogous to those which prevail in a vacuum tube under the conditions of a negative space charge resulting from an excess of electrons. Consequently,

Eq. (4-12), which relates the current density (in this case a positive-ion current density) with the potential, must be valid. Thus

$$J = K \frac{E_k^{\frac{3}{2}}}{d_k^2} \tag{12-23}$$

where E_k is the cathode-fall potential and d_k is the distance from the cathode to the edge of the negative glow.

This equation contains an explanation of the "normal" region of the glow discharge. Suppose, for example, that the current through a glow tube is measured for a given applied potential and external series resistor. According to the foregoing discussion, E_k is approximately the minimum breakdown voltage, and d_k is the distance at which this minimum occurs for the given pressure. This fixes both E_k and d_k in Eq. (12-23), and thus J may be calculated. Consequently, the area of the glow I/J is known. However, as the magnitude of the external resistor is varied, the magnitude of the current is changed, but E_k, d_k, and so J remain constant. Hence the area of the glow on the cathode increases directly with the magnitude of the current. This theory accounts for the "normal" discharge region that exists in such discharges.

If d_k varies inversely as p, then it follows from Eq. (12-23) that J varies directly as the square of the pressure. This has been verified experimentally.

Once the entire cathode is covered with glow, a further increase in current can be obtained only by a corresponding increase in the current density. This requires an increase in E_k and a decrease in d_k. This region is called the "abnormal" glow and is the region HK of Fig. 12-8.

It is not possible to maintain a glow discharge simply by applying the breakdown voltage between the electrodes, if the spacing is too small for a given pressure. Thus, if sparking occurs to the left of the minimum of the Paschen's curve (Fig. 12-7), then the breakdown voltage will be equal to the cathode-fall voltage, since this fall will occupy the entire tube. In order to be able to draw any current from the tube, a voltage in excess of the breakdown potential must be applied.

No adequate quantitative theory of the glow discharge has been given, and the above description certainly is not intended as such. However, the discussion is useful because it shows in a semiquantitative way approximately what takes place in the cathodic part of the discharge.

12-18. Arcs.[10] Upon increasing the current through a discharge tube beyond the region where the abnormal glow exists, a sudden transition takes place in which the voltage drop decreases markedly, the current density increases until the current concentrates itself in a small spot on the cathode, and the discharge becomes an arc. The current through the system is controlled wholly by the external circuit. Figure 12-10 shows the volt-ampere characteristic starting with a non-self-sustained

Townsend discharge and progressing through the glow to the arc. The tremendous current range covered should be noted (a logarithmic current scale is used).

Electric arcs are generally associated with the flow of large currents at low voltage or with very high current densities at the cathode, and with a volt-ampere characteristic that has a negative slope. The mechanism of initiating the arc need not be that of a transition from a glow by increasing the current. Other methods of starting an arc are given below.

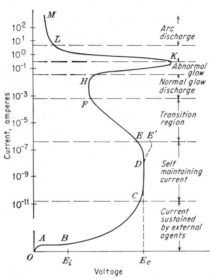

FIG. 12-10. Volt-ampere characteristic of a gaseous discharge. (*After M. J. Druyvesteyn and F. M. Penning, Revs. Mod. Phys.*, **12**, 87–174, 1940.)

The dividing line between an arc and a glow discharge is indistinct, and they have many features in common. Each discharge has associated with it the cathode fall and the plasma region. However, the discharges differ in respect to the mechanism by which the electrons are supplied from the cathode. In the glow discharge, the electrons are emitted from the cathode principally by positive-ion bombardment of the cathode. In the arc discharge, the emission of the electrons from the cathode occurs through the production of electrons by a hot cathode or a high field at the cathode surface. This fact leads to the following classification of arcs:

1. *Thermionic Arcs.* The cathode is heated to high temperatures *by the discharge*, the thermionic-emission current being of the same order as the self-maintained arc current.

2. *Externally Heated Arcs.* These are non-self-maintained arcs in which an externally heated thermionic cathode supplies the requisite arc current.

3. *Low-boiling-point Cathode Arcs.* The electron release occurs by the mechanism of high-field emission from a relatively cold cathode surface. The thermionic emission is negligible in this case.

Common examples of arcs of type 1 are the carbon-arc lamp and the "sun lamp" with tungsten electrodes. Arcs of types 2 and 3 are the most prevalent in engineering practice. The externally heated arcs (type 2) find wide use in gas-filled thermionic diodes and triodes. These units have moderate current capacities (up to perhaps 25 amp). The high-field emission arcs (type 3) are extremely important. The mercury-pool-cathode arcs used in high-current tank rectifiers presumably belong in this class. Arcs of type 3 also play a significant role in circuit breakers.

12-19. A Comparison of the Arc and Glow. A summary of the essential similarities and differences of glow and arc discharges follows.

Similarities. (1) Both have the same shape volt-ampere characteristic. The breakdown voltage is greater than the maintaining voltage, and the latter is essentially constant with load current. (2) Both have the same shape voltage-distance characteristic. It consists of a cathode fall and a plasma region.

Differences. (1) A glow is a low-current high-voltage discharge, whereas an arc is a high-current low-voltage discharge. (2) In the glow the electrons are supplied by the γ mechanism at the cold cathode. In the arc there is available a more efficient electron supply, such as thermionic or high-field emission. (3) The arc has no counterpart to the normal glow region of the glow tube.

12-20. The Plasma.[11] Consider a tube containing gas between parallel electrodes separated by a distance d. If there were no space charge the potential vs. distance curve would be the straight line 1 shown in Fig. 12-11. Assume now that the electrons liberated from the cathode (by any of the mechanisms discussed in connection with either glows or arcs) ionize some molecules. Since the electrons are much lighter than the ions, they are rapidly drawn out of the discharge, whereas the positive ions remain essentially stationary where they are formed. Hence, a positive space charge is built up. By Coulomb's law this raises the po-

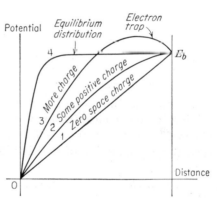

FIG. 12-11. Potential-distance curves as positive space charge is formed.

tential at every point in the interelectrode space, and curve 2 now represents the potential distribution. These curves and the discussion to follow should be compared with the somewhat analogous situation in Sec. 4-3, where the potential-distance curves for a negative-space-charge diode are developed.

If the positive space charge increases further, it may become large enough for the distribution to take on the shape of curve 3, which has a maximum greater than the applied plate potential E_b. However, in general, such a situation is not physically possible. To demonstrate this, refer to Fig. 12-12, where are shown the potential-energy curves for an electron corresponding to the potential curves of Fig. 12-11. (It should be recalled that potential energy equals potential times the charge on the electron—which is a negative number, so that the curves of Fig. 12-12 have the same shape as those of Fig. 12-11 but are inverted.) The potential maximum corresponds to a potential-energy minimum and hence to a potential-energy barrier for slow-moving electrons. For example, consider an electron that starts from the cathode with very little energy, travels a distance OD, collides with a gas molecule, and gives up an amount of energy DC. This electron will not be able to reach the anode

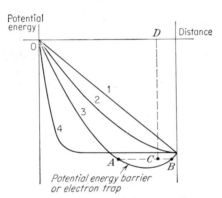

FIG. 12-12. Potential-energy-distance curves for an electron corresponding to the potential variations in Fig. 12-11.

but will collide with the barrier at point B. It will be "trapped" in the region between A and B. Similarly, if the collision causes ionization, the liberated electron will have very little energy and will also be trapped in the potential maximum. Hence, these electrons will effectively neutralize positive ions. In this manner the captured electrons reduce the net space charge to zero, and the potential maximum disappears. The equilibrium distribution, curve 4 of Fig. 12-11 (and Fig. 12-12), is one in which most of the space is an approximately equipotential volume containing equal concentrations of positive and negative charge—the plasma. The necessary condition for the generation of a plasma is that the rate of production of positive ions is sufficient to produce a potential maximum.

The impression should not be gained that the plasma contains only electrons and positive ions. In fact, it consists almost entirely of nonionized gas molecules. The concentration of electrons and ions rarely exceeds several per cent of the gas concentration and may actually be only a small fraction of 1 per cent of the latter.

Because of their smaller mass the electrons will diffuse out of the plasma more rapidly than the ions. They will go to the walls of the tube containing the gas and will charge it a few volts negative with respect to the main portion of the plasma. This negative potential will repel electrons and attract positive ions, and in the equilibrium state the net current to the walls must be zero.

The region between the plasma and a boundary across which there is a large potential gradient is designated by the name *sheath*. A sheath may form around any probe or electrode that is immersed in the plasma. The sheath that forms at the surface of an insulator which is negative with respect to the plasma (for example, the glass walls of the discharge tube) will arise from the presence of an excess number of positive ions. However, sheaths may contain either electrons or positive ions, an electron sheath forming about a probe which is positive with respect to the plasma.

Although the average energy of the electrons in the plasma is of the order of a few electron volts, nevertheless a few electrons possess energies that are high enough to cause ionization by collision. This situation must prevail because otherwise the random velocities of the ions would cause them all to pass ultimately through the sheaths at the boundaries of the plasma. This loss of ions must be compensated for by the production of other ions in order to maintain the plasma.

If the area of the plasma is large compared with the volume, then the rate at which deionization takes place at the walls will be high. For sufficient ionization to take place in the plasma to replace these lost ions, the plasma can no longer be an equipotential region but there must be an appreciable voltage drop across it. Such a situation exists in a neon advertising sign, which consists of a long tubular glass envelope of small cross section. The drop in the plasma in such a tube is found to be 100 to 200 volts/ft.

12-21. Probe Characteristics. Langmuir and Mott-Smith[12] obtained a great deal of information about what was happening physically inside a discharge by inserting a conductor, called a *probe*, into the plasma. If a known voltage (with respect to the cathode) is applied to the probe and the current to it is measured, the volt-ampere characteristic of Fig. 12-13 is obtained. For large negative potentials with respect to the plasma potential, positive ions will be attracted and electrons repelled. Hence, in the region AB a saturation positive-ion current I_i is collected, analogous to the reverse saturation current drawn in a semiconductor diode.

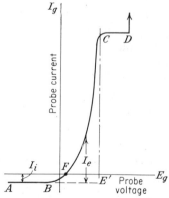

FIG. 12-13. Volt-ampere characteristic of a probe in the plasma of a discharge. This diagram is not drawn to scale since the maximum electron current is usually about 1,000 times the positive-ion current.

As the voltage of the probe is made more positive, all the electrons are no longer repelled, so that the difference between the positive-ion current and the electron current drifting to the probe will be collected. Hence, the true electron current I_e, at any voltage, is that indicated on the diagram by the curve BC. At a potential (point F) designated the *floating potential*, the number of positive ions collected and the number of electrons collected will be equal to each other, so that an ammeter in the external probe circuit will be zero. It follows from the discussion given in the preceding section that the potential at F must be negative with respect to the plasma. As the probe potential is increased beyond the point F, the number of electrons that are collected will increase exponentially, since the retarding action of the probe potential with respect to the plasma potential is being decreased. This current is analogous to the forward current drawn in a semiconductor diode as the junction potential barrier is reduced (Sec. 5-2).

When the probe is at the same potential as the plasma, the probe will exert no repelling force on the electrons and the ions and so those that wander to the probe because of their random motion will be collected. Consequently, further increases in potential of the probe will not result in an increased electron current. Potentials more positive than E' produce a field that repels the positive ions. But the random electron current is very much greater than the positive-ion current. Hence a region CD which is practically horizontal exists. Thus a more or less sharp break will exist in the curve at the potential E', which then represents the potential of the plasma. If the voltage of the probe is increased sufficiently, the electrons attracted to the probe may have sufficient energy to ionize the molecules in the sheath. These will neutralize the electron space charge, the probe current will rise rapidly, and the probe will become an auxiliary anode as at point D in Fig. 12-13.

In the region AB (Fig. 12-13), the electron current is zero, and the positive-ion current is a constant. What then is the consequence of variations of probe potential? The answer to this question can be found by a closer examination of the sheath that so effectively shields the plasma from the probe. This sheath is a region containing charges of one sign only (positive ions, in this case), and the conditions here differ very little from those which exist in the space-charge-limited vacuum diode. Within the range of probe voltages for which this analogy is valid, the same three-halves-power law must also be applicable. Thus, Eq. (4-12) may be written in the form

$$x = \left[\frac{2.33 \times 10^{-6}}{J_{ri}(m_i/m_e)^{\frac{1}{2}}} \right]^{\frac{1}{2}} E_r^{\frac{3}{4}} \tag{12-24}$$

where x now represents the sheath thickness, m_i/m_e is the mass ratio of ion to electron, and $E_r \equiv E' - E_g =$ the potential across the sheath.

Since from Eq. (12-10) the random ion current density J_{ri} is independent of E_g and hence of E_r, then Eq. (12-24) clearly indicates that the effect of varying the probe potential is simply to vary the thickness of the sheath. With nominal values of currents and voltage this equation yields a sheath thickness of approximately 10^{-4} m. This is so small that the probe disturbs the discharge hardly at all. In other words, *as the probe voltage is varied, the anode current remains unchanged.* The practical consequences of this result are discussed in Chap. 14 in connection with the thyratron tube.

12-22. Discharges in High-frequency Fields.[13]   An important class of discharges are those which occur in the very high-frequency fields that exist in certain microwave discharge tubes. The mechanism for the discharge in these tubes is completely different from that which maintains a low-frequency discharge.

As discussed at some length in Sec. 12-13, the d-c discharge mechanism is the cumulative ionization of the electrons that leave the cathode and multiply as they proceed toward the anode. Such discharges depend on the cathode. The high-frequency a-c discharge is maintained entirely from electrons which are obtained from ionization by collisions in the gas and does not depend on the electrodes. Breakdown occurs when the number of electrons that are produced by ionization by collision in the gas equals the number of electrons that are lost by diffusion in the gas.

High-frequency discharges find a very important application in what is called the TR (transmit-receive) switch of a radar set. The TR switch is a relatively simple plane-parallel gas diode mounted into the transmission line. The requirement is that during the interval when the high-frequency high-power generator (the magnetron) is sending out a pulse, it must not get to the receiver (since it would certainly overload the receiver).

The operation is as follows: The TR tube breaks down almost instantly under the excitation of the high voltage pulse, and the discharge essentially short-circuits the input to the receiver. The high-energy pulse radiates into space. The reflected echo is picked up by the antenna. This very weak echo does not have enough energy to excite the gas in the TR switch, and hence it passes down the transmission line to the receiver.

REFERENCES

1. RUTHERFORD, E., "The Scattering of α and β Particles by Matter and the Structure of the Atom," *Phil. Mag.*, **21**, 669–688, May, 1911.
2. BOHR, N., "On the Constitution of Atoms and Molecules. Part 2: Systems Containing Only a Single Nucleus," *Phil. Mag.*, **26**, 476–502, September, 1913.
3. For a discussion of the various experimental methods that have been used to determine the mean life of excited states, see K. K. DARROW, "Electrical Phenomena in Gases," pp. 125–132, The Williams & Wilkins Company, Baltimore, 1932.
4. ZEMANSKY, M. W., "The Diffusion of Imprisoned Resonance Radiation in Mercury Vapor," *Phys. Rev.*, **29**, 513–523, April, 1927.
5. VARNEY, R. N., L. B. LOEB, and W. R. HASELTINE, "The Role of Ionization by Positive Ions in Spark Breakdown," *Phil. Mag.*, **29**, 379–390, April, 1940.

6. DARROW, K. K., "Electrical Phenomena in Gases," pp. 123, 297, The Williams & Wilkins Company, Baltimore, 1932.

7. COBINE, J. D., "Gaseous Conductors," 1st ed., p. 159, McGraw-Hill Book Company, Inc., New York, 1941.

8. SLEPIAN, J., and R. C. MASON, "Discharges in Gases. III: Self-maintained Discharges," *Elec. Eng.*, **53**, 511–518, April, 1934.

9. HALE, D. H., and W. S. HUXFORD, "Concerning Estimates of the Minimum Sparking Potential Based upon the Cathode Work Function," *J. Appl. Phys.*, **18**, 586, June, 1947.

10. DRUYVESTEYN, M. J., and F. M. PENNING, "The Mechanism of Electrical Discharges in Gases of Low Pressure," *Revs. Mod. Phys.*, **12**, 87–174, April, 1940.

    COBINE, J. D., "Gaseous Conductors," 1st ed., p. 290, McGraw-Hill Book Company, Inc., New York, 1941.

11. LANGMUIR, I., "Electric Discharges in Gases at Low Pressures," *J. Franklin Inst.*, **214**, 275–298, September, 1932.

    MARSHALL, D. E., Electrical Conduction in Gases, in Westinghouse Electric Corporation "Industrial Electronics Reference Book," pp. 47–57, John Wiley & Sons, Inc., New York, 1948.

12. LANGMUIR, I., "Electric Discharges in Gases at Low Pressures," *J. Franklin Inst.*, **214**, 275, September, 1932.

13. MARGENAU, H., "Theory of High Frequency Gas Discharges. I: Methods for Calculating Electron Distribution Functions," *Phys. Rev.*, **73**, 297–308, February, 1948.

    MARGENAU, H., and L. M. HARTMAN, "Theory of High Frequency Gas Discharges. II: Harmonic Components of the Distribution Function," *ibid.*, **73**, 309–315, February, 1948.

    HARTMAN, L. M., "Theory of High Frequency Gas Discharges. III: High Frequency Breakdown," *ibid.*, **73**, 316–325, February, 1948.

    MARGENAU, H., "Theory of High Frequency Gas Discharges. IV: Note on the Similarity Principle," *ibid.*, **73**, 326–328, February, 1948.

    MacDONALD, A. D., and S. C. BROWN, "High Frequency Discharge Breakdown in Helium," *ibid.*, **75**, 411–418, February, 1949.

CHAPTER 13

COMMERCIAL GAS TUBES

G AS-FILLED tubes depend for their operation on the characteristics of gaseous discharges discussed in the preceding chapter. Many different types of gas-filled tubes are available commercially, the most important of which are the two-element hot-cathode tube (the low-voltage externally heated arc tube); the two-element cold-cathode tube (the glow tube); the pool-type tube (the mercury-tank rectifier); the three-element hot-cathode tube (the thyratron); the three-element cold-cathode tube (the grid glow tube); and a number of single-anode multielement pool-type tubes (the excitron and ignitron). The most important use of these tubes, that of rectification, will be discussed in detail in Chap. 14. Several of the other applications, such as voltage regulators, light sources, control devices, and sweep circuits, will be considered below.

13-1. Hot-cathode Gas-filled Diodes. These are low-voltage non-self-maintaining arc tubes and were discussed in essence in the previous chapter. These tubes are frequently referred to as "phanotrons." They may be provided with an inert gas (neon, argon, etc.) at low pressure, although more commonly the gas is mercury vapor. In the latter case, a few drops of mercury are added to the tube after evacuation. The pressure in the tube is then a function of the mercury-vapor condensation temperature. At an ambient room temperature the pressure is of the order of 0.01 mm Hg. The breakdown potential is usually of the order of magnitude of the ionization potential of the gas present in the tube, although it will vary with the gas pressure. There exists a generally falling breakdown potential with increasing gas pressures, indicating that the operating pressures are to the left of the Paschen minimum.

Once conduction has started, *the tube drop will remain substantially constant and independent of the tube current at a value that is of the order of the ionizing potential of the gas.* The tube drop at any pressure is generally several volts less than the breakdown potential. If the current is decreased continuously after conduction has started, either by decreasing the applied voltage or by increasing the magnitude of the external resistance, the arc will go out. This extinction will occur when insufficient ionization takes place to maintain the discharge.

It should be emphasized that the maximum current obtainable in a phanotron is the saturation thermionic emission from the cathode enhanced by the effect of the field at the surface of the cathode (see Sec. 3-11). This has been shown to be about 1.8 times the actual thermionic emission current.[1] *The sole function of the gas in these tubes is to provide ions for the neutralization of space charge*, thereby permitting the

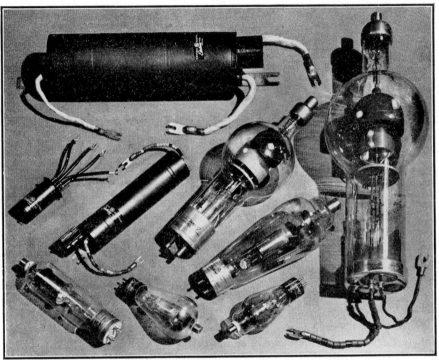

FIG. 13-1. Commercial hot-cathode diodes. (*Courtesy of General Electric Co.*)

The smallest tube is the FG-190 full-wave, gas-filled rectifier. It is approximately 3 in. long and 1.5 in. in diameter. The tube drop is 8 volts. The average anode current is 1.25 amp, the peak current is 5 amp, and the surge current for 0.1 sec is 20 amp.

The largest tube is the FG-166 half-wave all-metal mercury-vapor rectifier. It is approximately 14 in. long and 5 in. in diameter. The tube drop is 9 volts. The average anode current is 20 amp, the peak current is 75 amp, and the surge current is 750 amp. The tube is capable of delivering 50 kw of power.

high current to be obtained at much lower voltages than are required by the three-halves-power law in vacuum tubes. Under normal operating conditions, the total drop across a mercury-filled thermionic heater gas tube will range from 6 to 15 volts. If more current is passed through the tube than the cathode can deliver, the tube drop increases to the point where the additional electrons are produced by positive-ion bombardment. However, if the tube drop in such a tube exceeds about 22 volts, the positive-ion bombardment will cause the cathode to disintegrate. This voltage is known as the *disintegration* voltage. In operation, the voltage across a mercury-vapor tube should never be permitted to approach this value.

A group of phanotrons is shown in Fig. 13-1. The range of voltages and currents of these tubes is given in the caption.

To provide large tube currents, *heat-shielded cathodes* are used.[2] One form of such an emitter is indicated in Fig. 13-2. It resembles a furnace provided with oxide-coated vanes which extend radially outward from the center so that heat is radiated from vane to vane. The cathode is surrounded by a series of nickel cylinders which act as heat baffles, thereby providing for practically all the heat loss to occur from the relatively small area at the top of the cylinder. Consequently, *this type of cathode has a very large electron-emitting surface but a small effective radiating surface*, which accounts for the high efficiency and high currents obtainable from such a heat-shielded cathode. Another method of accomplishing a similar result is to wind a coated cathode ribbon either in the form of a spiral or in a form resembling the bellows of an accordion.[3]

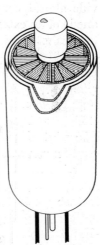

FIG. 13-2. A heat-shielded cathode. (*Courtesy of General Electric Co.*)

It is very important in the larger tubes which are equipped with the heat-shielded cathodes that sufficient time has elapsed for the cathode to reach its operating temperature before any anode potential is applied. This heating time may extend from perhaps 30 sec to as much as 30 min, depending upon the size of the cathode. If the anode potential is applied before the cathode can supply the electrons demanded of it, the tube will begin to operate as a self-maintained discharge, with the result that intense cathode sputtering will take place. In this case, the oxide-coated surface on the cathode will be flaked off, and the cathode will be permanently injured.

13-2. High-pressure Gas Diodes. These diodes contain argon or a mixture of argon and mercury at a pressure of about 5 cm Hg. They contain short heavy filaments located close to heavy graphite anodes. These tubes, which are used extensively for charging automobile storage batteries, are known as Tungar[4] or "rectigon" tubes.

The presence of the fairly high-pressure gas serves a twofold purpose. One is to provide the positive ions for reducing the space charge, in order to permit large currents. The second is to prevent the evaporation of the thorium or the oxide coating from the filament. This second effect is extremely important since the filament is operated at above-normal temperature, in order to provide the large currents from such a simple cathode structure.

Although these tubes have the advantage that fairly high currents are possible with a simple unit, they are limited in their application because the sparking potential on the inverse (nonconducting) half cycle is low at the high pressures that are used. These tubes are suitable only for use on low-voltage circuits.

13-3. The Thyratron.[5]   The insertion of a massive grid, so as to provide almost complete electrostatic shielding between the cathode and anode of an externally heated thermionic arc tube, permits control of the

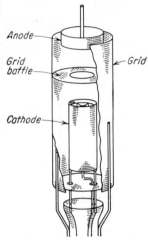

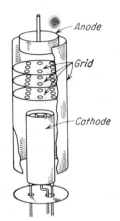

FIG. 13-3. Electrode structure of the type FG-27A (or FG-57) negative-control thyratron. (*From H. J. Reich, "Theory and Application of Electron Tubes," McGraw-Hill Book Company, Inc., New York, 1944.*)

FIG. 13-4. Electrode structure of the type FG-33 positive-control thyratron. (*From H. J. Reich, "Theory and Application of Electron Tubes," McGraw-Hill Book Company, Inc., New York, 1944.*)

initiation of the arc by controlling the potential of the grid. The grid usually consists of a cylindrical structure which surrounds both the anode and the cathode, a baffle or a series of baffles containing small holes being inserted between the cathode and the anode. Such tubes are illustrated in Figs. 13-3 and 13-4. Because of the almost complete shielding between the cathode and the anode, the application of a small grid potential before conduction is inaugurated is adequate to overcome the field at the cathode resulting from the application of a large anode potential. That is, a small grid voltage may neutralize the effects of a large anode potential and so prevent the arc from being initiated.

Once the arc has been initiated, the grid loses complete control over the arc, since now the grid is immersed in a plasma and is separated therefrom by the positive-ion sheath. The grid volt-ampere characteristic is that depicted in Fig. 12-13. Any variations in grid potential merely result in changing the thickness of the sheath. This behavior of the grid is to be expected in view of the theory of probes developed in Sec. 12-21. Grid control is reestablished only when the anode potential is reduced to a value below that necessary to maintain the arc. Once the arc has been extinguished by lowering the plate voltage, the grid once more determines when conduction will be initiated. This control characteristic is frequently referred to as the "trigger" action of the grid. The curve that relates the grid ignition potential with the potential on the anode is known as the *critical grid curve*. The control characteristics of the tube can be predicted from a knowledge of this one static curve.

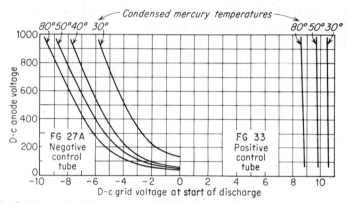

Fig. 13-5. Critical grid characteristics of a positive- and a negative-control thyratron with mercury condensation temperature as a parameter. (*Courtesy of General Electric Co.*)

Typical starting-characteristic curves of mercury-vapor thyratrons are given in Fig. 13-5. It will be observed that there are two distinct types of characteristic: those in which the grid potential must always be positive, and those in which the grid is generally negative, except for very low plate voltages. The physical distinction between these two types of tube lies essentially in the more complete shielding by the grid of the cathode from the anode in the positive-control tube. Compare the grid structures of the FG-27A and the FG-33 tubes illustrated in Figs. 13-3 and 13-4.

As is seen from Fig. 13-5, the grid potential of an FG-33 tube must be made positive for conduction to begin. That is, in order that the electrons that leave the cathode in a positive-control tube may acquire sufficient velocity to cause ionization of the gas molecules by collision, the grid must be made positive. As a matter of fact, the shielding of the anode is so complete that the potential of the plate exerts practically no influence on the control action. This means that the field at the cathode due to the anode potential is practically zero in the positive-control tubes, and the critical grid voltage is independent of the plate potential.

In the negative-control tube, where the shielding is far less complete, the effect of the plate voltage is clearly seen; the higher the plate potential, the more negative must the grid potential be in order to prevent conduction from taking place. For low plate voltages, positive grid voltages must be applied before ionization by collision, and hence conduction, can begin. If the plate voltage is reduced still further, even below the potential necessary for ionization, breakdown can still be obtained by making the grid sufficiently positive. Now, however, the function of the tube may be destroyed, since the main arc may take place between the cathode and the grid, with very little current to the plate. The thyratron will be converted into a gaseous diode under these circumstances with the plate acting as a dummy electrode, the cylindrical grid now acting as the anode.

It is necessary that the grid circuit contain sufficient current-limiting resistance in order to protect it from overload when such an arc takes place. Although the grid structure could handle high currents, the leads are not designed for high-current operation, and higher than rated current may overheat and crack the glass press at the point of entrance of the grid lead. It is good practice to fuse both the grid and the anode circuits.

As a specific illustration of the use of the starting characteristics, consider the circuit of Fig. 13-6, in which a thyratron is employed as a switch. In this circuit, the load may be a bell, a counter, or some other type of recording device. The control device,

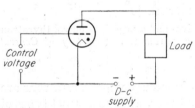

Fig. 13-6. A thyratron used as a switch. The load is not energized until the control voltage exceeds a critical value. (Heater circuit and an extinguishing circuit, if any, are not shown.)

which is in the grid circuit, may be a photocell circuit, a relay system of some type, or a mechanically or electrically operated switch. If an FG-27A tube is used in conjunction with the 120-volt d-c lines, the grid voltage must be at least 3 volts negative with respect to the cathode (for a condensation temperature of 50°C) in order that no conduction occur. If the control device in the grid circuit causes the grid voltage to become more positive than −3 volts, the tube will conduct and current will pass through the load. An extinguishing circuit must be used to stop the plate current, if it is desired that the grid regain control. Many practical applications of such circuits are possible.[6]

In addition to the mercury-vapor and gas-filled thyratrons of moderate current capacity, small argon-filled low-current-capacity tubes are available. The shielding between the cathode and the anode is not so complete in these tubes as in the higher power units. A typical critical grid curve for such an 885 or 884 tube is given in Fig. 13-7. The critical grid curve is independent of temperature since the number of gas molecules in the glass envelope is constant.

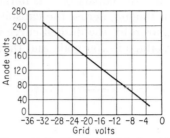

A group of thyratrons is shown in Fig. 13-8. The range of currents is given in the caption.

13-4. The Sweep-circuit Oscillator. An important use of the small argon-filled thyratron is as a relaxation-type sweep-circuit generator or saw-tooth oscillator for use with cathode-ray tubes. The diagram of a circuit that employs such a tube

Fig. 13-7. Typical critical grid characteristic of an 885 (or 884) argon-filled thyratron.

to produce a saw-tooth voltage wave of the type illustrated in Fig. 2-10

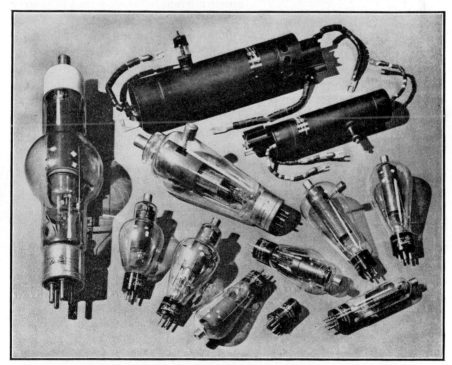

Fig. 13-8. Commercial thyratrons. (*Courtesy of General Electric Co.*)
The smallest tube is the GL-502A, which is $2\frac{5}{8}$ in. long and $1\frac{1}{32}$ in. in diameter. The peak forward voltage is 650 volts. The peak inverse voltage is 1,300 volts. The average current is 0.1 amp, the peak current is 1.0 amp, and the surge current for 0.1 sec is 10 amp.
The largest tube is the 414, which is over 15 in. long and $3\frac{1}{8}$ in. in diameter. The peak forward and the peak inverse voltage are each equal to 3,000 volts. The average current is 12.5 amp, the peak current is 100 amp, and the surge current is 1,500 amp.

is given in Fig. 13-9. To understand the operation of this circuit, assume that the capacitor C is initially uncharged. After switch S is closed, the voltage e_c across the capacitor will increase exponentially toward E_{bb}, as shown by the dashed curve in Fig. 13-10. Assume that the plate supply voltage is 250 volts and that the grid bias is 26 volts. The plate voltage corresponding to the grid voltage of 26 volts is found from Fig. 13-7 to be approximately 200 volts. Hence, the charging of the capacitor will continue only until the voltage across the capacitor reaches 200 volts. At this time the tube will break down. Charge will leak off the capacitor very rapidly, and the tube will stop conducting when the anode current falls below that necessary to maintain ionization. When the voltage e_c tries to fall below the maintaining voltage E_m the tube is extinguished and the capacitor will again begin to charge through the local RC

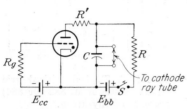

FIG. 13-9. A saw-tooth voltage generator employing an 885 thyratron. R_g is the protective resistor in the grid circuit, and R' is the protective resistor in the plate circuit. R' should be as small as possible in order that the capacitor may discharge very quickly through the tube.

circuit. This process will repeat itself, and Fig. 13-10 shows the resulting sweep voltage. If the amplitude E_s of the swing is small compared with E_{bb}, then the exponential portions become almost linear and a sweep voltage proportional to time is obtained.

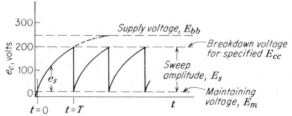

FIG. 13-10. The saw-tooth voltage wave shape across C in Fig. 13-9. The frequency is $f = 1/T$.

The period can be adjusted by varying R, C, or the voltages E_{cc} or E_{bb}. The amplitude of the oscillation is determined only by E_{cc} and E_m.

If t is measured from the instant the sweep starts ($e_c = E_m$), then the sweep voltage $e_s = e_c - E_m$ is given by

$$e_s = E(1 - \epsilon^{-t/RC}) \tag{13-1}$$

where $E = E_{bb} - E_m$. This equation is consistent with the following facts. At $t = 0$, $e_s = 0$. At $t = \infty$, e_c would equal the supply voltage E_{bb}, if the tube did not fire. And the time constant is RC.

VISITOR

ROBERT ADLER
NAME

U. C. L. A.
COMPANY AFFILIATION

20 December 1961
DATE

The amplitude of the sweep is given by the right-hand side of Eq. (13-1) with t equal to the period T of the oscillation.   If T/RC is much less than unity, the exponential term may be expanded in a power series, and, keeping the first three terms of the expansion, there results

$$e_s = E\, \frac{t}{RC} \left(1 - \frac{t}{2RC} \right)$$ (13-2)

This shows that the maximum deviation from linearity depends upon the ratio T/RC.   Hence, if the sweep is to be reasonably linear, the time constant RC must be large compared with the sweep time T.   Since $e_s = E_s$ when $t = T$, we have to a first approximation that

$$\frac{E_s}{E} = \frac{T}{RC}$$ (13-3)

In the case of a general-purpose cathode-ray oscillograph an important requirement of the sweep is that its speed (i.e., the rate of change of sweep voltage with time) be constant.   Hence, the deviation from linearity is given by the *slope* or *sweep speed error* ϵ_s defined by

$$\epsilon_s = \frac{\text{difference in slope at beginning and end of sweep}}{\text{initial value of slope}}$$

If this definition is applied to Eq. (13-1), we find that

$$\epsilon_s = \frac{E_s}{E}$$ (13-4)

where E_s is the sweep amplitude.   From Eq. (13-3) ϵ_s is approximately given by T/RC.

If the charging current of the capacitor is too large, the circuit may "block," *i.e.*, cease oscillating.   This arises because a steady-state d-c condition is possible in which the tube remains conducting, the capacitor stays charged at the maintaining tube drop, and the current through R passes through the tube.   In order to avoid this condition, the charging current must be less than that necessary to maintain the arc.   If the resistor R is chosen large enough so that the charging current is a fraction of a milliampere, then a steady arc will not be maintained.   Under these conditions the capacitor will discharge through the tube until its voltage is less than the extinction voltage of the tube.   The arc will then be extinguished, and a new charging cycle will begin.

If the capacitor is charged at a constant rate, then $e_c = I_0 t/C$, where I_0 is the constant current delivered to the capacitor, and a truly linear time axis results.   To achieve this requires that the capacitor be charged from a constant-current unit rather than exponentially through the resistor R.

13-5. Shield-grid Thyratrons.[7]   Before breakdown of the tube occurs, the current to the grid of a thyratron (such as the FG-27A) is a few tenths of a microampere. Although this is entirely negligible for most applications, it will introduce difficulties in circuits that require very high grid impedances, for example, in circuits that employ phototubes. For this reason a fourth electrode, or shield grid, has been added to the thyratron. Such a shield-grid thyratron is illustrated in Fig. 13-11. The massive cylindrical shield-grid structure encloses the cathode, control grid, and anode. This construction reduces the leakage current to a small fraction of its previous value.

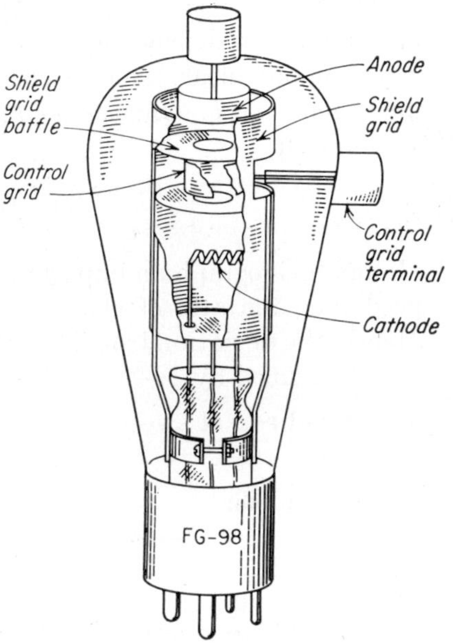

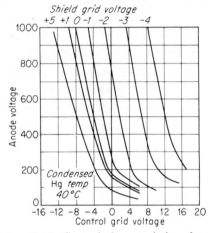

FIG. 13-11. Electrode structure of the FG-98 shield-grid thyratron. (*From H. J. Reich, "Theory and Application of Electron Tubes," McGraw-Hill Book Company, Inc., New York, 1944.*)

FIG. 13-12. Control characteristics of an FG-98 shield-grid thyratron.

Since the control grid is physically shielded from the cathode by the shield-grid baffle, the likelihood of contamination of the control grid resulting from cathode sputtering is greatly reduced. This reduces the possible effects of photoemission and thermal emission from the grid. As a result, the preignition grid current in this tube is of the order of $10^{-3}\,\mu\text{a}$. In addition to the low grid current, this tube possesses the additional advantage that the grid-cathode electrostatic capacitance is small. This low capacitance results from the electrostatic shielding of the grid from the cathode by the shield. The capacitance is also reduced because the grid in the gas tetrode is much smaller than that in the triode. Compare the size of the control grids in Figs. 13-3 and 13-11.

The critical grid starting characteristics of such a tube are shown in Fig. 13-12. It will be observed that these characteristics are functions of the shield-grid voltage. This feature adds to the versatility of the tube in possible applications.

The type 2050 and 2051 inert-gas tetrodes are low-current-capacity (75 to 100 ma average) shield-grid thyratrons. The shielding action of the control grid is much more complete than that in the 885 tube, and a steeper control characteristic is obtained. In fact, the critical grid characteristics are quite similar to those shown in Fig. 13-12. If the shield grid is connected to the cathode, the tetrode is converted into a very sensitive triode thyratron.

13-6. Mercury-pool Rectifiers. A basic form of this tube, which is primarily of historic interest, consists of two anodes, usually of carbon, sealed through arms in a glass envelope at the bottom of which is a pool of metallic mercury which acts as the cathode. Such a glass-bulb mercury rectifier tube is illustrated in Fig. 13-13.

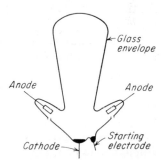

In these units the arc is started by tipping the bulb so that the mercury pool makes contact with the starting electrode and then setting the bulb in its upright position. This causes the mercury connection between the cathode and the starting electrode to break, and an arc is established. This arc forms the cathode spot on the surface of the mercury. Sufficient ionization is produced to allow the current to pass to the main electrodes, and continued operation is possible. The ionized mercury ions that are formed are neutralized at the glass surface of the envelope and condense on the walls. The evaporated mercury returns to the pool under the action of gravity.

FIG. 13-13. Glass-pool-cathode full-wave mercury-arc rectifier.

If the arc should be broken for any reason whatsoever, recombination of the mercury ions occurs and deionization of the vapor takes place. The arc will remain out until it is again initiated by tipping the tube. It is for this reason that certain tubes are provided with "keep-alive" electrodes, a steady arc being maintained between these auxiliary electrodes at all times. These auxiliary electrodes are not absolutely necessary for tubes of the multiple-anode type shown in Fig. 13-13 when used in an appropriate circuit. Such keep-alive electrodes would be necessary in single-anode mercury-cathode units, since otherwise the tube would be extinguished during the negative half cycle of an applied a-c voltage.

13-7. The Excitron.[8] As discussed in the preceding section, if the arc in a pool-cathode rectifier is broken for any reason whatsoever, the arc will remain extinguished until it is again initiated. Of course, if an auxiliary circuit is provided in order to maintain the arc, even when the main anode is not conducting, then continuous operation of the rectifier is possible. The *excitron* provides such an auxiliary circuit.

The excitron is a single-anode pool-cathode rectifier tube which is provided with a holding or excitation anode, a control grid, and the main anode. In this tube an arc is struck to and is continuously maintained by the excitation anode, which is connected in a d-c circuit. Control of the current in the main anode circuit is effected by the grid, precisely as in the thyratron. The tube possesses the control characteristics of a positive-type thyratron but likewise possesses the current capabilities of the pool cathode.

The ignition in these tubes is accomplished by means of a solenoid-operated mercury-spray splash device. The unit is placed in operation by the mercury spray, which is thrown upward to the excitation anode. As the mercury falls away from the excitation anode, the auxiliary arc is struck.

Excitrons are designed for high-current service and are used in banks as the individual elements of a polyphase rectifier system. Excitrons are made in both sealed-off and pumped types by the Allis-Chalmers Mfg. Co. One sealed excitron made by them carries a 400-amp d-c continuous-current rating. A unit assembly, comprising a 12-tank rectifier for railway service, is rated at 3,000 kw, 600 volts.

13-8. The Ignitron.[9] In distinction to the excitron, the *ignitron* is a single-anode pool tank which is provided with a starting ignitor electrode which initiates the arc when it is extinguished. A drawing of such a unit is given in Fig. 13-14.

With an a-c potential applied between the anode and the pool, the arc would become extinguished once each alternate half cycle, provided that the arc could be initiated regularly. It is the duty of the starting ignitor to provide this regular ignition once each alternate half cycle. The starting ignitor is made of a refractory material (among them being silicon carbide, boron carbide, and carborundum), which projects into the mercury-pool cathode, as seen in Fig. 13-14. The ignitor has a cold resistance of 20 to 100 ohms, which, under operating conditions, decreases to 2 to 10 ohms.

There is no generally accepted theory[9] for the mechanism of the starting. The most likely explanation is that the ignitor operates because of high field emission near the mercury-ignitor junction. Once ignition begins, the tiny spark expands into an arc between the cathode and the anode. This process is accomplished in short times, usually measured in microseconds.[10] If the point in the cycle at which the current passes through the ignitor rod is controlled, then the output of the tube is likewise controlled.

Ignitrons may have two[11] or three ignitors, only one of these being used at any time.   Owing to the high surge current through the ignitor rod it gradually deteriorates.   With several available as stand-bys, the life of the tube is extended.

Some ignitrons are equipped with an *auxiliary* or *holding* or *excitation* *anode*.   This auxiliary anode serves two functions.   It has been found that for steady operation, especially at relatively light loads, the current

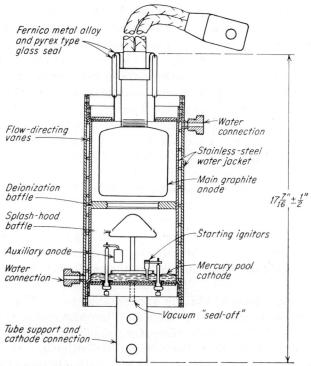

Fernico metal alloy and pyrex type glass seal

Flow-directing vanes

Deionization baffle

Splash-hood baffle

Auxiliary anode

Water connection

Tube support and cathode connection

Water connection

Stainless-steel water jacket

Main graphite anode

$17\frac{7}{16}" \pm \frac{1}{2}"$

Starting ignitors

Mercury pool cathode

Vacuum "seal-off"

Fig. 13-14. A sealed ignitron for power rectifier service.   (*Courtesy of General Electric Co.*)

surge through the ignitor should be maintained for an appreciable portion of the cycle.   However, in order to prolong the life of the ignitor rods, the ignition-current pulse duration should be made as short as possible, so that heating of the ignitor rod is small.   The use of the auxiliary anode permits a short excitation pulse and then serves to maintain the arc spot for the remainder of the main-anode cycle.   A second reason for the auxiliary anode is that it provides another arc-conduction circuit, which, because of its relatively close spacing to the cathode, will usually conduct even in those rare instances when the main arc circuit might not fire. Owing to the usual electrical connections (see Fig. 14-34) that are used for ignitor excitation, the duty on the ignitor rod and the rectifier in the firing circuit is likely to be very severe during a misfire. Some protection from this surge is afforded by the auxiliary-anode shunt path.

Some ignitrons are provided with a grid which may be used to perform a phase-shift control function in much the same way that the grid performs in a thyratron. Thus it can be used for controlling the point in the cycle at which the tube will conduct, assuming that an arc has previously been established to the auxiliary anode by the ignitor rod. However, it has been found that the ignitor often permits control over a larger portion of the cycle than does the grid. The single grid which surrounds the anode and is sometimes called the *anode shield* or *shield grid* also serves to reduce the tendency for arc back.

In multianode rectifiers, failure in the inverse direction frequently occurs because an arc may form between anodes. This unwanted initiation of an arc to an idle anode is known as *arc back*, *flash back*, or *backfire*. Arc back under these circumstances results in an internal short circuit between anodes, and so of the power transformers, and may result in permanent injury to the tube unless protective devices are employed. In single-anode rectifiers, conduction in the inverse direction between the cathode and anode is likewise called "backfire."

The exact nature of arc-back phenomena is not completely understood. They seem to occur at random times. That is to say, no arc backs may occur in a rectifier under normal operating conditions for some time, and then several may occur at relatively closely separated times.

The use of grids that surround each of the anodes is a frequent practice in order to reduce arc back. The presence of these grids serves several useful purposes. They shield the anodes, thus preventing droplets of mercury from condensing on the anodes. They also reduce the deionization time by furnishing large surfaces for recombination. Furthermore, the presence of the grid affects the voltage distribution in such a way as to prevent strong fields from forming. This reduction in potential gradient allows a higher total sparking potential. One three-grid (pentode) ignitron designed for rectification or inversion service at 20,000 volts at a continuous current of 200 amp is manufactured by the General Electric Co.

The ignitron has three principal applications: heavy-duty (above 25 amp) power rectification, inversion, and control switching of alternating currents, as in resistance welding. The first two are continuous-duty operation, and the third is an intermittent application.

13-9. Gas-tube Ratings. Gas- or vapor-filled rectifier tubes are given *average* current ratings rather than rms current ratings. The tube must dissipate an instantaneous power given by the product of the instantaneous anode current and the instantaneous tube voltage. Since this voltage is substantially constant and independent of the tube current, the average power is the product of this tube drop and the *average* tube current. Furthermore, units are given peak current ratings, specifying the maximum current that the tube should be permitted to reach in each conducting cycle and averaged over various time intervals.

The grid in the thyratron is also given average and peak ratings. These ratings should not be exceeded, for otherwise the glass press through which the leads pass may be ruptured.

The function of a rectifier is to act as a synchronous switch which permits current to pass in one direction only. That is, electrons must flow from the cathode to the anode only while the anode is positive with respect to the cathode. It is necessary, therefore, that the anode remain insulating during that portion of the voltage cycle when it is negative with respect to the cathode. The "maximum inverse peak voltage" specifies the largest safe instantaneous value of this negative voltage.

Conduction in the inverse direction occurs because of breakdown of the gas in the region between the cathode and the anode. This so-called "flash-back" voltage, which is nothing more than the sparking potential of the gas according to Paschen's law, is shown for an 866 tube in Fig. 13-15. For the pressures and spacing usually

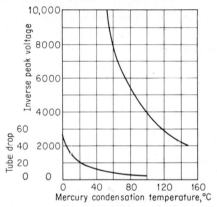

Fig. 13-15. Tube drop and peak inverse voltage of an 866 gas diode as a function of temperature. (*H. C. Steiner and H. T. Maser, Proc. IRE,* **18,** 67 83, 1930.)

employed in arc discharge tubes of the externally heated types, only the portion of the sparking-potential curve to the left of the minimum sparking value comes into consideration.

The "maximum peak forward voltage" is a quantity that is significant only for gas tubes controlled by means of a grid. It specifies the largest positive potential that may be applied to the anode before the grid loses its arc-initiation ability. That is, if the plate voltage exceeds this value, breakdown will first occur between the grid and the anode. The glow that results immediately changes to an arc between the cathode and the anode. Of course, once the arc forms, a sheath forms around the grid and it becomes ineffective.

The condensed-mercury temperature limits are specified for the safe and efficient operation of mercury-vapor tubes. The range usually extends from about 30° to 80°C, corresponding to vapor pressure of approximately 0.003 to 0.08 mm. The upper temperature limit is determined by the peak inverse voltage, since this voltage limit may fall below a safe value at the higher temperatures (see Fig. 13-15). The lower temperature limit is determined by several factors: As the pressure decreases, the tube drop increases (see Fig. 13-15), so that the power loss in the rectifier increases. This results in a decreased efficiency. In addition, the high tube drop may result in serious cathode disintegration.

It is desirable, therefore, especially in the large metal-tank rectifiers, that the mercury-condensation temperature be maintained in the proper range. For this reason, water cooling of the tank is usually employed.

13-10. Deionization Time.[12] Once the arc has been initiated in a thyratron, the grid loses its control feature, as already explained. Suppose that the anode potential is momentarily removed and is then quickly reapplied. The grid is supposed to be highly negative during this experiment. Will the tube again conduct, or will the grid, because of its large negative value, regain control and so prevent the arc from reigniting? The answer to this question is found by examining the conditions at the grid.

The grid loses control after conduction starts because of the formation of the positive-ion sheath around it, which effectively shields the electrostatic field of the grid and so prevents this field from altering conditions in the plasma. If, therefore, the positive ions in the sheath have had time enough to diffuse to the grid and recombine with electrons to form neutral molecules before the anode voltage is reapplied, then the grid regains control (see Sec. 12-11 for a discussion of recombination). The minimum time of this process is called the *deionization time*.

The deionization time t_d depends upon many factors. As the gas pressure increases, t_d increases, since the diffusion takes place at a slower rate. This is also affected by the increased probability of additional ion formation by electronic collisions. Also, large values of anode current result in large values of t_d, since the number of ions to be swept out of the sheath is correspondingly large. However, small deionization times are favored by small electrode spacings and by the presence of large surfaces at which recombination may occur. Furthermore, highly negative potentials on the inverse cycle favor small deionization times.

From this discussion, it is clear that the deionization time depends upon both the tube and the circuit in which the tube is used. For commercial tubes operated under rated conditions, it varies between 10 and 1,000 μsec. This time is so short that satisfactory operation of thyratrons on 60-cycle mains results. However, the deionization time may offer a serious limitation to the use of such tubes in applications at higher frequencies. Hydrogen is used as the gas in a thyratron when very fast deionization time is desired. A value of t_d about one-tenth[13] that for a mercury thyratron results because the small mass of the hydrogen ion allows it to diffuse more rapidly out of the sheath.

The *ionization time* is the time required for conduction to be established once the anode potential has been applied. It seldom exceeds 10 μsec and so can generally be neglected.

13-11. Industrial Power Tubes. It may be well to compare the industrial power tubes, *viz.*, phanotrons, thyratrons, and tubes with pool-type tubes. Tubes with pool cathodes require no cathode heating power and no cathode heating time. Consequently, these units are immediately ready for service. Large average currents (hundreds or thousands of amperes) and extremely high peak currents are possible without any harmful effects on the tube. There is no cathode sputtering as in the heater tubes.

For uncontrolled rectification, phanotrons are used. If control is desired, then thyratrons are used when the average current requirement is below about 25 amp. If the current exceeds this value pool-type tubes are employed.

If in a multianode mercury-pool tank each of the anodes is completely surrounded by a grid, then such a system will possess characteristics that are somewhat like those of a positive-control thyratron. Mercury-arc rectifiers equipped with these grids are known as *grid pool tanks*. The single-anode metal sealed-off tank rectifier unit is largely superseding the multianode tank, principally for the following reasons:

1. Each unit is complete and requires no auxiliary pumping apparatus. In the smaller sizes, only air cooling is necessary, although the larger units are provided with a water jacket for water cooling.

2. If a polyphase system is desired, a number of single-anode tanks are required. Since each anode is in a separate chamber, the cathode-anode distance can be made smaller than is possible in a multianode tank with a common pool. This reduces the length of the plasma region, with a consequent smaller tube drop, which produces a more efficient unit.

3. Single-anode tanks make the maintenance problem a relative simple one. Thus, it is necessary to hold only a single unit in reserve for purposes of emergency.

There is a fundamental difference between the control action in a thyratron or a grid pool tube and the action of the ignitor rod in an ignitron. In thyratrons and grid pool tubes, the grid *prevents* the formation of an arc, whereas the ignitor *initiates* the arc. In the former case the electrons already exist in the tube (owing to the presence of an externally heated cathode or of an arc to the keep-alive electrode), but the grid electrostatically prevents them from reaching the anode until a critical voltage is reached. In the ignitron, on the other hand, the tube is in a nonconducting state until the ignitor circuit is energized, when conduction is forced.

13-12. Glow Tubes. A glow tube is a cold-cathode gas-discharge diode. It operates in the normal-glow-discharge region and so is characterized by a fairly high tube drop and a low current-carrying capacity. The voltage drop across the tube over the operating range is fairly constant and independent of the current.

One commercial type of tube consists of a central anode wire which is coaxial with a cylindrical cathode, as shown in Fig. 13-16. The electrodes are of nickel, the inner surface of the cathode being oxide-coated. The gases commonly used are neon, argon, and helium. The tubes containing neon or helium usually contain a small amount (of the order of 1 per cent) of argon. The presence of the argon lowers the starting voltage

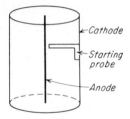

FIG. 13-16. Electrode structure in a glow tube.

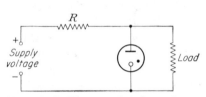

FIG. 13-17. The use of a glow tube as a voltage regulator to maintain approximately constant voltage across a load.

(see Sec. 12-10). The cathode fall in the normal-glow region of the discharge is determined solely by the material of the cathode and by the type of gas. Commercial tubes are available which have normal output voltages of 75, 90, 105, and 150 volts, respectively, with a normal current range of from 5 to 40 ma.

The current rating of these tubes is determined by the area of the cathode and by the pressure of the gas. It should be recalled that the normal current density in the normal-glow region remains substantially constant and that the area of the cathode glow increases in proportion to the current demanded by the circuit.

The principal use of these glow tubes is as voltage regulators. Since the voltage remains constant (within a few per cent) over the region of the normal glow, then the output voltage will remain substantially independent of the current over this range. For example, the voltage across the load in the circuit of Fig. 13-17 will be 150 volts over a range of currents from 5 to 40 ma if an OD3/150 tube is used. The difference between the supply voltage and the operating tube volt drop will appear across the resistor R. The supply voltage must be greater than the breakdown voltage of the tube in order to make the operation possible. The sparking potential may exceed the maintaining voltage by 50 per cent or more. It is observed in Fig. 13-16 that a piece of metal is attached to the cathode and is directed toward and near to the anode. It is the function of this "starting probe" to lower the breakdown voltage of the tube. Sparking takes place first to the starting probe and then spreads to the rest of the cathode.

Glow tubes may be connected in series in order to provide a constant voltage that is the sum of the tube drops of the tubes that are used. Thus, the use of an OD3/150 and an OC3/105 tube in series will provide a constant 255-volt source.

A glow lamp may be connected as in Fig. 13-9 (with the grid circuit omitted) to produce oscillations of the saw-tooth variety.

It must be emphasized that the glow tube is far from an ideal voltage regulator.[14] As already stated above, its output voltage varies by perhaps 5 per cent over its normal-glow region. Also, the voltage characteristics of the tubes vary with age mainly because of the deterioration of the cathode, caused by sputtering. The maintaining voltage is not precisely the same value each time the tube is fired. The cathode is photosensitive, and the tube voltage will depend somewhat upon the illumination falling on the cathode. The tube characteristics are also slightly temperature-sensitive. Voltage changes of a few tenths of a per cent sometimes occur abruptly and for no apparent reason. Also, the tube may break out into high-frequency oscillations (which often can be prevented by shunting a capacitor across the tube). One of the most stable voltage-regulator tubes available is the type 5651. Over the normal operating range of 1.5 to 3.5 ma, the manufacturers claim that the maintaining voltage (87 volts) of this tube under continuous operation will not drift with age by more than 0.3 volt.

The Zener diode (Sec. 5-2) is replacing the VR tube in many applications.

Glow tubes having smaller ratings than those considered above are available. Several such tubes having ratings ranging from $\frac{1}{25}$ to 3 watts are available. These smaller lamps are used extensively as test lamps.[15] For example, they will indicate circuit continuity; by brilliancy, whether the circuit potential is 110 volts or higher; by flicker, whether the circuit frequency is 25 cps or higher; by glow, which terminal is positive, since the negative electrode is covered with glow on a d-c source. They are also used to indicate the presence of a high-intensity radio-frequency field, since the gas will glow in such a field. The tube need not be connected conductively into the circuit. It is operating not as a normal glow tube but rather as an electrodeless discharge (see Sec. 12-22). The tubes may also be used as pilot lights to indicate that a circuit is energized, and as a dim-light source for exit markers, for fire-station markers, or for location markers in general.

13-13. Cold-cathode Triodes.[16] This tube is referred to as a "grid glow tube," although the third element is more appropriately named the

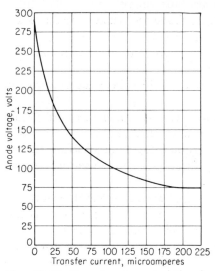

"control electrode," "control anode," or "starter anode" rather than the "grid." The geometry of the electrodes is such that a discharge takes place from the cathode to the control electrode at a lower voltage than is required for a discharge from the cathode to the anode. Once the control gap has been broken down, however, it is possible for the discharge to transfer to the main anode. The anode-cathode voltage that is required for this transfer to occur is a function of the transfer current, *i.e.*, the current in the cathode-to-control-electrode circuit. These features are evident from an inspection of the curve of Fig. 13-18. Such a curve is called the "transfer" or "transition" characteristic.

Fig. 13-18. Transfer characteristic of a cold-cathode triode. RCA OA4-G. Control-gap-maintaining voltage is 60 volts and main-gap-maintaining voltage is 75 volts.

For zero transfer current, which means that the control electrode is not connected in the circuit, the anode voltage is equal to the breakdown voltage between the cathode and the anode. It is noted that the required anode-cathode voltage falls rapidly as the transfer current, which provides more ionization, is increased. Regardless of the magnitude of the transfer current, however, the anode-cathode voltage can never fall below the maintaining voltage for this gap. Hence, the transfer characteristic approaches this sustaining voltage asymptotically. The transfer characteristic depends upon the type of gas, the gas pressure, and the electrode structure.

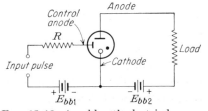

Fig. 13-19. A cold-cathode triode as a relay.

The use of the tube as a relay is illustrated in Fig. 13-19. The plate supply voltage E_{bb2} is greater than the main-gap sustaining voltage but less than the main-gap breakdown voltage. The voltage E_{bb1} is less than the control-gap breakdown voltage. It is now possible for a positive pulse to raise the control-anode voltage above the breakdown point so that a discharge will occur between these two electrodes. If the transfer current is sufficiently high so that E_{bb2} will cause breakdown, then the discharge will transfer to the anode circuit. In this way a small input-circuit current is able to control milliamperes in the load circuit.

Here, as in the case of thyratrons, once conduction between the cathode and anode has begun, the discharge cannot be controlled or extinguished by means of the control electrode. It is necessary that the anode-cathode voltage be lowered below the sustaining value for a time that is long enough to permit deionization to take place. The deionization time of these tubes is of the order of 10 msec.

Among the applications in which these tubes have been used, the most important are as rectifiers in selective-ringing telephone circuits; as voltage regulators, providing two different output voltages, the anode-cathode drop or the control electrode–cathode voltage; as relaxation oscillators; and as relays or switching units.

A special cold-cathode glow-discharge tube called a *Dekatron*[17] contains 1 anode, 10 cathodes, and 20 control electrodes. It is used as a decade counter which delivers 1 output pulse for every 10 input pulses.

13-14. Gaseous Discharges as Sources of Light.[18] Gaseous-discharge lamps generally possess a higher luminous efficiency[19] than lamps of the incandescent-filament type. As a result, the former are rapidly supplementing the latter in many applications.

In addition to the higher luminous efficiencies, the gaseous-discharge lamps possess features characteristic of these sources. Because of this, various types of gaseous-discharge tubes are applied to a very diversified field of application. In the advertising field, neon, helium, and argon signs are very common; sodium-vapor lamps are found in the field of highway illumination; high-intensity mercury-vapor lamps are used for industrial lighting and floodlighting, as the intense point sources of light for projection work, for searchlights, for locomotive headlights, and for photoprinting; and fluorescent lighting is a common source of illumination for indoor lighting.

1. *"Neon" Signs.*[20] These are glow lamps in long tubular form. They contain an inert gas (not necessarily neon) at a few millimeters pressure between cold electrodes. The mechanism of the discharge is that discussed in Sec. 12-16. The cathode glow is now an insignificant part of the light-emitting region of the discharge, and most of the luminosity comes from the long plasma in the tube. If the tube is filled with neon, the glow is red-orange. If helium is used, the glow is yellow. And if mercury (mixed with argon and neon) is used, the glow is blue. Various other distinctive colors are obtained by using colored glass tubing. For example, a mercury-argon mixture in a yellow glass tube gives a green light.

Such tubes require a high voltage for breakdown but need only moderate voltages to maintain the discharge. It is for this reason that luminous-sign transformers are provided with magnetic leakage shunts so as to provide poor regulation. In this way, high voltages are made available at light load, and low voltages result after the discharge occurs. Under normal conditions of operation, these luminous signs require 100 to 200 volts/ft, depending upon the dimensions of the glass tubing used. A typical transformer supplies 10,000 volts on open circuit and 30 ma on short circuit.

2. *Sodium-vapor Lamps.*[21] These lamps are provided with an oxide-coated filament, and they operate, therefore, as low-voltage arcs and not as glow discharges. The bulb contains a small quantity of metallic sodium (less than 0.5 g) which vaporizes to some extent as the temperature of the unit rises to its normal operating value (200° to 300°C). The vapor pressure of the sodium is so low, even under steady operating conditions, that neon gas is added (at a pressure of about 1.5 mm Hg) both for starting and for continuing the operation of the lamp.

To operate the lamp, the filament is first heated and then an arc is struck. At the outset of operation the color of the discharge is the distinctive red-orange that is characteristic of the neon gas. This color gives way gradually to the yellow light that is characteristic of the normal sodium discharge. The explanation of this change of color is very simple. Initially, the neon pressure is so much higher than that of sodium that most of the electrons from the hot filament collide with neon atoms. However, once the discharge is established, most of the region in the bulb will be a plasma in which a considerable number of low-energy electrons will exist. Although these electrons may make many collisions with the plentiful neon atoms, these collisions will be elastic ones because the first excitation potential of neon is 16.6 volts. Since the first excitation potential of sodium is only 2.11 volts, then the probability of sodium excitation in the plasma will be high because many electrons will possess sufficient energy for this process although they may not possess as much as 16.6 volts energy. The light is emitted in the transition from the first excitation level to the normal state of sodium.

3. *Mercury-vapor Lamps.*[22] The luminous efficiency of a low-pressure mercury-vapor lamp is approximately the same as that of an incandescent-filament source. However, as the pressure is increased, the luminous efficiency also increases. As a consequence, the design of these lamps has been toward higher and higher pressure. For example, the 1,000-watt type A-H6 lamp operates at a pressure of 75 atm. The entire arc is concentrated in a water-cooled quartz chamber only 1 in. long and 0.1 in. in diameter. This results in a 65,000-lumen light source, having a brightness of 30,000 candles/cm², or about one-fifth that of the sun. A gas such

as neon or argon at a few centimeters pressure is used to initiate the arc. The cold electrodes are thereby raised to a temperature at which they emit electrons thermionically. The high temperature causes the mercury to vaporize, and the pressure increases to 1 atm or more.

The reason for the necessity of high pressures in order to obtain a high luminous output in a mercury-vapor lamp is found by studying the mercury spectrum. The strongest line in the spectrum is the ultraviolet line, 2,537 A. As shown in the energy-level diagram of Fig. 12-2, this line is excited when an atom falls back from its 4.88-ev level to the ground state. The lines in the visible part of the spectrum arise from transitions between higher energy levels. These high-energy transitions are favored by high current density and a high pressure because, under these conditions, many collisions will take place, particularly with the metastable atoms. Furthermore, for sufficiently high pressures, the resonance line 2,537 A is entirely absent from the spectrum. This results from the process of self-absorption (see Sec. 12-8). As a result, some of the energy that would appear in this ultraviolet line at the low pressures is transformed (by multiple collisions) into visible radiation. In addition, because of the high temperatures at which these arc sources operate, a considerable part of the radiation appears as a continuous visible spectrum, characteristic of an incandescent solid.

In contrast with this, the sodium-vapor lamp possesses a high efficiency at low pressures because its yellow radiation originates from transitions between the 2.11-ev level and the ground state. The sodium atom is easily excited to its resonance potential by an electronic collision, and so multiple collisions are unnecessary for the efficient production of light with this source, as is the case with the mercury radiation.

4. *Fluorescent Lamps.*[23] The fluorescent lighting units consist generally of a coated emitter and an anode that have been sealed in the opposite ends of a glass tube that contains mercury at low pressure. Tubes for use on a-c lines are frequently provided with emitters at each end of the glass tube, these acting alternately as cathode and anode upon potential reversal. The inner wall of these lamps is covered with a thin layer of fluorescent material. The thickness of this layer must be sufficient to absorb most of the impinging excitation radiation, although it must not be so thick that it will absorb any appreciable amount of its own light. Excitation is generally provided by the ultraviolet light contained in the spectrum of the mercury discharge. The fluorescent materials used in these lamps are particularly sensitive to the middle ultraviolet region (2,000 to 3,000 A).

In order to start a fluorescent tube, it is necessary to strike an arc in the discharge tube. This requires the application of a high voltage across electrodes. These high voltages are obtained either by the use of a step-up transformer or by means of an inductive surge produced by the associated starting device.   Starting is accomplished in the usual household lighting unit by one of the circuits shown in Fig. 13-20.   Refer to Fig. 13-20a.

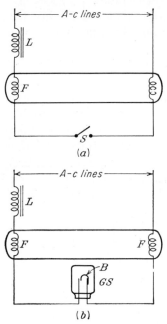

When the switch S is closed, the line current passes through the ballast unit L (a small inductor) and the filaments F. After a short time has elapsed during which the filaments have become heated, the switch S is opened. The interrupted current through L generates a high voltage across it, and in consequence a high voltage appears across the tube. Once the arc has been struck, the positive-ion bombardment of the emitter will maintain its temperature and continued operation results.

Figure 13-20b provides for automatic starting. The starter is a rather interesting combination of a glow-discharge tube (which operates in the abnormal-glow region) and a bimetallic element. When the unit is switched on, the starter glow discharge begins. The bimetallic element, which is part of the glow electrode, heats, so that the contacts close and the glow discharge is extinguished. This connects the filaments into the circuit, and at the same time the bimetallic element cools. After a short time, the bimetallic unit contacts open and thereby produce the high voltage across the tube, as with the manual start. Once the lamp discharge starts, the

FIG. 13-20. Fluorescent lamp starting by (a) manual start, (b) automatic start. L is the ballast unit, F are the filaments, S is the manual switch, GS is the glow switch, B is the bimetallic strip.

voltage across it is not high enough to restrike the glow in the starter and it remains out.

The luminous efficiency of fluorescent lamps exceeds that of the usual incandescent lamp. Furthermore, this highly efficient lighting occurs with the lamps operating at a relatively low temperature. Because the operating temperature of these units is about 40°C, these tubes have been said to produce "cold" light.

REFERENCES

1. WHEATCROFT, E. L. E., "Gaseous Electrical Conductors," p. 189, Oxford University Press, New York, 1938.
2. HULL, A. W., "Hot-cathode Thyratrons," *Gen. Elec. Rev.*, **32**, 213–223, April, 1929.

3. Lowry, E. F., "Thermionic Cathodes for Gas-filled Tubes," *Electronics*, **6**, 280–281, October, 1933.

4. Hull, A. W., "New Vacuum Valves and Their Applications," *Gen. Elec. Rev.*, **35**, 622–629, December, 1932.

   Hull, A. W., "Gas-filled Thermionic Tubes," *Trans. AIEE*, **47**, 753–763, July, 1928.

5. Hull, A. W., "Gas-filled Thermionic Tubes," *Trans. AIEE*, **47**, 753–763, July, 1928.

   Hull, A. W., "Hot-cathode Thyratrons," *Gen. Elec. Rev.*, **32**, 213–223, 390–399, July, 1929.

6. Reich, H. J., "Theory and Application of Electron Tubes," 2d ed., McGraw-Hill Book Company, Inc., New York, 1944.

   Henney, K., "Electron Tubes in Industry," 2d ed., McGraw-Hill Book Company, Inc., New York, 1937.

7. Livingston, O. W., and H. T. Maser, "Shield Grid Thyratrons," *Electronics*, **7**, April, 114–116, 1934.

8. Marti, O. K., "Excitron Mercury-arc Rectifiers," *Supplement to Electrical Engineering—Transactions Section*, pp. 927–931, December, 1940.

   Mulder, J. G. W., "New Metal Rectifying Valve with Mercury Cathode," *Philips Tech. Rev.*, **1**, 65–69, March, 1936.

   Winograd, H., "Development of Excitron-type Rectifier," *Trans. AIEE*, **63**, 969–978, December, 1944.

9. Slepian, J., and L. R. Ludwig, "A New Method of Starting an Arc," *Elec. Eng.*, **52**, 605–608, September, 1933.

   Cage, J. M., "Theory of Immersion Mercury-arc Ignitor," *Gen. Elec. Rev.*, **38**, 464–465, October, 1935.

   Toepfer, A. H., "Low Current Ignitors," *Elec. Eng.*, **56**, 810–812, July, 1937.

   Mierdel, G., "Ueber die Zeundung von Quecksilberdampflichtboegen durch Innenzuender (Ignitron)," *Wiss. Veroffentl. Siemens-Werken*, **15**, 35–50, 1936.

   Klemperer, H., "New Ignitron Firing Circuit," *Electronics*, **12**, 12–15, December, 1939.

10. Dow, W. G., and W. H. Powers, "Firing Time of Ignitor Type of Tube," *Trans. AIEE*, **54**, 942–949, September, 1935.

11. Herskind, C. C., and E. J. Remscheid, "Excitation, Control, and Cooling of Ignitron Tubes," *Trans. AIEE*, **65**, 632–635, October, 1946.

12. Hull, A. W., "Hot-cathode Thyratrons," *Gen. Elec. Rev.*, **32**, 213–223, April, 1929.

    Ostendorf, W., "Entionisierungszeiten von Stromrichtern," *Elektrotech. Z.*, **59**, 87–89, Jan. 27, 1938.

13. Glasoe, G. N., and J. V. Lebacqz (eds.), "Pulse Generators," 1st ed., Radiation Laboratory Series, Vol. 5, p. 336, McGraw-Hill Book Company, Inc., New York, 1948.

14. Kirkpatrick, G. M., "Characteristics of Certain Voltage-regulator Tubes,' *Proc. IRE*, **35**, 485–489, May, 1947.

    Titterton, E. W., "Some Characteristics of Glow-discharge Voltage Regulator Tubes," *J. Sci. Instr.*, **26**, 33–36, February, 1949.

    Benson, F. A., W. E. Cain, and B. D. Lucas, "Variations in the Characteristics of Some Glow-discharge Voltage-regulator Tubes," *ibid.*, **26**, 399–401, December, 1949.

15. Ferree, H. M., "Some Characteristics and Applications of Negative-glow Lamps," *Trans. AIEE*, **60**, 8–12, January, 1941.

16. Ingram, S. B., "Cold-cathode Gas-filled Tubes as Circuit Elements," *Elec. Eng.*, **58**, 342–346, July, 1939.

KNOWLES, D. D., "The Theory of the Grid Glow Tube," *Elec. J.*, **27**, 232–236, April, 1930.

KNOWLES, D. D., and S. P. SASHOFF, "Grid-controlled Glow and Arc Discharge Tubes," *Electronics*, **1**, 182–185, July, 1930.

17. MILLMAN, J., and H. TAUB, "Pulse and Digital Circuits," pp. 335–339, McGraw-Hill Book Company, Inc., New York, 1956.

18. DUSHMAN, S., "Search for High Efficiency Light Sources," *JOSA*, **27**, 1–24, January, 1937.

COTTON, H., "Electrical Discharge Lamps," Chapman & Hall, Ltd., London, 1946.

19. FREEMAN, G. A., "Trends in High-intensity Mercury Lamps," *Elec. Eng.*, **59**, 444–447, November, 1940.

20. MILLER, S. C., and D. G. FINK, "Neon Signs," McGraw-Hill Book Company, Inc., New York, 1935.

21. GORDON, N. J., "Operating Characteristics of Sodium-vapor Lamps," *Gen. Elec. Rev.*, **37**, 338–341, July, 1934.

FOUND, C. G., "Fundamental Phenomena in Sodium-vapor Lamps," *ibid.*, **37**, 269–277, June, 1934.

BUTTOLPH, L. J., "High Efficiency Mercury and Sodium Vapor Lamps," *JOSA*, **29**, 124–130, March, 1939.

HELLER, G., "Comparison between Discharge Phenomena in Sodium and Mercury Vapor Lamps," *Philips Tech. Rev.*, **1**, 2–5, January, 1936; **1**, 70–75, March, 1936.

22. HELLER, G., "Comparison between Discharge Phenomena in Sodium and Mercury Vapor Lamps," *Philips Tech. Rev.*, **1**, 2–5, January, 1936; **1**, 70–75, March, 1936.

FREEMAN, G. A., "Trends in High-intensity Mercury Lamps," *Elec. Eng.*, **59**, 444–447, November, 1940.

BUTTOLPH, L. J., "High-efficiency Gaseous-conduction Lamps," *ibid.*, **55**, 1174–1180, November, 1936.

MARDEN, J. W., N. C. BEESE, and G. MEISTER, "High-intensity Mercury-arc Lamps," *ibid.*, **55**, 1186–1190, November, 1936.

23. INMAN, G. E., and R. N. THAYER, "Low Voltage Fluorescent Lamps," *Elec. Eng.*, **57**, 245–248, June, 1938.

FONDA, G. R., "Fundamental Principles of Fluorescence," *Trans. AIEE*, **57**, 677–681, December, 1938.

MARDEN, J. W., N. C. BEESE, and G. MEISTER, "Effect of Temperature on Fluorescent Lamps," *Trans. Illum. Eng. Soc. (N.Y.)*, **34**, 55–64, January, 1939.

INMAN, G. E., "Characteristics of Fluorescent Lamps," *ibid.*, **34**, 65–82, January, 1939.

O'DAY, A. B., and R. F. CISSELL, "Fluorescent Lamps and Their Applications," *ibid.*, **34**, 1165–1180, 1939.

CLAUDE, A., "L'Éclairage par luminescence," *Bull. soc. franç. élec.*, **9**, 307–336, April, 1939.

CLEAVER, O. P., "Fluorescent Lighting after Two Years," *Elec. Eng.*, **59**, 261–266, July, 1940.

CHAPTER 14

RECTIFIERS

A$_{\text{NY}}$ electrical device which offers a low resistance to the current in one direction but a high resistance to the current in the opposite direction is called a *rectifier*. An *ideal* rectifier is one with zero resistance in the forward direction and with infinite resistance in the reverse direction. In effect, therefore, a rectifier is a synchronized switch that opens and closes the circuit as the a-c voltage that is applied across the device changes its polarity. A number of devices have characteristics which approximate those of the ideal rectifier. Among these are high-vacuum thermionic diodes, gas-filled thermionic diodes, pool-cathode mercury arcs, and semiconductor rectifiers.

Vacuum-tube (and semiconductor) rectifiers possess a small and approximately constant forward resistance, whereas a gas tube is characterized by an almost constant tube drop during conduction. Because of this difference in the volt-ampere characteristic, the operation of rectifier circuits involving vacuum tubes will be considered separately from that of circuits using gas tubes. The analysis for a semiconductor rectifier is identical with that for a vacuum diode, provided that the plate resistance of the vacuum

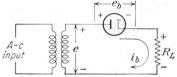

Fig. 14-1. Basic circuit for half-wave rectification.

tube is replaced by the forward resistance of the crystal diode. The back resistance of the junction diode is not as high as that of a vacuum tube, but it is usually so much higher than the load resistance that little error is introduced in assuming the semiconductor back resistance to be infinite.

14-1. Single-phase Half-wave Vacuum Rectifier. The basic circuit for half-wave rectification is shown in Fig. 14-1. We shall assume that the diode forward resistance is r_p and is constant so that during conduction $e_b = i_b r_p$. If the transformer secondary voltage is $e = E_m \sin \omega t$ it follows from Fig. 14-1 that

$$e = e_b + i_b R_L = i_b(r_p + R_L) = E_m \sin \omega t \tag{14-1}$$

or

$$i_b = \frac{E_m}{r_p + R_L} \sin \omega t = I_m \sin \omega t \qquad \text{when } 0 \leq \omega t \leq \pi$$
$$i_b = 0 \qquad\qquad\qquad\qquad\qquad \text{when } \pi \leq \omega t \leq 2\pi \qquad (14\text{-}2)$$

where

$$I_m \equiv \frac{E_m}{r_p + R_L} \qquad (14\text{-}3)$$

This analysis permits one to draw an electrical circuit that is equivalent to the circuit of Fig. 14-1. This equivalent circuit is shown in Fig. 14-2.

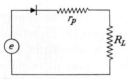

FIG. 14-2. Equivalent circuit of a single-phase half-wave rectifier.

The symbol ← represents an ideal synchronized switch which permits current to pass through the circuit during the conduction period and which opens the circuit on the inverse cycle. The arrow points in the direction of forward current flow.

Example. A d-c ammeter, an a-c ammeter, and the current coil of a wattmeter are inserted in series with the load of Fig. 14-1. The potential coil of the wattmeter is across the transformer secondary. A d-c voltmeter is placed across the diode. What do these four instruments read?

Solution. A d-c ammeter reads the full-cycle average current passing through it. However, by definition, the average value of a periodic function is given by the area of one cycle of the curve divided by the base. Expressed mathematically,

$$I_{dc} = \frac{1}{2\pi} \int_0^{2\pi} i_b \, d\alpha \qquad (14\text{-}4)$$

where $\alpha \equiv \omega t$. It follows from Eq. (14-2) that

$$I_{dc} = \frac{1}{2\pi} \int_0^{\pi} I_m \sin \alpha \, d\alpha = \frac{I_m}{\pi} \qquad (14\text{-}5)$$

Note that the upper limit of the integral has been changed from 2π to π since the instantaneous current in the interval between π and 2π is zero and so contributes nothing to the integral.

An a-c ammeter indicates the effective or rms current passing through it. By definition, the effective or rms value squared of a periodic function of the time is given by the area of one cycle of the curve representing the function squared divided by the base. Expressed mathematically,

$$I_{\text{rms}} = \left(\frac{1}{2\pi} \int_0^{2\pi} i_b^2 \, d\alpha \right)^{\frac{1}{2}} \qquad (14\text{-}6)$$

This becomes, by use of Eq. (14-2),

$$I_{\text{rms}} = \left(\frac{1}{2\pi} \int_0^{\pi} I_m^2 \sin^2 \alpha \, d\alpha \right)^{\frac{1}{2}} = \frac{I_m}{2} \qquad (14\text{-}7)$$

It should be noted that the rms value of this wave is different from the rms value of a sinusoidal wave.

A d-c voltmeter reads the average value of the voltage across its terminals. Since the voltmeter is across the tube, the instantaneous tube voltage must be plotted and the area under one cycle of this curve must be found. When the tube is conducting, it has a resistance r_p and the voltage across it is $i_b r_p$. When the tube is nonconducting, the current is zero and from Fig. 14-1 it is seen that the transformer secondary voltage e appears across the tube. Thus,

$$\left.\begin{aligned} e_b &= i_b r_p = I_m r_p \sin \alpha & 0 \le \alpha \le \pi \\ e_b &= E_m \sin \alpha & \pi \le \alpha \le 2\pi \end{aligned}\right\} \tag{14-8}$$

A plot of the tube voltage is shown in Fig. 14-3. The reading of the voltmeter is

$$\begin{aligned} (E_{dc})_{\text{tube}} &= \frac{1}{2\pi}\left(\int_0^\pi I_m r_p \sin \alpha \, d\alpha + \int_\pi^{2\pi} E_m \sin \alpha \, d\alpha\right) \\ &= \frac{1}{\pi}(I_m r_p - E_m) = \frac{1}{\pi}[I_m r_p - I_m(r_p + R_L)] \end{aligned}$$

where use has been made of Eq. (14-3). Hence

$$(E_{dc})_{\text{tube}} = -\frac{I_m R_L}{\pi} \tag{14-9}$$

This result is negative, which means that if the voltmeter is to read upscale, its positive terminal must be connected to the cathode of the diode. Since $I_{dc} = I_m/\pi$, the d-c tube voltage is seen to be equal to $-I_{dc}R_L$ or to the negative of the d-c voltage across the load resistor. This result is evidently correct because the sum of the d-c voltages around the complete circuit must add up to zero.

It should be noted that the voltmeter reading does *not* equal the product of the direct current I_{dc} times the tube resistance r_p. The reason for this is that the tube is a nonlinear device whose resistance is constant (and equals r_p) only when the plate voltage is positive. On the other hand, the

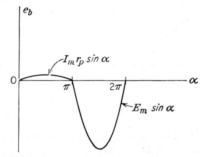

FIG. 14-3. The tube voltage across the vacuum diode in Fig. 14-1.

d-c voltage across the load does equal the product of direct current I_{dc} times the output resistance R_L because the load is a truly constant resistor.

A *wattmeter indicates the average value of the product of the instantaneous current through its current coil and the instantaneous voltage across its potential coil.* Hence the power read by the wattmeter will be

$$P_i = \frac{1}{2\pi}\int_0^{2\pi} e i_b \, d\alpha \tag{14-10}$$

This becomes, by Eq. (14-2),

$$P_i = \frac{1}{2\pi}\int_0^{2\pi} i_b^2 (r_p + R_L) \, d\alpha$$

This may be written, by virtue of Eq. (14-6), as

$$P_i = I_{\text{rms}}^2 (r_p + R_L) \tag{14-11}$$

This result could have been written down immediately by arguing physically that all the power supplied by the transformer must be used to heat the load and the tube resistances.

Equation (14-11) expresses the total power supplied to the plate circuit of the rectifier. This quantity can readily be calculated in any specific application. The total input power to the rectifier system cannot, in general, be predicted theoretically. The total input power includes the transformer losses, the filament heating power, and the power losses in any auxiliary apparatus.

The above illustration indicates the general method of calculating what d-c or a-c instruments will read in any electronic circuit. It is *not* restricted to the simple diode rectifier. The wave forms, in general, may be more complicated than those of the simple diode considered above, but the method is the same. For assistance in the calculations, rough sketches of the curves are made, and the readings of the instruments are obtained from an evaluation of the area under the curve (for a d-c instrument) or the area under the squared function (for an a-c instrument). If a wattmeter reading is desired, the curve representing the current through its current coil is multiplied by the curve representing the voltage across its potential coil and the area under the product curve is then evaluated.

The d-c power supplied to the load will be defined as the product of the reading of a d-c ammeter in the load circuit and a d-c voltmeter across the load. Thus,

$$P_{dc} \equiv E_{dc}I_{dc} = I_{dc}{}^2 R_L \qquad (14\text{-}12)$$

For the half-wave vacuum diode,

$$P_{dc} = \left(\frac{1}{\pi}\right)^2 \left(\frac{E_m}{r_p + R_L}\right)^2 R_L \qquad (14\text{-}13)$$

It is important to note that P_{dc} given in Eq. (14-13) is quite different from P_i given in (14-11), or from the reading of a wattmeter placed across the load. In those applications which are d-c operated, as, for example, d-c machinery and electroplating, the presence of a-c components, in addition to the d-c component, may contribute to the over-all heating of the system without contributing to the useful operation. Hence, usually a filter (Chap. 19) is interposed between the rectifier and the load in order to remove these a-c components. If the filter were completely effective, then the power delivered to the load would be P_{dc}.

As a measure of the efficiency of the rectification process, and also as a comparison of the various types of rectifiers to be discussed, it is convenient to define the *efficiency of rectification* (also called the "conversion efficiency" or the "theoretical efficiency") η_r as the ratio of the d-c output power to the plate-circuit power. This is

$$\eta_r \equiv \frac{P_{dc}}{P_i} \times 100\% = \frac{I_{dc}{}^2 R_L}{I_{rms}{}^2(r_p + R_L)} \times 100$$

$$= \left(\frac{I_{dc}}{I_{rms}}\right)^2 \frac{100}{1 + r_p/R_L} \quad \% \qquad (14\text{-}14)$$

By combining this with Eqs. (14-5) and (14-7), there results

$$\eta_r = \left(\frac{I_m/\pi}{I_m/2}\right)^2 \frac{100}{1 + r_p/R_L} = \frac{40.6}{1 + r_p/R_L} \quad \% \quad (14\text{-}15)$$

This indicates that the theoretical maximum efficiency of a single-phase half-wave circuit is 40.6 per cent. Actually, of course, the over-all efficiency of the system, which is obtained by considering the power supplied to the entire system, is considerably less than this.

It may be easily shown that the maximum power output of such a system occurs for $R_L = r_p$. At this load, the plate-circuit efficiency is only one-half its maximum possible value, or 20.3 per cent.

There are several features of the single-phase half-wave circuit that warrant special attention. First, it is noticed that on the inverse cycle, *viz.*, that part of the cycle during which the tube does not conduct, the maximum potential across the tube is equal to the transformer maximum potential. That is, the peak inverse voltage to which the tube is subjected during operation is equal to the transformer maximum value.

In order to prevent stray charges from building up on various parts of the system, it is desirable to ground either the positive or the negative side of the load. An inspection of Fig. 14-4, with the negative terminal of the system connected to ground, indicates that the heater winding of the transformer is at a high d-c potential with respect to ground. For example, suppose that the output voltage is 10,000 volts. Then, the center tap of the filament-transformer secondary is 10,000 volts above ground. Since one side of the a-c power line is generally grounded, there will be 10,000 volts between

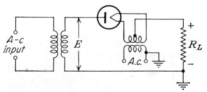

Fig. 14-4. To investigate the insulation stress in the filament transformer when one side of the load is grounded.

the primary and secondary windings of the filament transformer even though the primary voltage rating is only 115 volts and the secondary rating, perhaps, 5 volts. This requires that the insulation between the windings of the filament transformer be capable of withstanding this high voltage without rupture.

If the positive output terminal is grounded, then the center tap of the secondary of the filament transformer is at ground potential also. Hence, the high output voltage does not appear between the primary and secondary of the heater transformer, and it is now not necessary to use a specially built high-insulation transformer.

Example. Calculate the regulation and the efficiency of rectification of a type 5U4-GB diode used in the circuit of Fig. 14-1. The rated output current is 225 ma-

The transformer secondary voltage is 230 volts rms. Also, find the current at which maximum power is obtained.

Solution. By regulation is meant the variation of d-c output voltage as a function of d-c output current. This is given by

$$E_{dc} = I_{dc}R_L$$

and, from Eqs. (14-5) and (14-3),

$$I_{dc} = \frac{I_m}{\pi} = \frac{E_m/\pi}{r_p + R_L} \qquad (14\text{-}16)$$

Solve this for $I_{dc}R_L$ and combine with the first equation. The result is

$$E_{dc} = \frac{E_m}{\pi} - I_{dc}r_p \qquad (14\text{-}17)$$

This result (which is consistent with Thévenin's theorem) shows that E_{dc} equals E_m/π at no load and that the d-c voltage decreases linearly with the d-c output current. The larger the magnitude of the tube resistance, the greater is the rate of decrease.

From the volt-ampere curve for the type 5U4-GB tube given in Fig. A9-4 it is found that this characteristic can be approximated by a straight line, from which a value of $r_p = 260$ ohms is calculated. Also, the peak transformer voltage is $E_m = \sqrt{2}\, E_{\text{rms}}$ (for a sine wave) $= (\sqrt{2})\,(230) = 325$ volts. Hence,

$$E_{dc} = 103.5 - 260 I_{dc}$$

It follows from this expression that the d-c voltage drops from 103.5 volts at no load to 45.0 volts at the rated value of 225 ma. By definition, the percentage regulation is

$$\%\ \text{regulation} \equiv \frac{E_{\text{no load}} - E_{\text{full load}}}{E_{\text{full load}}} \times 100\%$$

If the output voltage does not vary with load, then the percentage regulation is zero. In the present illustration,

$$\%\ \text{regulation} = \frac{103.5 - 45.0}{45.0} \times 100 \cong 130\%$$

This extremely poor regulation, combined with the low efficiency and high harmonic content of the output wave, explains why half-wave high-vacuum diodes are seldom used when appreciable currents are required.

A more accurate way of estimating the effective tube resistance than that employed above using the static characteristic is to obtain a regulation plot E_{dc} vs. I_{dc} in the laboratory. The negative slope of the resulting straight line is r_p. The result so obtained includes the resistance of the transformer as well as the tube resistance. It also includes the effect of the transformer regulation.

To obtain the conversion efficiency as a function of load current, eliminate the term R_L from Eq. (14-15) as was done above for the regulation. This simple substitution yields

$$\eta_r = 40.6\left(1 - \frac{\pi r_p}{E_m} I_{dc}\right) \qquad \% \qquad (14\text{-}18)$$

This shows that the plate-circuit efficiency decreases linearly with the plate current. Using the numerical values found for the type 5U4-GB tube gives

$$\eta_r = 40.6(1 - 2.51 I_{dc}) \qquad \%$$

Thus η_r decreases from 40.6 per cent at no load to 17.6 per cent at full load.

The current at which maximum power is obtained from the rectifier is readily found by equating the plate-circuit efficiency η_r to 20.3 and then solving for I_{dc}. This leads to the value 200 ma for this tube. A second method of obtaining the same result is to set $R_L = r_p = 260$ in Eq. (14-16).

14-2. Ripple Factor. Although it is the purpose of a rectifier to convert alternating into direct current, the simple circuit considered above does not achieve this. Nor, in fact, do any of the more complicated rectifier circuits have a truly constant output. What is accomplished is the conversion from an alternating current into a unidirectional current, periodically fluctuating components still remaining in the output wave. It is for this reason that filters are frequently used in order to decrease these a-c components. A measure of the fluctuating components is given by the *ripple factor r*, which is defined as

$$r \equiv \frac{\text{rms value of the alternating components of the wave}}{\text{average value of the wave}}$$

This may be written as

$$r \equiv \frac{I_{\text{rms}}'}{I_{dc}} = \frac{E_{\text{rms}}'}{E_{dc}} \tag{14-19}$$

where the terms I_{rms}' and E_{rms}' denote the rms value of the a-c components of the current and voltage, respectively.

In order to measure the ripple factor of a given rectifier system experimentally, the measurement of the ripple voltage or the ripple current in the output should be made with instruments that respond to higher than power frequencies, so that the contributions from the higher harmonic terms will be recorded. These measurements may be made using a "square-law" voltmeter of either the thermocouple or the vacuum-tube type. A capacitor must be used in series with the input to the meter in order to "block" the d-c component. This capacitor charges up to the average value of the voltage and only the ripple components in the wave are recorded by the meter.

An analytical expression for the ripple factor, defined in Eq. (14-19), is possible. By noting that the instantaneous a-c component of current is given by

$$i' = i - I_{dc}$$

then

$$I_{\text{rms}}' \equiv \sqrt{\frac{1}{2\pi} \int_0^{2\pi} (i - I_{dc})^2 \, d\alpha} = \sqrt{\frac{1}{2\pi} \int_0^{2\pi} (i^2 - 2I_{dc}i + I_{dc}^2) \, d\alpha}$$

The first term of the integral becomes simply I_{rms}^2 of the total wave.

Since $\dfrac{1}{2\pi} \displaystyle\int_0^{2\pi} i \, d\alpha$ is I_{dc} by definition, then the second term under the integral sign is

$$(-2I_{dc})(I_{dc}) = -2I_{dc}^2$$

The rms ripple current then becomes

$$I_{rms}' = \sqrt{I_{rms}^2 - 2I_{dc}^2 + I_{dc}^2} = \sqrt{I_{rms}^2 - I_{dc}^2}$$

By combining this result with Eq. (14-19),

$$r = \frac{\sqrt{I_{rms}^2 - I_{dc}^2}}{I_{dc}} = \sqrt{\left(\frac{I_{rms}}{I_{dc}}\right)^2 - 1} \tag{14-20}$$

This result is independent of the current wave shape and is *not* restricted to a half-wave vacuum diode. In the case of the half-wave single-phase rectifier, the ratio

$$\frac{I_{rms}}{I_{dc}} = \frac{I_m/2}{I_m/\pi} = \frac{\pi}{2} = 1.57$$

from Eqs. (14-5) and (14-7). Hence

$$r = \sqrt{1.57^2 - 1} = 1.21 \tag{14-21}$$

This result indicates that the rms ripple voltage exceeds the d-c output voltage. This shows that the single-phase half-wave rectifier is a relatively poor device for converting alternating into direct current.

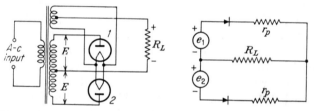

Fig. 14-5. Schematic wiring diagram and equivalent circuit of a full-wave vacuum rectifier.

14-3. Single-phase Full-wave Vacuum Rectifier. The circuit of the single-phase full-wave rectifier is shown in Fig. 14-5. This circuit is seen to comprise two half-wave circuits which are so connected that conduction takes place through one tube during one half of the power cycle and through the other tube during the second half of the power cycle.

The current to the load, which is the sum of these two currents, has the form shown in Fig. 14-6. The d-c and rms values of the load current in such a system are readily found, from the definitions (14-4) and (14-6), to be

$$I_{dc} = \frac{2I_m}{\pi} \qquad I_{rms} = \frac{I_m}{\sqrt{2}} \tag{14-22}$$

where I_m is the maximum value of the current wave. The d-c output power is, therefore,

$$P_{dc} = I_{dc}{}^2 R_L = \left(\frac{2}{\pi}\right)^2 \frac{E_m{}^2 R_L}{(r_p + R_L)^2} \tag{14-23}$$

where E_m is the peak transformer secondary voltage from one end to the center tap. It is noted, by comparing Eq. (14-22) with Eq. (14-5), that the direct current supplied to the load for the full-wave connection is twice that for the half-wave connection. Hence the power delivered to the load is larger by a factor of 4 in the full-wave circuit. However, the power depends upon the circuit constants and parameters in the same way as for the half-wave circuit.

A little thought should convince the reader that the input power supplied to the plate circuit in the full-wave case is given by the same expression as for the half-wave case, viz.,

$$P_i = I_{\text{rms}}{}^2(r_p + R_L) \tag{14-24}$$

The efficiency of rectification of the rectifier is then easily found to be

$$\eta_r = \frac{P_{dc}}{P_i} \times 100$$

$$= \frac{81.2}{1 + r_p/R_L} \quad \% \tag{14-25}$$

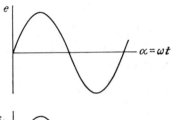

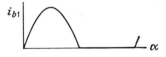

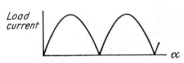

FIG. 14-6. The transformer voltage, the individual tube currents, and the load-current wave forms in a single-phase full-wave rectifier.

This expression shows a theoretical maximum twice that obtained for the half-wave circuit.

The required current ratio that appears in the expression for the ripple factor is

$$\frac{I_{\text{rms}}}{I_{dc}} = \frac{I_m/\sqrt{2}}{2I_m/\pi} = 1.11$$

The ripple factor for the full-wave circuit is, from Eq. (14-20),

$$r = \sqrt{1.11^2 - 1} = 0.482 \tag{14-26}$$

A comparison of this value with the value given by Eq. (14-21) for the half-wave circuit shows that the ripple factor has dropped from 1.21 in the half-wave case to 0.482 in the present case. Clearly, therefore, the full-wave circuit gives more efficient rectification with a larger fraction of the a-c input power being converted into d-c power.

The d-c output voltage is given by

$$E_{dc} = \frac{2E_m}{\pi} - I_{dc}r_p \tag{14-27}$$

Full-wave rectification is usually accomplished through the use of a tube that is so constructed as to contain both diodes within a single envelope, such as the type 5U4-GB tube. Semiconductor junction power diodes are also packaged in pairs for full-wave rectification.

Let us consider the diagram of Fig. 14-5 from the point of view of peak inverse voltages. Suppose that tube 1 is conducting, whence tube 2 is in the nonconducting state. Except for the $i_b r_p$ drop in tube 1, the peak potential between the transformer mid-point and the cathode is E_m, the

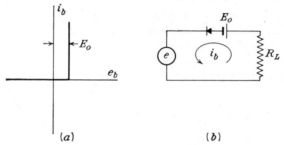

(a)   (b)

FIG. 14-7. (a) Idealized voltage-ampere characteristic of a gas diode. The break-down, maintaining, and extinction voltages are all assumed to be equal to E_0. (b) The equivalent circuit.

transformer maximum value. This is the voltage that appears across the load R_L. But the potential difference between the mid-point and the anode of tube 2 is also E_m, so that the potential between the cathode and anode of tube 2 is $2E_m$. Hence, the peak inverse voltage of each diode in a full-wave system is twice the transformer maximum voltage to center tap if the tube drop is neglected.

The conditions imposed on the insulation between the primary and the secondary of the filament heating transformer are the same as those which exist in the case of the half-wave circuit. Thus, if the negative of the system is grounded, it is necessary to use a filament transformer having interwinding insulation that will withstand the full d-c potential. If the positive of the system is grounded, this insulation stress will not exist.

14-4. Circuits with Gas Diodes. Although the general characteristics of the circuits for diode operation remain substantially unchanged when the high-vacuum diodes are replaced by gas-filled or vapor-filled tubes, certain differences do exist which we shall now investigate.

A gas tube will not conduct until the potential difference between the anode and the cathode reaches the breakdown value. During conduction, a constant voltage drop will exist between the cathode and the anode. When the anode potential falls below the extinction voltage, conduction ceases. The situation is illustrated in Fig. 14-7; (a) gives the idealized volt-ampere characteristic and (b) gives the equivalent circuit. The wave forms are indicated in Fig. 14-8. Actually, the breakdown and the extinction potentials are not exactly the same, and as a result, Fig. 14-8 is only approximate. However, very little practical error is introduced by this approximation.

A limitation to the use of gaseous diodes of the mercury-vapor type lies in the fact that the electrons in the plasma of the discharge perform oscillations of high frequencies.[1] This high-frequency disturbance

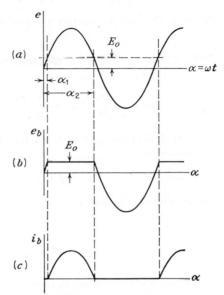

FIG. 14-8. The wave forms for a half-wave circuit using an ideal gas diode. (a) Input voltage. (b) Voltage across the tube. (c) Plate current.

may prove annoying in certain cases, although it may be suppressed by connecting radio-frequency chokes in series with each anode lead.

Example. Calculate the regulation and efficiency of rectification of a half-wave circuit using a gas-filled rectifier tube. Assume that the constant tube drop during conduction E_0 is small compared with the transformer secondary peak value E_m.

Solution. The instantaneous load voltage e_L equals the instantaneous transformer voltage less the constant tube drop. Hence, during conduction,

$$e_L = E_m \sin \alpha - E_0$$

The corresponding expression for the current is

$$i_b = \frac{E_m \sin \alpha - E_0}{R_L}$$

The d-c load voltage is found by taking the average value of e_L. Thus

$$E_{dc} = \frac{1}{2\pi} \int_{\alpha_1}^{\alpha_2} (E_m \sin \alpha - E_0)\, d\alpha$$

where α_1 is the angle at which the tube fires and α_2 is the angle at which conduction ceases. However, if $E_m \gg E_0$, little error will be made by assuming that $\alpha_1 = 0$ and $\alpha_2 = \pi$. By changing the limits as indicated, and carrying out the indicated integration, there results

$$E_{dc} = \frac{E_m}{\pi} - \frac{E_0}{2} = \frac{E_m}{\pi}\left(1 - \frac{\pi}{2}\frac{E_0}{E_m}\right) \tag{14-28}$$

This equation does not contain the load current. This means, of course, that E_{dc} remains constant, independent of the load current. Thus perfect regulation is indicated.

To calculate the efficiency of rectification, it is necessary to know the input power to the plate circuit. This is given by

$$P_i = \frac{1}{2\pi}\int_0^\pi ei_b\, d\alpha = \frac{1}{2\pi}\int_0^\pi (E_m \sin \alpha)\left(\frac{E_m \sin \alpha - E_0}{R_L}\right) d\alpha$$

where the limits have again been taken as 0 and π instead of α_1 and α_2. This expression reduces to

$$P_i = \frac{E_m{}^2}{4R_L}\left(1 - \frac{4}{\pi}\frac{E_0}{E_m}\right) \tag{14-29}$$

The d-c power to the load is

$$P_{dc} = E_{dc}I_{dc} = \frac{E_{dc}{}^2}{R_L}$$

$$= \frac{E_m{}^2}{\pi^2 R_L}\left(1 - \frac{\pi}{2}\frac{E_0}{E_m}\right)^2 \tag{14-30}$$

The efficiency of rectification is, therefore,

$$\eta_r = \frac{P_{dc}}{P_i} = \frac{4}{\pi^2}\frac{\left(1 - \frac{\pi}{2}\frac{E_0}{E_m}\right)^2}{1 - \frac{4}{\pi}\frac{E_0}{E_m}} \tag{14-31}$$

This expression shows that η_r is independent of the load current. If the numerator of Eq. (14-31) is divided by the denominator, and if all powers of E_0/E_m higher than the first are neglected, this may be written in the form

$$\eta_r = 40.6\left(1 - 1.87\frac{E_0}{E_m}\right) \qquad \% \tag{14-32}$$

To the same approximation as that of this problem, the ripple factor is given by

$$r = 1.21\left(1 + 0.5\frac{E_0}{E_m}\right) \tag{14-33}$$

The foregoing shows that the result of using gas tubes in a rectifier circuit is to yield a slightly lower d-c output voltage and efficiency of rectification than the maximum possible values with vacuum diodes. However, the values are substantially constant and independent of the load current, and under normal operation these values are generally higher than actually exist when vacuum diodes are used. The ripple voltage with gas tubes is slightly higher than with vacuum diodes.

If the tube drop is very small compared with E_m, the foregoing expressions reduce to

$$E_{dc} = \frac{E_m}{\pi} \qquad \eta_r = 40.6\% \qquad r = 1.21$$

These are exactly the values that would be obtained from the corresponding equations for the vacuum diode, if the plate resistance r_p were set equal to zero.

The analysis of the full-wave gas-tube circuit is similar to that made above for the half-wave rectifier.

14-5. Other Full-wave Circuits. A variety of other rectifier circuits find extensive use. Among these are the bridge circuit, several voltage-doubling circuits, and a number of voltage-multiplying circuits. The bridge circuit finds application not only for power circuits but also as a rectifying system in rectifier a-c meters for use over a fairly wide range of frequencies.

The essentials of the bridge circuit are shown in Fig. 14-9. In order to understand the action of this circuit, it is necessary only to note that two tubes conduct simultaneously. For example, during that portion of the cycle when the transformer polarity is that indicated in Fig. 14-9, tubes 1 and 3 are conducting, and current passes from the positive to the negative end of the load. The conduction path is shown on the figure. During the next half cycle, the transformer voltage reverses its

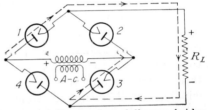

FIG. 14-9. Single-phase full-wave bridge circuit.

polarity, and tubes 2 and 4 send current through the load in the same direction as that during the previous half cycle.

The principal features of the bridge circuit are the following: The currents drawn in both the primary and the secondary of the supply transformer are sinusoidal, and therefore a smaller transformer may be used than for the full-wave circuit of the same output; a transformer without a center tap is used; and each tube has only transformer voltage across it on the inverse cycle. The bridge circuit is thus suitable for high-voltage applications. For example, if the output is 10,000 volts, then the peak inverse voltage across each tube is 10,000 volts. However, if a full-wave circuit were used, then the peak inverse voltage would be 20,000 volts. The transformers supplying the heaters of the tubes must be properly insulated for the high voltage.

The rectifier meter which is illustrated in Fig. 14-10 is essentially a bridge-rectifier system, except that semiconductor elements replace the tubes, and, of course, no transformer is required. Instead, the voltage to be measured is applied through a multiplier resistor R to two corners of

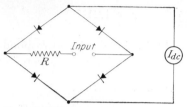

the bridge, a d-c milliammeter being used as an indicating instrument across the other two corners. Since the d-c milliammeter reads average values of current, the meter scale is calibrated to give rms values when a sinusoidal voltage is applied to the input terminals.

FIG. 14-10. The rectifier voltmeter.

As a result, this instrument will not read correctly when used with wave forms which contain appreciable harmonics.

A common voltage-doubling circuit, which delivers a d-c voltage approximately equal to twice the transformer maximum voltage at no load, is shown in Fig. 14-11. This circuit is operated by alternately charging each of the two capacitors to the transformer peak voltage E_m, current being continually drained from the capacitors through the load. The capacitors also act to smooth out the ripple in the output.

This circuit is characterized by poor regulation unless very large capacitors are used. The inverse voltage across the tubes during the nonconducting cycle is twice the transformer voltage. If ordinary rectifier tubes are used, two separate filament transformers or one transformer with windings well insulated from each other must be used. The latter difficulty can be avoided in low-voltage systems by using special tubes, for example, the 25Z5, which is equipped with separated, indirectly heated cathodes, each being surrounded by its own anode. The heaters are con-

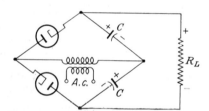

FIG. 14-11. The bridge voltage-doubler circuit. This is the single-phase full-wave bridge circuit of Fig. 14-9 with two capacitors replacing two tubes.

nected in series internally but are well insulated from the cathodes. The action of this circuit will be better understood after the capacitor filter is studied in Chap. 19.

Circuits for obtaining n-fold multiplication,[2] n even or odd, are given in Probs. 14-14 and 14-15.

14-6. Controlled Rectifiers. A number of applications exist which require a controlled amount of current. These include electric-welding operations, lighting-control installations in theaters, motor-speed control, and a variety of other industrial control applications. It is possible to vary the amount of current supplied to the load either by controlling the transformer secondary voltage or by inserting a controlling resistor in the output circuit. Neither of these methods is desirable. The first method may require expensive auxiliary equipment, and the second is characterized by poor efficiency. The development of thyratrons, ignitrons, and excitrons has made control a relatively inexpensive process.

It was pointed out in Sec. 13-3 that the presence of the massive grid structure between the cathode and the anode of the thyratron to provide complete electrostatic shielding between these electrodes permits control of the initiation of the arc by controlling the grid potential. With an applied a-c potential to the anode, the arc is extinguished once each alternate half cycle provided that the arc is initiated regularly. The average rectified current can be varied over wide limits by controlling the point in each half cycle at which the arc initiation occurs.

In order to analyze the action of a thyratron in a controlled rectifier circuit, use is made of the critical grid breakdown characteristic of Fig.

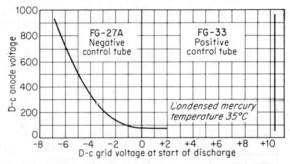

FIG. 14-12. The breakdown characteristics of a negative- and a positive-control thyratron.

14-12. This curve gives the minimum grid potential required for conduction to occur for each value of plate potential. Thus, if a sinusoidal plate voltage is applied to the tube, the potential of the grid just to permit conduction at each point in the cycle is found from the critical grid curve. The important curves are illustrated in Fig. 14-13. In this figure the sine waves represent the plate potential as a function of time. On these same curves are drawn the critical grid (cg) voltages corresponding to these values of plate voltage. The critical grid curves for the negative-control tube in Fig. 14-13a and for the positive-control tube in Fig. 14-13b are obtained from the critical grid breakdown curves of Fig. 14-12, which are plotted for 35°C (the approximate operating temperature in air).

The critical grid breakdown curve is drawn only for positive anode voltages, since conduction does not take place if the anode is negative. For the positive tube the critical grid curve is a straight line parallel to the time axis, indicating that the breakdown voltage is substantially independent of the anode potential. For the negative tube, a point-by-point plot is required to draw the critical grid curve, as in Fig. 14-13a. This is obtained from the critical grid starting curve as follows: Corresponding to any time t_1 in the positive half cycle, the plate voltage e_{b1} is obtained from the impressed voltage curve. Then corresponding to this value e_{b1}, the critical grid point e_{g1} (the minimum value of grid potential at which conduction will just take place) is read off the curve of Fig. 14-12. This

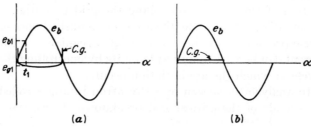

(a)   (b)

FIG. 14-13. The sinusoidal plate supply voltage and the corresponding critical grid (cg) curve for (a) a negative-control tube and (b) a positive-control tube.

point is plotted on Fig. 14-13a at the point corresponding to the time t_1. (The grid-voltage values are so small that it is difficult to draw the critical grid curve to scale.)

Suppose that the circuit is so arranged that the grid potential exceeds the critical grid breakdown value at some angle, say φ. Conduction will start at this point in the cycle. The voltage drop across the tube during conduction of the thyratron, like that of any gas tube, remains substantially constant at a low value that is independent of the current. This tube drop is of the order of 10 to 15 volts. If the tube drop after conduction has begun is denoted by E_0, the current that flows through a pure resistance plate load R_L during the time that the tube is conducting is given by

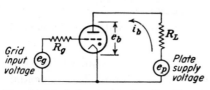

FIG. 14-14. A thyratron circuit with a-c plate and grid excitation.

$$i_b = \frac{E_m \sin \omega t - E_0}{R_L} \tag{14-34}$$

where E_m is the maximum value of the applied potential. This expression is seen to follow directly from the circuit of Fig. 14-14.

The resulting form of the output current is illustrated in Fig. 14-15. The breakdown or ionization time is so small[3] that it need not be taken into consideration in most applications. This accounts for the vertical rise in the plate-current curve at the angle φ. The current is seen to rise abruptly at this angle and then follows the sine variation given in Eq.

(14-34) until the supply voltage e_p falls below E_0 at the phase $\pi - \varphi_0$. The current will remain zero until the phase φ is again reached in the next cycle.

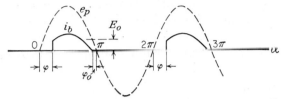

FIG. 14-15. The wave shape of the load current i_b in a thyratron. Conduction starts at the angle φ and stops at $\pi - \varphi_0$ in each cycle. The broken curve e_p is the impressed plate voltage.

The average rectified current (the value read on a d-c ammeter) will be

$$I_{dc} = \frac{1}{2\pi} \int_{\varphi}^{\pi - \varphi_0} i_b\, d\alpha = \frac{E_m}{2\pi R_L} \int_{\varphi}^{\pi - \varphi_0} \left(\sin \alpha - \frac{E_0}{E_m} \right) d\alpha$$

which integrates to

$$I_{dc} = \frac{E_m}{2\pi R_L} \left[\cos \varphi + \cos \varphi_0 - \frac{E_0}{E_m} (\pi - \varphi_0 - \varphi) \right] \quad (14\text{-}35)$$

where $\alpha = \omega t$ and where φ_0 is the smallest angle defined by the relation

$$E_0 \equiv E_m \sin \varphi_0 \quad (14\text{-}36)$$

If the ratio E_0/E_m is very small, then φ_0 may be taken as zero and Eq. (14-35) reduces to the form

$$I_{dc} \cong \frac{E_m}{2\pi R_L} (1 + \cos \varphi) \quad (14\text{-}37)$$

The limits of variation of the angle φ in Eq. (14-37) are from 0 to π.

This analysis shows that the average rectified current can be controlled by varying the position at which the grid potential exceeds the critical grid starting value. The maximum current is obtained when the arc is initiated at the beginning of each cycle; and the minimum current is obtained when

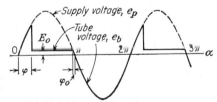

FIG. 14-16. The wave shape of the anode voltage e_b of a thyratron.

the grid potential is applied at a point where no conduction occurs, viz., at the end of the positive half cycle.

The voltages across the thyratron for the conditions illustrated in Fig. 14-15 are shown in Fig. 14-16. The applied voltage appears across the tube until conduction begins. After breakdown the tube voltage is a constant equal to E_0. When the applied voltage falls to such a low value that the tube is extinguished, then the tube voltage is again equal to the applied voltage.

The reading of a d-c voltmeter placed across the tube will be

$$E_{dc} = \frac{1}{2\pi} \int_0^{2\pi} e_b \, d\alpha$$

$$= \frac{1}{2\pi} \left(\int_0^{\varphi} E_m \sin \alpha \, d\alpha + \int_{\varphi}^{\pi-\varphi_0} E_0 \, d\alpha + \int_{\pi-\varphi_0}^{2\pi} E_m \sin \alpha \, d\alpha \right)$$

which integrates to

$$E_{dc} = \frac{E_0}{2\pi} (\pi - \varphi_0 - \varphi) - \frac{E_m}{2\pi} (\cos \varphi + \cos \varphi_0) \qquad (14\text{-}38)$$

If $E_m \gg E_0$, this reduces to

$$E_{dc} \cong -\frac{E_m}{2\pi} (1 + \cos \varphi) \qquad (14\text{-}39)$$

The appearance of the negative sign means that the cathode is more positive than the plate for most of the cycle. This is in agreement with Fig. 14-16. It is to be emphasized that a d-c voltmeter does not read E_0, if an a-c potential is applied to the plate. If the voltmeter is to read upscale, it must be connected with its positive terminal at the cathode.

It should be noted that the d-c load voltage is the negative of the d-c tube voltage [compare Eqs. (14-37) and (14-39)]. This follows from the fact that the sum of the d-c voltages around the circuit is zero.

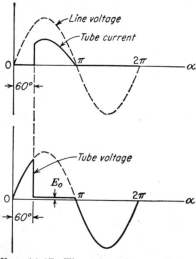

FIG. 14-17. The wave shapes of the tube current and tube voltage in a thyratron. Conduction begins at 60 deg and (since $E_m \gg E_0$) ceases at 180 deg.

Example. A thyratron is connected according to Fig. 14-14 and supplies power to a 200-ohm resistance load from a 230-volt source of supply. If the grid voltage is adjusted so that conduction starts 60 deg after the start of each cycle, calculate the readings of the following meters: (1) an a-c ammeter in series with the load, (2) an a-c voltmeter across the tube, (3) a wattmeter inserted in the circuit so as to read the total power delivered by the a-c supply. Assume that the tube drop during conduction equals 15 volts.

Solution. Since $E_m \gg E_0$, little error will be made by assuming that conduction continues until the end of each positive half cycle. The instantaneous current through the tube and the voltage across the tube will have the forms shown in Fig. 14-17.

1. The instantaneous current during the conduction is

$$i_b = \frac{230 \sqrt{2} \sin \alpha - 15}{200} \\ i_b = 1.625 \sin \alpha - 0.075 \Bigg\} \quad \text{for } \frac{\pi}{3} \leqq \alpha \leqq \pi$$

An a-c ammeter reads the rms value of the current wave. For the wave sketched,

$$I_{\text{rms}} = \sqrt{\frac{1}{2\pi} \int_{\pi/3}^{\pi} (1.625 \sin \alpha - 0.075)^2 \, d\alpha}$$

$$= \sqrt{\frac{1}{2\pi} \int_{\pi/3}^{\pi} (2.65 \sin^2 \alpha - 0.244 \sin \alpha + 0.00564) \, d\alpha}$$

$$= \sqrt{0.533 - 0.058 + 0.002} = 0.69 \text{ amp}$$

If the tube drop is neglected, then

$$I_{\text{rms}} = \sqrt{\frac{1}{2\pi} \int_{\pi/3}^{\pi} (1.625 \sin \alpha)^2 \, d\alpha} = \sqrt{0.533} = 0.73 \text{ amp}$$

The limits of integration are from 60 to 180 deg, the current being zero outside of this range.

2. The a-c voltmeter reads the rms value of the voltage wave sketched. It is noted that between 0 and $\pi/3$ the tube voltage equals the line voltage; between $\pi/3$ and π, it is constant and equal to E_0; and between π and 2π, it again equals the line voltage. Thus,

$$E_{\text{rms}} = \sqrt{\frac{1}{2\pi} \left[\int_0^{\pi/3} (230 \sqrt{2} \sin \alpha)^2 \, d\alpha + \int_{\pi/3}^{\pi} 15^2 \, d\alpha + \int_{\pi}^{2\pi} (230 \sqrt{2} \sin \alpha)^2 \, d\alpha \right]}$$
$$= 178 \text{ volts}$$

If the tube drop is neglected, then very little error is introduced.

3. The instantaneous power from the a-c supply is the product of the instantaneous line current and the instantaneous line voltage. The wattmeter will read the average value of this product. Hence

$$P = \frac{1}{2\pi} \int_{\pi/3}^{\pi} (1.625 \sin \alpha - 0.075)(230 \sqrt{2} \sin \alpha) \, d\alpha = 101 \text{ watts}$$

The integration extends only from $\pi/3$ to π, for there can be no power when the current is zero. If the tube drop is neglected, the calculated power equals 107 watts.

14-7. Phase-shift Control. In the phase-shift method of control, the point in each half cycle at which conduction will take place is varied by changing the phase angle between the plate and grid potentials. These conditions are illustrated in Fig. 14-18. In this figure the grid voltage e_g lags the plate voltage e_p by an angle θ, as indicated by the sinors that represent the sine waves. An examination of this figure shows that at the time corresponding to the phase φ the grid voltage just equals the critical breakdown value, so that conduction starts at this point in the cycle. The arc will be extinguished, of course, when the plate potential falls to a value too small to maintain conduction.

It should be noted that the curve marked e_p in Fig. 14-18 (and e_b in Fig. 14-13) is really the plate supply voltage and not the anode voltage e_b. However, before conduction begins in each cycle, $e_p = e_b$, and hence the foregoing method of determining the angle φ at which conduction begins is valid.

If the magnitude of the applied grid voltage is large compared with the critical grid voltage (appropriate to the plate potential at any phase), the

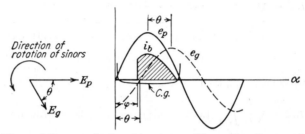

FIG. 14-18. Phase-shift control of a thyratron. The grid voltage e_g lags the plate voltage e_p by an angle θ. Conduction begins at the angle φ at which the grid-voltage curve intersects the critical grid curve. The sinors (phasors) which generate the plate and grid voltages are indicated to the left.

angle φ is approximately equal to the angle θ. *Under these circumstances the critical grid curve may be assumed to coincide with the zero voltage axis.* Furthermore, if the maximum value of the plate voltage is much larger than the tube drop, then Eq. (14-37) will give the dependence of d-c load current upon the phase angle for all values of φ for which the grid voltage *lags* the plate voltage. When the grid voltage *leads* the plate voltage by *any* angle, an inspection of Fig. 14-18 reveals that conduction will occur

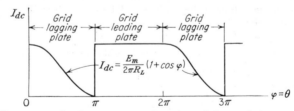

FIG. 14-19. The average load current as a function of the angle between the grid and plate voltages. The tube drop has been neglected, and the critical grid characteristic has been assumed to coincide with the zero voltage axis.

very nearly at the beginning of each cycle. The maximum possible rectified current is obtained under these conditions. These results are illustrated in Fig. 14-19.

It is observed from this curve that the current is very small for an angle slightly less than 180 deg. For an angle slightly larger than 180 deg, the plate current suddenly rises to its full value. Since, when the grid is 180 deg leading, the tube will be on, and, when it is 180 deg lagging, the tube will be off, the 180-deg point is a critical one.   This critical point may be obtained in the laboratory by using a phase-shifting system that allows a shift through the 180-deg point.

For those cases where a small plate potential or a small grid potential may be employed, the generalization that $\varphi \cong \theta$ will no longer be valid. Such cases can, however, be analyzed by drawing the plate, grid, and critical grid curves to scale in the manner shown in Fig. 14-18.   Under some extreme conditions, it may be found that φ differs considerably from θ.   Also, if the tube drop is not negligible compared with the peak plate voltage, the d-c plate current will be given by Eq. (14-35) and not by the simplified expression (14-37).   However, the approximations introduced above, viz., the neglect of the tube drop and the assumption that the critical grid curve coincides with the zero voltage axis, are valid in many practical problems.

14-8. Phase-shifting Circuits.   A number of methods exist by which the phase between the plate and grid voltages may be varied.   A direct way is to employ a polyphase phase shifter. These devices are essentially wound-rotor induction motors, generally with unity transformation ratio, the rotor of which may be set at any fixed desired angle with respect to the stator.   The primary is excited with a three-phase supply.   This causes a rotating magnetic field to be set up, the phase of the emfs induced in the secondary windings being a function of the angular position of the rotor.   A so-called "three-phase selsyn" may be used for this purpose in exactly this way.

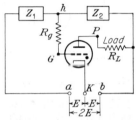

Fig. 14-20.   A network which allows the phase of the grid voltage to be shifted with respect to the phase of the plate voltage.

The more customary method of shifting the phase is through the use of simple phase-shifting networks.   The phase-shifting network of Fig. 14-20 is frequently employed.[4]   The cathode return K is connected to the mid-point of a single-phase system.   The phase between the grid and plate voltages is controlled by means of the two impedances Z_1 and Z_2, arranged as shown.

In order to analyze this phase-shifting network, it is convenient to draw a sinor diagram of this circuit.   Consider the case where

$$Z_1 = R \text{ (a resistor)}$$

and

$$Z_2 = \omega L \text{ (an inductor)}$$

The voltage notation conventions used here are explained in Appendix VIII.   The reader is urged to study these carefully before proceeding further; otherwise, the diagrams which follow may not be clear to him.

The first step in the analysis is to label the cathode, plate, and grid with the letters K, P, and G, respectively. Other letters (a, b, and h) are also added at the junction points in the network. Conditions are then considered *before conduction begins in each cycle.* The plate current, the grid current, and the cathode current are all zero before conduction begins, and the tube may be removed from the circuit without any effect. The simple network of Fig. 14-21 is obtained. Before conduction, there is no voltage drop in the load resistor R_L, and points b and P are at the same potential as indicated on the diagram. Similarly, h and G are at the same potential.

The sinor diagram is given in Fig. 14-22. The voltage drop $\mathbf{E}_{pa}$ from P to a is drawn along the horizontal axis. Since the cathode is connected to the mid-point of the system, then the point K is located midway

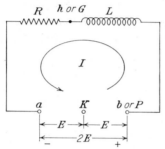

FIG. 14-21. Before conduction begins in each cycle the circuit of Fig. 14-20 reduces to this network.

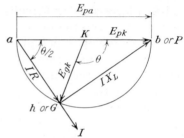

FIG. 14-22. Circle diagram for the circuit of Fig. 14-20 for conditions before conduction starts in each cycle. The diagram is used to determine the phase angle θ between the plate and grid voltages.

between the end points a and P of the sinor $\mathbf{E}_{pa}$. Since the circuit is inductive, the current $\mathbf{I}$ lags the voltage $\mathbf{E}_{pa}$. The IR drop from G to a is in phase with the current, and the IX_L drop leads the current by 90 deg. The sum of the two drops must, of course, equal the line voltage drop $\mathbf{E}_{pa}$. The angle aGP is a right angle. As either R or L is varied, the point G has as its locus a semicircle whose diameter is the voltage drop $E_{pa} = 2E$ or whose radius is E. This is referred to as a "circle diagram."

Since the points K and G are already located on the diagram, then the sinor $\mathbf{E}_{gk}$ can be drawn between them. The sinor diagram shows that the grid voltage $\mathbf{E}_{gk}$ lags the plate voltage $\mathbf{E}_{pk}$ by the angle θ. As either R or L is varied, this angle changes but *the magnitudes of both the plate and the grid voltages remain constant and equal to the input voltage E.*

With the system of Fig. 14-20, the load current will decrease as the resistance decreases, provided that X_L is constant. This result is evident from the following: If R decreases, I increases, IX_L will increase, and the angle θ increases. From Fig. 14-19, it is seen that I_{dc} decreases as

θ increases. The phase angle can be obtained from Fig. 14-22. The result is seen upon inspection to be

$$\tan \frac{\theta}{2} = \frac{Z_2 I}{Z_1 I} = \frac{Z_2}{Z_1} \tag{14-40}$$

where

$$Z_2 = X_L = \omega L \quad \text{and} \quad Z_1 = R$$

If Z_1 and Z_2 are interchanged, then a sinor diagram similar to the foregoing for the new conditions indicates that now θ becomes an angle of *lead* of the grid voltage over the plate voltage. For this case there can be no control over the magnitude of the rectified current, I_{dc} remaining constant and independent of θ, as indicated in Fig. 14-19.

A similar analysis shows that, for the case where $Z_1 = 1/\omega C$ and $Z_2 = R$, the angle θ is also given by Eq. (14-40). Here with X_C held constant and R adjustable, the rectified plate current decreases as R increases. The possible arrangements for L and C constant, with an adjustable R, are tabulated.

Z_1	Z_2	Control
R	X_L	I_{dc} increases as R increases
X_L	R	No control; maximum conduction
R	X_C	No control; maximum conduction
X_C	R	I_{dc} decreases as R increases

The quantity R that appears in the phase-shift circuit need not necessarily be an ohmic resistor but may be a thermionic tube whose resistance is varied by changing one of the control voltages; it may be a photocell whose resistance varies with illumination; or it may be any other resistor. Of course, R could be maintained fixed in any of these circuits, and the phase angle could be controlled by varying L or C.

Numerous other phase-shifting networks exist. The following illustration shows another such circuit.

Example. Two similar capacitors C and two similar resistors R are employed in the phase-shifting network sketched in Fig. 14-23. Show that phase-shift control of the thyratron is obtained by varying C. In particular, if $R = 10^6$ ohms and $C = 0.001$ μf, what will be the d-c plate current through the 200-ohm plate load?

Solution. Since the plate and grid voltages are large, little error is made by neglecting the tube drop and by assuming that the critical grid curve coincides with the zero voltage axis.

The first step in the analysis is to label the cathode, plate, and grid with the letters K, P, and G, respectively. Other letters are also added at the junction points in the network as shown. Before conduction begins in each cycle, the tube represents an open circuit, and the network of Fig. 14-23 reduces to that shown in Fig. 14-24.

To construct the sinor diagram of the control network, the grid transformer secondary voltage sinor $\mathbf{E}_{ba}$ is taken, for convenience, along the horizontal axis in Fig. 14-25. The currents through both parallel branches bga and bka are equal, since each circuit contains the same elements R and C. This current is denoted by $\mathbf{I}$, and it leads the voltage $\mathbf{E}_{ba}$, since each branch is capacitive. The voltage drop from point k to point a equals $\mathbf{I}R$ and is in phase with $\mathbf{I}$. Similarly, the voltage drop from b to k is $\mathbf{E}_{bk} = \mathbf{I}X_C$

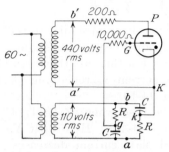

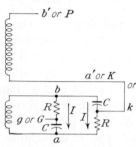

Fig. 14-23. A phase-shifting network for thyratron control.

Fig. 14-24. The equivalent circuit of the network in Fig. 14-23 before conduction begins in each cycle.

and lags $\mathbf{I}$ by 90 deg, since X_C is a capacitive reactance. Since the sinors $\mathbf{E}_{ka}$ and $\mathbf{E}_{bk}$ are mutually perpendicular, this locates the point k on a semicircle with $\mathbf{E}_{ba}$ as the diameter and drawn above the horizontal axis.

By employing a similar analysis, the point g is located on a semicircle with $\mathbf{E}_{ba}$ as diameter but drawn below the horizontal axis, as shown by the broken semicircle in Fig. 14-25. The grid voltage $\mathbf{E}_{gk}$ is seen to be equal in magnitude to the secondary grid transformer voltage and is therefore independent of the particular values of R and C. The angle between $\mathbf{E}_{gk}$ and $\mathbf{E}_{ba}$ is θ and represents the angle between the grid and plate voltages. This follows from the fact that $\mathbf{E}_{b'a'} = \mathbf{E}_{pk}$ (before conduction starts in each cycle) and $\mathbf{E}_{ba}$ is either in phase with or 180 deg out of phase with $\mathbf{E}_{b'a'}$.

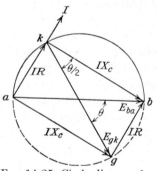

Fig. 14-25. Circle diagram for the network of Fig. 14-23.

When $\mathbf{E}_{ba}$ is 180 deg out of phase with $\mathbf{E}_{b'a'}$, the angle θ is one of lead of grid voltage over plate voltage and so no control of the output current is possible. Hence the maximum current will flow for all values of θ. If $\mathbf{E}_{b'a'}$ is in phase with $\mathbf{E}_{ba}$, then the current can be controlled from zero to a maximum value by varying C from very large values to very small values.

It is seen from the geometry of the circle diagram that

$$\tan \frac{\theta}{2} = \frac{R}{X_C} = \omega RC$$

For the present case with $R = 10^6$ ohms, $C = 0.001$ μf, and $\omega = 120\pi$, then tan $(\theta/2) = 0.377$, from which $\theta = 41.2°$. By Eq. (14-37), the direct current is found to be

$$I_{dc} = \frac{440 \sqrt{2}}{400\pi} (1 + \cos 41.2°) = 0.87 \text{ amp}$$

14-9. D-c Bias Control.   It is possible to control the magnitude of the average rectified current of a thyratron by varying the d-c grid bias voltage E_c on the tube.   An a-c plate supply voltage must be used.   This is called the "bias-control" method.   This method of control is most easily understood by referring to Fig. 14-26.

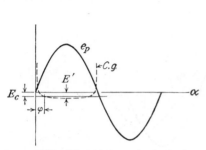

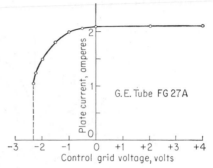

FIG. 14-26. The bias method of control.   Conduction starts at the phase φ at which the d-c grid voltage E_c equals the critical grid voltage.

FIG. 14-27. The experimentally determined average plate current in a thyratron as a function of the d-c grid voltage in the bias method of control.

The tube will conduct at the point where E_c intersects the critical grid curve, the angle φ of the diagram.   Clearly, if the negative grid voltage is too large ($E_c > E'$), the grid-voltage line will not intersect the critical grid characteristic and conduction will not be possible.   The maximum negative bias is that for which the grid voltage line is tangent to the critical grid curve, and the tube conducts for one-quarter of the cycle.   For less negative values of the bias voltage, the angle φ at which conduction begins is less than 90 deg.   Control is evidently possible over the range from full conduction to half conduction.

A curve showing the variation of the d-c plate current with bias voltage is shown in Fig. 14-27.   As predicted, the plate current can be varied from a maximum value to a value about one-half of this maximum. If one attempts to obtain smaller values of rectified current, the tube ceases to conduct and the current falls to zero, as shown.

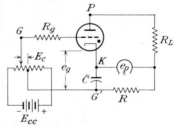

FIG. 14-28. A circuit for bias phase control of a thyratron. The grid voltage is the sum of the a-c voltage across the capacitor C and the d-c bias voltage E_c.

An unstable critical condition analogous to that which prevails in the phase-shift method of control for $\theta = 180°$ occurs here at the point $\varphi = 90°$.

14-10. Bias Phase Control.   It is a shortcoming of the d-c bias method of control discussed in Sec. 14-9 that it provides control only over the range from maximum current to approximately one-half this value. It is possible to extend the range of control by combining a-c and d-c grid excitation. A circuit for such control is illustrated in Fig. 14-28. The *RC* network serves to provide a fixed shift between the grid and plate voltages. Control is then obtained by varying the d-c grid bias E_c either positively or negatively.

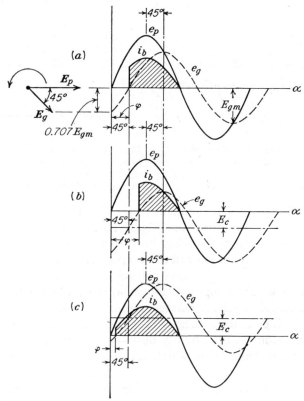

Fig. 14-29. Current variations with bias phase control. The phase angle between plate and grid voltages is kept constant at 45 deg and the bias voltage is varied: (a) $E_c = 0$; (b) E_c negative; (c) E_c positive. The sinors generating the e_p and e_g curves are shown to the left.

Suppose, for convenience, that $R = X_C$. The a-c grid voltage will then *lag* the plate voltage by 45 deg and will have a maximum value that is 0.707 times the maximum of the plate voltage, as can easily be seen from a simple sinor diagram. Assume also that the critical grid curve coincides with the zero voltage axis. Then, with zero bias $E_c = 0$, conduction will start at the 45-deg point in each positive half cycle, as shown in Fig. 14-29a. From Eq. (14-37) the direct current is closely approximated by

$$I_{dc} = \frac{I'}{2}(1 + \cos \varphi) \qquad (14\text{-}41)$$

where $I' = E_m/\pi R_L$ represents the maximum possible direct current. For $\varphi = 45°$,

$$\frac{I_{dc}}{I'} = \frac{1}{2}(1 + \cos 45°) = 0.85$$

This is indicated in Fig. 14-30.

If now a negative d-c bias is applied, this is equivalent to sliding the e_g curve downward with respect to the e_p curve. This is indicated in Fig. 14-29b. The a-c grid voltage e_g intersects the zero voltage axis farther along in the cycle, and the plate current is decreased. It can be seen from the diagram that the minimum rectified current will exist when the negative bias E_c equals the peak a-c grid voltage E_{gm}. Conduction will then start at an angle $\varphi = 135°$. Under this condition, $I_{dc}/I' = \frac{1}{2}(1 + \cos 135°) = 0.15$.

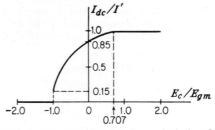

FIG. 14-30. The control characteristic of the network in Fig. 14-28.

If the d-c bias is made more negative than this value, no conduction is possible.

If the bias is made positive, this is equivalent to sliding the e_g curve upward with respect to the e_p curve. Conduction will start at some angle that is smaller than 45 deg. This is shown in Fig. 14-29c. An inspection of this diagram shows that when the d-c bias equals 0.707 times the peak grid alternating voltage ($E_c = 0.707E_{gm}$), conduction will take place over the full half cycle and maximum current will be delivered.

A plot of I_{dc}/I' as a function of E_c/E_{gm} is given in Fig. 14-30. Different shapes of control curves of this type are obtained for each phase-shift angle. An angle of lead results in a quite different control characteristic from the same angle of lag. The method of obtaining these control curves is summarized as follows: The sinor $\mathbf{E}_p$ is drawn horizontally, and the sinor $\mathbf{E}_g$ is drawn at the given angle with respect to it. Then the e_p and e_g curves are drawn as the vertical projections of the corresponding sinors, as they are imagined to rotate in a counterclockwise direction. This ensures the proper orientation of the a-c grid voltage with respect to the plate voltage. The entire analysis may be invalid unless this is done carefully. The e_g curve is now moved upward for a positive d-c bias and downward for a negative d-c bias. The angle at which the e_g curve intersects the zero voltage axis is noted for each value of bias, and the corresponding direct current is calculated from Eq. (14-41).

One special case is of importance. If the phase-shift angle is 90 deg with the grid voltage lagging the plate voltage, then linear control from zero to maximum current is obtained as illustrated in Fig. 14-31. The proof of this statement is left to the reader (Prob. 14-31e).

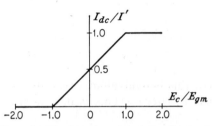

FIG. 14-31. Linear control is obtained with the bias phase method if the grid voltage lags the plate voltage by 90 deg.

14-11. On-Off Control. A variety of circuits exist which permit on-off control of a thyratron. Such circuits would be employed when it is desired to use the thyratron as a switch or contactor.

Consider a positive-grid thyratron which operates with alternating current on the plate and with a d-c bias on the grid. The critical grid characteristic is a straight line, as can be seen from Fig. 14-12. If the grid voltage is more positive than this critical grid voltage, conduction takes place. If the grid voltage is less than this critical value, the tube does not conduct. Thus the tube acts as a power switch, with the grid controlling the "on" or "off" status.

There are other instances when continuous control is not obtained, only an on-off control being exercised. Consider, for example, the phase-shift control circuits of Sec. 14-8. It is seen from Fig. 14-19 that if the circuit parameters are so adjusted that the phase shift between the grid and plate potentials is in the neighborhood of 180 deg either full rectified current or zero current is obtained.

Another example of on-off control is illustrated in the circuit of Fig. 14-32. The switch S serves as an arcless contactor to control considerable power through the load R_L. With S open, no conduction occurs since E_{cc} is so adjusted that it is more negative than the maximum

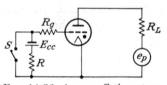

FIG. 14-32. An on-off thyratron control circuit.

negative critical grid value (the voltage E' of Fig. 14-26). When the switch S is closed, the grid is tied to the cathode and approximately maximum rectified current is delivered. The resistor R serves to prevent short-circuiting the battery E_{cc} when S is closed. The resistor R_g is large enough to keep the grid current after breakdown within safe limits.

14-12. D-c Operation of Thyratrons. Since the grid provides a means of initiating the discharge but not of extinguishing it, the plate voltage must be reduced below the extinction voltage before conduction will cease.

In those circuits considered above, the application of an a-c plate voltage resulted in arc extinction once each cycle. If the thyratron is operated with a d-c voltage applied to the plate, then for control it is necessary that some means be provided for extinguishing the arc. This can be accomplished manually by opening a switch in the plate circuit, by means of a relay in the plate circuit, or by suitable electrical means.

A variety of electrical methods exist for extinguishing the arc in a thyratron. In one method, a series LC circuit is connected between the plate and the cathode. With such an oscillatory circuit, the output when the tube fires will be a pulse of current that tends to oscillate from a positive to a negative value. Since the tube cannot pass a reverse current, the arc will be extinguished. This method has been used to permit voltage pulses applied to the grid to be recorded on a mechanical counter in the plate circuit.

A second method, which is used extensively for the generation of rectangular pulses of relatively short duration, is quite like that just described except that an open-circuited artificial transmission line replaces the LC circuit.[5]

Many other electrical circuits exist which effectively open the plate circuit.[6] In one such circuit one thyratron is used as a means for extinguishing the arc in a second thyratron (see Prob. 14-47).

14-13. Control of Ignitrons. The general features of the ignitron are discussed in Sec. 13-8. In this tube, the arc is established once each cycle of the applied power by means of a high-current surge to the ignitor circuit. Since ignition may be established at any point in the cycle, then control of the average anode current is possible.

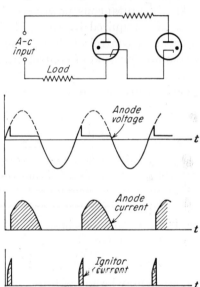

Fig. 14-33. A simple ignitron circuit and the wave forms of the anode voltage, anode current, and ignitor current.

The fundamental circuit of the ignitron for simple rectification without phase control is illustrated in Fig. 14-33. The wave forms of the anode voltage, the anode current, and the ignitor current are also shown. Conduction occurs if the anode potential is sufficiently positive to maintain the arc that results from the ignition spark. After conduction begins, the anode-cathode voltage across the ignitron is the arc drop (about 10 to 20 volts). If this is less than the maintaining voltage of the diode, the current through the ignitor rod falls to zero. These conditions are illustrated in the figure. If the drop across the ignitron is greater than the diode maintaining voltage, the ignitor-rod current is not reduced to zero but falls to a small value.

The series rectifier serves two purposes, to limit the ignitor current after ignition on the positive half cycle to a small value (or zero) and to prevent inverse currents on the negative half cycle. The instantaneous power required by the ignitor is relatively high, although the total energy involved is small, owing to the short time interval

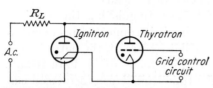

Fig. 14-34. An ignitron controlled by means of a thyratron.

during which the ignitor operates. Hence, the average ignitor power is small.

The instantaneous power required for ignition is considerably higher than that required by the grid circuit of a thyratron, and the general methods of control of thyratrons are not applicable to ignitron control. A common method of control utilizes a thyratron in the circuit. In this method, which is illustrated in Fig. 14-34, the point of ignition in each cycle is controlled by controlling the breakdown point of the thyratron,

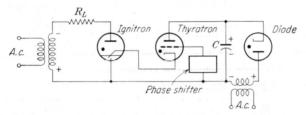

Fig. 14-35. An ignitron control circuit in which the ignitor-rod current does not pass through the load R_L.

which is in series with the ignitor rod. The grid-control circuit of the thyratron may be any of those studied above, viz., a phase shifter, a phase-shifting network, etc. It should be noted that, in this circuit, the ignitor current passes through the load. This may not be desirable in some applications and can be avoided by using the circuit of Fig. 14-35. In this circuit the thyratron plate current, which is also the ignitor current, is supplied by the energy stored in the capacitor C in the thyratron plate circuit.

To understand the operation of this circuit, suppose that the thyratron is nonconducting. The capacitor C will become charged to the peak value of the transformer voltage through the series gas diode. This auxiliary charging circuit must be so connected as to provide the capacitor polarity as shown. It must also be phased properly with respect to the ignitron supply transformer, as shown by the polarity markings on Fig. 14-35, so that the capacitor is charged during the half cycle when the ignitron anode is negative. If the thyratron grid voltage is now adjusted so that conduction will occur *in the next half cycle*, the capacitor charge will flow through the thyratron and ignitor-rod circuits and breakdown will occur provided that the ignitron anode voltage is sufficiently positive.

The current surge through the thyratron and ignitor-rod circuit will quickly discharge the capacitor. As a result the thyratron plate current will fall below that necessary to maintain the arc, and the current through the thyratron and ignitor-rod circuit will fall to zero. The diode rectifier must now supply enough current to charge the capacitor again before the cycle is over so that the plate voltage of the thyratron will be at its full value when the grid again assumes control. This action is repeated in each cycle.

14-14. Polyphase Rectifiers. Single-phase rectifiers are used extensively to provide sources of rectified power at voltages up to several kilovolts and for currents up to several amperes. If larger powers are required, polyphase rectifiers are employed. Such polyphase systems are used for supplying power for railway systems, for supplying the large direct currents required for electroplating, for supplying the moderate-current high-voltage power required for the plate circuits of radio transmitters, or, in fact, for any application that requires large direct currents.

A number of reasons exist for preferring polyphase rectifiers for high-power service. First, most a-c power is generated and distributed as three-phase power, and a rectifying system which operates directly from the three-phase lines is clearly desirable. Second, the ripple in the output of a polyphase rectifier which operates without a filter decreases with an increase in the effective number of phases. Moreover, the lowest harmonic that exists in the output of a rectifier is directly dependent on the number of effective phases. The larger the number of phases, the higher the frequency of the first harmonic term, and consequently it is easier to obtain effective filtering with a simple and generally inexpensive filter. Third, the transformers and associated equipment are utilized to better advantage in certain polyphase circuits than with single-phase circuits, so that for a given rectifier output, the rating of the auxiliary equipment is smaller than with the single-phase system.

Although the primary source of power is usually a three-phase system, considerable advantage may be realized by using more than three phases. The desired phase transformation is effected by means of transformers to yield 6-phase, 12-phase, or other polyphase power.

Because of the greater current capacity of gas tubes and the fact that the tube drop remains substantially constant during the conducting portion of the cycle (thereby providing a high and substantially constant efficiency), polyphase rectifiers seldom, if ever, employ vacuum diodes. If moderate values of current are required at high voltage, mercury-vapor diodes are usually employed. If high currents are required at low voltage, semiconductor rectifiers may be used. For very high-current sources at moderate values of voltage, polyphase pool-cathode tanks or banks of ignitrons or excitrons are employed. The general operating theory is substantially the same in either case.

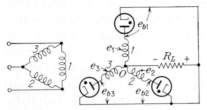

FIG. 14-36. Three-phase half-wave rectifier.

The circuit of the three-phase half-wave rectifying system is given in Fig. 14-36. *The corresponding primary and secondary transformer windings are shown parallel to each other*, a method of representation that will be adhered to throughout the text. The symbol e_s represents the voltage at anode S with respect to the neutral O of the transformer secondary.

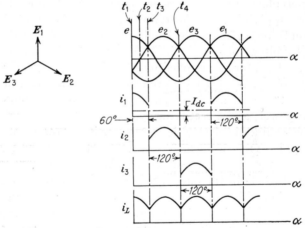

FIG. 14-37. Transformer voltages, tube currents, and load current in a three-phase half-wave rectifier. The sinors generating the three-phase wave forms are shown at the left.

The operation of such a system is made clear by reference to Figs. 14-36 and 14-37. At a time such as t_1 (indicated on Fig. 14-37), only e_1 is positive, and so only anode 1 is passing current. Since the voltage drop across the tube is small, most of the voltage appears across the load R_L. At an instant later than t_2, the transformer voltage e_2 also becomes positive. However, the second tube remains nonconducting because the voltage of the plate with respect to the cathode, e_{b2}, is still negative. From

Fig. 14-36 we observe that

$$e_{b2} = e_2 - e_L$$

where e_L is the voltage across the load R_L. However, when tube 1 conducts, then $e_L = e_1 - E_0$, where E_0 is the constant tube drop. Hence

$$e_{b2} = e_2 - e_1 + E_0 \qquad (14\text{-}42)$$

Thus, so long as e_1 is greater than e_2, e_{b2} will be less than E_0 and tube 2 will not conduct.

At the time t_3, however, e_2 equals e_1. At an instant later, e_2 exceeds e_1, and tube 2 will fire because $e_{b2} > E_0$. Further, since the plate voltage on the first rectifier is

$$e_{b1} = e_1 - e_2 + E_0$$

as is evident from the way Eq. (14-42) has been derived, then e_{b1} will fall below E_0 and conduction of tube 1 will cease when e_2 exceeds e_1.

By following the same sequence of arguments, we see that the current will transfer to tube 3 at the time $t = t_4$. Thus each tube conducts for 120 deg, or one-third of the total cycle. The output current is the sum of the currents through each of the anodes and is given by i_L of Fig. 14-37.

Also indicated in Fig. 14-37 is the average or d-c component of current I_{dc} that exists in anode 1. Since this is the value of the direct current through each transformer secondary winding, it will cause some saturation of the transformer core. This is undesirable, for a distortion of the output wave form may result.

For the same reasons that the single-phase full-wave circuit is more desirable than the single-phase half-wave circuit, the three-phase full-wave circuit is more desirable than the three-phase half-wave system. The full-wave circuit supplies higher power at a higher efficiency than the half-wave circuit.

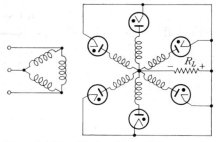

FIG. 14-38. Three-phase full-wave or six-phase half-wave rectifier connections.

If three transformers with center taps or with double secondary windings are available, the six rectifier units may be connected as in Fig. 14-38. The physical behavior of this circuit is identical with that of the three-phase half-wave rectifier, except that each tube conducts for 60 instead of 120 deg. Furthermore, since the average current through each secondary winding is zero, there is no saturation of the transformer core.

If three transformers without center taps are available, then full-wave rectification is possible through the use of the three-phase bridge circuit, shown schematically in Fig. 14-39. The output wave shape is the same as that for the six-phase half-wave circuit. However, the individual tube currents differ from those in the six-phase half-wave circuit, since each pair of tubes conducts for two successive 60-deg intervals during each cycle. As was also true in the case of the single-phase bridge circuit, two tubes always act in series to pass current to the load.

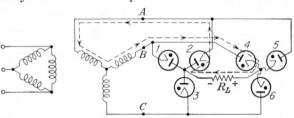

FIG. 14-39. Three-phase full-wave bridge circuit. At the instant shown, the potential of point B is positive with respect to point A, and tubes 4 and 2 are conducting. The corresponding current path is indicated by the broken line.

From the way in which the circuit diagram has been drawn, it is noted that tubes 1, 2, and 3 form a Y-connected system which is connected in parallel with a second group of tubes 4, 5, and 6. This latter group has the plates connected to the lines feeding the cathodes of the first group.

To understand the operation of this rectifier, refer to Fig. 14-40, in which the three-phase line voltages e_{BA}, e_{AC}, and e_{CB} are indicated by solid lines. The negative of these voltages e_{AB}, e_{CA}, and e_{BC}, respectively, are indicated by the broken lines. The diodes that conduct over each 60-deg interval of the output voltage are also indicated. Thus, at the instant when the voltage e_{BA} is a maximum (B being positive with respect to A), the plates of tubes 4 and 2 are positive, so that these tubes are conducting current. The current path through these tubes, the transformer secondaries, and the load is given in Fig. 14-39. When the voltage e_{BC} exceeds e_{BA}, then the current will switch from tubes 4 and 2 to tubes 4 and 3. The explanation for this commutation

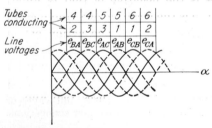

FIG. 14-40. In the three-phase bridge circuit two tubes pass current simultaneously. Each tube conducts for 120 deg of each cycle as shown.

is very similar to that given for Fig. 14-37 for the three-phase half-wave circuit. The reader should check the commutation sequence indicated in Fig. 14-40. In particular, note that the tubes conduct in pairs and that each tube carries current for 120 deg in each cycle, as predicted.

14-15. The Double-Y Rectifier Circuit. A very important rectifier circuit, which is known as a *double-Y circuit*,[7] is illustrated in Fig. 14-41. Pool-cathode multianode or single-anode tanks may be used with this circuit so that advantage is taken of the very high currents that are available from the pool cathode. Also, the peak anode current in such a system is one-half the total load current, whereas in the bridge circuit the peak anode and the load currents are equal. Consequently, the double-Y connection recommends itself for systems that are to supply high currents, and it is used on most large six-phase or higher-phase rectifiers.

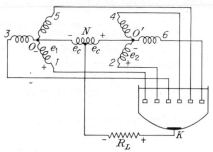

It will be noted that this system consists essentially of two separate three-phase Y-connected secondary systems whose corresponding windings are displaced by 180 electrical degrees with respect to each other.

Fig. 14-41. The double-Y rectifier connections.

The two three-phase systems have their neutral points connected together by a center-tapped reactor, generally referred to as the "interphase transformer," which is marked ONO' in the diagram.

The three-phase system of voltages of group I, consisting of anodes 1, 3, and 5, are shown in Fig. 14-42. Directly below are indicated the three-phase voltages of group II, consisting of anodes 2, 4, and 6. It should be noted that the voltage of anode 4 is the negative of that of anode 1, 5 is the negative of 2, and 6 is the negative of 3. The action of the circuit can best be understood if the interphase transformer is considered simply as a "commutating reactor"[8] that causes two anodes to fire simultaneously.

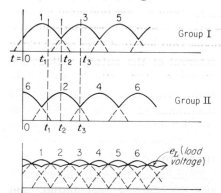

Fig. 14-42. The internal and external behavior of a double-Y-connected rectifier.

Consider, for example, the instant of time t_1 shown on the curves of Fig. 14-42. At this instant, the voltages e_3, e_4, and e_5 are negative, so that anodes 3, 4, and 5 are not conducting. The voltages e_1 and e_2 are positive, and anodes 1 and 2 conduct *simultaneously*. Although the voltage e_6 is positive, the anode-cathode voltage of anode 6 is $+e_6 - e_2$, which is negative, so that anode 6 is not conducting. (The tube drop is neglected, for simplicity.)

Consider the path $1ONO'2K1$, which connects anodes 1 and 2 together through the interphase transformer. If e_c (the "commutating voltage") is the voltage to the center tap of this reactor, then Kirchhoff's law around this path gives

$$e_c = \tfrac{1}{2}(e_1 - e_2) \tag{14-43}$$

Anodes 1 and 2 are passing current simultaneously, and it is the difference in voltage between the two conducting anodes that appears across the reactor.

The load voltage is found by choosing a path through the load, through one half of the interphase reactor, and through either anode 1 or anode 2. The result is either

$$e_L = e_1 - e_c \qquad \text{or} \qquad e_L = e_2 + e_c \tag{14-44}$$

By adding these expressions,

$$e_L = \tfrac{1}{2}(e_1 + e_2) \tag{14-45}$$

This equation shows that *the load voltage is the average value of the transformer voltages e_1 and e_2* and is so indicated in Fig. 14-42.

At the time t_2 when e_1 equals e_3, the current shifts from anode 1 to anode 3, exactly as in a simple three-phase system. However, anode 2 continues to carry current. At the time t_3 the current transfers from anode 2 to anode 4, which then conducts simultaneously with tube 3.

From the foregoing reasoning, we can conclude that internally group I behaves independently of group II, each functioning as an ordinary three-phase half-wave rectifier, and each tube conducts for 120 deg/cycle. Since two anodes always conduct simultaneously, these two groups may be considered to be acting essentially in parallel. The difference in voltage between the transformer potentials to the anodes that are conducting appears across the commutating reactor. The load voltage is the average value of the output voltage of group I and group II. This load voltage is seen from Fig. 14-42 to have twice the frequency of either group I or group II.

14-16. Rectifier-design Data. The main results of the analysis of the uncontrolled rectifier circuits outlined above are summarized in Table 14-1.

Suppose that the three circuits that yield effective six-phase output are compared. We note from Table 14-1 that the six-phase half-wave circuit requires the largest transformer kilovolt-ampere (kva) rating. Furthermore, this circuit possesses no features that compensate for the low transformer utilization factors,* and so this circuit is seldom used.

---

* The transformer utilization factor is defined as the ratio of the d-c power output supplied to the load to the volt-ampere rating of the transformer bank.

TABLE 14-1*

RECTIFIER-DESIGN DATA

Circuit	One-phase full-wave	One-phase bridge	Three-phase half-wave	Three-phase bridge	Double-Y	Six-phase half-wave
Circuit diagram......	14–5	14–9	14–36	14–39	14–41	14–38
Transformer secondary rms volts/leg..	$1.11E_{dc}$	$1.11E_{dc}$	$0.855E_{dc}$	$0.427E_{dc}$	$0.855E_{dc}$	$0.741E_{dc}$
Peak inverse voltage..	$3.14E_{dc}$	$1.57E_{dc}$	$2.09E_{dc}$	$1.045E_{dc}$	$2.09E_{dc}$	$2.09E_{dc}$
Average tube current.	$0.5I_{dc}$	$0.5I_{dc}$	$0.33I_{dc}$	$0.33I_{dc}$	$0.167I_{dc}$	$0.167I_{dc}$
Peak tube current....	I_{dc}	I_{dc}	I_{dc}	I_{dc}	$0.5I_{dc}$	I_{dc}
Transformer secondary kva rating.....	$1.57P_{dc}$	$1.11P_{dc}$	$1.481P_{dc}$	$1.047P_{dc}$	$1.481P_{dc}$	$1.814P_{dc}$
Transformer primary kva rating.........	$1.11P_{dc}$	$1.11P_{dc}$	$1.21P_{dc}$	$1.047P_{dc}$	$1.047P_{dc}$	$1.283P_{dc}$
Principal ripple frequency...........	$2f$	$2f$	$3f$	$6f$	$6f†$	$6f$
Ripple factor........	0.472	0.472	0.177	0.0404	0.0404	0.0404

* The values in this table are based upon the following assumptions: zero transformer resistance; zero transformer reactance; zero tube drop; very large reactance in series with the load so that the tube current is constant (except for the ripple frequency and ripple factor).

† The load ripple frequency is $6f$, but the interphase reactor ripple frequency is $3f$.

The three-phase bridge circuit is characterized by (1) high transformer primary and secondary utilization factors, (2) two tubes in series during the conduction period, (3) low inverse peak voltage per tube. Though (1) and (3) are desirable features, the drop in the two conducting tubes results in a reduced rectifier efficiency. This circuit is used extensively for high-voltage moderate-current service.

The double-Y circuit is characterized by (1) poor transformer secondary utilization factor, but with a high primary utilization factor, (2) high inverse peak voltage per anode, (3) low average tube current. By virtue of (3), this circuit is recommended for moderate-voltage high-current service. Other advantages arise from the fact that the arc drop is lowered as a result of the low peak current. This results in an increased efficiency. Furthermore, since a lower current is commutated, the regulation is improved.

Example. The plates of a certain radio-frequency power amplifier require 4.5 amp at 16,000 volts. Design a polyphase rectifier that will supply this power from a 220-volt three-phase supply.

Solution. The three-phase bridge circuit is used for the reasons given in the foregoing discussion. From the data in column 5 of Table 14-1, it is found that

$$\text{Peak-inverse voltage} = 1.045 \times 16{,}000 = 16{,}700 \text{ volts}$$
$$\text{Average tube current} = 0.33 I_{dc} = 1.5 \text{ amp}$$
$$\text{Peak-tube current} = 4.5 \text{ amp}$$

Western Electric type 255-A mercury-vapor diodes, for which

$$\text{Peak-inverse-voltage rating} = 20{,}000 \text{ volts}$$
$$\text{Peak-tube-current rating} = 5.0 \text{ amp}$$

would be satisfactory tubes to use in this circuit.

Transformer characteristics:

$$\text{Transformer-secondary rating} = \frac{1.047 \times 16{,}000 \times 4.5}{3} = 25.1 \text{ kva}$$

$$\text{Transformer-primary rating} = 25.1 \text{ kva}$$
$$\text{Transformer-secondary voltage} = 0.427 \times 16{,}000 = 6{,}830 \text{ volts rms}$$
$$\text{Transformer-primary voltage} = 220 \text{ volts rms}$$

14-17. Controlled Polyphase Rectifiers.[9] Many of the circuits considered above for polyphase rectifiers have been adopted for use with grid pool tanks, ignitrons, and excitrons.

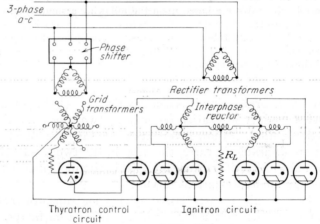

FIG. 14-43. A double-Y ignitron circuit with thyratron control. The complete ignitor-rod control circuit is shown for only one ignitron.

Figure 14-43 shows a typical circuit of a three-phase double-Y controlled ignitron circuit.[10] Each ignitron is controlled by an individual thyratron. For simplicity, only one ignitron is shown connected to its control thyratron. The Δ-connected primaries of the grid transformers are supplied from the three-phase supply through a phase shifter. The output voltage of this system for a pure resistance load with an angle of delay φ is shown as a heavy line in Fig. 14-44. The d-c value of this voltage is, of course, controlled by varying φ.

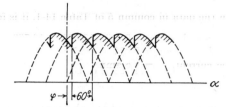

FIG. 14-44. The output-voltage wave shape of a controlled six-phase rectifier.

Another common circuit for grid pool tanks is the bias phase control discussed in Sec. 14-10,[11] which has been extended for polyphase operation

REFERENCES

1. TONKS, L., and I. LANGMUIR, "Oscillations in Ionized Gases," *Phys. Rev.*, **33**, 195–210, February, 1929.
2. GREINACHER, H., "Über eine Methode, Wechselstrom mittels elektrischer Ventile und Kondensatoren in hochgespannten Gleichstrom umzuwandeln," *Z. Physik*, **4**(2), 195–205, 1921.
   COCKCROFT, J. D., and E. T. S. WALTON, "Experiments with High Velocity Positive Ions. I: Further Developments in the Method of Obtaining High Velocity Positive Ions," *Proc. Roy. Soc. (London)*, **136**, 619–630, June, 1932.
   GARSTANG, W. W., "New Voltage Quadrupler," *Electronics*, **4**, 50–51, February, 1932.
   WAIDELICH, D. L., "Voltage Multiplier Circuits," *ibid.*, **14**, 28–29, May, 1941.
   WAIDELICH, D. L., "The Full-wave Voltage-doubling Rectifier Circuit," *Proc. IRE*, **29**, 554–558, October, 1941.
   WAIDELICH, D. L., and C. L. SHACKELFORD, "Characteristics of Voltage-multiplying Rectifiers," *ibid.*, **32**, 470–476, August, 1944.
   WAIDELICH, D. L., and H. A. K. TASKIN, "Analyses of the Voltage-tripling and Quadrupling Rectifier Circuits," *ibid.*, **33**, 449–457, July, 1945.
3. SNODDY, L. B., "Low Voltage Impulse Circuits," *Physics*, **4**(9), 327–331, 1933.
4. HULL, A. W., "Hot-cathode Thyratrons," *Gen. Elec. Rev.*, **32**, 390–399, July, 1929.
   HERSKIND, C. C., and E. J. REMSCHEID, "Excitation, Control, and Cooling of Ignitron Tubes," *Trans. AIEE*, **65**, 632–635, October, 1946.
5. SEELY, S., "Electron-tube Circuits," 1st ed., McGraw-Hill Book Company, Inc., New York, 1950.
6. REICH, H. J., "Theory and Application of Electron Tubes," 2d ed., McGraw-Hill Book Company, Inc., New York, 1944.
   HENNEY, K., "Electron Tubes in Industry," 2d ed., McGraw-Hill Book Company, Inc., New York, 1937.
7. MILLMAN, J., and S. SEELY, "Electronics," 2d ed., pp. 433–440, McGraw-Hill Book Company, Inc., New York, 1951.
8. DORTORT, I. K., "Interphase Transformers for Mercury Arc Rectifiers," *Allis-Chalmers Elec. Rev.*, **4**, 9–16, March, 1939.
9. MILLMAN, J., and S. SEELY, "Electronics," 2d ed., pp. 440–449, McGraw-Hill Book Company, Inc., New York, 1951.
10. COX, J. H., and G. F. JONES, "Ignitrons for the Transportation Industry," *Trans. AIEE*, **58**, 618–622, December, 1939.
11. JOURNEAUX, D., "Voltage Control of Vapor Rectifiers," *Elec. Eng.*, **53**, 976–998, June, 1934.

CHAPTER 15

UNTUNED VOLTAGE AMPLIFIERS

In this chapter, we consider the following problem: Given a low-level input wave form which is not necessarily sinusoidal but which may contain frequency components from a few cycles to a few megacycles, how can this voltage signal be amplified with a minimum of distortion?

We shall also discuss many topics associated with the general problem of amplification, such as the classification of amplifiers, power sources for amplifiers, hum and noise in amplifiers, etc.

15-1. Classification of Amplifiers. Amplifiers are described in many ways, according to their frequency range, the method of operation, the ultimate use, the type of load, the method of interstage coupling, etc. The frequency classification includes d-c (from zero frequency), audio (20 cps to 20 kc), video or pulse (up to a few megacycles), radio-frequency (a few kilocycles to hundreds of megacycles), and ultrahigh-frequency (hundreds or thousands of megacycles) amplifiers.

The position of the quiescent point and the extent of the characteristic that is being used determine the method of operation. Whether the tube or transistor is being operated as a Class A, Class AB, Class B, or Class C amplifier is determined from the following definitions:

1. A Class A amplifier is one in which the operating point and the input signal are such that the plate or collector current flows at all times. A Class A amplifier operates essentially over a linear portion of its characteristic.

2. A Class B amplifier is one in which the operating point is at an extreme end of its characteristic so that the quiescent power is extremely small. Hence, either the quiescent current or the quiescent voltage is approximately zero. If the signal voltage is sinusoidal, amplification takes place for only one-half a cycle. For example, if the quiescent plate or collector current is zero, then this current will remain zero for one-half a cycle.

3. A Class AB amplifier is one operating between the two extremes defined for Class A and Class B. Hence, the plate or collector current (or voltage) is zero for part but less than one-half of an input sinusoidal signal cycle.

4. A Class C amplifier is one in which the operating point is chosen so that the plate or collector current (or voltage) is zero for more than one-half of an input sinusoidal signal cycle.

In the case of a vacuum-tube amplifier the suffix 1 may be added to the letter or letters of the class identification to denote that grid current does not flow during any part of the input cycle. The suffix 2 may be added to denote that grid current does flow during some part of the input cycle.

The classification according to use includes voltage, power, current, or general-purpose amplifiers. In general, the load of an amplifier is an impedance. The two most important special cases are the idealized resistive load and the tuned circuit operating near its resonant frequency.

Class AB and Class B operation are used with untuned power amplifiers, whereas Class C operation is used with tuned radio-frequency amplifiers. Many important wave-shaping functions may be performed by Class B or C overdriven amplifiers. This chapter considers only the untuned audio or video voltage amplifier with a resistive load operated in Class A.

15-2. Distortion in Amplifiers. The application of a sinusoidal signal to the grid of an ideal Class A amplifier will result in a sinusoidal output wave. Generally, the output wave form is not an exact replica of the input-signal wave form because of various types of distortion that may arise, either because of the inherent characteristics of the tubes or transistors or from the influence of the associated circuit. The types of distortion that may exist either separately or simultaneously are nonlinear distortion, frequency distortion, and delay distortion.

Nonlinear distortion results from the production of new frequencies in the output which are not present in the input signal. These new frequencies, or harmonics, result from the existence of a nonlinear dynamic curve and are considered in some detail in Secs. 16-2 and 16-3. This distortion is sometimes referred to as "amplitude distortion."

Frequency distortion exists when the signal components of different frequency are amplified differently. In vacuum tubes this distortion arises from the characteristics of the associated circuit and must be distinguished from nonlinear distortion. As seen in Sec. 8-3, if the load circuit is reactive in character, then the gain **A** is a complex number whose magnitude and phase angle depend upon the frequency of the impressed signal. A plot of gain (magnitude) vs. frequency of an amplifier is called the *amplitude frequency response characteristic*. If this plot is not a horizontal straight line over the range of frequencies under consideration, the circuit is said to exhibit frequency distortion over this range.

Delay distortion, also called "phase-shift distortion," results from unequal phase shifts of waves of different frequency. This distortion is due to the fact that the phase angle of the complex gain **A** depends upon the frequency. For the idealized special case where the phase shift is proportional to the frequency, a time delay will occur although no distortion is introduced. To prove this statement, suppose that a complex input signal of the form

$$e_i = E_{m1} \sin (\omega t + \theta_1) + E_{m2} \sin (2\omega t + \theta_2)$$
$$+ E_{m3} \sin (3\omega t + \theta_3) + \cdots \quad (15\text{-}1)$$

is impressed on an amplifier. If the gain **A** is constant in magnitude but possesses a phase shift that is proportional to the frequency, the output will then be of the form

$$e_o = A E_{m1} \sin (\omega t + \theta_1 + \psi) + A E_{m2} \sin (2\omega t + \theta_2 + 2\psi)$$
$$+ A E_{m3} \sin (3\omega t + \theta_3 + 3\psi) + \cdots$$

Choose a new time variable t', defined by

$$\omega t + \psi \equiv \omega t' \quad (15\text{-}2)$$

Then

$$e_o = A E_{m1} \sin (\omega t' + \theta_1) + A E_{m2} \sin (2\omega t' + \theta_2)$$
$$+ A E_{m3} \sin (3\omega t' + \theta_3) + \cdots \quad (15\text{-}3)$$

which is simply the expression given by Eq. (15-1) multiplied by A, which has been plotted to the new time scale t'. This analysis shows that *an amplifier which has a flat amplitude response and for which the phase angle is proportional to the frequency (or is zero) will preserve the signal in form, although it will be delayed in time.* Unless these conditions are true, the input and output waves will no longer have the same wave shape.

Delay distortion is not of much importance in amplifiers of the audio type, since delay distortion is not perceptible to the ear. It is very objectionable in systems that depend on visual observation or on wave-shape preservation for their operation, as in radar, television, or other pulse systems.

15-3. The Decibel. In many problems it is found very convenient to compare two powers on a logarithmic rather than on a direct scale. The unit of this logarithmic scale is called the decibel (abbreviated db). The number N of decibels by which the power P_2 exceeds the power P_1 is defined by

$$N \equiv 10 \log_{10} \frac{P_2}{P_1} \quad (15\text{-}4)$$

It should be noted that the specification of a certain power in decibels is meaningless unless a standard reference level is implied or is stated specifically. A negative value of N means that the power P_2 is less than the reference power P_1.

If the input and output impedances are equal resistances, then $P_2 = E_2^2/R$ and $P_1 = E_1^2/R$, where E_2 and E_1 are the output and input voltage drops. Under this condition, Eq. (15-4) reduces to

$$N = 20 \log_{10} \frac{E_2}{E_1} = 20 \log_{10} A \qquad (15\text{-}5)$$

where A is the magnitude of the voltage gain of the unit. The input and output resistances are not equal in general. However, *this expression is adopted as a convenient definition of the decibel voltage gain of an amplifier, regardless of the magnitudes of the input and output resistances*. That is, if the voltage amplification is 10, then its decibel voltage gain is 20; if the voltage amplification is 100, the decibel voltage gain is 40; etc. If there is the possibility of confusion between voltage and power gain, then the designation dbv can be used for decibel voltage gain.

15-4. Cascading of Amplifiers. When the amplification of a single amplifier is insufficient for a particular purpose, two or more stages may be connected in cascade. The output voltage from the first stage serves as the input voltage of the second stage, that from the second stage serves as the input voltage to the third stage, and so forth. *The resultant voltage gain equals the product of the individual voltage gains of each stage.* This statement is verified as follows:

$$\mathbf{A_1} \equiv \frac{\mathbf{E_2}}{\mathbf{E_1}} = \frac{\text{output voltage of the first stage}}{\text{input voltage to the first stage}} = A_1/\theta_1$$

and

$$\mathbf{A_2} \equiv \frac{\mathbf{E_3}}{\mathbf{E_2}} = \frac{\text{output voltage of the second stage}}{\text{input voltage to the second stage}} = A_2/\theta_2$$

The resultant or over-all amplification is defined as

$$\mathbf{A} \equiv \frac{\mathbf{E_3}}{\mathbf{E_1}} = \frac{\text{output voltage of the second stage}}{\text{input voltage to the first stage}} = A/\theta$$

It follows from these expressions that

$$\boxed{A = A_1 A_2} \qquad (15\text{-}6)$$

or

$$A/\theta = A_1 A_2/\theta_1 + \theta_2 \qquad (15\text{-}7)$$

The logarithm of the magnitude of this expression is

$$\log_{10} A = \log_{10} A_1 + \log_{10} A_2 \qquad (15\text{-}8)$$

By comparing this result with Eq. (15-5), which defines the decibel voltage gain, it is seen that *the over-all decibel voltage gain of a multistage amplifier is the sum of the decibel voltage gains of the individual stages.*

Since, from Eq. (15-7), $\theta = \theta_1 + \theta_2$, *the resultant phase shift of a multi-stage amplifier is the sum* of the phase shifts introduced by each stage.

The above considerations are independent of the type of interstage coupling and are valid for both transistor and vacuum-tube amplifiers. However, it must be emphasized that, in calculating the gain of one stage, the loading effect of the next stage must be taken into account.

15-5. Resistance-Capacitance (RC) Coupled Vacuum-tube Amplifiers. This type of coupling, often called "resistance coupling," is one of the simplest and one of the most widely used methods of coupling between stages of an audio- or video-frequency amplifier. It is used when substantially constant amplification over a wide range of frequencies is desired. The schematic diagram of the system is shown in Fig. 15-1.

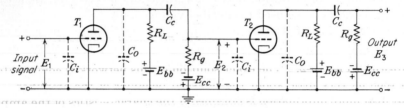

Fig. 15-1. Two RC-coupled vacuum-tube amplifier stages in cascade.

Although only two stages are shown, more stages may be added. The tubes used in such an amplifier may be pentodes, although, for simplicity, the diagram indicates the use of triodes. The following analysis is valid for either type of tube, it being necessary only that the screen voltage remain constant when pentodes are used. We shall assume throughout this chapter that the signal amplitude is small enough so that each tube operates linearly, unless specifically stated otherwise.

The function of the "blocking" or "coupling" capacitor C_c is to prevent any d-c voltages that may be present in the circuit of one stage from appearing in any other stage. Thus, C_c prevents any d-c voltage that may exist at the plate of T_1 from appearing at the grid of T_2 and changing the grid-biasing voltage. Values of the coupling capacitors are determined, as will be seen later, by the low-frequency response. They range from about 0.001 μf to 0.5 μf. The resistor R_g, which is known as the *grid leak,* serves as the path whereby the grid bias voltage is impressed on the tube. It also serves as the path that permits any charge which may be collected by the grid of the tube to be returned to the cathode. A typical value for R_g is 1 megohm. The load resistor R_L is determined principally by the gain and frequency response desired.

The capacitors C_o and C_i represent, respectively, the output and input capacitances of the tube (Sec. 8-9). These capacitors have been indicated by dashed lines because they have not been included deliberately but are rather unavoidable attributes of the vacuum tubes employed. In any practical arrangement of the amplifier components there are also capacitances associated with the tube sockets and the proximity to the chassis of components and signal leads. We shall assume that these additional stray capacitances have been included in C_o and C_i.

15-6. Amplitude and Phase Response of a Broadband RC-coupled Vacuum-tube Amplifier Stage. The linear current equivalent circuit from the grid of one tube to the grid of the succeeding tube of Fig. 15-1

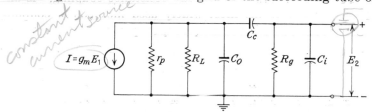

FIG. 15-2. The equivalent circuit of an RC-coupled amplifier stage.

is drawn in Fig. 15-2. The exact solution of this network is complicated and tells us very little about the physical behavior of the amplifier. A great deal more information is obtained if the characteristics of the amplifier are studied in three separate frequency ranges. There is one region where the frequency is so low that the shunt capacitances have no appreciable effect but the influence of C_c is marked. There is a second range where the frequency is high enough to permit us to neglect the series capacitance C_c but in which the influence of the shunt capacitances must be taken into account. Finally, there is the range, which falls between the low- and high-frequency regions, in which we may neglect all capacitances, without introducing appreciable error.

1. *Intermediate (Mid-band) Frequencies*. In this range all capacitances can be neglected, and the circuit of Fig. 15-2 reduces to that shown in Fig. 15-3.

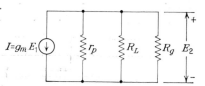

FIG. 15-3. The mid-band equivalent circuit of an RC-coupled amplifier stage.

The output voltage E_2 is given by $\mathbf{E}_2 = -g_m R \mathbf{E}_1$, where R is the parallel combination of r_p, R_L, and R_g, or R is the total impedance from plate to cathode,

$$\frac{1}{R} \equiv \frac{1}{r_p} + \frac{1}{R_L} + \frac{1}{R_g} \tag{15-9}$$

The mid-band gain $\mathbf{A}_o$, defined as the ratio $\mathbf{E}_2/\mathbf{E}_1$, is given by

$$\mathbf{A}_o = -g_m R \tag{15-10}$$

This result was obtained in Sec. 8-5. For a pentode amplifier both r_p and

R_g usually are much larger than R_L. Hence $R \cong R_L$ and $\mathbf{A}_o \cong -g_m R_L$.

2. *High Frequencies.* In this range the capacitance C_c may be neglected, and the equivalent circuit is that shown in Fig. 15-4a and b. In the latter figure R is given by Eq. (15-9) and $C_s \equiv C_o + C_i$. The out-

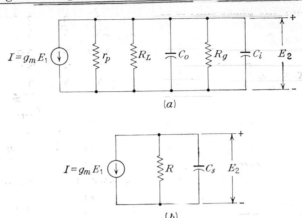

(a)

(b)

FIG. 15-4. The high-frequency equivalent circuit of an RC-coupled amplifier stage.

put voltage is calculated by multiplying the short-circuit current $-g_m\mathbf{E}_1$ by the impedance of R and C_s in parallel, or

$$\mathbf{E}_2 = \frac{-g_m\mathbf{E}_1}{1/R + j\omega C_s} \tag{15-11}$$

The ratio of the high-frequency gain $\mathbf{A}_2 \equiv \mathbf{E}_2/\mathbf{E}_1$ to the mid-band gain $\mathbf{A}_o = -g_m R$ is given by

$$\frac{\mathbf{A}_2}{\mathbf{A}_o} = \frac{1}{1 + j\omega R C_s} = \frac{1}{1 + j(f/f_2)} \tag{15-12}$$

where f_2 is defined by

← COMPLEX JAZZ !

$$f_2 \equiv \frac{1}{2\pi R C_s} \tag{15-13}$$

We see that f_2 is that frequency for which the reactance of the total shunt capacitance C_s equals the effective parallel resistance R. The magnitude of the amplification A_2/A_o and the phase angle θ_2 are found from Eq. (15-12) to be

MAGNITUDE ONLY.

$$\frac{A_2}{A_o} = \frac{1}{\sqrt{1 + (f/f_2)^2}} \qquad \theta_2 = \arctan \frac{f}{f_2} \tag{15-14}$$

Note that θ_2 is the angle by which the output lags the input, with the initial 180-deg phase shift through the amplifier neglected. If $f = f_2$, $A_2/A_o = 1/\sqrt{2} = 0.707$ and $20 \log (A_2/A_o) = -3$ dbv. Hence, f_2 is the upper frequency at which the amplification falls to 0.707 of its mid-band value or at which the voltage gain has decreased by 3 dbv. Therefore f_2 is called the *upper 3-dbv frequency, the upper half-power frequency,* or the *upper corner frequency.* At this frequency the phase shift is 45 deg.

3. *Low Frequencies.* In this range the shunting capacitances may be neglected, and the equivalent circuit is that shown in Fig. 15-5a. The impedance to the left of points A and B is R', the parallel combination of r_p and R_L, or

$$R' \equiv \frac{r_p R_L}{r_p + R_L} \quad (15\text{-}15)$$

The open-circuit voltage between A and B is $-g_m R' E_1$. Hence, if the portion of Fig. 15-5a to the left of A and B is replaced by its Thévenin's equivalent the result shown in Fig. 15-5b is obtained. The output voltage is given by

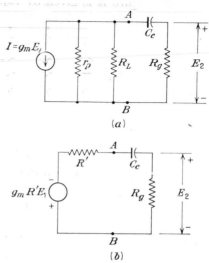

Fig. 15-5. The low-frequency equivalent circuit of an RC-coupled amplifier stage,

$$\begin{aligned}
\mathbf{E}_2 &= -g_m R' \mathbf{E}_1 \frac{R_g}{R_g + R' - j/\omega C_c} \\
&= -g_m \mathbf{E}_1 \frac{R' R_g}{R_g + R'} \frac{1}{1 - j/\omega C_c (R_g + R')} \quad (15\text{-}16)
\end{aligned}$$

Since $R' R_g/(R_g + R')$ equals the parallel resistance of R' and R_g, this expression represents the parallel combination of r_p, R_L, and R_g. Hence, from Eq. (15-9), $R' R_g/(R_g + R') = R$, and the ratio of the low-frequency gain $\mathbf{A}_1 \equiv \mathbf{E}_2/\mathbf{E}_1$ to the mid-band gain $\mathbf{A}_o = -g_m R$ is given by

$$\boxed{\frac{\mathbf{A}_1}{\mathbf{A}_o} = \frac{1}{1 - j/\omega C_c R_g'} = \frac{1}{1 - j(f_1/f)}} \quad (15\text{-}17)$$

where $R_g' \equiv R_g + R'$ and f_1 is defined by

$$f_1 \equiv \frac{1}{2\pi C_c R_g'} \quad (15\text{-}18)$$

We see that f_1 is the frequency for which the reactance of the coupling capacitance C_c equals the resistance R_g'. Incidentally, in practice it is usually true that $R_g \gg R'$ so that $R_g' \cong R_g$. The magnitude A_1/A_o and the phase angle θ_1 are found from Eq. (15-17) to be

MAGNITUDE
ONLY

$$\frac{A_1}{A_o} = \frac{1}{\sqrt{1 + (f_1/f)^2}} \qquad \theta_1 = -\arctan\frac{f_1}{f} \qquad (15\text{-}19)$$

Note that θ_1 is the angle by which the output lags the input, neglecting the initial 180-deg phase shift through the amplifier. If $f = f_1$, $A_1/A_o = 1/\sqrt{2} = 0.707$. Hence, f_1 is the lower frequency at which the voltage gain falls to 0.707 of its mid-band value or at which the gain has decreased by 3 dbv. Therefore f_1 is called the *lower 3-dbv frequency*, the *lower half-power frequency*, or the *lower corner frequency*. At this frequency the phase shift is 45 deg.

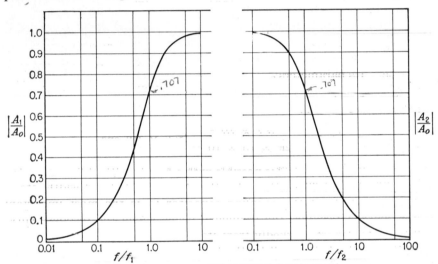

Fig. 15-6. The band-pass characteristic of an *RC*-coupled amplifier stage.

15-7. Discussion of RC-coupled Amplifier Characteristics. Universal curves of voltage gain and phase shift can be drawn, based upon Eqs. (15-14) and (15-19). For example, the relative gain of *any* broadband *RC*-coupled amplifier is indicated in Fig. 15-6. The frequency scale is logarithmic because it is desired to cover a very large range of frequencies. The frequency range from f_1 to f_2 is called the *band width* of the amplifier stage. We may anticipate in a general way that a signal, all of whose Fourier components of appreciable amplitude lie well within the range f_1 to f_2, will pass through the stage without excessive distortion. The criterion must, however, be applied with some caution.[1]

The mid-band region may be defined as the range which extends over frequencies greater than $10f_1$ and less than $0.1f_2$. Over this range the amplification is constant to within 0.5 per cent, and the phase shift is less than ± 0.1 rad or less than ± 6 deg.

The upper frequency that can be included in the substantially flat portion of the amplitude response curve can be increased by decreasing C_s. Hence, every attempt must be made to keep this shunt capacitance as small as possible by careful wiring and proper choice of tube type. The upper 3-db frequency can also be increased by decreasing the load resistance and hence R. However, a decrease of R simultaneously decreases the gain. A figure of merit F which is useful in comparing tube types is the magnitude of the gain–band-width product. Since $f_2 \gg f_1$, then this product may be defined by $f_2 A_o$, or

$$F \equiv f_2 A_o = \frac{1}{2\pi R C_s} g_m R = \frac{g_m}{2\pi C_s} \qquad (15\text{-}20)$$

Thus the larger the ratio of transconductance to the sum of output and input capacitances of a tube, the better is this tube as a wide-band amplifier. The 6AK5 pentode has one of the largest figures of merit of any tube. Its parameters are $g_m = 5.1$ millimhos and $C_o + C_i = 6.8 \ \mu\mu f$. Taking stray capacitances into account, we shall assume a total shunt capacitance $C_s = 15 \ \mu\mu f$, so that

$$f_2 A_o = \frac{5.1 \times 10^{-3}}{2\pi \times 15 \times 10^{-12}} \cong 6 \times 10^7 \text{ cps}$$

Hence, a voltage gain of 10 is possible with a band width of 6 megacycles, an amplification of 60 is attained with a 1-megacycle band width, etc.

The magnitude of the coupling capacitor C_c is the most important factor which determines the frequency below which the response curve will begin to depart markedly from its mid-band value. The larger its capacitance, the better will be the low-frequency response. There are, however, several practical limitations to the size of the capacitor that may be employed in this connection. It must be of high quality; $i.e.$, the leakage current must be small. Otherwise, a conduction path from the plate circuit of one stage to the grid circuit of the next stage may exist. Good-quality capacitors in sizes much larger than 1.0 μf are relatively expensive and are usually rather large physically. The larger the size of the capacitor, the greater will be the capacitance between its terminals and ground. This shunting capacitance must be included in C_s. Hence, too large a value of C_c will adversely affect the high-frequency response.

The grid leak R_g is made large in order to obtain a low value of f_1. The upper limit to this value is set by the grid current. The grid current is ordinarily very small, but if R_g is made very much larger than about 1 megohm, the small grid current through R_g may cause an appreciable voltage drop. Since grid current is not a stable quantity, an erratic spurious voltage may be generated at the grid.

The value of R_g should usually be kept below several megohms for another reason. Assume that the tube is slightly "gassy." Then the grid will act somewhat as a probe in a gas tube, and with a negative bias it will collect positive ions. The small positive-ion current through a large R_g may give an appreciable voltage drop, which will tend to make the grid less negative. This increases the plate current which in turn means a greater positive-ion current. This phenomenon may become cumulative, and the tube may be damaged by the excessive currents drawn.

Typical values for the coupling capacitors and resistors as well as recommended tubes and operating voltages for audio amplifiers may be found in the receiving-tube manuals published by tube manufacturers.

The upper 3-dbv frequency for n cascaded stages is $f_2^{(n)}$ and equals the frequency for which the over-all voltage gain falls to $1/\sqrt{2}$ (3 dbv) of its mid-band value. Thus $f_2^{(n)}$ is calculated from

$$\left[\frac{1}{\sqrt{1 + (f_2^{(n)}/f_2)^2}}\right]^n = \frac{1}{\sqrt{2}}$$

to be

$$\frac{f_2^{(n)}}{f_2} = \sqrt{2^{1/n} - 1} \tag{15-21}$$

For example, for $n = 2$, $f_2^{(2)}/f_2 = 0.64$. Hence two cascaded stages, each with a band width $f_2 = 10$ kc, have an over-all band width of 6.4 kc. Similarly, three cascaded 10-kc stages give a resultant upper 3-db frequency of 5.1 kc, etc.

If the lower 3-dbv frequency for n cascaded stages is $f_1^{(n)}$, then corresponding to Eq. (15-21) we find

$$\frac{f_1^{(n)}}{f_1} = \frac{1}{\sqrt{2^{1/n} - 1}} \tag{15-22}$$

If the amplitude response for a single stage is plotted on log-log paper the resulting graph will approach a straight line whose slope is 6 dbv/octave both at the low and at the high frequencies. For example, it follows from Eq. (15-14) that, for $f/f_2 \gg 1$, $20 \log (A_2/A_o) = 20 \log (f_2/f)$. Hence every time the frequency f doubles (which, by definition, is one octave) the response drops by $20 \log 2 = 6$ db. For an n-stage amplifier it follows that the amplitude response falls $6n$ decibels per octave or, equivalently, $20n$ decibels per decade.

Other characteristics of wide-band amplifiers not considered in this text are the following: Both the high- and low-frequency range may be extended with the use of special passive compensating networks.[2] The high-frequency response may be extended to hundreds of megacycles with a distributed amplifier.[3] The frequency and phase response discussed above are steady-state characteristics and give the output of the amplifier for a given *sinosoidal* input signal. From these characteristics it is difficult to calculate the behavior of the amplifier for a nonsinusoidal input (for example, a video pulse). The transient behavior of RC-coupled amplifiers is discussed in Ref. 4.

15-8. Transformer-coupled Vacuum-tube Amplifiers. The coupling from the output of one stage to the input of the next stage may be made by means of a transformer. The primary winding is in series with the plate of the first tube, and the secondary is in series with the grid of the second tube. The low-frequency response of a transformer-coupled amplifier is limited by the primary magnetizing inductance. If this amplifier is to be used at low audio frequencies, L must be very large (tens of henrys) and hence a bulky iron-core transformer is required. Such a transformer will have considerable leakage inductance and shunt capacitance which will consequently limit the high-frequency response to the audio range. Since RC coupling requires less space, makes use of less expensive equipment, and has a better frequency response characteristic than transformer coupling, an audio interstage transformer is now seldom employed with vacuum-tube amplifiers. An exception to this statement is the use of a transformer to drive the grid of a stage positive during part of the cycle. Since audio transformer coupling finds such limited application, it will not be discussed further here. A complete analysis is given in Ref. 5.

If a narrow pulse (of the order of a microsecond) is to be amplified, it is not necessary to have good low-frequency response. The primary inductance need only be large enough (of the order of millihenrys) so as not to distort appreciably the flat top of the wave. Small inexpensive iron-core transformers make excellent interstage coupling elements for pulse amplifiers.[6]

15-9. Cascaded Transistor Stages. Since the voltage gain of a grounded-collector stage is less than unity, it is not possible (without a transformer) to increase the over-all amplification by cascading such stages. Hence, grounded-collector stages are not used in cascade.

Grounded-base RC-coupled stages also are seldom cascaded because the voltage gain of such an arrangement is approximately the same as that of the output stage alone. This statement may be verified as follows: The voltage gain of a stage equals the short-circuit current gain times the effective load resistance R divided by the input resistance. The resistance R is the parallel combination of the actual load resistance R_L, the output impedance R_o of the stage under consideration, and (except for the last stage) the input resistance R_i of the following stage. This parallel combination is certainly less than R_i, and hence for identical stages the effective load impedance is less than the input impedance. The maximum current gain is α, which is less than unity (but approximately equal to unity). Hence, the voltage gain of any stage (except the last or output stage) is less than unity. [This analysis is not strictly correct because R_i is a function of the effective load resistance and hence will vary somewhat from stage to stage (Prob. 15-13).]

Since the short-circuit current gain of a grounded-emitter stage is much greater than unity, it is possible to increase the over-all voltage amplification by cascading such stages. Two stages of an RC-coupled amplifier consisting of common-emitter stages are indicated in Fig. 15-7. It should

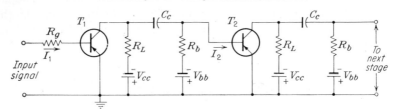

Fig. 15-7. Two common-emitter transistor stages in cascade.

be emphasized that, since the input impedance R_i of each stage is very much smaller than the output impedance R_o ($R_i \cong 2$ kilohms, $R_o \cong 80$ kilohms; see Table 10-3), each stage is almost short-circuited by the following stage. Despite this fact, it is possible to obtain voltage gain because the current gain is large. If R_g is the resistance in series with the first stage, if R_{i1} is the input resistance of the first stage, if R_L is the load on the last stage, and if $\mathbf{A}_{i1}'$, $\mathbf{A}_{i2}'$, $\mathbf{A}_{i3}'$, . . . are the current gains of the first, second, third, . . . stages, then the over-all voltage gain $\mathbf{A}$ is, from Eqs. (10-30), (10-31), and (10-36),

$$\mathbf{A} = (\mathbf{A}_{i1}'\mathbf{A}_{i2}'\mathbf{A}_{i3}' \cdot \cdot \cdot) \frac{R_L}{R_g + R_{i1}} \tag{15-23}$$

The amplitude and phase response of the RC-coupled transistor amplifier can be determined by considering three frequency ranges (low, intermediate, and high) just as was done in Sec. 15-6 for the vacuum-tube amplifier. The equivalent circuit at low frequencies for any stage (except the last) is given in Fig. 15-8a, where $\mathbf{A}_i$ is the short-circuit current gain and $\mathbf{I}_1$ is the input current to the stage (Fig. 10-7b). The resistor R_b is used to supply the proper quiescent base current, and its resistance is very large ($\cong 100$ kilohms) compared with R_i ($\cong 2$ kilohms). Hence R_b may be omitted from Fig. 15-8. The resistance of R_L is usually of the same order as that of R_o. Let R' denote the parallel combination of

R_o and the load resistance R_L of the stage under consideration so that

$$R' \equiv \frac{R_L R_o}{R_L + R_o} \tag{15-24}$$

The equivalent circuit reduces to that given in Fig. 15-8b.   The output

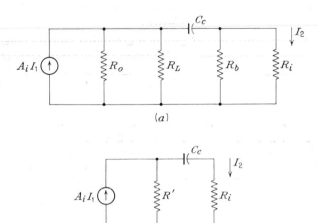

(a)

(b)

Fig. 15-8. The equivalent circuit of an RC-coupled transistor amplifier stage.

current $\mathbf{I}_2$ is given by

$$\mathbf{I}_2 = \mathbf{A}_i \mathbf{I}_1 \frac{R'}{R' + R_i - j/\omega C_c}$$

The *low-frequency current gain* $(\mathbf{A}_i')_{\text{low}}$ is given by

$$(\mathbf{A}_i')_{\text{low}} \equiv \frac{\mathbf{I}_2}{\mathbf{I}_1} = \frac{\mathbf{A}_i R'}{R' + R_i - j/\omega C_c} \tag{15-25}$$

In the mid-band region we may neglect the small series reactance of C_c, and the equivalent circuit is given in Fig. 15-9.   The *mid-band current gain* $\mathbf{A}_{io}'$ is given by

$$\mathbf{A}_{io}' = \mathbf{A}_i \frac{R'}{R' + R_i} \tag{15-26}$$

The low-frequency current gain relative to the mid-band gain is

$$\frac{(\mathbf{A}_i')_{\text{low}}}{\mathbf{A}_{io}'} = \frac{R' + R_i}{R' + R_i - j/\omega C_c} = \frac{1}{1 - j(f_1/f)} \tag{15-27}$$

where

$$f_1 \equiv \frac{1}{2\pi C_c(R' + R_i)} \tag{15-28}$$

is the lower 3-db frequency. Equations (15-27) and (15-28) correspond
to Eqs. (15-17) and (15-18) for the RC-coupled vacuum-tube amplifier.

As a numerical example, consider $C_c = 1\ \mu f$ and $R' + R_i = 10$ kilohms.
Then from Eq. (15-28) we find $f_1 = 16$ cps. The voltages required for
a transistor are low (a few volts or tens of volts) and hence a low-voltage
capacitor may be used for C_c. Capacitors of small physical size and large
capacitance (tens of microfarads) are available commercially. If we
choose $C_c = 10\ \mu f$ for the above illustration, then f_1 is 1.6 cps, indicating
that it is possible to obtain excellent
low-frequency response with transistor
amplifiers.

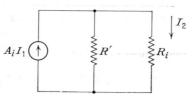

FIG. 15-9. The mid-band equivalent
circuit of an RC-coupled transistor
amplifier stage.

In order to calculate f_1 the value
of R_o must be used. If the circuit
parameters are given, then R_o can
be calculated from Table 10-2. This
equation contains R_g, which represents the effective resistance in series
with the base input circuit. For the first stage the value of R_g is known.
For all other stages R_g is assumed infinite (see the illustrative example in
Sec. 10-5).

The transistor amplifier response for high frequencies is usually determined by the frequency characteristic of α. For the grounded-emitter
stage the upper 3-db frequency f_2 is given by Eq. (11-16), namely,

$$f_2 = (1 - \alpha)f_\alpha \tag{15-29}$$

where f_α is the α cutoff frequency.

The maximum current gain is (Table 10-3)

$$A_i = \frac{\alpha}{1 - \alpha} \tag{15-30}$$

and the *current-gain–band-width product* is

$$A_i f_2 = \alpha f_\alpha \cong f_\alpha \tag{15-31}$$

As $\alpha \to 1$ the band width decreases, although the current gain increases.
Hence, for a video amplifier α should not be too close to unity. For
example, if $f_\alpha = 5$ megacycles and $\alpha = 0.98$, then $f_2 = 100$ kc, which is
a very low video frequency. If $f_\alpha = 50$ megacycles and if $\alpha = 0.9$, then
a current gain of 9 at a band pass of 5 megacycles is possible. Transistors
with such large values of f_α are available commercially but are expensive.
This illustration indicates that it is difficult and costly to obtain excellent
high-frequency response with a transistor amplifier. It must also be
recalled that if n stages are cascaded the over-all upper 3-db frequency is
multiplied by $\sqrt{2^{1/n} - 1}$, which is less than unity.

Transformer coupling is sometimes used with cascaded transistor amplifiers. The step-down transformer matches the high output impedance of one stage to the low input impedance of the following stage. With such a connection higher gain can be realized than with RC coupling. However, the transformers have poorer frequency response and are more costly than the RC networks. Hence, usually RC coupling is used even though more stages may be required for the same gain than would be necessary if the stages were transformer-coupled.

It is not necessary that all cascaded stages be of the same type. For example, if the source impedance is high, then a common-collector stage may be used at the input, although all other stages are of the common-emitter variety. Similarly, a grounded-base input stage may be used to match a very low signal-source impedance.

15-10. Voltage Sources for Amplifiers. The potentials required for the several electrodes of a vacuum tube are supplied as follows:

1. *The Heater or A Supply.* The most common method of energizing the heater is from a low-voltage winding of a transformer whose primary operates from the a-c power lines. Sometimes a number of tubes in a system are connected with their heaters in series so that the total voltage is 115 volts. Such a combination can be excited directly from the a-c supply mains, thus saving the expense of a heater transformer. Storage batteries are used when d-c heating is necessary (see Sec. 15-11). Special low-drain tubes operate from dry cells.

2. *The Plate, B-supply, or E_{bb} Voltage.* The d-c plate supply necessary for most tubes ranges from about 90 to 500 volts. These d-c voltages are obtained from a rectifier, which is provided with sufficient filtering so that the ripple is not excessive (Chap. 19). It must be noted that the ripple in the plate circuit of one stage appears directly across the grid of the second stage and so is amplified along with the signal. This imposes severe requirements on the power-supply design. Sometimes one or more VR tubes are used to maintain constant B-supply voltage (see Sec. 13-12). If better voltage stabilization and regulation are necessary, then electronically regulated power supplies must be used (Chap. 19). Special low-drain tubes use batteries for the plate supply.

3. *The Grid or C Supply.* The grid of a voltage amplifier ordinarily requires very little current, and so low-power dry cells may be used for this purpose. Sometimes VR tubes fed from a separate negative supply voltage are used. This arrangement is the fixed-bias method.

In most cases, however, the necessary bias voltage is obtained without the use of a separate grid battery by the self-bias method illustrated in Fig. 15-10. A resistor R_k is connected in series with the cathode of the tube. The quiescent current I_b passes through R_k, and this voltage furnishes the grid bias. The correct self-biasing resistor is $R_k = E_{cc}/I_b$, where E_{cc} is the desired bias.   If a pentode is used, then the screen current I_s also passes through the cathode resistor.   Hence, $R_k = E_{cc}/(I_b + I_s)$.

Note that a capacitor C_k shunts R_k in Fig. 15-10.   To see the purpose of this capacitor, suppose that the input signal voltage increases.   Then the plate current increases, the voltage across R_k increases, and the increase in voltage between grid and cathode is less than the increase in

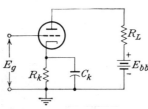

input signal.   Hence the gain of the amplifier is less than it would be if fixed bias were used. In order to avoid this loss in gain due to the "feedback" from the output to the input circuit, the resistor R_k is shunted by the capacitor C_k, the reactance of which must be small compared with R_k over the operating frequency range.   [It follows from Fig. 17-7b that, if feedback is to be avoided, $(\mu + 1)|\mathbf{Z}_k|$

FIG. 15-10. A resistor in the cathode lead of a tube provides the grid bias.

$\ll |R_L + r_p|$, where $\mathbf{Z}_k$ is the impedance in the cathode circuit.]   If the amplifier is to operate without loss of gain at low frequencies, then large-capacitance capacitors are required.   Low-voltage electrolytic capacitors having capacitances of 50 or more micro-farads in a very small volume are commercially available for this specific application.

Self-bias leads to more stable quiescent operation (d-c stability) than fixed bias.   Consider, for example, that for some reason (such as a change in E_{bb} voltage or aging of a tube or a tube re-placement, etc.) the current tends to increase.   Then this current through R_k will increase the bias and so the quies-cent current will change much less than it would have were fixed bias used.

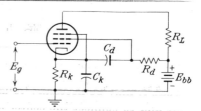

FIG. 15-11. A resistor in the screen lead of a tube provides the screen bias.

4. *The Screen Supply.*   Either a portion of the B-supply voltage is tapped off (sometimes a VR tube is used) or else the full B supply is applied to the screen through a series voltage-dropping resistor R_d.   In either case a capacitor C_d is used between the screen and cathode.   The capacitance of C_d is made large enough so that the voltage from cathode to screen remains sensibly constant independent of variations in the screen current as the signal is applied.   This statement implies that R_d must be much greater than $1/\omega C_d$ for the frequency band under consideration. The self-bias method of feeding the screen is illustrated in Fig. 15-11 and is to be preferred over the fixed-bias method for reasons of d-c sta-bility (as explained under 3 above).   If I_s and E_s are the quiescent screen

current and voltage, respectively, then the required value of R_d is given by $R_d = (E_{bb} - E_s)/I_s$.

The complete wiring diagram for a typical two-stage resistance-coupled amplifier employing pentode tubes is given in Fig. 15-12. It should be noted that a common B supply is used to supply the plates of both tubes. The center tap of the filament transformer is usually grounded. However, if a cathode is at a high voltage (over 100 volts) with respect to

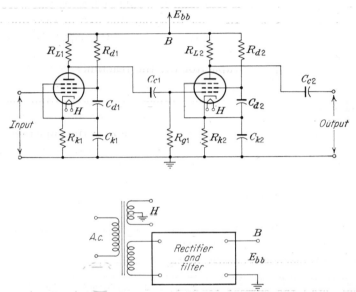

FIG. 15-12. The schematic wiring diagram of a two-stage RC-coupled amplifier.

ground it may be necessary to use a separate heater transformer for this tube and to connect the center tap to the cathode.

It should be noted that coupling exists between stages of a multistage amplifier through the impedance of the common B supply. In the above circuit the point marked B is not at a fixed voltage with respect to ground but varies with the current demand because of the regulation of the B supply. For example, as the relatively large current in the output stage varies, it will cause a voltage drop in the internal impedance of the power supply. This will appear as a spurious voltage in the first tube (and also in all other stages). This feedback may become large enough and be of the proper phase to cause the amplifier to oscillate.

Another undesirable feature of using a common B supply is that any ripple appearing in the filter output is impressed on the grids of all the tubes (except the first). Specifically, in Fig. 15-12, if the reactance of C_{c1} is neglected, then the fraction $R_{gp}/(R_{gp} + R_{L1})$ of the ripple voltage of the B supply will appear as a spurious signal on the grid of the second stage, where R_{gp} represents R_{g1} and r_{p1} in parallel.

These interactions which result from the use of a common B supply can be greatly reduced by the proper use of RC combinations, known as *decoupling filters.* Such decoupling filters are included in Fig. 15-13 for a resistance-coupled two-stage amplifier. Triodes are shown in this circuit for the sake of simplicity. These filters must be designed so that the resistance is much greater than the reactance of the capacitor for the frequencies under consideration. Under these conditions, most of the a-c

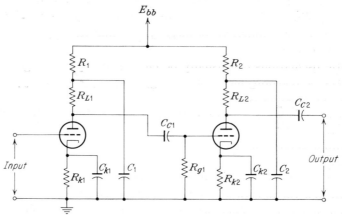

FIG. 15-13. A two-stage amplifier using decoupling filters $R_1 C_1$ and $R_2 C_2$.

variations in the B-supply impedance appear across the resistor of these units. Hence, the voltage across the capacitor of the decoupler is very nearly constant and independent of any B-supply variations. Since the voltage across C_1 is the effective plate supply for the first tube and the voltage across C_2 is the effective plate supply of the second tube, the two stages have been rendered independent of each other. These decoupling filters also serve to reduce hum from the power supply.

The power source for the collector circuit of a transistor is either a battery or a low-voltage power supply as described under 2 above. To avoid interaction between stages, RC decoupling filters of the type indicated in Fig. 15-13 are often used in the collector circuit. The base circuit may be supplied from a battery although more commonly self-bias is used for reasons of d-c stability, as explained in Sec. 9-12.

15-11. Spurious Input Voltages. It often happens that with no apparent input signal to an amplifier an output voltage of considerable magnitude may be obtained. The amplifier may be oscillating because some part of the output is inadvertently being fed back into the input. This oscillation may result from the nonzero output impedance of the power supply and can usually be prevented by the use of appropriately placed decoupling filters, as discussed in the preceding section.

Feedback may occur through the interelectrode capacitance from grid to plate of a tube, through lead inductances, stray wiring, etc., the exact path often being very difficult to determine. The undesired or *parasitic* oscillation may occur with any type of circuit, such as audio-, video-, or radio-frequency amplifier, oscillator, modulator, pulse wave form generating circuits, etc. Parasitic oscillations are particularly prevalent with circuits in which (physically) large tubes are used, tubes or transistors are operated in parallel or push-pull, and in power stages.[7] The frequency of oscillation may be in the audio range but is usually much higher and often is so high (hundreds of megacycles) that its presence cannot be detected with an oscilloscope.

Parasitic oscillations can usually be eliminated by a change in circuit parameters, a rearrangement of wiring, some additional bypassing or shielding, a change of tube or transistor, the use of an r-f inductor in the plate circuit, r-f chokes in series with filament lead, etc. A small resistance (50 to 1,000 ohms) placed in series with a grid and as close to the grid terminal as possible is often very effective in reducing high-frequency oscillations.

Even if an amplifier is not oscillating, undesirable output voltages may be present in a vacuum-tube amplifier in the form of hum from the use of a-c heated filaments.[8] There are several sources of this hum.

1. The magnetic field produced by the filament current will deflect the electron stream. During some portion of each half cycle the electrons may be deflected to such an extent as to miss the plate. A 120-cycle hum results (if a 60-cycle power source is used).

2. Effective capacitances exist between each side of the heater and the grid. If these capacitances are not equal, an effective 60-cycle voltage is impressed upon the grid.

3. The heater-cathode insulation is not infinite. If self-bias is used, leakage will take place from the heater through this insulation resistance in series with the cathode impedance Z_k. The voltage across Z_k appears as hum.

4. The heating and cooling of the cathode, because the heating power is periodic, introduces a 120-cps hum. This would not be true if the plate current were strictly space-charge-limited since it would then be independent of the temperature of the emitter. However, some parts of the cathode are at a low enough temperature so that some temperature-limited current exists. Furthermore, the effect of the initial velocities is a function of temperature.

Hum from the above sources can be eliminated completely only by using d-c heating power.

In addition to hum that is inherent in the tube construction, some hum may appear from pickup resulting from the stray magnetic fields of the power transformer or from the fields produced by the heater current in the connecting leads. The effect of the former is negligible with properly shielded transformers, and that of the latter may be reduced if the heater leads are twisted. There may also be electrostatic pickup from the a-c line. Finally, there is the possibility of pickup of r-f signals radiated through space. These spurious voltages can often be eliminated by proper shielding or bypassing.

It should be emphasized that hum troubles are usually of importance only in the first stage of a high-gain amplifier, for the small spurious voltages introduced in this stage are amplified by all succeeding stages.

Microphonics is the name given to the spurious output voltages caused by the vibrations of the electrodes because of mechanical or acoustical jarring of the tube. Some tubes are much more microphonic than others of presumably identical construction, and this source of trouble can often be eliminated by changing tubes. In many cases, it is necessary to mount the tubes in rubber or in special supports. In addition, special tubes are available in which the microphonic effect and also the heater hum effects outlined above have been minimized. A transistor is, of course, completely nonmicrophonic because there can be no mechanical motion between the emitter, base, and collector.

15-12. Noise. It is found that there is an inherent limit to the amplification obtainable from an amplifier even after the above-mentioned sources of hum have been eliminated. Under these conditions, the output of the amplifier when there is no impressed input signal is called *amplifier noise.*[9] If, therefore, only a very small voltage is available, such as a weak radio, television, radar, etc., signal, it may be impossible to distinguish the signal from the background noise.

There are two important contributing factors to the noise of an amplifier. The first results from the fact that the electrons in the circuit elements of the amplifier are in a state of incessant activity. The random fluctuations produced by the thermal agitation of the electrons appears as a thermal noise voltage called the *Johnson noise.* The second cause, which arises within the tube itself, is produced primarily by the random motion of the electrons in the cathode-anode space.

The electrons in a conductor possess varying amounts of energy by virtue of the temperature of the conductor. The slight fluctuations in energy about the values specified by the most probable distribution are very small, but they are sufficient to produce small noise potentials within a conductor. In particular, if this conductor is the grid-leak resistor, this voltage will be applied to the grid of the tube and will be equivalent to an input signal. The rms value of the *thermal noise voltage* E_n is given by the expression

$$E_n{}^2 = 4kTRB \qquad (15\text{-}32)$$

where k is the Boltzmann constant, T is the resistor temperature in degrees Kelvin, R is the resistance in ohms, and $B = f_2 - f_1$ is the frequency band width in cycles per second.

An idea of the order of magnitude of the voltage involved is obtained by calculating the noise voltage generated in a 1-megohm resistor at room temperature over a 10-kc band pass. Equation (15-32) yields for E_n the value 13 μv. Clearly, if the band pass of an amplifier is wider, then the input resistor must be smaller, if excessive noise is to be avoided. Thus, if the amplifier considered is 10 megacycles wide, its input resistance cannot exceed 1,000 ohms, if the fluctuation noise is not to exceed that of the 10-kc audio amplifier.

It is obvious that the band pass of an amplifier should be kept as low as possible (without introducing excessive frequency distortion) because the noise power is directly proportional to the band width. It should also be observed that the same noise power exists in a given band width regardless of the center frequency. Such a distribution which gives the same noise per unit band width anywhere in the spectrum is called *white noise*.

Among the various possible sources of noise in the tube itself, one of the most important is the *shot effect*. Normally, one assumes that the current in a tube under d-c conditions is a constant at every instant. Actually, however, the current from the cathode to the anode consists of a stream of individual electrons, and it is only the time average flow which is constant. These fluctuations in the number of electrons emitted constitute the shot noise. If the cathode emission is temperature-limited, then the rms noise current I_n amperes in a diode is given by the expression

$$I_n{}^2 = 2eI_bB \qquad (15\text{-}33)$$

where e is the electronic charge, I_b is the emission current in amperes, and B is the band width in cycles per second. If the load resistor is R, then a noise voltage of magnitude I_nR will appear across the load. Temperature-limited diodes are used as constant-current white-noise generators for test purposes.

If the tube is space-charge-limited, the irregularities in emission are decreased, and the plate-current fluctuation is much less in a space-charge-limited tube than in one which is temperature-limited. This fact is explained qualitatively by the automatic-valve action of the space-charge cloud in the neighborhood of the cathode, as discussed in Sec. 4-3. The space-charge-limited noise power is of the order of 10 per cent of the temperature-limited value.

Other sources of noise in vacuum tubes are the following: *Gas noise* caused by the random ionization of the few molecules remaining in the tube; *secondary-emission* noise arising from the random variations of secondary emission from the grid and plate; *flicker noise* caused by the spontaneous emission of particles from an oxide-coated cathode, an effect particularly noticeable at low frequencies; and *induced grid noise* resulting from the random nature of the electron stream near the grid. In addition to the above, we also have in a pentode *partition noise* which arises from the random fluctuation in the current division between the screen and the plate. Because of this partition effect a pentode may be much noisier (perhaps by a factor of 10) than a triode. Hence, the input stage to a high-gain amplifier is usually a triode. We should note that it is the input stage whose noise must be kept extremely low because any noise generated in this tube is amplified by all the following stages.

A transistor is much noisier than a vacuum tube. In addition to thermal noise, there exists noise due to the random motion of the carriers crossing the emitter and collector junctions. There is also a partition effect arising from the random fluctuation in the division of current between the collector and base. It is found that a transistor does not generate white noise, but rather that the noise power is inversely proportional to frequency. Also, the amount of noise generated depends upon the quiescent conditions. Hence, in specifying the noise in a transistor the center frequency and the operating point must be given.

A *noise figure F* has been introduced in order to be able to specify quantitatively how noisy a circuit is. By definition, F is the ratio of the noise power output of the circuit under consideration to the noise power output which would be obtained in the same band width if the only source of noise were the thermal noise in the internal resistance of the signal source. Thus, the noise figure is a quantity which compares the noise in an actual amplifier with that in an ideal (noiseless) amplifier. Usually F is expressed in decibels. The noise figure of a triode may be as low as a few decibels throughout the video-frequency range whereas 10 to 30 db is representative for a junction transistor and 40 to 70 db for the point-contact type.

REFERENCES

1. MILLMAN, J., and H. TAUB, "Pulse and Digital Circuits," pp. 61–63, McGraw-Hill Book Company, Inc., New York, 1956.
2. MILLMAN, J., and H. TAUB, "Pulse and Digital Circuits," Secs. 3-6 and 3-13, McGraw-Hill Book Company, Inc., New York, 1956.
3. MILLMAN, J., and H. TAUB, "Pulse and Digital Circuits," pp. 315–321, McGraw-Hill Book Company, Inc., New York, 1956.
4. MILLMAN, J., and H. TAUB, "Pulse and Digital Circuits," Chap. 3, McGraw-Hill Book Company, Inc., New York, 1956.

5. TERMAN, F. E., "Electronic and Radio Engineering," 4th ed., pp. 275–280, McGraw-Hill Book Company, Inc., New York, 1955.
6. MILLMAN, J., and H. TAUB, "Pulse and Digital Circuits," pp. 253–272, McGraw-Hill Book Company, Inc., New York, 1956.
7. TERMAN, F. E., "Electronic and Radio Engineering," 4th ed., pp. 503–506, McGraw-Hill Book Company, Inc., New York, 1955.
8. *RCA Application Note* 88.
9. VAN DER ZIEL, A., "Noise," Prentice-Hall, Inc., Englewood Cliffs, N.J., 1954.
   TERMAN, F. E., "Electronic and Radio Engineering," 4th ed., pp. 434–442, 796–798, McGraw-Hill Book Company, Inc., New York, 1955.
   SEELY, S., "Radio Electronics," pp. 143–149, McGraw-Hill Book Company, Inc., New York, 1956.
   VALLEY, G. E., Jr., and H. WALLMAN, "Vacuum Tube Amplifiers," Radiation Laboratory Series, Vol. 18, pp. 496–720, McGraw-Hill Book Company, Inc., New York, 1948.

CHAPTER 16

AUDIO POWER AMPLIFIERS

A POWER amplifier serves to supply power to some devices such as a loud-speaker, a servo motor, a relay, or a switching circuit. Power amplifiers may be operated as Class A, AB, B, or C, depending upon the particular purpose of the unit. If the amplifier is to reproduce the audio spectrum without distortion, the amplifier must be operated in Class A, if a single tube or transistor is used. If two devices are used in a balanced (push-pull) circuit, then the amplifier may be operated in Class AB or Class B.

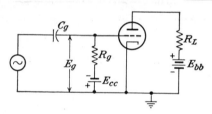

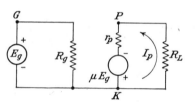

FIG. 16-1. The schematic wiring diagram and the equivalent circuit of a simple series-fed power amplifier.

Only audio-frequency power amplifiers will be considered in this chapter. Particular emphasis will be placed upon the types of circuits used, the power output, the distortion, and the efficiency.

16-1. Class A Triode Power Amplifiers. Consider a simple triode amplifier that supplies power to a pure resistance load R_L. The schematic and equivalent circuits of this amplifier are indicated in Fig. 16-1. The plate current is given by

$$I_p = \frac{\mu E_g}{r_p + R_L}$$

and the power supplied to the load is

$$P = I_p{}^2 R_L = \left(\frac{\mu E_g}{r_p + R_L}\right)^2 R_L \tag{16-1}$$

The conditions for maximum power transfer to the load may readily be determined. *If it is assumed that μ, r_p, and E_g are constants*, the power

400

transfer is a maximum when

$$\frac{dP}{dR_L} = 0$$

from which it follows that

$$R_L = r_p \tag{16-2}$$

Under these conditions, the maximum output power is

$$P_{\max} = \left(\frac{\mu E_g}{2r_p}\right)^2 r_p = \frac{\mu^2 E_g{}^2}{4r_p} = \frac{\mu g_m E_g{}^2}{4} \tag{16-3}$$

A plot of Eq. (16-1) is given in Fig. 16-2, and we observe that although a maximum exists for $R_L = r_p$ this maximum is quite broad.

For a given operating point the power supply voltage required will increase with the magnitude of R_L. Since the maximum power transfer occurs when the load resistor equals the internal plate resistance of the tube, it is necessary to have tubes with low values of r_p in order to obtain reasonable amounts of out-

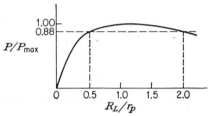

FIG. 16-2. The power output from the amplifier in Fig. 16-1 as a function of R_L/r_p.

put power with nominal values of plate supply voltage. Tubes with low values of r_p also usually possess rather low values of μ. As a result, large grid-excitation voltages are required for appreciable amounts of output power. It is noted from Eq. (16-3) that the product μg_m is a figure of merit for a power tube.

If the amplitude distortion is negligible and if the amplifier supplies power to a pure resistance load, then the power output may be found graphically as follows:

$$P = E_p I_p = I_p{}^2 R_L$$

where E_p and I_p are the rms output voltage and current, respectively, and where R_L denotes the magnitude of the load resistance. The numerical values of E_p and I_p can be determined graphically in terms of the maximum and minimum voltage and current swings, as indicated in Fig. 16-3. Under the conditions of negligible distortion, it is seen that

$$I_p = \frac{I_m}{\sqrt{2}} = \frac{I_{\max} - I_{\min}}{2\sqrt{2}}$$

and

$$E_p = \frac{E_m}{\sqrt{2}} = \frac{E_{\max} - E_{\min}}{2\sqrt{2}}$$

so that the power becomes

$$P = \frac{E_m I_m}{2} = \frac{I_m^2 R_L}{2} \tag{16-4}$$

which may also be written in the form

$$P = \frac{(E_{max} - E_{min})(I_{max} - I_{min})}{8} \tag{16-5}$$

This equation allows the output power to be calculated very simply.

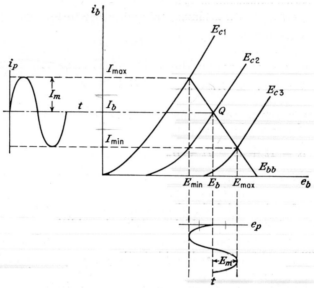

Fig. 16-3. The output-current and voltage wave forms of a triode power amplifier.

All that is necessary is to plot the load line on the volt-ampere characteristics of the tube and to read off the values of E_{max}, E_{min}, I_{max}, and I_{min}.

16-2. Second Harmonic Distortion in Triodes. In the preceding section the tube was idealized as a perfectly linear device. However, in general, the dynamic characteristic is not a straight line. This non-linearity arises because the static plate characteristics are not equidistant straight lines for constant-grid-voltage increments. If the dynamic curve is nonlinear over the operating range, the wave form of the output voltage differs from that of the input signal. Distortion of this type is called nonlinear or amplitude distortion.

In order to investigate the magnitude of this distortion we shall assume that the dynamic curve of a triode with respect to the quiescent point Q can be represented by a parabola rather than a straight line. Thus, instead of relating the alternating plate current i_p with the grid excitation voltage e_g by the relation

$$i_p = Ge_g \qquad G \equiv \frac{\mu}{r_p + R_L} \qquad (16\text{-}6)$$

that arises from the linear equivalent circuit of the triode, we assume that the relationship between i_p and e_g is given more accurately by the expression

$$i_p = G_1 e_g + G_2 e_g{}^2 \qquad (16\text{-}7)$$

where the G's are constants. Actually, these two terms are the beginning of a power series expansion of i_p as a function of e_g.

If the input wave form is sinusoidal and of the form

$$e_g = E_{gm} \cos \omega t$$

the substitution of this expression in Eq. (16-7) leads to

$$i_p = G_1 E_{gm} \cos \omega t + G_2 E_{gm}{}^2 \cos^2 \omega t$$

Since $\cos^2 \omega t = \frac{1}{2} + \frac{1}{2} \cos 2 \omega t$, the expression for the instantaneous total current i_b reduces to the form

$$i_b = I_b + i_p = I_b + B_0 + B_1 \cos \omega t + B_2 \cos 2\omega t \qquad (16\text{-}8)$$

where the B's are constants which may be evaluated in terms of the G's. The physical meaning of this equation is evident. It shows that the application of a sinusoidal signal on a parabolic dynamic characteristic results in an output current which contains, in addition to a term of the same frequency as the input, a second harmonic term and also a constant current. This constant term B_0 adds to the original d-c value I_b to yield a total d-c component of current $I_b + B_0$. Hence, *a sinusoidal input signal has changed the average value of the output current* and hence rectification has taken place.

The amplitudes B_0, B_1, and B_2 for a given load resistor are readily determined from either the static or the dynamic characteristics. We observe from Fig. 16-4 that when

$$\left. \begin{array}{ll} \omega t = 0, & i_b = I_{\max} \\[4pt] \omega t = \dfrac{\pi}{2}, & i_b = I_b \\[4pt] \omega t = \pi, & i_b = I_{\min} \end{array} \right\} \qquad (16\text{-}9)$$

By substituting these values in Eq. (16-8) there results

$$\left. \begin{array}{l} I_{\max} = I_b + B_0 + B_1 + B_2 \\ I_b = I_b + B_0 - B_2 \\ I_{\min} = I_b + B_0 - B_1 + B_2 \end{array} \right\} \qquad (16\text{-}10)$$

This set of three equations determines the three unknowns B_0, B_1, and B_2.

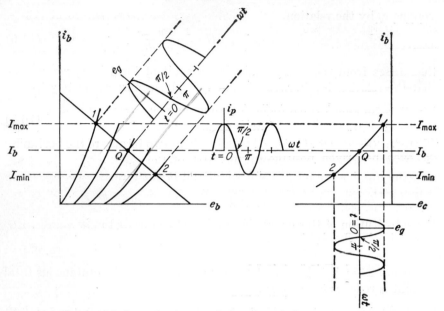

FIG. 16-4. Static and dynamic characteristics of a triode. The output current has zero-axis symmetry provided only that the input is assumed to be of the form $e_g = E_{gm} \cos \omega t$.

It follows from the second of this group that

$$B_0 = B_2 \tag{16-11}$$

By subtracting the third equation from the first, there results

$$B_1 = \frac{I_{max} - I_{min}}{2} \tag{16-12}$$

With this value of B_1, the value for B_2 may be evaluated from either the first or the last of Eqs. (16-10) as

$$B_2 = B_0 = \frac{I_{max} + I_{min} - 2I_b}{4} \tag{16-13}$$

The second harmonic distortion D_2 is defined as

$$D_2 \equiv \frac{|B_2|}{|B_1|} \tag{16-14}$$

(To find the per cent second harmonic distortion, D_2 is multiplied by 100.) The quantities I_{max}, I_{min}, and I_b appearing in these equations are obtained directly from the characteristic curves and the load line.

If the dynamic characteristic is given by the parabolic form (16-7) and if the input contains two frequencies ω_1 and ω_2, then the output will consist of a d-c term and sinusoidal components of frequencies ω_1, ω_2, $2\omega_1$, $2\omega_2$, $\omega_1 + \omega_2$, and $\omega_1 - \omega_2$ (Prob. 16-2). The sum and difference frequencies are called _intermodulation_ or _combination_ frequencies.

16-3. Harmonic Generation in a Tube. The analysis of the previous section has assumed a parabolic dynamic characteristic. This approximation is usually valid for voltage amplifiers where the swing is small. However, for a triode power amplifier with a large input swing (the grid may even be driven positive during part of the input cycle) it is an inadequate assumption. It is likewise true that the parabolic approximation may not be sufficiently accurate to describe the behavior of tetrodes and pentodes as circuit elements.

It is frequently necessary, therefore, to express the dynamic curve with respect to the Q point by a power series of the form

$$i_p = G_1 e_g + G_2 e_g{}^2 + G_3 e_g{}^3 + G_4 e_g{}^4 + \cdots \tag{16-15}$$

If we assume that the input wave is a simple cosine function of time, of the form

$$e_g = E_{gm} \cos \omega t \tag{16-16}$$

then the output current will have the form

$$i_b = I_b + B_0 + B_1 \cos \omega t + B_2 \cos 2\omega t + B_3 \cos 3\omega t + \cdots \tag{16-17}$$

This equation results when Eq. (16-16) is inserted in Eq. (16-15) and the proper trigonometric transformations are made.

That the output-current wave form must be expressible by a relationship of this form is made evident from an inspection of Fig. 16-4. It is observed from this figure that the plate-current curve must possess _zero-axis symmetry_, or that the current is an _even_ function of time. Expressed mathematically, $i(\omega t) = i(-\omega t)$. Physically, it means that the wave shape for every quarter cycle of the plate-current curve as the operating point moves from point Q to point 1 is similar to the shape of the curve that is obtained as the operating point moves back from point 1 to point Q. Similarly, the wave shape of the current generated by the operating point as it moves from point Q to point 2 is symmetrical with that generated as it moves from point 2 back to point Q. These conditions are true regardless of the curvature of the characteristics. Since i is an even function of time, the Fourier series in Eq. (16-17) representing a periodic function possessing this symmetry contains only cosine terms. (If any sine terms were present they would destroy the symmetry since they are _odd_ and not _even_ functions of time.)

If in Eq. (16-15) one assumes, as is frequently done in the literature, that the excitation voltage is a sine instead of a cosine function of the time, the resulting output current is no longer expressed by a series of cosine terms only. Though a sine function differs from a cosine function in the shift of the time axis by an amount $\omega t = \pi/2$, nevertheless such a shift destroys the above-noted zero-axis symmetry. It is found in this case that the Fourier series representing the output current contains odd sine components and even cosine components.

Any one of a number of methods[1] may be used in order to obtain the coefficients B_0, B_1, B_2, etc. These include the standard procedures employed in conventional Fourier analysis, viz., the schedule method or the Fischer-Hinnen average selected ordinate method. The method due to Espley, which is a combination of the two standard procedures and which is simply an extension of the method of procedure of the last section, will be described here. It was assumed in the foregoing section that only three terms, B_0, B_1, and B_2, of the Fourier series were different from zero. These three values were evaluated in terms of three measured values of current, I_{max}, I_{min}, and I_b. As the next approximation, it will be assumed that only five terms, B_0,

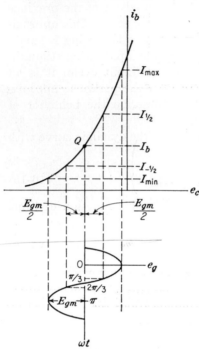

FIG. 16-5. The values of signal voltage and the corresponding values of plate current that are used in the five-point schedule for determining the Fourier components B_0, B_1, B_2, B_3, and B_4 of the current.

B_1, B_2, B_3, and B_4, exist in the resulting Fourier series. In order to evaluate these five coefficients, the values of the currents at five different values of e_g are needed. These are chosen at equal intervals in the grid swing. Thus, I_{max}, $I_{\frac{1}{2}}$, I_b, $I_{-\frac{1}{2}}$, and I_{min} correspond, respectively, to the following values of e_g: maximum positive value, $\frac{1}{2}$ the maximum positive value, zero, $\frac{1}{2}$ the maximum negative value, and the maximum negative value. These values are illustrated in Fig. 16-5.

By assuming that the grid voltage has the form

$$e_g = E_{gm} \cos \omega t$$

as illustrated, then when

$$\begin{aligned}
\omega t &= 0, & i_b &= I_{\max} \\
\omega t &= \frac{\pi}{3}, & i_b &= I_{\frac{1}{2}} \\
\omega t &= \frac{\pi}{2}, & i_b &= I_b \\
\omega t &= \frac{2\pi}{3}, & i_b &= I_{-\frac{1}{2}} \\
\omega t &= \pi, & i_b &= I_{\min}
\end{aligned} \right\} \qquad (16\text{-}18)$$

By combining these conditions with Eq. (16-17), five equations containing five unknowns are obtained. The solution of these equations yields

$$\left.\begin{aligned}
B_0 &= \tfrac{1}{6}(I_{\max} + 2I_{\frac{1}{2}} + 2I_{-\frac{1}{2}} + I_{\min}) - I_b \\
B_1 &= \tfrac{1}{3}(I_{\max} + I_{\frac{1}{2}} - I_{-\frac{1}{2}} - I_{\min}) \\
B_2 &= \tfrac{1}{4}(I_{\max} - 2I_b + I_{\min}) \\
B_3 &= \tfrac{1}{6}(I_{\max} - 2I_{\frac{1}{2}} + 2I_{-\frac{1}{2}} - I_{\min}) \\
B_4 &= \tfrac{1}{12}(I_{\max} - 4I_{\frac{1}{2}} + 6I_b - 4I_{-\frac{1}{2}} + I_{\min})
\end{aligned}\right\} \qquad (16\text{-}19)$$

This method might be termed a "five-point schedule." Higher harmonics can be obtained by employing a seven-point, a nine-point, etc., schedule.

If a large number of determinations of harmonic distortion are to be made, it might be advantageous to use specially constructed direct-reading scales or certain trigonometric simplifications that are described in the literature.[2]

The harmonic distortion is defined as

$$D_2 = \frac{|B_2|}{|B_1|} \qquad D_3 = \frac{|B_3|}{|B_1|} \qquad D_4 = \frac{|B_4|}{|B_1|} \qquad (16\text{-}20)$$

where D_s ($s = 2, 3, 4, \ldots$) represents the distortion of the sth harmonic. An example illustrating how these equations may be used to determine the distortion in multielectrode tubes is given in Sec. 16-8.

If the distortion is not negligible, the power output at the fundamental frequency is

$$P_1 = \frac{B_1{}^2 R_L}{2} \qquad (16\text{-}21)$$

However, the total power output is

$$P = (B_1{}^2 + B_2{}^2 + B_3{}^2 + \cdots) \frac{R_L}{2}$$

which may be written as

$$P = (1 + D_2{}^2 + D_3{}^2 + \cdots)P_1$$

or

$$P = (1 + D^2)P_1 \qquad (16\text{-}22)$$

where *the total distortion* or *distortion factor* is defined as

$$D \equiv \sqrt{D_2{}^2 + D_3{}^2 + D_4{}^2 + \cdots} \qquad (16\text{-}23)$$

If the total distortion is 10 per cent of the fundamental, then

$$P = [1 + (0.1)^2]P_1 = 1.01P_1$$

The total power output is only 1 per cent higher than the fundamental power when the distortion is 10 per cent. Hence, little error is made in using only the fundamental term in calculating the power output.

In passing it should be noted that the total harmonic distortion is not necessarily indicative of the discomfort to someone listening to music. Usually the same amount of distortion is more irritating, the higher the order s of the harmonic frequency.

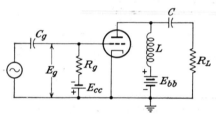

FIG. 16-6. A power amplifier employing parallel or shunt feed. Usually $X_L \gg R_L$ and $X_C \ll R_L$.

16-4. Output Circuits. If the load resistance is connected directly in the plate circuit of the power tube, as shown in Fig. 16-1, the quiescent current passes through this resistance. This current represents a considerable waste of power, as it does not contribute to the a-c component of power. Furthermore, it is generally inadvisable to pass the d-c component of current through the output device, for example, the voice coil of a loud-speaker. For these reasons a parallel-feed arrangement or an output transformer is usually employed.

The parallel-feed circuit is illustrated in Fig. 16-6. The plate supply voltage is connected across the tube through a high inductance L instead of being in series with the load resistor. The blocking capacitor C prevents the d-c battery voltage from appearing across the load R_L. The magnitude of this capacitor must be sufficiently high so that its reactance is small compared with R_L. Furthermore, the inductance L must be high enough to prevent an appreciable fraction of the alternating current from passing through it. In this way the alternating component of the tube current passes through the RC branch, while a negligible reactance drop exists across the capacitor.

The voltage and current relations for this type of circuit are shown in

Fig. 16-7. The construction differs from that of the simple series-fed circuit in that the resultant resistance is now higher for the a-c than for the d-c component. This indicates the need for distinguishing between the "dynamic" resistance and the "static" resistance of the load. The quiescent point is determined by drawing a load line through the point $i_b = 0$, $e_b = E_{bb}$, with a slope determined by the d-c resistance of the choke R_1. Since this resistance is generally small, this static load line will be almost vertical. The point Q is, as before, the intersection of this load line with the grid characteristic corresponding to the bias voltage E_c.

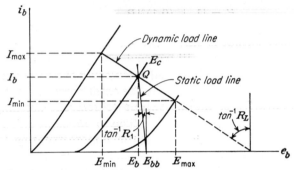

FIG. 16-7. The dynamic and static load lines of a shunt-fed or transformer-coupled amplifier.

However, for the frequencies at which the amplifier is to be used, the impedance of the inductor is so large that no alternating current passes through it. Since, at these frequencies, the reactance of C is considered negligible, the tube works into a resistance load R_L. Thus, the dynamic load line is drawn through the point Q with a slope determined by R_L, as shown in Fig. 16-7.

If a dynamic loud-speaker, the impedance of the voice coil of which may be of the order of from 5 to 15 ohms, were used in a shunt-fed circuit, only a small output power would be possible. This follows from the fact that the internal resistance of the tube is very much higher than that of the speaker, and so most of the power generated would be lost in the tube itself. If an output-matching transformer is used, however, it is possible to match the load resistance with that of the tube. Figure 16-8 illustrates such an output circuit.

The impedance-matching properties of an ideal transformer follow from the simple transformer relations

$$E_1 = \frac{N_1}{N_2} E_2 \quad \text{and} \quad I_1 = \frac{N_2}{N_1} I_2 \qquad (16\text{-}24)$$

where E_1 is the primary voltage, E_2 is the secondary voltage, I_1 is the primary current, I_2 is the secondary current, N_1 is the number of primary turns, and N_2 is the number of secondary turns. When $N_2 < N_1$, these equations show that the transformer reduces the voltage in proportion to the turns ratio $n = N_2/N_1$ and steps the current up in the same ratio. The ratio of these equations yields

$$\frac{E_1}{I_1} = \frac{1}{n^2}\frac{E_2}{I_2}$$

Since, however, E_1/I_1 represents the effective input resistance R_L', whereas E_2/I_2 is the output resistance R_L, then

$$R_L' = \frac{1}{n^2} R_L \qquad (16\text{-}25)$$

If, for example, $R_L = 10$ ohms and $n = \frac{1}{15}$, then $R_L' = 2{,}250$ ohms, a value which is comparable with the internal resistance of a power triode.

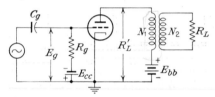

The same distinction between the static and dynamic load lines must be made for the transformer-coupled load as for the shunt-fed circuit. Thus, Fig. 16-7 is also valid for the transformer-coupled unit provided that R_1 is interpreted as the resistance of the primary winding of the transformer and that R_L denotes the effective load R_L'.

FIG. 16-8. A low-resistance load is matched to a high-resistance tube through an output transformer.

16-5. Frequency Response of an Output Transformer. Since an output transformer is never "ideal," the frequency-response curve will not be flat for all frequencies. The tube load will be a pure resistance only in the mid-frequency range. At low frequencies, the gain will fall, owing to the small reactance of the transformer magnetizing inductance L which will act as a shunt across the load. At the high frequencies, the transformer leakage reactance σ will act effectively as a high impedance in series with the load, and the gain will again fall. The transformer and tube capacitances usually play an unimportant role over the entire audio range for a triode-amplifier load. The equivalent circuit is shown in Fig. 16-9. If L_p is the primary inductance and K is the coefficient of coupling between primary and secondary, then it can be shown that[3] the magnetizing inductance is $L = KL_p$ and the leakage inductance is $\sigma = 2L_p(1 - K)$. The secondary output voltage is E_o.

1. *Intermediate Frequencies.* All reactances are negligible, and hence σ may be short-circuited and L may be open-circuited. Then the gain is

given by

$$\mathbf{A}_o = \frac{\mathbf{E}_o}{\mathbf{E}_g} = \frac{\pm \mu R_L/n}{R_1' + R_2'} \qquad (16\text{-}26)$$

where $R_1' \equiv r_p + R_1$ is the total primary resistance

$R_2' \equiv R_2/n^2 + R_L/n^2$ is the total secondary resistance referred to the primary

$n \equiv N_2/N_1$ is the ratio of secondary to primary turns and is less than unity

2. *Low Frequencies.* The leakage reactances are negligible, and σ may be shorted, but the reactance of L now parallels R_2'. The solution of this series-parallel circuit for the gain relative to the mid-band gain is found to be

$$\frac{\mathbf{A}_1}{\mathbf{A}_o} = \frac{1}{1 - j(f_1/f)} \qquad (16\text{-}27)$$

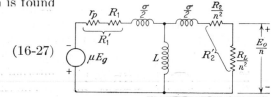

where

$$f_1 \equiv \frac{R_1' R_2'}{(2\pi L)(R_1' + R_2')} \qquad (16\text{-}28)$$

FIG. 16-9. The equivalent circuit of a tube containing an output transformer. The transformer primary and secondary winding resistances are R_1 and R_2, respectively. The magnetizing inductance is L, and the total leakage inductance is σ.

We see that the lower 3-db frequency f_1 is that frequency for which the magnetizing reactance equals the parallel combination of R_1' and R_2'.

3. *High Frequencies.* The reactance of L is so large that its shunting action may be ignored, but the leakage reactance σ must be taken into consideration. A simple series circuit results, and the gain relative to the mid-band gain is found to be

$$\frac{\mathbf{A}_2}{\mathbf{A}_o} = \frac{1}{1 + j(f/f_2)} \qquad \text{GOOD ONLY for A TRIODE} \qquad (16\text{-}29)$$

where

$$f_2 \equiv \frac{R_1' + R_2'}{2\pi\sigma} \qquad (16\text{-}30)$$

We see that the upper 3-db frequency f_2 is that frequency for which the total series leakage reactance equals the total series resistance.

These expressions for $\mathbf{A}_1/\mathbf{A}_o$ and $\mathbf{A}_2/\mathbf{A}_o$ are identical with those obtained for an RC-coupled amplifier in Chap. 15 (except that f_1 and f_2 have different meanings). Hence, the universal-gain and phase-shift curves of Fig. 15-6 are applicable here.

According to these results, the response characteristics of a transformer-coupled output stage can be improved greatly if a transformer having a very high primary inductance and very low leakage inductance is used. If the quiescent current is not allowed to pass through the transformer primary, d-c saturation of the core is avoided and the primary inductance may be greatly increased by using high-permeability iron. Furthermore, smaller wire can be used, and more turns can be wound on the same-sized core. Hence a combination of transformer coupling and shunt feed (to keep the quiescent current out of the transformer primary) is often used to improve the frequency response of an output stage.

Equation (16-29) is valid only for a triode. For a pentode or a beam power tube for which the plate resistance is very large, the primary shunting capacitance C_s can no longer be neglected. It often happens for such a circuit that there is a resonance between C_s and σ in the audio range. Under these circumstances the response at high frequencies may rise above the mid-band value before finally falling to a low value.

16-6. Maximum Undistorted Power Output. The maximum output power and the corresponding value of load resistance depend upon the method of operation.[4] Three cases will be discussed below. These are (1) the small-signal condition, (2) the fixed quiescent plate voltage condition, and (3) the fixed quiescent operating condition.

1. *The Small-signal Condition.* In Sec. 16-1 it is shown (assuming linear operation) that if the signal amplitude is kept constant the maximum power output is obtained for $R_L = r_p$. However, the requirement that E_g must remain constant is an artificial and unnecessary limitation. A large grid swing may be obtained by using several stages of voltage amplification before the power, or output, stage. Hence, in what follows it is assumed that any required signal voltage E_g is available.

2. *The Fixed Quiescent Plate Voltage Condition.* A transformer or shunt-fed arrangement is much more common for power amplifiers than the series-fed circuit. Under this method of operation, $E_b = E_{bb}$ (except for the small d-c voltage drop in the choke resistance). It now seems reasonable to ask: What must be the value of the load resistance in order that the power output be a maximum for a small allowable distortion and for a fixed value of quiescent plate voltage? An analysis[5] shows that the answer to this query is $R_L = 2r_p$. The solution will not be given here because the conditions set forth above are not practical since no consideration was given to the allowable plate dissipation of the tube. It turns out that, if the tube were to be operated under these conditions, in most cases the allowable plate dissipation would be exceeded.

3. *The Fixed Quiescent Operating Condition.* Since the tube manufacturers specify both the maximum allowable plate voltage and the maximum allowable plate dissipation, a very practical problem is the following:

Find the value of the load resistance in order that the power output be a maximum for a small allowable distortion and a specified quiescent point.

The answer to this problem is obtained graphically. If P_p is the maximum specified plate dissipation and E_b the quiescent specified plate voltage, then the quiescent current is $P_p/E_b = I_b$. A series of load lines are passed through this quiescent point, and in each case the output power and the distortion are calculated corresponding to a grid-cathode swing up to zero voltage and down to a grid voltage equal to twice the quiescent grid voltage.

The results of the above indicated calculations for a 2A3 power triode (Fig. A9-6) are shown in Fig. 16-10. The specified plate dissipation is 15 watts, and the specified plate voltage is 250 volts, which gives a quiescent current of $15/250$ amp $= 60$ ma. From the plate characteristics of the 2A3, the corresponding quiescent grid voltage is 45 volts. Hence, the grid swing is from zero to -90 volts.

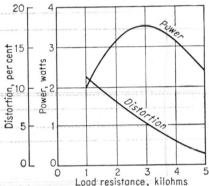

FIG. 16-10. Power output and second harmonic distortion of a type 2A3 triode as a function of load resistance. Conditions of operation: $I_b = 60$ ma, $E_b = 250$ volts, $E_c = -45$ volts, $r_p = 800$ ohms.

It is observed from this diagram that the maximum power of 3.5 watts is obtained at about 3,000 ohms, which is approximately four times the plate resistance of the tube. The second harmonic distortion is not negligible at this point, although the 5 per cent that exists is usually tolerable. The curves of Fig. 16-10 show that the power output has a very broad maximum with respect to load resistance but that the distortion varies rapidly with R_L. Hence, we have a choice of resistance to give a low value of distortion without too much sacrifice of output power.

16-7. Plate-circuit Efficiency. The various components of power in an amplifier circuit will now be examined. Suppose that the tube is supplying power to a pure resistance load. The average power input from the d-c supply is $E_{bb}I_b$. The power absorbed by the output circuit is $I_b{}^2R_1 + I_pE_p$, where I_p and E_p are the rms output current and voltage, respectively, and where R_1 is the *static* load resistance. If P_p denotes the average power dissipated by the plate, then, in accordance with the principle of the conservation of energy,

$$E_{bb}I_b = I_b{}^2R_1 + E_pI_p + P_p \tag{16-31}$$

Since, however,

$$E_{bb} = E_b + I_b R_1$$

P_p may be written in the form

$$P_p = E_b I_b - E_p I_p \tag{16-32}$$

If the load is not a pure resistance, $E_p I_p$ must be replaced by $E_p I_p \cos \theta$, where $\cos \theta$ is the power factor of the load.

Equation (16-32) expresses the amount of power that must be dissipated by the plate. It represents the kinetic energy of the electrons which is converted into heat upon bombardment of the plate by these electrons. If the a-c power output is zero, *i.e.*, if no applied signal exists, then P_p has its maximum value of $E_b I_b$. Otherwise, the heating of the anode is reduced by the amount of the a-c power converted by the tube and supplied to the load. Hence, a tube is cooler when delivering power to a load than when there is no such a-c power transfer. Obviously, then, the maximum plate dissipation is determined by the zero-excitation value.

The *theoretical efficiency, conversion efficiency,* or *plate-circuit efficiency* η_p gives a measure of the ability of the tube to convert the d-c power of the plate supply into the a-c power supplied to the load and is defined as

$$\eta_p \equiv \frac{\text{a-c power output to the load}}{\text{d-c power input to the plate circuit}} \times 100\% \tag{16-33}$$

If the distortion components are negligible, then

$$\eta_p = \frac{E_p I_p}{E_{bb} I_b} \times 100\% \tag{16-34}$$

The plate-circuit efficiency differs from the over-all efficiency because the grid power, the cathode heating power, and (for a pentode) the screen power are not included in the denominator of Eq. (16-33).

It is possible to obtain an approximate expression for η_p for triodes, if certain idealizations are made in the characteristic curves. These idealizations will, of course, introduce errors in the analysis. However, the results will permit an estimate of the order of magnitude of the plate-circuit efficiency and in particular will furnish an upper limit to the value. It will be assumed that the static curves of the tube are parallel straight lines which are equidistant for equal bias intervals, as illustrated in Fig. 16-11. The dynamic load

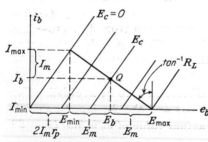

Fig. 16-11. The graphical construction from which the plate-circuit efficiency of an ideal amplifier with a resistance load is calculated.

is a resistor R_L. This figure may be used to analyze the results of either a series-fed or a shunt- (or transformer-) fed output tube. The only difference between the two is that the B-supply voltage E_{bb} equals E_{max} in the series-fed case, whereas E_{bb} is equal to the quiescent-point voltage E_b (on the assumption that the static d-c drop is negligible) in the shunt-fed amplifier.

We shall also assume that the grid does not swing beyond $E_c = 0$ but that it may swing to give zero current. Then

$$I_b = I_m$$

and

$$\eta_p = \frac{E_p I_p}{E_{bb} I_b} = \frac{E_m I_m}{2 E_{bb} I_b} = 50 \frac{E_m}{E_{bb}} \qquad \% \qquad (16\text{-}35)$$

The type of coupling used must now be taken into consideration before the analysis can be carried further. For the transformer or shunt-fed load,

$$E_{bb} = E_b = E_m + 2 I_m r_p$$

so that

$$\eta_p = \frac{50 E_m}{E_m + 2 I_m r_p} \qquad \%$$

which reduces to the form

$$\eta_p = \frac{50}{1 + 2 r_p / R_L} \qquad \% \qquad (16\text{-}36)$$

This result shows that the theoretical maximum value of η_p is 50 per cent. This optimum value cannot be obtained since to do so would require an infinite load resistance. For the 2A3 operating near the peak power output of 3.5 watts, as indicated in Fig. 16-10, we see that $R_L = 3{,}000$ ohms and $r_p = 800$ ohms. The value of η_p as calculated from Eq. (16-36) is 33 per cent. The true value of plate-circuit efficiency is less than that given by Eq. (16-36) because, in practice, the operating range will be smaller than that assumed in the above derivation. That is, the minimum current cannot be zero if excessive distortion is to be avoided. For example, since the output power is 3.5 watts and the d-c input power is 15 watts for the 2A3 amplifier, then the actual value of η_p is $3.5/15 = 23$ per cent.

Alternative forms for the output power P and the conversion efficiency η_p which do not involve r_p or R_L are easily obtained from the above relationships. These are

$$P = \tfrac{1}{8}(I_{max} - I_{min})(E_{max} - E_{min}) \qquad \eta_p = 25 \frac{E_{max} - E_{min}}{E_{bb}} \qquad \%$$

$$(16\text{-}37)$$

where $E_{\min} = 2I_m r_p$ is the minimum tube voltage, $E_{\max}$ is the maximum tube voltage, $I_{\max}$ is the peak value, and $I_{\min} \cong 0$ is the minimum value of the tube current.

An analysis similar to that just given shows that the maximum theoretical efficiency of a series-fed power amplifier is 25 per cent, or one-half that of the shunt-fed configuration. This is another reason why the series arrangement is seldom used.

Increased output power and plate-circuit efficiency may be obtained by driving the grid positive. However, the signal source impedance must

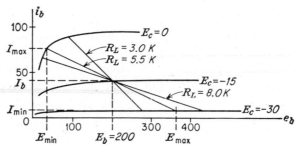

Fig. 16-12. Plate characteristics of a 6F6 pentode. Three load lines corresponding to resistance values of 3,000, 5,500, and 8,000 ohms are shown passing through the quiescent point, $E_b = 200$ volts, $E_c = -15$ volts.

be low compared with the grid input impedance. Otherwise, this mode of operation will introduce a high nonlinear distortion.

16-8. Power Pentodes and Beam Power Tubes.[6] The desirable features of a power pentode or beam tube are the ability to deliver a large power output with a small grid swing (high power sensitivity), a high efficiency, and possibly lower distortion.

The discussion (Sec. 16-3) of harmonic generation in a vacuum tube resulting from the nonlinear dynamic characteristic is applicable to multi-electrode tubes as well as to triodes. Under ordinary conditions of operation of a triode, the second harmonic is the principal component of distortion. It will be shown below that it is possible to eliminate completely, by the proper choice of the load resistance, the second-harmonic-distortion component in a multielectrode tube. The third-order-distortion term is then the most important.

Consider a 6F6 pentode operating under the following conditions: $E_f = 6.3$ volts, $E_{c2} = 250$ volts, $E_b = 200$ volts, and $E_c = -15$ volts. Three load lines corresponding to load resistances of 3,000, 5,500, and 8,000 ohms pass through the quiescent point, as shown in Fig. 16-12. Suppose that a signal voltage having a peak value of 15 volts is impressed on the grid. The grid will then swing from 0 to -30 volts. Oscillograms of the output-*current* wave forms reveal the following: The wave form closely resembles a sine wave for the case $R_L = 5,500$ ohms. For $R_L = 8,000$ ohms, the upper half of the wave is decidedly smaller than the lower loop, whereas for $R_L = 3,000$ ohms the upper half is larger. The lower half of the current wave is identical for all three resistances.

An inspection of the static characteristics of the 6F6 (Fig. 16-12) reveals the reason for these results. The bottom half of the wave is obtained as the grid swings from -15 to -30 volts. At the quiescent point (-15 volts) the current is the same for all three loads. At -30 volts the current is still practically the same for all loads, for the i_b-e_b characteristic is practically a horizontal line, as seen in Fig. 16-12. Consequently, the lower halves of the current waves are almost identical for the three loads.

The upper loop of the output-current wave is obtained as the grid swings from -15 volts to zero. Since the i_b-e_b characteristic for $e_c = 0$ is a rapidly varying one in the region of low values of e_b, the peak current depends critically upon the point of intersection of the load line with this characteristic. For low resistances the point of intersection will be on the upper portion of the $e_c = 0$ curve. This results in a peaked output wave. For high resistances, the point of intersection will be on the rapidly falling portion of this curve and gives rise to a flat-topped curve.

The choice of $R_L = 5,500$ ohms was determined by the requirement that the second harmonic distortion be zero. From Eqs. (16-19),

$$B_2 = \tfrac{1}{4}(I_{max} - 2I_b + I_{min})$$

and I_{max} must equal $2I_b - I_{min}$ in order that $B_2 = 0$. It is found from Fig. A9-7 that I_b, under the prescribed conditions of operation, is equal to 37 ma. Also, I_{min} (corresponding to $E_c = -30$ volts) is substantially independent of the load line and is found to be 7 ma. Hence, I_{max} must equal

$$2 \times 37 - 7 = 67 \text{ ma}$$

The corresponding value of e_b (for $e_c = 0$, $i_b = 67$ ma) is 35 volts. It follows that

$$R_L = \frac{200 - 35}{67 - 37} = 5.5 \text{ kilohms}$$

The other two values of load resistance were arbitrarily chosen in order to illustrate the distortion.

Example. Calculate the distortion and the power output of the amplifier discussed above, if it is working into an 8,000-ohm load.

Solution. A load line corresponding to 8,000 ohms is drawn through the quiescent point, $E_c = -15$, $E_b = 200$, on the static curves of Fig. A9-7. The following points of intersection of this line with the plate characteristics are obtained:

e_c	0	-5	-10	-15	-20	-25	-30
i_b	59	56	48	37	26	15	7

TO GET LOAD LINE

$e_b = E_{bb} - i_b R_L$ ∴ $E_{bb} = 200 + (37)(8)$ I_{bq}

E_{bq}

$= 496$
SO NOW HAVE 2 PTS & DRAW LINE

The values of $I_{\frac{1}{2}}$ and $I_{-\frac{1}{2}}$ introduced in Sec. 16-3 are the current values when the grid swings to one-half its peak values (positively and negatively, respectively). The peak swing in this case is 15 volts, so that $I_{\frac{1}{2}}$ is the current for $e_c = -7.5$ volts. $I_{-\frac{1}{2}}$ represents the current for $e_c = -22.5$ volts. These values do not appear in the table and must be obtained either by interpolation or from the plotted dynamic curve (i_b vs. e_c). The latter method yields $I_{\frac{1}{2}} = 52$ ma and $I_{-\frac{1}{2}} = 21$ ma. From the table, $i_{max} = 59$ ma, $I_b = 37$ ma, and $I_{min} = 7$ ma. These are the five values required for the five-point schedule. Using the formulas of Eqs. (16-19), there result

$$B_0 = -1.7 \qquad B_1 = 28 \qquad B_2 = -2.0 \qquad B_3 = -1.7 \qquad B_4 = 0.3 \text{ ma}$$

Hence, the second-, third-, and fourth-harmonic-distortion components are

$$D_2 = 100 \frac{|B_2|}{|B_1|} = \frac{200}{28} = 7\%$$

$$D_3 = 100 \frac{|B_3|}{|B_1|} = \frac{170}{28} = 6\%$$

$$D_4 = 100 \frac{|B_4|}{|B_1|} = \frac{30}{28} = 1\%$$

The total distortion is

$$D = \sqrt{7^2 + 6^2 + 1^2} = 9.3\%$$

The total power is

$$P = \frac{(1 + D^2)B_1{}^2 R_L}{2} = 3.15 \text{ watts}$$

Suppose that it is desired to investigate the proper load resistance of a power pentode for which the *quiescent point is specified.* This is operating condition 3 of Sec. 16-6, and the procedure is essentially the same as that outlined in that section for a triode. However, since considerable distortion is introduced if the magnitude of the load resistance is not correctly chosen, the first step in the analysis is to choose a load resistor that will give zero second harmonic distortion. The values of the third- and higher-harmonic components are then calculated. Several values of resistance above and below this load resistor are chosen, and the corresponding distortion components are calculated for each case. Also, the output power under the several conditions of load is calculated either from the expression

$$P = \tfrac{1}{2} B_1{}^2 R_L \tag{16-38}$$

or from

$$P = \tfrac{1}{8}(E_{max} - E_{min})(I_{max} - I_{min}) \tag{16-39}$$

These expressions assume that the contribution to the power by the harmonics is negligible, a justifiable assumption under most circumstances. The calculated values of the power output and the corresponding values of distortion are plotted as a function of the load resistance. The optimum load is that which gives the largest output power without excessive distortion.

It is fortunate that a large power output is obtainable in power pentodes for a value of load resistance for which the distortion is low. The power output and harmonic distortion for a 6L6 beam power tube operating at the quiescent point $E_b = E_{c2} = 250$ volts and a plate dissipation of 19 watts are shown in Fig. 16-13. We see that the maximum in the power-output curve is quite broad. For example, it is possible to obtain at least 6.5 watts of output power with less than 10 per cent distortion for any load resistance in the range from 2.5 to 4.5 kilohms. The plate-circuit efficiency under these conditions is $650/19 = 34$ per cent. Note that the optimum value of R_L for a pentode is a small fraction of the plate resistance (22.5 kilohms for the 6L6) whereas for a triode the optimum value of R_L is several times r_p.

16-9. Shift of Dynamic Load Line.[7] The analysis of the preceding section must be corrected slightly if an appreciable change in direct current occurs because of rectification caused by the non-linearity of the dynamic characteristic. Consider Fig. 16-14, on which are indicated the static and dynamic load lines of a pentode working into a transformer-coupled resistive load. Point Q is the qui-

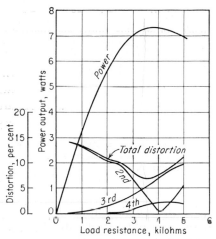

FIG. 16-13. Power output and distortion of a 6L6 beam tube as a function of load resistance. (Operating conditions: $E_b = E_{c2} = 250$ volts, $I_b = 72$ ma, $E_{c1} = -14$ volts.)

escent point if there is no rectification. If a calculation reveals that $B_0 \neq 0$, then it is no longer valid to draw the dynamic load line through the point Q. Instead, it must now pass through some other point D of the static load line. The new dynamic load line $D'DD''$ is drawn parallel to the original dynamic line through the point D. The new "quiescent" point Q' is located on the quiescent grid characteristic E_c, and the corresponding quiescent current is I_b'.

The point D must be determined by trial and error. The correct location is that for which $I_{dc} = I_b' + B_0'$. The component B_0' due to rectification may be either positive or negative. A negative value of B_0' is indicated in Fig. 16-14 so that the average tube current decreases with applied signal. As a first estimate of the correct location of the point D, the following procedure may be adopted: The dynamic load line is drawn through point Q and the rectification component B_0 is calculated. Then D is located so that $I_{dc} = I_b + B_0$. The new values of I_b and B_0, which are the terms I_b' and B_0', respectively, are found. If the correct value of D has been located, then the assumed direct current I_{dc} will equal the calculated direct current $I_b' + B_0'$. This will usually be the case if the rectification is small. For example, for the 6F6 operating under the conditions given in Sec. 16-8 into an 8,000-ohm load ($E_c = -15$ volts, $E_b = 200$ volts), the value of I_b is 37 ma and $B_0 = -3$ ma so that

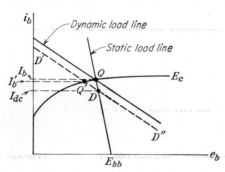

FIG. 16-14. The operating point shifts when rectification occurs because of a nonlinear dynamic curve.

the point D is assumed to correspond to a current $I_{dc} = 34$ ma and $E_b = 200$ volts. In this calculation the d-c resistance of the transformer is neglected so that the line QD is a vertical line. If an 8,000-ohm line is drawn through point D, it is found that $I_b' + B_0'$ yields 34 ma very closely. Thus the assumed value of D is the correct one. If the rectification is very large, several estimates might be necessary before the correct point D is found.

It should be noted that these considerations are not restricted to pentodes but are also applicable to beam tubes and triodes. The method of analysis would be the same in all cases.

16-10. Push-Pull Amplifiers. A great deal of the distortion that is introduced by the nonlinearity of the dynamic characteristic may be eliminated by means of the arrangement shown in Fig. 16-15 which is known as a "push-pull" circuit. In this circuit the excitation voltage is introduced through a center-tapped transformer. Thus, when the signal voltage on one tube is positive, the signal voltage on the other tube is negative by an equal amount. Any other circuit that provides two equal voltages which differ in phase by 180 deg may be used in place of the transformer.

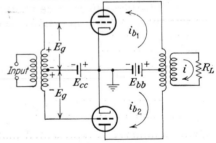

FIG. 16-15. A push-pull circuit using fixed bias.

Circuits involving vacuum tubes to provide this phase reversal have been devised, and several are discussed in Sec. 17-7. Suppose that the signal input grid voltage to one tube is of the form

$$e_{g1} = E_{gm} \cos \omega t$$

The plate current of this tube will be represented by the expression

$$i_{b1} = I_b + B_0 + B_1 \cos \omega t + B_2 \cos 2\omega t + B_3 \cos 3\omega t + \cdots \quad (16\text{-}40)$$

This Fourier series contains only cosine components, as explained in Sec. 16-3. The corresponding input signal to the second tube is

$$e_{g2} = -e_{g1} = E_{gm} \cos (\omega t + \pi)$$

The output current of this tube is obtained by replacing ωt by $\omega t + \pi$ in the expression for i_{b1}. That is,

$$i_{b2}(\omega t) = i_{b1}(\omega t + \pi) \quad (16\text{-}41)$$

whence

$$i_{b2} = I_b + B_0 + B_1 \cos (\omega t + \pi) + B_2 \cos 2(\omega t + \pi) + \cdots$$

which is

$$i_{b2} = I_b + B_0 - B_1 \cos \omega t + B_2 \cos 2\omega t - B_3 \cos 3\omega t + \cdots \quad (16\text{-}42)$$

As illustrated in Fig. 16-15, the currents i_{b1} and i_{b2} are in opposite directions through the output-transformer primary windings. The total output current is then proportional to the difference between the plate currents in the two tubes. That is,

$$i = k(i_{b1} - i_{b2}) = 2k(B_1 \cos \omega t + B_3 \cos 3\omega t + \cdots) \quad (16\text{-}43)$$

This expression shows that a push-pull circuit will balance out all even harmonics in the output and will leave the third harmonic term as the principal source of distortion. This conclusion was reached on the assumption that the two tubes are identical. If the characteristics of the two tubes differ appreciably, then the appearance of even harmonics must be expected.

The fact that the output current contains no even harmonic terms means that the push-pull system possesses "half-wave" or "mirror symmetry," in addition to the zero-axis symmetry. Half-wave symmetry requires that the bottom loop of the wave, when shifted 180 deg along the axis, will be the mirror image of the top loop. The condition of mirror symmetry is represented mathematically by the relation

$$i(\omega t) = -i(\omega t + \pi) \quad (16\text{-}44)$$

If $\omega t + \pi$ is substituted for ωt in Eq. (16-43), it will be seen that Eq. (16-44) is satisfied.

Because no even harmonics are present in the output of a push-pull system, such a circuit will give more output per tube for a given amount of distortion. For the same reason, a push-pull arrangement may be used to obtain less distortion for a given power output per tube.

Another feature of the push-pull system is evident from an inspection of Fig. 16-15.   It is noticed that the d-c components of the plate current oppose each other magnetically in the transformer core.   This eliminates any tendency toward core saturation and consequent nonlinear distortion that might arise from the curvature of the transformer magnetization curve.   Another advantage of this system is that the effects of ripple voltages that may be contained in the power supply because of inadequate filtering will be balanced out.   This cancellation results because the cur-

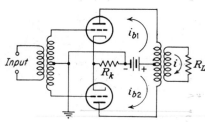

rents produced by this ripple voltage are in opposite directions in the transformer winding and so will not appear in the load.   Of course, the power-supply hum will also act on the voltage-amplifier stages and so will be part of the input to the power stage.   This hum will not be eliminated by the push-pull circuit.

FIG. 16-16   A self-biased push-pull circuit.

The wiring diagram of a self-biased push-pull amplifier is illustrated in Fig. 16-16.   The voltage developed across the self-bias resistor R_k at any instant of time is $(i_{b1} + i_{b2})R_k$, which, from Eqs. (16-40) and (16-42), becomes

$$(i_{b1} + i_{b2})R_k = 2R_k(I_b + B_0 + B_2\cos 2\omega t + B_4\cos 4\omega t + \cdots) \quad (16\text{-}45)$$

That is, the current through the self-biasing resistor contains only *even* harmonics.   If it is assumed that the tubes are operating on the substantially linear portions of their characteristics (that is, for a Class A system), then $B_0 = B_2 = B_4 = 0$, and the voltage across R_k remains fixed at its bias value of $2I_bR_k$.   In other words, no feedback exists, and it is therefore not necessary to use a bypass capacitor.   The correct bias resistor for a desired bias voltage E_{cc} is evidently $R_k = E_{cc}/2I_b$.   If the tubes are operating over a nonlinear region, then a capacitor is needed to bypass the second and higher harmonics.

The larger the applied grid signal, the greater will be the distortion arising from the nonlinearity of the tube characteristics.   Under the conditions of large grid swing (and so of large power output) the "rectification" component $2B_0R_k$ will no longer be negligible and will add to the bias $2I_bR_k$.   Thus, the greater the grid swing, the more negative will be the effective bias of the triodes in a push-pull circuit.   The rectification component is so large in Class B systems (the quiescent current being very small or zero) that self-bias cannot be used for this type of operation.

16-11. Equivalent Circuit of a Push-Pull Class A System.   Suppose that both tubes of the push-pull system are identical and that μ and r_p

remain constant over the range of operation. The equivalent circuit of the system may then be drawn according to the rules of Sec. 8-3. This circuit is given in Fig. 16-17. We see from this figure that the voltage drop from grid to the cathode of the first tube is $E_{gk1} = E_g$ whereas the corresponding quantity for the second tube is $E_{gk2} = -E_g$.

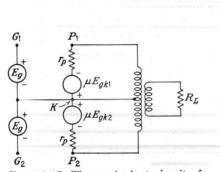

FIG. 16-17. The equivalent circuit of the Class A push-pull amplifier of Fig. 16-15.

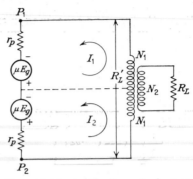

FIG. 16-18. A circuit equivalent to the circuit of Fig. 16-17.

The equivalent plate circuit can be redrawn as in Fig. 16-18. It is clear from the symmetry of this figure that $I_1 = I_2$. The connection (drawn dashed) between the cathode terminal and the mid-point of the output transformer carries no fundamental frequency component of current, owing to the cancellation that occurs in this line. This line may be omitted from the diagram without affecting the analysis. By replacing the coupling transformer and load resistor R_L by the *effective plate-to-plate load resistance R_L'*, the final simplified equivalent circuit becomes that shown in Fig. 16-19. The resistance R_L of the secondary is related to the resistance R_L' by the expression

$$R_L' = \left(\frac{2N_1}{N_2}\right)^2 R_L \qquad (16\text{-}46)$$

in accordance with Eq. (16-25), *the total number of primary turns being $2N_1$.*

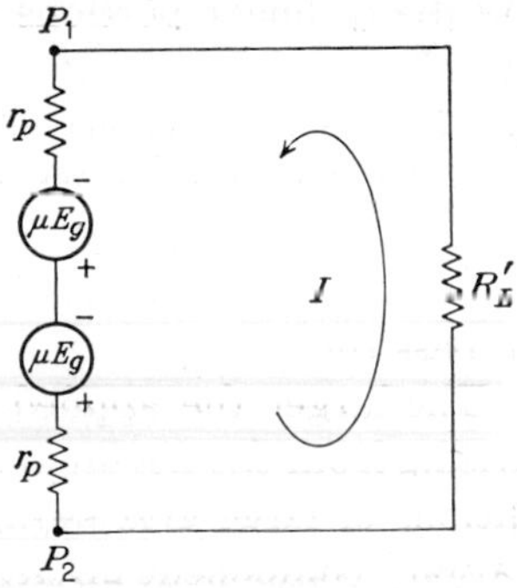

The resultant current is given by

$$I = \frac{2\mu E_g}{2r_p + R_L'} \qquad (16\text{-}47)$$

FIG. 16-19. The simplified equivalent circuit of the Class A push-pull amplifier.

which may be written in the form

$$I = \frac{\mu E_g}{r_p + R_L'/2} \qquad (16\text{-}48)$$

The total power delivered to the load is

$$P = I^2 R_L' = 2 \left(\frac{\mu E_g}{r_p + R_L'/2} \right)^2 \frac{R_L'}{2} \tag{16-49}$$

This expression may be interpreted as showing that the total output power is twice the power of each tube working into the equivalent load resistance $R_L'/2$.

Equation (16-49) may also be written in the more significant form

$$P = \left(\frac{\mu E_g}{r_p/2 + R_L'/4} \right)^2 \frac{R_L'}{4} \tag{16-50}$$

This expression reveals that the Class A push-pull amplifier may be represented by a single composite generator having an emf μE_g with an internal resistance equal to $r_p/2$ and working into a load resistance equal to $R_L'/4$. It is possible, in fact, to derive a set of static characteristics of the composite tube from the plate characteristics of the individual tube and to obtain significant operating information therefrom. This matter is examined in the following sections.

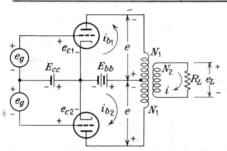

16-12. Composite Static Characteristic Curves.[8] The equivalent circuits are valid only if μ, r_p, and g_m of the tubes are constant over the entire range of operation. Under such conditions, no harmonics are generated. However, push-pull circuits are generally operated over such a range that harmonics are introduced. If due account is to be taken of the nonlinearity of the tube characteristics, a graphical construction must be employed. The explanation of this method is somewhat involved. However, it is extremely easy to carry out the graphical construction in any specific case.

Fig. 16-20. When the grid voltage of one tube increases by an amount e_g, the grid voltage of the other tube decreases by this amount. When the plate voltage of one tube decreases by an amount e, the plate voltage of the other tube increases by this amount. (Total number of primary turns is $2N_1$.)

The theory that forms the basis for the graphical construction follows from the circuit diagram of Fig. 16-15, which is redrawn as Fig. 16-20 for convenience. An ideal transformer is assumed. The voltage across each half of the primary is e, as shown. The load voltage is, therefore,

$$e_L = \frac{N_2}{N_1} e \tag{16-51}$$

For an ideal transformer, the net primary ampere turns are equal to the secondary ampere turns at any instant of time.   That is,

$$N_1 i_{b1} - N_1 i_{b2} = N_2 i \tag{16-52}$$

The load voltage is

$$e_L = i R_L = (i_{b1} - i_{b2}) \frac{N_1}{N_2} R_L \tag{16-53}$$

By combining Eqs. (16-51) and (16-53) there results

$$e = (i_{b1} - i_{b2}) \frac{R_L'}{4} \tag{16-54}$$

where the plate-to-plate resistance R_L' is given by

$$R_L' = \left(\frac{2N_1}{N_2}\right)^2 R_L \tag{16-55}$$

The following relationships are evident from an inspection of Fig. 16-20:

$$e_{b1} = E_b - e \qquad e_{b2} = E_b + e \qquad e_{c1} = E_c + e_g \qquad e_{c2} = E_c - e_g \tag{16-56}$$

where E_c equals the *negative* of the grid-supply voltage (or $E_c = -E_{cc}$) and E_b equals the plate-supply voltage E_{bb}, the transformer primary resistance being neglected.

These equations state that when the plate voltage e_{b1} of tube 1 decreases from the quiescent-point value E_b by an amount e, then the corresponding voltage e_{b2} of tube 2 increases from the quiescent value by the same amount.   Likewise, when the grid voltage e_{c1} of tube 1 increases from the quiescent voltage E_c by the signal voltage e_g, the corresponding voltage e_{c2} of tube 2 decreases from the quiescent value by the same amount.   These conditions are depicted in Fig. 16-21, which shows three members of the plate family of the triodes under consideration.

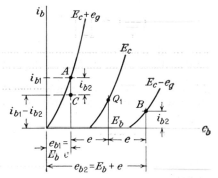

FIG. 16-21. The construction for obtaining a point C on a composite static characteristic of a push-pull amplifier.

The quiescent point of tube 1 is Q_1 and is determined by the grid voltage E_c and the plate voltage E_b.   Point A corresponds to $e_{b1} = E_b - e$ and $e_{c1} = E_c + e_g$, the tube current being i_{b1}.   Point B corresponds to $e_{b2} = E_b + e$ and $e_{c2} = E_c - e_g$, the tube current being i_{b2}.   If the ordinate at B is subtracted from the ordinate at A, then the point C is located.

(A pair of dividers is useful in this connection.) Point C has the ordinate $i_{b1} - i_{b2}$ *for the arbitrarily chosen instantaneous values of e and e_g.*

The *composite static plate characteristics* denote the family of $(i_{b1} - i_{b2})$ vs. e_{b1} curves, with the grid signal voltage as a parameter. Hence, point C is one point on the composite curve for the signal voltage e_g. Other points on this curve are found by maintaining e_g constant and by vary-

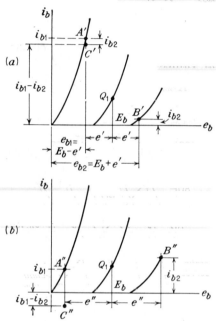

ing e. The constructions for two other values e' and e'' are shown in Fig. 16-22a and 16-22b. These locate two other points C' and C'' on the composite characteristic. The locus of these points is the complete composite characteristic corresponding to the signal

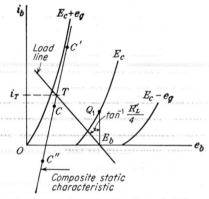

FIG. 16-22. The construction in Fig. 16-21 repeated for two other points C' and C''.

FIG. 16-23. Points C', C, and C'' replotted from Figs. 16-21 and 16-22 determine the composite static characteristic corresponding to the input signal e_g.

voltage e_g. This composite static curve is given in Fig. 16-23. It is seen to extend above and below the zero-current axis and to be much more linear than the plate characteristics of the individual tubes.

To find the load line corresponding to a given R_L to be used with the composite curves, it is noted from Eqs. (16-56) and (16-54) that

$$e_{b1} = E_b - (i_{b1} - i_{b2}) \frac{R_L'}{4} \tag{16-57}$$

This is the equation of a straight line that passes through the point $i_{b1} - i_{b2} = 0$, $e_{b1} = E_b$, with a slope determined by $R_L'/4$, as shown in Fig. 16-23. The point of intersection T of this line with the composite static characteristic gives the current

$$i_{b1} - i_{b2} = i_T$$

The actual load current in the transformer secondary circuit is, according to Eq. (16-52),

$$i = \frac{N_1}{N_2}(i_{b1} - i_{b2}) = \frac{N_1}{N_2}i_T \qquad (16\text{-}58)$$

for the signal voltage e_g.

A family of composite static characteristics may be obtained by repeating the construction above for several values of e_g. Such a family of curves for a type 2A3 tube is shown in Fig. 16-24. The composite curves are shown broken for the sake of clarity. The quiescent point of each tube was taken as Q_1 with $E_c = -40$ volts, and $E_b = 240$ volts. The quiescent point Q of the push-pull system corresponds to these same values of E_c and E_b but to zero net current $i_{b1} - i_{b2} = 0$ and to the signal voltage $e_g = 0$, as shown. The composite characteristics are labeled according to the relationship $e_g = e_c + 40$ volts.

An alternative method of obtaining the composite characteristics was described by Thompson.[8] According to this method, the plate characteristics of the tube are plotted in the usual way. These same curves are

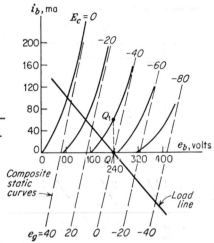

FIG. 16-24. The family of composite static characteristics for a 2A3 push-pull amplifier. Each tube operates at the Q point, $E_b = 240$ volts and $E_c = -40$ volts.

plotted again, this time with the plate current plotted downward, with the origin to the right, and with the voltage scale shifted so that the voltages E_b of both sets of curves coincide. This construction is shown in Fig. 16-25. These inverted curves represent the plate family of tube 2. At any given ordinate, the plate current i_{b2} for $e_{c2} = E_c - e_g$ is added algebraically to the plate current i_{b1} for $e_{c1} = E_c + e_g$. For example, point C in the diagram is obtained by subtracting from the magnitude of the current i_A ($e_{c1} = -40 + 40 = 0$) the magnitude of the current i_B ($e_{c2} = -40 - 40 = -80$ volts). This gives one point on the composite characteristic corresponding to the signal voltage $e_g = 40$ volts. A little thought will convince the reader that this procedure is essentially equivalent to the

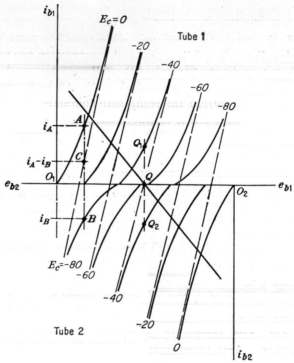

Fɪɢ. 16-25. The Thompson method of obtaining the composite static characteristic curves of a push-pull amplifier.

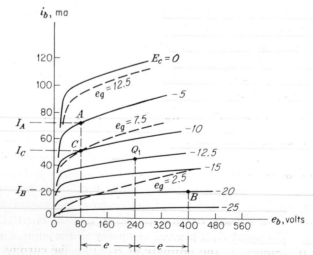

Fɪɢ. 16-26. The composite static characteristics of the 6V6 beam-power-tube push-pull amplifier.   Each tube operates at the Q point, $E_b = 240$ volts and $E_c = -12.5$ volts.

method considered above. The Thompson method of construction is very common in the literature, but the other method is to be preferred since it avoids the necessity of redrawing the complete plate family.

The foregoing discussion of the graphical construction has been entirely general, so that it applies to Class A, AB, or B operation and to any type of tube, whether triode, beam, or pentode. For Class B operation with exactly zero quiescent current the composite characteristics (for one-half a cycle) coincide with the static characteristics.

Although the discussion assumed that the tubes are triodes, the method is actually somewhat easier to apply to multielectrode tubes. This simplification results because the current i_{b2} remains substantially constant for large variations in e_b. The composite static characteristics for the 6V6 beam power tube are shown in Fig. 16-26. Specifically, it should be noted that any point C on the $e_g = 7.5$ volt curve (with $E_c = -12.5$ volts) is obtained by considering the two plate characteristics for $e_c = -12.5 + 7.5 = -5$ volts and $e_c = -12.5 - 7.5 = -20$ volts. For any voltage e, I_A is located on $e_c = -5$, and I_B is located on $e_c = -20$ volts, as shown. Then the point C is that for which $I_C = I_A - I_B$. Since I_B is fairly constant for all values of e, the composite curve for $e_g = 7.5$ volts is essentially that for $e_c = -5$ volts except that it is shifted downward by the amount I_B. This composite curve is shown dashed in Fig. 16-26. The curves for $e_g = 12.5$ volts (obtained from the static curves for $e_c = -12.5 + 12.5 = 0$ and $e_c = -12.5 - 12.5 = -25$ volts) and for $e_g = 2.5$ volts (obtained from the static curves for $e_c = -12.5 + 2.5 = -10$ volts and $e_c = -12.5 - 2.5 = -15$ volts) are also indicated. Again it is emphasized that the ordinates at the points A and B corresponding to the same e and located on the curves $e_c = E_c + e_g$ and $e_c = E_c - e_g$, respectively, can be measured and subtracted very rapidly if a pair of dividers or a millimeter ruler is employed.

16-13. Push-Pull Dynamic Characteristics. The composite dynamic curve of a push-pull amplifier can be determined from the composite static curves in much the same way that the dynamic curve is obtained from the static curves of a single-tube amplifier for any load resistance. Thus the points A, B, Q, C, D are the intersections of the equivalent load line $R_L'/4$ with the composite static curves (Fig. 16-27). These points are replotted in Fig. 16-28 to form the composite dynamic curve.

The dynamic characteristic of each tube is determined in the following manner: The total current for $E_c = 0$ is represented by I_A in Fig. 16-27. For the same plate voltage E_A and the same grid bias, the current in tube 1 is I_{A1}. The point A_1 is plotted vertically above point A and on the curve $E_c = 0$. Similarly, the ordinate at B_1 gives the current in tube 1 when the composite current is determined by the ordinate at B for $E_c = -20$. The same method is used to determine all the other points.

From the construction described above it should be clear that C and B are located symmetrically about the Q point. The current at C is the negative of the current at B. The same is true for the currents at D and A. Hence, *it is unnecessary to draw either the push-pull load line or the composite static characteristics to the right of the Q point.* To complete the load line of tube 1, point C_1 (or D_1) is located the same distance to the right of Q as B_1 (or A_1) is to the left of Q.

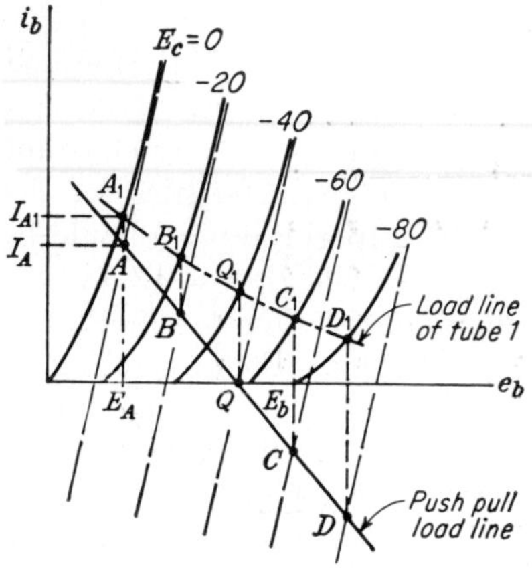

The individual dynamic curves of each tube are shown in Fig. 16-28. The points A_2, B_2, Q_2, C_2, D_2 for tube 2 are obtained by symmetry from the corresponding points of tube 1. It is seen that, although the composite dynamic characteristic is practically a straight line, the individual dynamic characteristics are curved. Thus, for a given sinusoidal input, the current delivered by each tube is not sinusoidal, in general. However, the output current, as determined from the composite dynamic characteristic, is almost an exact sinusoidal curve. This construction again demonstrates that a push-pull circuit eliminates considerable distortion.

FIG. 16-27. The push-pull load line and the load line of one tube of the push-pull amplifier. It is observed that the load line (dynamic characteristic) of the single tube is not linear.

It is unnecessary to determine the individual-tube dynamic curves if only the output current is desired. These individual dynamic curves are required if the plate-circuit efficiency is under survey. This statement follows from the fact that the power input to the system is $2I_{dc}E_{bb} = 2(I_b + B_0)E_{bb}$ and B_0 must be found from the individual-tube dynamic characteristics by the method of harmonic analysis considered in Sec. 16-3.

16-14. Output Power and Distortion in Push-Pull Circuits. To find the distortion in a push-pull amplifier, which is known to be predominantly a third harmonic of the signal-voltage frequency, the five-point schedule of Sec. 16-3 can be used. Since, however, the output of a push-pull system always possesses mirror symmetry, the following relationships are true: $I_b = 0$, $I_{max} = -I_{min}$, and $I_{\frac{1}{2}} = -I_{-\frac{1}{2}}$ (Fig. 16-28). Under these circumstances, Eqs. (16-19) reduce to

$$B_0 = B_2 = B_4 = 0 \qquad B_1 = \tfrac{2}{3}(I_{max} + I_{\frac{1}{2}}) \qquad B_3 = \tfrac{1}{3}(I_{max} - 2I_{\frac{1}{2}})$$

$$\text{(16-59)}$$

The third harmonic distortion is given by B_3/B_1. The values I_{max} and

$I_{\frac{1}{2}}$ are the values of current when the grid signal is at its maximum value and at one-half of this maximum value, respectively. These current values are readily determined from the composite dynamic characteristic or from the composite static characteristics and the load line $R_L'/4$. If the composite dynamic characteristic possesses an appreciable curvature, the fifth and higher harmonic components may not be negligible. Under

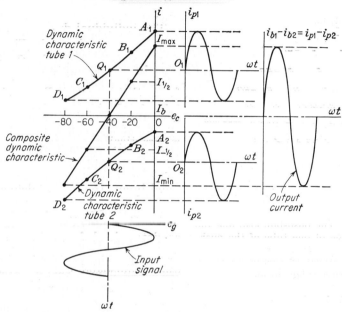

FIG. 16-28. The current wave shapes of each tube and the output-current wave shape from a push-pull amplifier for a sinusoidal input signal. The dynamic curves are determined from Fig. 16-27.

such circumstances, it is necessary to use a schedule that will permit the calculation of these higher-order terms.

The fundamental power output is given by the product of the rms fundamental current squared and the effective resistance, or

$$P_1 = \left(\frac{B_1}{\sqrt{2}}\right)^2 \frac{R_L'}{4} = \frac{B^2{}_1 R_L'}{8} \qquad (16\text{-}60)$$

If, as is usually the case, it is permissible to neglect the harmonic power, then the total power is given by

$$P = \frac{E_m I_m}{2} \qquad (16\text{-}61)$$

where E_m and I_m denote the peak values of the alternating output voltage and current, respectively. These values can be read directly from the curves and are determined by the intersection of the load line $R_L'/4$ with the appropriate composite static curve. For example, the output power for the conditions shown in Fig. 16-27, since $I_m = I_A$ and $E_m = E_b - E_A$, is simply

$$P = \frac{(E_b - E_A)I_A}{2} \tag{16-62}$$

It is unnecessary to draw a complete set of composite characteristics in order to calculate the output power. All that is necessary is to locate point A. This may be done very quickly by a method of trial and error. Thus, the load line representing $R_L'/4$ is drawn through the given Q point

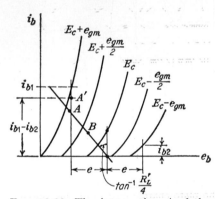

$(e_b = E_b, i = 0)$ on the plate characteristics supplied by the tube manufacturer. Point A will lie on this line and somewhat to the right of the static curve corresponding to the peak grid signal per tube, e_{gm}. As a first approximation, a value of e is assumed that will give a resultant current point in this neighborhood. Suppose, for example, that the point A' in Fig. 16-29 is thus located. Since this point lies above the load line, the chosen value of e

Fig. 16-29. The intersection A of the load line with the composite static characteristic corresponding to a given signal voltage (e_{gm}) is easily found by the method of trial and error.

is too small. A slightly larger value of e is chosen as a second trial. Several successive trials will permit the point A on the load line to be located. This is an extremely simple and rapid method. If the value of e originally chosen had been too large, point A' would have fallen below the load line.

Any other point on the dynamic curve can be found in a similar way without first drawing the complete composite static family. In particular, in order to calculate the third harmonic distortion, all that is necessary is to locate two points on the dynamic curve, viz., $I_{max} = I_A$, and $I_{\frac{1}{2}}$. The current $I_{\frac{1}{2}}$ is found just as I_A above, except that the plate characteristics for $e_c = E_c \pm \frac{1}{2}e_{gm}$ are used instead of the curves for $e_c = E_c \pm e_{gm}$. This locates the point B in Fig. 16-29 so that $I_B = I_{\frac{1}{2}}$.

As was true with a single-tube amplifier, the load resistance that must be used in order to obtain maximum power from a push-pull system depends upon the particular type of tube used and upon the conditions of operation. Consider a set of triodes to be used in a push-pull circuit, the composite static characteristics of which are very nearly straight lines with equal spacings for equal increments in e_g. For a given operating point and a given grid swing, the maximum power output will exist when the effective load resistance $R_L'/4$ equals the resistance corresponding to the slope of the resultant composite characteristic.

If the composite characteristics are not linear (as would certainly be the case if triodes were operated in Class B or if pentodes were used), then the optimum load line to use is determined by the methods described in Secs. 16-6 and 16-8.

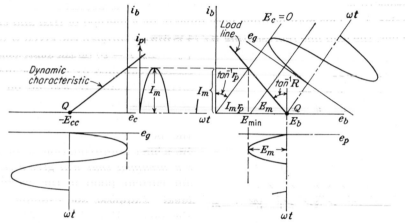

Fig. 16-30. Graphical construction for determining the output-current wave shape for a single-tube Class B amplifier from either the plate characteristics or the dynamic characteristic for a given input signal voltage. The characteristics are assumed to be straight lines with the plate line for $e_c = 0$ passing through the origin.

16-15. Class B Push-Pull Amplifiers. The circuit for the Class B push-pull system is the same as that for the Class A system except that the tubes are biased approximately at cutoff. The advantages of Class B as compared with Class A operation are the following: It is possible to obtain greater power output, the plate-circuit efficiency is higher, and there is negligible power loss at no signal. The disadvantages are that the harmonic distortion is higher, self-bias cannot be used, and the supply voltages must have good regulation.

In order to investigate the plate-circuit efficiency of the system, it will be assumed, as in Sec. 16-7, that the plate characteristics of the tubes are straight lines equally spaced for equal intervals of grid voltage. Since the tubes are biased to cutoff, current exists in the plate circuit only when e_c, the instantaneous grid potential, is more positive than $-E_{cc}$, the grid bias of the tube. The conditions for one tube are illustrated graphically in Fig. 16-30. These diagrams show that the application of a sinusoidal grid-exciting voltage to a Class B amplifier results in a plate-current wave form which is substantially sinusoidal during one-half of each period and is zero during the second half cycle. This is the same wave form as that obtained from a half-wave rectifier (Chap. 14).

The results illustrated in Fig. 16-30 represent one tube only. The output of the second tube is, of course, a series of sine loop pulses that are 180 deg out of phase with those of tube 1. The load current which is proportional to the difference between the two tube currents is, therefore, a perfect sine wave for the ideal conditions assumed. The rms value of the output current is $I_m/\sqrt{2}$, and the power output is

$$P = \frac{I_m{}^2}{2} R \tag{16-63}$$

where $R = R_L'/4$ is the effective load resistance. The corresponding direct plate current in each tube under load is the average value of the half sine loop of Fig. 16-30. This is, from Eq. (14-5), $I_{dc} = I_m/\pi$. Hence, the d-c input power from the B supply is

$$P_i = 2 \frac{I_m E_{bb}}{\pi} \tag{16-64}$$

The factor 2 that appears in this expression arises because two tubes are used in the push-pull system.

The plate-circuit efficiency is given by the expression

$$\eta_p = \frac{P}{P_i} = \frac{\pi}{4} \frac{I_m{}^2 R}{I_m E_b} = \frac{\pi}{4} \frac{I_m R}{E_b} \tag{16-65}$$

where $E_b = E_{bb}$, since for zero quiescent current the plate-supply voltage must equal the quiescent plate voltage. We see from Fig. 16-30 that

$$E_b = I_m r_p + E_m$$

assuming that the grid does not swing positive. Also, since $E_m = I_m R$, this becomes

$$E_b = I_m(r_p + R)$$

from which it follows that

$$\eta_p = \frac{\pi}{4} \frac{R}{r_p + R} \times 100\% \tag{16-66}$$

This reduces to the form

$$\eta_p = 78.5 \frac{1}{1 + r_p/R} \% \tag{16-67}$$

This expression shows that the maximum possible plate-circuit efficiency is 78.5 per cent for a Class B system compared with a maximum of 50 per cent for a Class A system. This increase in efficiency results from the fact that there is no current in a Class B system if there is no signal, whereas there is a drain from the plate power supply in a Class A system even at zero signal.   We also note that in a Class B amplifier the dissipation at the plates is zero in the quiescent state and increases with excitation, whereas the heating of the plates of a Class A system is a maximum at zero input and decreases as the signal increases.   Since the direct current increases with signal in a Class B amplifier, the power supply must have good regulation.

Alternative forms for P and η_p which do not involve r_p or R are easily obtained from the above relationships.   These are

$$P = \tfrac{1}{2}I_{\max}(E_b - E_{\min}) \qquad \eta_p = \frac{\pi}{4}\left(1 - \frac{E_{\min}}{E_b}\right) \times 100\% \quad (16\text{-}68)$$

where $E_{\min} = I_m r_p$ is the minimum tube voltage and $I_{\max} = I_m$ is the peak value of the tube current.

If the typical triodes that are used in Class A applications are used for

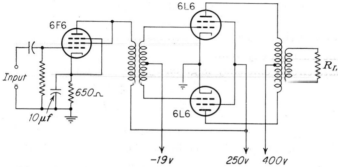

Fig. 16-31. The schematic circuit diagram of a high-power Class AB$_2$ push-pull amplifier.

Class B operation, the bias voltage necessary to secure cutoff is large. This results from the low amplification factors of these tubes and the large voltages that are necessary in order to obtain appreciable amounts of power.   In order to avoid the use of sources of large fixed (grid bias) voltage, special tubes which have high amplification factors and which operate at zero bias have been designed.   These tubes are therefore driven positive during operation.

Beam tubes in Class AB$_1$ permit as high an output as, or even a higher one than, the triodes in Class B$_2$.   Although the plate-circuit efficiency may not be so high as in Class B operation, it is reasonably good.   In addition, Class AB operation is possible with lower distortion.   Also, self-bias may be used.   If greater power is desired, Class AB$_2$ can be used. This system will require less driving power than Class B$_2$, and the distortion will be smaller.   Figure 16-31[9] shows the circuit of two 6L6 tubes operated in Class AB_2 capable of delivering approximately 40 watts with 7 per cent distortion.   In this circuit, 400 volts is applied to the plates and 250 volts to the screens, and a -19-volt grid bias is used.   The plate-to-plate load is 5,000 ohms.   A 6F6 tube connected as a triode is used as the driver tube.

It is found that nonlinear distortion can be reduced considerably if the screen voltages are obtained from taps on the output transformer, instead of from a fixed d-c voltage.   Such an *ultralinear circuit*[10] has found wide acceptance among high-fidelity enthusiasts.

16-16. Driver Stages for Push-Pull Amplifiers.   The *driver stage* of the push-pull amplifier is the circuit that supplies the two signal voltages to the grids of the push-pull tubes.   These voltages must be equal in magnitude but must be of opposite polarity.   For high-power applications the driver is usually an amplifier with a transformer in the plate circuit, as in Fig. 16-31.   The secondary of this transformer is center-tapped, each end of the winding being connected to one of the grids.

The grids of zero-bias tubes are driven positive during normal operation, and frequently negative-bias tubes draw some grid current over a portion of the signal peaks.   Consequently the power requirements of the driver stage depend on the circuit that it feeds, but this is a small percentage[11] (usually much less than 15) of the output of the push-pull stage.   If the driver stage is called upon to supply power, it should have a low internal resistance, if no distortion is to be introduced into the grid circuit of the push-pull stage.   Such distortion will arise if the relationship between the grid current and the grid voltage is not a linear one.   Clearly, if the effective resistance in the driver stage is high, an appreciable nonlinear voltage drop will be subtracted from the sinusoidal input voltage, resulting in the application of a distorted signal to the grids of the push-pull tubes.   It is advisable, for this reason, to use a step-down transformer to couple the driver stage to the push-pull input, since the step-down transformer will reduce the effective resistance in the grid circuit.

Because of their expense, bulk, and relatively poor frequency response, the use of transformers should be avoided wherever possible.   If the grid current of the push-pull tubes is negligible, then RC coupling may be used between the driver and the output tubes.   Several such *phase-inverter circuits* are given in Sec. 17-7.

16-17. Transistor Power Amplifiers.[12]   A power transistor has a larger cross-sectional area and hence can deliver a greater current than can be obtained from a voltage transistor.   The voltage ratings of both types are approximately the same, but because of the increased current (of the order of 0.5 amp) the power rating of the former may extend to several watts or tens of watts.   In order to be able to dissipate safely the collector power, these transistors are built with radiating cooling fins and/or are enclosed in a metal case. The latter is connected to the collector internally, and the case is mounted on the metal chassis which houses the circuit, directly or through some thin mica (for electrical insulation) so as to allow maximum heat transfer away from the collector.

The types of circuits and general principles studied in this chapter in connection with vacuum-tube power amplifiers are applicable with very little modification for transistors. For example, a transistor may be used in a Class A or Class B circuit, with a series-fed or shunt-fed load, single-ended or in a push-pull arrangement, etc. The methods of calculating conversion efficiency, power output, per cent harmonic distortion, etc., are the same for the transistor as for tube circuit.

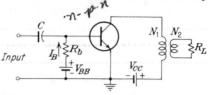

FIG. 16-32. A power transistor in a Class A circuit with a transformer-coupled output.

As a matter of fact, most of the equations derived in the preceding sections are applicable to transistors (the principal exceptions to this statement are the formulas involving r_p, which symbol has no meaning for transistors).

An n-p-n power transistor in a Class A circuit with a transformer-coupled output is indicated in Fig. 16-32. The dynamic load line for $R_L' = (N_1/N_2)^2 R_L$ is drawn through the quiescent point Q (corresponding to quiescent base current I_B and quiescent collector voltage V_{CC}) on the collector characteristics of Fig. 16-33. The power output and the collector-circuit efficiency are given by Eqs. (16-37) or in the semiconductor notation indicated in Fig. 16-33.

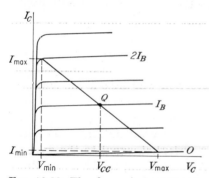

FIG. 16-33. The dynamic load line is drawn on the collector characteristics.

$$P = \tfrac{1}{8}(I_{max} - I_{min})(V_{max} - V_{min}) \qquad \eta_c = 25\,\frac{V_{max} - V_{min}}{V_{CC}}\ \%$$

$$(16\text{-}69)$$

Since the collector volt-ampere characteristics resemble the plate characteristics of a pentode, the distortion components may be calculated as indicated in Sec. 16-8. The power output and distortion are computed for each value of load resistance R_L. Then that value of R_L is chosen as optimum which gives nearly maximum power output with a reasonable value of distortion. This load line will pass through the knee of the collector characteristic (corresponding to $2I_B$), and hence the minimum collector voltage V_{min} will be quite small compared with the supply voltage V_{CC}. Under these circumstances we see from the second of Eqs. (16-69) that an efficiency close to 50 per cent is attainable. If series feed rather than shunt feed had been employed, the maximum efficiency would have been 25 per cent for either the transistor or the vacuum-tube circuit.

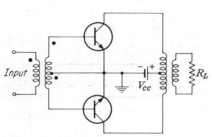

Transistor push-pull amplifiers are analyzed in exactly the same manner as were their vacuum-tube counterparts. Such an amplifier has an output wave shape which contains no even harmonics and, in addition, possesses mirror symmetry (Sec. 16-10). The composite characteristics are constructed as explained in Sec. 16-12 for a pentode except, of course, that the collector volt-ampere curves instead of the plate characteristics are used.

FIG. 16-34. Two transistors in a Class B push-pull arrangement.

Most transistor power amplifiers use two transistors in a Class B push-pull arrangement, as in Fig. 16-34. The important features of such a circuit are that the quiescent current (and hence the battery drain) is practically zero and that the efficiency is very high. The power output and conversion efficiency are given by Eqs. (16-68) or, in the notation of Eq. (16-69),

$$ P = \tfrac{1}{2}I_{max}(V_{CC} - V_{min}) \qquad \eta_c = 78.5 \left(1 - \frac{V_{min}}{V_{CC}} \right) \qquad \% $$

Because $V_{min} \ll V_{CC}$, efficiencies approaching the theoretical value of 78.5 per cent can be approached in practice.

In Fig. 16-34 the base and emitter are shorted together in the quiescent state. This connection results in a very slight forward bias of the emitter and a quiescent collector current of the order of $4I_{CO}$ (Sec. 9-5). Low-level distortion may be improved by using a small amount of forward fixed bias, obtained from a divider across the V_{CC} battery. A circuit which dispenses with the output transformer is shown in Fig. 16-35. This arrangement requires a power supply whose center tap is grounded, a condition which is not difficult to obtain with batteries.

A circuit[13] which requires neither an output nor an input transformer is shown in Fig. 16-36. This arrangement uses transistors having complementary symmetry (one n-p-n and one p-n-p type), and hence there is no vacuum-tube counterpart of this circuit. The difficulty with the circuit is that of obtaining matched complementary transistors. If there is an unbalance in the characteristics of the two transistors in Fig. 16-36 (or also in Figs. 16-34 and 16-35), then considerable distortion will be introduced; even harmonics will no longer be canceled. In Fig. 16-36 the power supply "floats" with respect to ground. This difficul y may be avoided by inserting the sources V_{CC} in series with each emitter.

In addition to that introduced by not using matched transistors, the distortion in any of the circuits discussed above is due to the nonlinearity

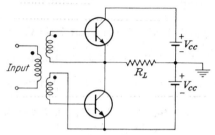

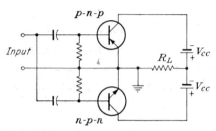

FIG. 16-35. A push-pull transistor circuit which does not use an output transformer.

FIG. 16-36. A push-pull circuit using transistors having complementary symmetry.

of the collector characteristics and to the nonlinearity of the input impedance. An examination of the 2N156 collector characteristics in Fig. A0 3 shows that the curves crowd together at the higher currents. This decrease in spacing of the characteristics arises because the current gain α_e decreases with current.[14] For the 2N156, α_e varies from approximately 50 at $I_C = 0$ to 22 at $I_C = -1.0$ amp. If the input current is sinusoidal, then the nonconstancy of α_e causes the output wave shape to be flatter ("squashed") on one half a cycle than on the next half. The input impedance is a function of emitter current principally because r_e varies inversely with I_E. Hence, at low values of I_E the input impedance may become appreciable compared with the driver impedance. Under these circumstances

FIG. 16-37. Illustrating cross-over distortion.

a sinusoidal excitation of the driver stage will not result in a sinusoidal current into the power stage. This effect is particularly noticeable in a Class B amplifier where the quiescent current is almost zero and results in "cross-over distortion," as indicated in Fig. 16-37. This type of distortion would not occur if the driver were a true current generator (infinite output impedance). As already mentioned, this distortion may be decreased by biasing the transistors at a higher stand-by current. A compromise must be made between distortion and efficiency.

Power transistors may also be used in the common-base and common-collector arrangements as well as the common-emitter circuits discussed above. Because of its low input impedance a common-base configuration may require considerable drive. However, the common-collector input drive is the same as that of the common-emitter circuit. Because of degeneration, the former reduces distortion considerably and is often used for this reason.

REFERENCES

1. ESPLEY, D. C., "The Calculation of Harmonic Production in Thermionic Valves with Resistive Loads," *Proc. IRE*, **21**, 1439–1446, October, 1933.
   CHAFFEE, E. L., "A Simplified Harmonic Analysis," *Rev. Sci. Instr.* **7**, 384–389, October, 1936.
2. ESPLEY, D. C., and L. I. FARREN, "Direct Reading Harmonic Scales," *Wireless Eng.*, **11**, 183–188, April, 1934.
   BLOCK, A., "Distortion in Valves with Resistive Loads," *ibid.*, **16**, 592–596, December, 1939.
3. MILLMAN, J., and H. TAUB, "Pulse and Digital Circuits," pp. 253–255, McGraw-Hill Book Company, Inc., New York, 1956.
4. NOTTINGHAM, W. B., "Optimum Conditions for Maximum Power in Class A Amplifiers," *Proc. IRE*, **29,** 620–623, December, 1941.
5. MILLMAN, J., and S. SEELY, "Electronics," 1st ed., pp. 633–637, McGraw-Hill Book Company, Inc., New York, 1941.
6. *RCA Application Note* 78.
7. KILGOUR, C. E., "Graphical Analysis of Output Tube Performance," *Proc. IRE*, **19**, 42–50, January, 1931.
8. THOMPSON, B. J., "Graphical Determination of Performance of Push-pull Audio Amplifiers," *Proc. IRE*, **21**, 591–600, April, 1933.
9. *RCA Application Note* 72.
10. LANGFORD SMITH, F., and A. R. CHEATERMAN, "Ultra Linear Amplifiers," *Radiotronics*, **20**(5,6,7), May, June, July, 1955.
11. GORDON, M., "Class B Audio Frequency Amplification," *Wireless Eng.*, **16**, 457–459, September, 1939.
12. WOLL, H. J., Low-frequency Amplifiers, in L. P. HUNTER (ed.), "Handbook of Semiconductor Electronics," pp. 11-28 to 11-43, McGraw-Hill Book Company, Inc., New York, 1956.
    LO, A. W., et al., "Transistor Electronics," pp. 197–224, Prentice-Hall, Inc., Englewood Cliffs, N.J., 1956.
13. LOHMAN, R. D., "Complementary Symmetry Transistor Circuits," *Electronics*, **26**, 140–143, September, 1953.
14. WEBSTER, W. M., "On the Variation of Junction-transistor Current-amplification Factor with Emitter Current," *Proc. IRE*, **42**, 914–920, June, 1954.

CHAPTER 17

FEEDBACK AMPLIFIERS

IT IS possible to modify greatly the characteristics of an amplifier through feedback, *i.e.*, by combining a portion of the output with the external signal. There are many advantages to be gained by the use of feedback. These will now be studied. Feedback-amplifier circuits find extensive application in many fields. Among such circuits to be described in this chapter are the cathode follower, phase inverters, difference amplifiers, and the basic building blocks of an analog computer.

17-1. Voltage Feedback in Amplifiers.[1] A feedback amplifier (vacuum tube or transistor) may be defined as one in which the amplifier input signal is in part derived from an external source and in part from the amplifier output. Any amplifier, whether it involves feedback or not, may be analyzed by replacing it by its linear equivalent circuit. Where feedback is involved, however, it is more fruitful to try to deal separately with the amplifier proper and with the feedback network in order to be able to appreciate the influence of the feedback on the amplifier characteristics. Since, with respect to its output terminals, the amplifier is specified by the voltage gain and output impedance, we shall inquire into the manner in which these two features of the amplifier are modified by feedback.

Consider the feedback arrangement of Fig. 17-1. The input terminals are 1 and 2, and the input voltage between these terminals is E_i. The output terminals are 3 and 4, and the output voltage is E_o. The net voltage at the input terminals is the sum of the externally impressed signal voltage E_s and a feedback voltage $E_f = \beta E_o$. The ratio of feedback voltage to output voltage β is determined by the feedback network. The feedback network may be active or passive, and in general β may be a complex quantity. The convention with respect to the polarity of all signals is indicated, and this convention will be adhered to consistently in what follows.

Let **A** be the *forward voltage gain without feedback* (the *open-loop gain*) between the input and output terminals of the amplifier with the load Z_L removed.* We may define **A** by the following operational procedure.

---

* In Chap. 8 the open-circuit voltage amplification was designated by $\mathbf{A}_v$ but we shall now drop the subscript v for simplicity.

Remove $\mathbf{E}_s$, and apply a voltage $\mathbf{E}_i$ directly to the terminals 1 and 2. The gain $\mathbf{A}$ is given by $\mathbf{A} \equiv \mathbf{E}_o/\mathbf{E}_i$.

The *output impedance without feedback* $\mathbf{Z}_o$ of the amplifier is defined as follows: Remove $\mathbf{E}_s$, and short-circuit terminals 1 and 2. Under these conditions $\mathbf{Z}_o$ is the impedance seen looking back into the output terminals 3 and 4. Note that the definitions of $\mathbf{A}$ and $\mathbf{Z}_o$ take into account the loading effect of the impedance of the feedback network.

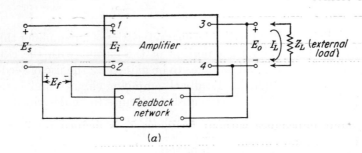

(a)

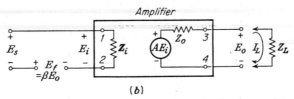

(b)

FIG. 17-1. (a) A block diagram of a voltage-feedback amplifier. The feedback factor β is defined by $\beta = \mathbf{E}_f/\mathbf{E}_o$, where $\mathbf{E}_f = \mathbf{E}_i - \mathbf{E}_s$. (b) The equivalent circuit. The input (output) impedance without feedback is $\mathbf{Z}_i$ ($\mathbf{Z}_o$).

The Thévenin equivalent circuit corresponding to Fig. 17-1a is indicated in Fig. 17-1b. *The distinguishing feature of voltage feedback is that the feedback voltage* $\mathbf{E}_f$ *is related to the output voltage* $\mathbf{E}_o$ *by* $\mathbf{E}_f = \beta\mathbf{E}_o$, *in which* β *is fixed independently of the external load* $\mathbf{Z}_L$. We may write

$$\mathbf{E}_o = \mathbf{A}\mathbf{E}_i - \mathbf{I}_L\mathbf{Z}_o \quad \text{and} \quad \mathbf{E}_i = \mathbf{E}_s + \beta\mathbf{E}_o$$

Eliminating $\mathbf{E}_i$ from these equations, we find

$$\mathbf{E}_o = \frac{\mathbf{A}}{1 - \mathbf{A}\beta} \mathbf{E}_s - \frac{\mathbf{Z}_o}{1 - \mathbf{A}\beta} \mathbf{I}_L \tag{17-1}$$

This equation is in the form of Eq. (8-25) and hence we conclude that the gain and output impedance with feedback are given by $\mathbf{A}_f$ (the *closed-loop gain*) and $\mathbf{Z}_f$, respectively, where

$$\mathbf{A}_f = \frac{\mathbf{A}}{1 - \beta\mathbf{A}} \tag{17-2}$$

and

$$Z_f = \frac{Z_o}{1 - \beta A} \qquad (17\text{-}3)$$

The Thévenin equivalent circuit is indicated in Fig. 17-2. The effect of the feedback is, therefore, to modify both gain and impedance by the same factor. If $|A_f| < |A|$, the feed-back is termed *negative* or *degenerative*. If $|A_f| > |A|$, the feedback is termed *positive* or *regenerative*. In the case of negative feedback, which is of principal interest to us, the magnitude of both gain and output impedance is divided by the factor $|1 - \beta A|$.

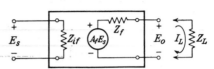

Fig. 17-2. The Thévenin equivalent circuit of an amplifier, with feedback taken into account.

The input impedance without feedback Z_i is defined by $Z_i \equiv E_i/I_i$, where I_i is the input current. The input impedance with feedback Z_{if} is defined by $Z_{if} \equiv E_s/I_i$. From these definitions we find that

$$Z_{if} = Z_i(1 - A\beta) \qquad (17\text{-}4)$$

If $|1 - A\beta| \gg 1$, then the input impedance may be greatly increased by means of the feedback. This result is of particular importance with a transistor amplifier because the input impedance of this device without feedback is fairly low.

The voltage E_i is multiplied by A in passing through the amplifier and then multiplied by β in passing through the feedback network. Since such a path takes us from the input terminals around the loop consisting of the amplifier and feedback network back to the input, the product $A\beta$ is called the *loop gain, loop transmission feedback factor*, or *return ratio*. Also, the amount of feedback introduced into an amplifier is often expressed in decibels by the definition

$$N = \text{db of feedback} \equiv 20 \log_{10} \left| \frac{A_f}{A} \right| = 20 \log_{10} \left| \frac{-1}{1 - A\beta} \right| \qquad (17\text{-}5)$$

If negative feedback is under consideration, then N will be a negative number.

17-2. Voltage-feedback Amplifier Characteristics. Since negative feedback reduces the amplification, why is it used? The answer to this question is that many desirable characteristics are obtained for the price of this reduction in gain. We shall now examine some of these advantages of voltage feedback.

Stability of Amplification. The variation due to aging, temperature, replacement, etc., of the circuit components and tube or transistor characteristics is reflected in a corresponding lack of stability of the amplifier gain. The fractional change in gain with feedback is related to the fractional change without feedback by

$$\left| \frac{d\mathbf{A}_f}{\mathbf{A}_f} \right| = \frac{1}{|1 - \beta\mathbf{A}|} \left| \frac{d\mathbf{A}}{\mathbf{A}} \right| \tag{17-6}$$

This equation is obtained by differentiating Eq. (17-2). If the feedback is negative, so that $|1 - \beta\mathbf{A}| > 1$, the feedback will have served to improve the gain stability of the amplifier. For example, for an amplifier with 20 db of negative feedback, $|1/(1 - \mathbf{A}\beta)| = 0.1$, and a 1 per cent change in the gain without feedback is reduced to a 0.1 per cent change after feedback is introduced.

In particular, if $|\beta\mathbf{A}| \gg 1$, then

$$\mathbf{A}_f = \frac{\mathbf{A}}{1 - \beta\mathbf{A}} \cong -\frac{\mathbf{A}}{\beta\mathbf{A}} = -\frac{1}{\beta}$$

and the gain may be made to depend entirely on the feedback network. The worst offenders with respect to stability are usually the vacuum tubes and transistors involved. If the feedback network should then contain only passive elements, the improvement in stability may indeed be pronounced.

Feedback is used to improve stability in the following way. Suppose an amplifier of gain $\mathbf{A}_1$ is required. We start by building an amplifier of gain $\mathbf{A}_2 = k\mathbf{A}_1$, in which k is a large number. Feedback is now introduced to divide the gain by the factor k. The stability will be improved by the same factor k, since both gain and stability are divided by the factor $k = |1 - \beta\mathbf{A}_2|$. If now the instability of the amplifier of gain $\mathbf{A}_2$ is not appreciably poorer than the instability of the amplifier of gain without feedback equal to $\mathbf{A}_1$, this procedure will have been useful. It often happens as a matter of practice that an amplifier gain may be increased appreciably without a corresponding loss of stability. Consider, for example, the case of a one-tube pentode amplifier. The gain is $-g_m R_L$, g_m being the tube transconductance and R_L the plate-circuit resistor. The principal source of instability is in g_m. Hence the fractional change in gain is the same for a given fractional change in g_m independently of the size of R_L.

Frequency Distortion. It follows from the equation $\mathbf{A}_f \cong -1/\beta$ that if the feedback network does not contain reactive elements then the overall gain is not a function of frequency. Under these circumstances a substantial reduction in frequency and phase distortion is obtained. It is to be noted, however, that negative feedback improves frequency response only at the expense of gain.

Example. A fraction β (real and positive) of the output voltage from a single-stage RC-coupled amplifier is fed back to the input circuit, as indicated in Fig. 17-3. Investigate the effect of this feedback upon the upper and lower 3-db frequencies f_2 and f_1, respectively. (We shall assume that C_k is arbitrarily large so that the self-biasing arrangement in the cathode circuit introduces no frequency distortion.)

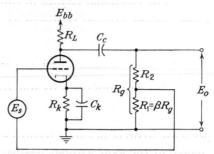

Solution. The high-frequency gain $\mathbf{A}_2$ without feedback is given by Eq. (15-12),

$$\mathbf{A}_2 = \frac{A_o}{1 + j(f/f_2)}$$

where A_o (real and negative) is the mid-band gain without feedback. The gain with feedback is given by Eq. (17-2),

FIG. 17-3. Voltage feedback applied to a single-stage RC-coupled amplifier.

$$\mathbf{A}_{2f} = \frac{\mathbf{A}_2}{1 - \beta\mathbf{A}_2} = \frac{\dfrac{A_o}{1 + j(f/f_2)}}{1 - \dfrac{\beta A_o}{1 + j(f/f_2)}}$$

$$= \frac{A_o}{1 - \beta A_o + j(f/f_2)}$$

By dividing numerator and denominator by $1 - \beta A_o$, this equation may be put in the form

$$\mathbf{A}_{2f} = \frac{A_{of}}{1 + j(f/f_{2f})}$$

where

$$A_{of} \equiv \frac{A_o}{1 - \beta A_o} \quad \text{and} \quad f_{2f} \equiv f_2(1 - \beta A_o) \tag{17-7}$$

We see that the *mid-band amplification with feedback* A_{of} equals the mid-band amplification without feedback A_o divided by $1 - \beta A_o$. Also, the *upper 3-db frequency with feedback* f_{2f} equals the corresponding 3-db frequency without feedback f_2 multiplied by the same factor $1 - \beta A_o$. The gain-frequency product has not been changed by feedback because, from Eq. (17-7),

$$A_{of}f_{2f} = A_o f_2 \tag{17-8}$$

By starting with Eq. (15-17) for the low-frequency gain of a single RC-coupled stage and proceeding as above, we can show that the *lower 3-db frequency with feedback* f_{1f} is decreased by the same factor as is the gain, or

$$f_{1f} = \frac{f_1}{1 - A_o\beta} \tag{17-9}$$

For an audio or video amplifier $f_2 \gg f_1$ and hence the band width $f_2 - f_1 \cong f_2$. Under these circumstances, Eq. (17-8) may be interpreted to mean that the gain–band-width product is the same with or without feedback.

In the above discussion β was considered to be independent of frequency. If, on the other hand, a frequency selective feedback network is used, the amplification may depend markedly upon frequency. For example, it is possible to obtain an amplifier with a high-Q band-pass characteristic by using a feedback network which gives little feedback at the center of the band and a great deal of feedback on both sides of this frequency.

Nonlinear Distortion. Suppose that a large amplitude signal is applied to a stage of an amplifier so that the operation of the tube extends slightly beyond its range of linear operation and as a consequence the output signal is slightly distorted. Negative feedback is now introduced, and the input signal is increased by the same amount by which the gain is reduced so that the output signal amplitude remains the same. For simplicity, let us consider that the input signal is sinusoidal and that the distortion consists of simply a second-harmonic signal generated within the tube. We shall also assume that the second-harmonic component, in the absence of feedback, is equal to $\mathbf{B}_2$. Because of the effects of feedback, a component $\mathbf{B}_{2f}$ actually appears in the output. To find the relationship that exists between $\mathbf{B}_{2f}$ and $\mathbf{B}_2$, it is noted that the output will contain the term $\mathbf{A}\beta\mathbf{B}_{2f}$, which arises from the component $\beta\mathbf{B}_{2f}$ that is fed back to the input. Thus the output contains two terms: $\mathbf{B}_2$, generated in the tube, and $\mathbf{A}\beta\mathbf{B}_{2f}$, which represents the effect of the feedback. Hence,

$$\mathbf{A}\beta\mathbf{B}_{2f} + \mathbf{B}_2 = \mathbf{B}_{2f}$$

or

$$\mathbf{B}_{2f} = \frac{\mathbf{B}_2}{1 - \mathbf{A}\beta} \qquad (17\text{-}10)$$

Since $\mathbf{A}$ and β are generally functions of the frequency, they must be evaluated at the second-harmonic frequency.

The signal voltage $\mathbf{E}_s$ to the feedback amplifier may be the actual signal externally available, or it may be the output of an amplifier preceding the feedback stage or stages under consideration. In order to multiply the input to the feedback amplifier by the factor $|1 - \mathbf{A}\beta|$, it is necessary either to increase the nominal gain of the preamplifying stages or to add a new stage. If the full benefit of the feedback amplifier in reducing nonlinear distortion is to be obtained, these preamplifying stages must not introduce additional distortion because of the increased output demanded of them. Since, however, appreciable harmonics are introduced only when the output swing is large, most of the distortion arises in the last stage. The preamplifying stages are of smaller importance in considerations of harmonic generation.

It has been assumed in the derivation of Eq. (17-10) that the harmonic distortion generated within the tube depends only upon the grid swing of the fundamental signal voltage. The small amount of additional distortion that might arise from the second-harmonic component fed back from the output to the input has been neglected. Ordinarily, this will lead to little error. Further, it must be noted, the result given by Eq. (17-10) applies only in the case of small distortion. The principle of superposition has been used in the derivation, and for this reason it is required that the tube must be considered to operate with at least approximate linearity.

Reduction of Noise. By employing the same reasoning as that in the discussion of nonlinear distortion, it can be shown that the noise (Secs.

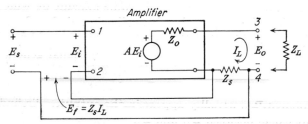

FIG. 17-4. A block diagram of a current-feedback amplifier.

15-11 and 15-12) introduced in an amplifier is multiplied by the factor $1/|1 - A\beta|$ if the feedback is employed. If $|1 - A\beta|$ is much larger than unity, this would seem to represent a considerable reduction in the output noise. However, as noted above, for a given output the amplification of the preamplifier for a specified over-all gain must be increased by the factor $|1 - A\beta|$. Since the noise generated is independent of the signal voltage, there may be as much noise generated in the preamplifying stage as in the output stage. Furthermore, this additional noise will be amplified as well as the signal by the feedback amplifier, so that the complete system may actually be noisier than the original amplifier without feedback. If the additional gain required to compensate that which has been lost because of the presence of inverse feedback can be obtained by a readjustment of the circuit parameters rather than by the addition of an extra stage, a definite reduction will result from the presence of the feedback. In particular, the hum introduced into the circuit by a poorly filtered power supply may be decreased appreciably.

Output Impedance. As indicated in Eq. (17-3), the output impedance with voltage feedback is $1/(1 - A\beta)$ times the output impedance without feedback. If $|1 - A\beta|$ is large, then voltage feedback will result in a significant reduction in the output impedance. Because of its small output impedance, an amplifier with voltage feedback will tend to maintain constant voltage with changing loads and hence approximates the ideal voltage source.

17-3. Current Feedback in Amplifiers. A *current-feedback* amplifier is shown in Fig. 17-4. The amplifier without feedback has a gain **A** and an impedance $\mathbf{Z}_o$. The distinguishing feature of the present circuit is that *the feedback voltage is proportional to the current which flows through the external load $\mathbf{Z}_L$ and the factor of proportionality between $\mathbf{E}_f$ and $\mathbf{I}_L$ is independent of the output voltage $\mathbf{E}_o$.* The feedback voltage is developed across the impedance $\mathbf{Z}_s$, which is in series with the load.

We have

$$\mathbf{E}_o = \mathbf{A}\mathbf{E}_i - (\mathbf{Z}_o + \mathbf{Z}_s)\mathbf{I}_L \quad \text{and} \quad \mathbf{E}_i = \mathbf{E}_s + \mathbf{Z}_s\mathbf{I}_L \quad (17\text{-}11)$$

from which

$$\mathbf{E}_o = \mathbf{A}\mathbf{E}_s - [\mathbf{Z}_o + \mathbf{Z}_s(1 - \mathbf{A})]\mathbf{I}_L \quad (17\text{-}12)$$

Comparing with Eq. (8-25), we see that the gain and impedance in the presence of current feedback are therefore

$$\mathbf{A}_f = \mathbf{A} \qquad \mathbf{Z}_f = \mathbf{Z}_o + \mathbf{Z}_s(1 - \mathbf{A}) \quad (17\text{-}13)$$

The gain has not been changed as a result of the current feedback. This result is clear from Fig. 17-4, where $\mathbf{Z}_L$ is considered as an external load and not part of the amplifier. However, if $\mathbf{Z}_L$ is not connected to the output terminals, then $\mathbf{I}_L = 0$ and the feedback voltage is zero. Under these circumstances the unloaded amplification with feedback must be the same as that without feedback.

If the amplifier were unaltered except that the feedback voltage were not returned to the input, the output impedance between terminals 3 and 4 of Fig. 17-4 (across which the load is placed) would be $\mathbf{Z}_o + \mathbf{Z}_s$. The effect of the current feedback is therefore to add to the output impedance the additional impedance $-\mathbf{A}\mathbf{Z}_s$. If, for example, $\mathbf{A}$ is a real negative number and $\mathbf{Z}_s$ is resistive, the output impedance with feedback will be greater than the impedance without feedback.

In Fig. 17-4 we have assumed that the entire load current passes through $\mathbf{Z}_s$ and that none of it is shunted away by the input circuit of the amplifier. In other words, in order for the above theory to be valid the input impedance of the device (vacuum tube or transistor) must be large compared with $|\mathbf{Z}_s|$.

Many of the characteristics discussed in Sec. 17-2 for the *output voltage* of a voltage-feedback amplifier are equally valid for the *output current* of a current-feedback amplifier. This statement may be confirmed as follows: From Fig. 17-2 and Eq. (17-13) the load current in a current-feedback amplifier is given by

$$\mathbf{I}_L = \frac{\mathbf{A}\mathbf{E}_s}{\mathbf{Z}_o + \mathbf{Z}_s(1 - \mathbf{A}) + \mathbf{Z}_L} \simeq \frac{-\mathbf{E}_s}{\mathbf{Z}_s} \quad (17\text{-}14)$$

provided that $|\mathbf{Z}_s\mathbf{A}| \gg |\mathbf{Z}_o + \mathbf{Z}_s + \mathbf{Z}_L|$. Under these circumstances we note that the current depends only upon $\mathbf{Z}_s$ and not upon the other amplifier features. Hence, if the feedback impedance $\mathbf{Z}_s$ is a stable element, the load current is stable with respect to aging, temperature, and replacement of circuit components and device characteristics. If $\mathbf{Z}_s$ is a resistor, then $\mathbf{I}_L$ is independent of frequency and the distortion in frequency and phase is greatly reduced. Note that this conclusion is valid even if the load impedance is a function of frequency. If $\mathbf{Z}_s$ is a linear element, then virtually no nonlinear distortion of load current results.

We may summarize the above discussion by stating that the load current in a current-feedback amplifier is approximately independent of load impedance. In other words, the circuit behaves as a current device, the magnitude of the load current being obtained by dividing the signal voltage by the feedback impedance $\mathbf{Z}_s$.

17-4. Feedback Circuits. The configuration in Fig. 17-3 suffers the disadvantage that the input signal must be isolated from ground. Since usually one terminal of a signal source is grounded, this circuit is of little practical importance. Figure 17-3 may be modified to include a transformer to couple either the signal or the feedback voltage into the input circuit. With such a connection the limited frequency response of the transformer must be taken into consideration. In an audio push-pull amplifier (Fig. 16-31) it is a simple matter to introduce voltage feedback by coupling part of the voltage from the secondary of the output transformer into the secondary

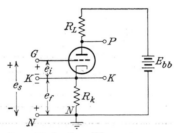

FIG. 17-5. Amplifier with plate and cathode resistors. Instantaneous variations from the quiescent point are indicated by lower-case letters.

of the input transformer. Separate resistive feedback dividers are used for each grid circuit.

We shall consider the simple feedback-amplifier configuration of Fig. 17-5 which does not use a transformer and yet allows a common ground between the external signal source and the output terminals. Depending upon how this circuit is used, it may exhibit voltage feedback or current feedback or fit into neither of these two classifications, as we shall now demonstrate.

Suppose that in the circuit of Fig. 17-5 we *define* the output terminals to be K and N so that $e_o = e_{kn}$ and the input terminals to be G and K so that $e_i = e_{gk}$. The external signal generator is connected to G and N so that $e_s = e_{gn}$. The circuit may now be redrawn as in Fig. 17-6a, which corresponds to Fig. 17-1b. Independently of whether the resistor R_k is considered a part of the amplifier or an external load, we have a case of voltage feedback in which $\beta = -1$ since $e_f = -e_o$. Let us consider that R_k is an external load and not a part of the amplifier. Then

$$A = \frac{e_o}{e_i} = \frac{e_{kn}}{e_{gk}} = \mu$$

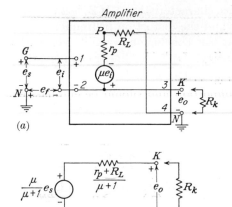

(a)

(b)

FIG. 17-6. (a) Circuit of Fig. 17-5 redrawn as a voltage-feedback amplifier. (b) Equivalent circuit with respect to output terminals between cathode and ground.

and $1 - \beta A = 1 + \mu$. The impedance without feedback seen looking to the left between terminals K and N is $r_p + R_L$. The gain and impedance with feedback are found from Eqs. (17-2) and (17-3) to be

$$
\left.\begin{array}{l}
A_f = \dfrac{\mu}{\mu + 1} \\[2ex]
R_f = \dfrac{r_p + R_L}{\mu + 1}
\end{array}\right\} \quad (17\text{-}15)
$$

and

The equivalent circuit is as indicated in Fig. 17-6b.

Next, referring again to Fig. 17-5, let us consider that again $e_i = e_{gk}$ and $e_s = e_{gn}$ but that now $e_o = e_{pn}$. The circuit is redrawn in Fig. 17-7a, which corresponds exactly to the circumstances of current feedback in Fig. 17-4. Observe that here we have no choice but to require that R_L be considered an external load. The gain, with or without feedback, is

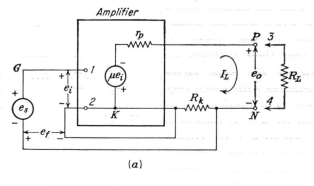

(a)

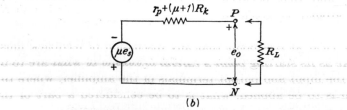

(b)

FIG. 17-7. (a) Amplifier with plate and cathode resistors drawn as a current-feedback amplifier. (b) Equivalent circuit with respect to output terminals between plate and ground.

$A = A_f = e_{pn}/e_{gk} = -\mu$. The output impedance between terminals 3 and 4, neglecting feedback, is $r_p + R_k$, so that we have

$$A_f = -\mu \quad \text{and} \quad R_f = r_p + (1 + \mu)R_k \quad (17\text{-}16)$$

The equivalent circuit is shown in Fig. 17-7b.

The above results are extremely important and should be emphasized. *If we look into the cathode of an amplifier, we see an equivalent circuit* (Fig. 17-6b) *consisting of a generator of value* $\mu/(\mu + 1)$ *times the signal-source voltage and an impedance* $(r_p + R_L)/(\mu + 1)$. The latter may be small if μ is large. On the other hand, *if we look into the plate of an amplifier, we see an equivalent circuit* (Fig. 17-7b) *consisting of a generator of value* $-\mu$ *times the signal-source voltage and an impedance* $r_p + (\mu + 1)R_k$. The latter may be large if μ is large.

The above results may be generalized to include a voltage source e_k in series with the cathode and a signal e_a in series with the anode, as indicated in Fig. 17-8a. It turns out that these voltages are transformed by the same factor as the resistances with which they are in series. For example, if R_k is multiplied by $\mu + 1$, then e_k is also multiplied by $\mu + 1$. Hence, the equivalent circuit between plate and ground is as indicated in Fig. 17-8b, and that between cathode and ground is given in Fig. 17-8c.

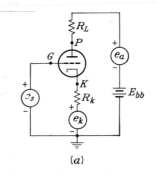

(a)

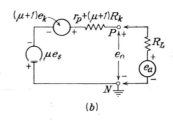

(b)

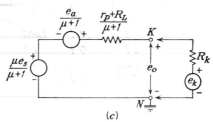

(c)

FIG. 17-8. (a) A useful configuration. (b) The equivalent circuit between plate and ground. (c) The equivalent circuit between cathode and ground.

It should be clear at this point that any discussion of feedback must necessarily take as its starting point a careful *definition* of what are to be considered as the input and output terminals of the amplifier, where the external signal is to be applied, what is to be considered a part of the amplifier, and what is external to the amplifier. For example, if, in connection with Fig. 17-7, the resistor R_L were to be considered part of the amplifier, then the resultant circuit would correspond neither to voltage nor to current feedback as we have defined them. It might still be profitable in this latter case to consider the amplifier as some new type of feedback amplifier. But the point to note is that a circuit must conform in every detail to the circumstances specified in Figs. 17-1 and 17-4 before we can confidently apply to them the feedback formulas stated above.

Another example of a feedback circuit which cannot be classified as either a voltage-feedback or a current-feedback configuration is obtained if the cathode bypass capacitor C_k in Fig. 17-3 is omitted. The resulting circuit is a combination of both types of feedback since it obtains current feedback through R_k and voltage feedback from the divider R_1-R_2. Such a configuration is called a *compound-* or *bridge-feedback circuit*.

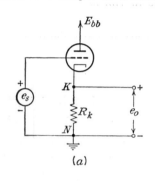

(a)

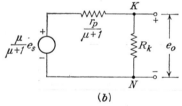

(b)

FIG. 17-9. The cathode follower and its equivalent circuit.

In a multistage amplifier the feedback network may be local, extending from output to input of a single stage, or it may be connected from input to output of all stages in cascade. If the feedback arrangement is of the type indicated in Fig. 17-3, an odd number of stages must be used in order to have negative feedback. If an even number of stages is used, then the feedback is positive and the circuit may oscillate (Sec. 17-9).

Transistor feedback circuits,[2] analogous to the vacuum-tube configurations just discussed, can be constructed. Compare, for example, Fig. 9-18 with Fig. 17-5.

17-5. The Cathode Follower. An example of a circuit which may profitably be viewed as a feedback amplifier is the cathode follower of Fig. 8-15a, which is redrawn in Fig. 17-9a for convenience. Its equivalent circuit, given in Fig. 8-17a and repeated in Fig. 17-9b, may be drawn directly by setting $R_L = 0$ in Fig. 17-6b. The gain is always less than unity and is given by

$$A_f = \frac{\mu R_k}{r_p + (\mu + 1)R_k} \qquad (17\text{-}17)$$

If $(\mu + 1)R_k \gg r_p$, then the gain is $\mu/(\mu + 1)$ or approximately unity. A gain of 0.95 or larger is not difficult to achieve. The polarity of the voltage at the cathode, the output signal, is the same as at the grid. The cathode voltage therefore *follows* very closely the grid voltage, and this feature accounts for the name given to the circuit.

If numerator and denominator of Eq. (17-17) are divided by r_p and if we recognize that usually $\mu + 1 \cong \mu$, we may rewrite Eq. (17-17) in the form

$$A_f = \frac{g_m R_k}{1 + g_m R_k} \tag{17-18}$$

in which $g_m = \mu/r_p$ is the transconductance of the tube.

The impedance between output terminals of the cathode follower is determined by the parallel combination of R_k and $r_p/(\mu + 1)$. Since $r_p/(\mu + 1) \cong 1/g_m$, this impedance may be written, with small error, as

$$R = \frac{R_k}{1 + g_m R_k} \tag{17-19}$$

For $g_m R_k \gg 1$, $R = 1/g_m$. Since g_m for a large variety of receiving-type tubes lies in the range 1 to 10 millimhos, R includes the range 100 to 1,000 ohms. A low output impedance is often an asset in an amplifier since it reduces the influence of the load on the amplifier output voltage. The output impedance of a cathode follower is frequently appreciably smaller than the output impedance encountered in a conventional amplifier where the output signal is developed across an impedance in the plate circuit.

The conventional amplifier, however, provides gain. To make a fair comparison between the two amplifier types, let us compare, for the two cases, a figure of merit F, which is defined as *the ratio of gain to output impedance.* If, in the conventional amplifier, the resistor R_L is small in comparison with the tube plate resistance (in order that a low output impedance may be obtained), then $A = g_m R_L$ and $R = R_L$ approximately. Therefore

$$F \text{ (conventional amplifier)} = \frac{g_m R_L}{R_L} = g_m$$

For a cathode follower,

$$F \text{ (cathode follower)} = \frac{g_m R_k}{1 + g_m R_k} \frac{1 + g_m R_k}{R_k} = g_m$$

It appears that if the gain of a conventional amplifier is made equal to that of a cathode follower, then the output impedance of the two circuits is the same.

Nevertheless, where an amplifier of low output impedance is required, the cathode follower might still be the circuit of choice since it offers an advantage with respect to *stability* of gain not shared by the conventional amplifier. In the light of the discussion in Sec. 17-2 this feature might well have been anticipated. Consider, for example, that the g_m of the tube changes by, say, 10 per cent. The gain of the conventional amplifier also changes by 10 per cent. On the other hand, if a cathode follower were adjusted for approximately unity gain $(g_m R_k \gg 1)$, the change in gain would be appreciably reduced. We have

$$\frac{dA_f}{A_f} = \frac{1}{1 + g_m R_k} \frac{dg_m}{g_m}$$

so that, if, say, $g_m R_k = 10$ and $dg_m/g_m = 0.1$, then $dA/A = 0.1/11 \cong 0.01$. Thus, a 10 per cent change in g_m has now resulted in only a 1 per cent change in gain. This is an improvement by a factor of 10 over the conventional amplifier.

A second advantage of the cathode follower lies in the linearity with which the output signal follows the input signal. The advantage is most pronounced when a cathode follower of maximum possible gain, nominally unity, is compared with a conventional amplifier of comparable gain and consequently comparable output impedance. Consider first a cathode follower in which R_k is made very large.

If an output signal swing Δe_o is required, the tube current must change by $\Delta e_o/R_k$, which is small since R_k is large. Since the nonlinearity introduced by a vacuum tube is largely determined by the range over which its current must vary, we may anticipate that the operation will be quite linear. The comparable conventional amplifier will require a plate-circuit resistor R_L nominally equal to $1/g_m$, which is only of the order of several hundred ohms. The tube current must then change by $\Delta e_o/R_L$, which is very much larger than $\Delta e_o/R_k$, and the linearity will suffer. With a cathode follower for which $g_m R_k \gg 1$ it is not difficult to achieve a linear output voltage whose peak-to-peak value is comparable to the total supply voltage. With a unity-gain amplifier the maximum output swing is the grid base (defined as the voltage swing from zero bias to cutoff). This swing is approximately $1/\mu$ times the supply voltage. Hence the swing obtainable from a unity-gain conventional amplifier is much smaller than that from a cathode follower.

Consider a circuit which is to drive a low-impedance load, such as a long cable terminated in its characteristic impedance, say, 75 ohms. Then with a tube for which $g_m = 5$ millimhos, $g_m R_k = 0.375$, and the condition $1 + g_m R_k \gg 1$ is not satisfied. Under these circumstances, the choice between a grounded-cathode and a cathode-follower circuit is not clear-cut.[3]

17-6. Characteristics and Applications of the Cathode Follower. The principal characteristics of the cathode follower may be summarized as follows:

1. High input impedance (low input capacitance).
2. Low output impedance.
3. Stability of amplification with tube changing, voltage variation, etc.

4. Output is linearly related to the input.

5. No inversion of the signal.

6. Gain is less than one but can be made almost equal to unity.

7. The input swing may be very large, approaching the supply voltage in magnitude.

8. The quiescent output voltage may be adjusted easily.

9. Any ripple in the supply voltages appears at the output greatly attenuated (see Prob. 17-6).

The first characteristic is discussed in Sec. 8-10, where the high-frequency behavior of the cathode follower is considered. The other characteristics mentioned above have been studied in the preceding sections.

Only a few applications will be listed, although many are suggested by the above properties. A cathode follower is usually employed when a high input impedance or a low output impedance or both are required. The input stage to almost all good-quality cathode-ray oscilloscopes is a cathode follower. Whenever it is required to transmit a signal over a relatively long distance, the capacitive loading of the long wires (or shielded cable) is minimized by taking advantage of the low output impedance of the cathode follower. One such application is the use of the cathode follower to couple the early stages of the amplifier of an oscilloscope, located near the front-panel input terminals, to the output

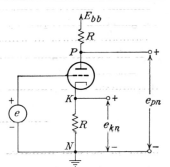

Fig. 17-10. The split-load phase inverter.

stages, which are located near the back of the chassis at the base of the cathode-ray tube. Another such application is the use of the cathode follower to feed video signals, by means of a coaxial cable, from a receiver to a number of indicators many feet away.

If the output from one circuit acts as the input to another circuit and if the second circuit reacts back onto the first, then a cathode follower may be used as a buffer stage to eliminate this reaction.

Many electronic instruments take advantage of the great stability and linearity of cathode followers.

17-7. Circuits with a Cathode Resistor.[4] There are many practical feedback networks which involve the use of a resistor in the cathode circuit. Some of the most important of these "cathode-follower-type" circuits are described in this section.

The Split-load Phase Inverter. This circuit appears in Fig. 17-10. A single input signal provides two output signals: e_{kn}, which is of the same polarity as the input, and e_{pn}, which is of opposite polarity. Further, if the plate and cathode resistors are identical, the magnitudes of the two signals must be the same, since the currents in the plate and cathode resistors are equal. The amplification $|A| \equiv |e_{kn}/e| = |e_{pn}/e|$ may be written directly by comparison with either of the equivalent circuits of Fig. 17-6b or 17-7b, with the result that

$$|A| = \frac{\mu R}{r_p + (\mu + 2)R} \cong \frac{g_m R}{1 + g_m R} \qquad (17\text{-}20)$$

The exact result differs from that given for the cathode follower, Eq. (17-17), only in the appearance of a factor $\mu + 2$ in place of the factor $\mu + 1$. The gain may be made to approach 1 if $g_m R \gg 1$. The ratio of the plate-to-cathode signal to the input signal may then approach 2. The output impedances at the plate and at the cathode are different, the plate impedance being higher than the cathode impedance.

If the capacitance from the plate to ground is greater than that from cathode to ground, it is possible to equalize the frequency response of the two outputs by adding capacitance across the cathode resistor. A phase inverter, also called a *paraphase amplifier*, is used to convert a voltage, one terminal of which is grounded (a single-ended signal) into symmetrical voltages, for example, for an oscilloscope or for a push-pull amplifier (Sec. 16-16).

The Cathode-coupled Phase Inverter. This circuit, shown in Fig. 17-11a, serves the same purpose as the split-load phase inverter but additionally provides some gain and equal output impedances. The two signals e_{o1} and e_{o2} are of opposite polarity and are nominally of equal amplitude. The equivalent circuit of Fig. 17-6b may again be used to advantage to analyze the operation of the cathode-coupled phase inverter. We replace each tube by its equivalent circuit *as seen from the cathode*. The resulting circuit is shown in Fig. 17-11b. The *signal* currents flowing, respectively, out of the cathode of T_1 and into the cathode of T_2 are i_1 and i_2. The output signals are $e_{o1} = -i_1 R_L$ and $e_{o2} = i_2 R_L$.

The output signals will be of equal magnitude if $i_1 = i_2$. This require-

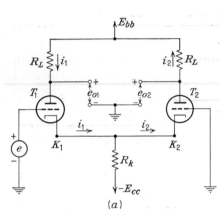

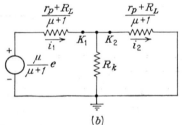

Fig. 17-11. (a) The cathode-coupled phase inverter. (b) Its equivalent circuit from cathode to ground.

ment will be satisfied nominally if $R_k \gg (r_p + R_L)/(\mu + 1)$. Typically if, say, $r_p = R_L = 10$ kilohms and $\mu + 1 = 20$ as for a 12AU7 tube, $(r_p + R_L)/(\mu + 1) = 1$ kilohm and R_k should be selected to be about 10 kilohms if an unbalance of no more than about 10 per cent is desired (see Prob. 17-19). It is possible to obtain balanced outputs by choosing unequal values for the two plate load resistors.

By applying Kirchhoff's voltage law to the outside loop of Fig. 17-11b we find for the plate-to-plate gain

$$A \equiv \frac{e_{o2} - e_{o1}}{e} = \frac{(i_1 + i_2)R_L}{e} = \frac{\mu R_L}{r_p + R_L} \tag{17-21}$$

which is the same gain that would be provided by a single-tube grounded-cathode amplifier with plate resistor R_L.

If each tube carries a quiescent current of, say, 5 ma, the quiescent drop across R_k is 100 volts. We may require for convenience that the quiescent grid voltages be ground potential. In the linear range of operation the grid-to-cathode voltage of a tube is usually only of the order of several volts. The voltage at the cathodes is therefore also required to be in the neighborhood of ground potential. These requirements with respect to quiescent operating voltages may be satisfied by returning the cathode resistor, as in Fig. 17-11a, to an appropriately large negative voltage (in this example, $E_{cc} = 100$ volts).

Other paraphase amplifier circuits exist which do not involve feedback and hence have greater voltage gain but less stability of amplification, etc., than the circuits described above.

The Difference Amplifier. Suppose that we have two signals e_1 and e_2, each measured with respect to ground. It is desired to generate a third signal, also to be referred to ground, which signal is to be proportional to the voltage difference $e_1 - e_2$. One such application would occur if it were required to convert the symmetrical signal, which appears at the plates of a paraphase amplifier, back to an unsymmetrical signal. A possible arrangement for this purpose would involve connecting a transformer primary from plate to plate in Fig. 17-11a. The required signal is taken from the transformer secondary, one side of which is grounded. The impedance of the transformer must be high enough not to load down the circuit appreciably, and its frequency response must be adequate for the application at hand. A much more generally applicable method is indicated in the difference amplifier of Fig. 17-12a. In this circuit one of the signals, e_2, is applied directly to the grid of the tube T_2 and the second signal, e_1, is applied to the cathode through the cathode follower T_1. The output of T_2 is proportional to its cathode-to-grid voltage and hence approximately proportional to the difference $e_1 - e_2$.

The equivalent circuit is given in Fig. 17-12b, where again each tube has been replaced by its equivalent seen looking back into the cathode. The output voltage is $i_2 R_L$. If we assume that $(\mu + 1)R_k \gg r_p$ and consequently neglect entirely the presence of R_k, then $i_1 = i_2$ and the output is exactly proportional to the difference $e_1 - e_2$, being given by

$$e_o = \frac{\mu R_L (e_1 - e_2)}{2r_p + R_L} \qquad (17\text{-}22)$$

Ideally, in a difference amplifier, if the input signals were identical, $e_1 = e_2 = e_c$, the output signal would be zero. An identical signal on

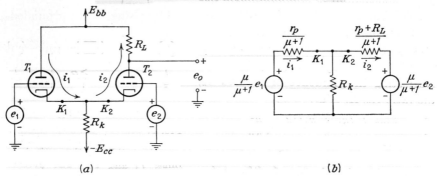

Fig. 17-12. (a) A difference amplifier. (b) The equivalent circuit from cathode to ground.

both grids is known as a *common-mode* signal. The amplification A_c for the common-mode signal would indeed be zero if R_k were infinite. However, if R_k is finite but if $(\mu + 1)R_k \gg r_p$ and $\mu \gg 1$, we find that

$$A_c \equiv \frac{e_o}{e_c} = \frac{-R_L r_p}{R_k(2r_p + R_L)} \qquad (17\text{-}23)$$

If the signals are of equal amplitude and opposite polarity, $e_d/2$ and $-e_d/2$, respectively, then e_d represents the *difference* voltage. The gain for this difference signal is given approximately, for $(\mu + 1)R_k \gg r_p$, by Eq. (17-22) as

$$A_d = \frac{e_o}{e_d} = \frac{\mu R_L}{2r_p + R_L} \qquad (17\text{-}24)$$

The matter may be summarized in the following manner. The output for any two arbitrary signals e_1 and e_2 may be expressed in terms of a difference signal $e_d \equiv e_1 - e_2$ and a common-mode signal $e_c \equiv (e_1 + e_2)/2$ as

$$e_o = A_d e_d + A_c e_c \qquad (17\text{-}25)$$

in which A_d is the gain for the difference signal and A_c is the gain for the common-mode signal. These gains are given by Eqs. (17-24) and (17-23), respectively.

A quantity called the *common-mode rejection ratio* which serves as a figure of merit for a difference amplifier is $A_d/A_c = -\mu R_k/r_p = -g_m R_k$. If, for example, the common-mode rejection ratio is 1,000, this means that a 1-mv difference of voltage at the two grids gives the same output as 1 volt applied with the same polarity to both grids. Since μ and r_p vary with signal voltage, this ratio is *not* a constant independent of common-mode signal amplitude.

The discussion above neglects the possibility that the amplification factors of the two tubes may be slightly different. Neglecting the influence of a finite R_k, the ratio A_d/A_c is given by

$$\frac{A_d}{A_c} = \frac{\mu_1\mu_2 + (\mu_1 + \mu_2)/2}{\mu_1 - \mu_2} \cong \frac{\mu^2}{\Delta\mu} \quad (17\text{-}26)$$

in which $\Delta\mu = \mu_1 - \mu_2$ and μ is the nominal amplification factor of either tube. High-μ tubes are therefore of advantage in difference amplifiers.

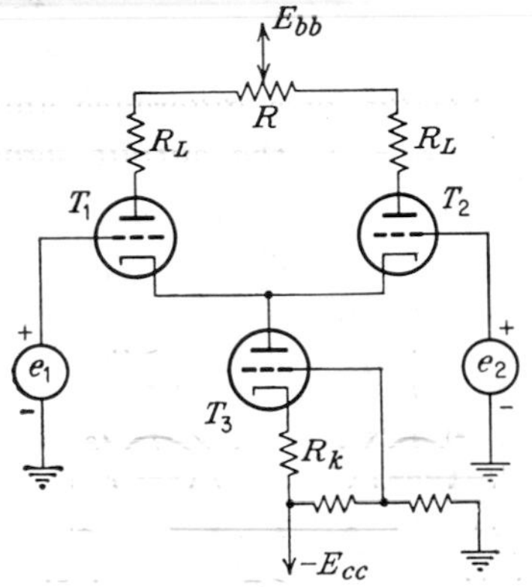

FIG. 17-13. Tube T_3 acts as a very high dynamic resistance of value $r_p + (\mu + 1)R_k$ in the cathode of tubes T_1 and T_2. The potentiometer R is used to balance the outputs from the two plates.

Current-feedback Amplifier as a Constant-current Source. The cathode follower, paraphase amplifier, and difference amplifier all operate with improved performance as the cathode resistance becomes larger. A large cathode resistance, however, results in a large d-c voltage drop due to the quiescent tube current. In Sec. 17-3 we showed that current feedback serves to increase the output impedance of an amplifier. If the output impedance is much greater than the load impedance, a current-feedback amplifier may be considered as a constant-current device (for no input signal) and used to advantage in the cathode circuit to replace a large ordinary resistor. An arrangement of this type is shown in Fig. 17-13. Referring to Fig. 17-7b, it appears that the impedance seen looking into the plate of the tube T_3 in the cathode circuit is $r_p + (1 + \mu)R_k \cong \mu R_k$, if R_k is large. Under typical circumstances $-E_{cc}$ might be -300 volts, $R_k = 500$ kilohms, and the cathode tube a 12AX7 with $\mu = 100$ and $r_p = 100$ kilohms. The effective cathode impedance of the difference amplifier would then be about 50 megohms. In the circuit of Fig. 17-13, high-μ, low-current tubes would be appropriate. Suppose, then, that the individual tubes carried only 0.1 ma of current. The total cathode current is 0.2 ma, and if an ordinary 50-megohm resistor were used, a negative supply voltage of 10,000 volts would be required. This voltage is, of course, impractically high, which demonstrates the advantage of tube T_3 over an ordinary 50-megohm resistor in this application.

17-8. A Cascode Amplifier. This circuit consists of two triodes in series (the same current in each) and should not be confused with cascaded amplifier stages. This configuration is indicated in Fig. 17-14.

That this circuit behaves like a pentode can be seen as follows: The

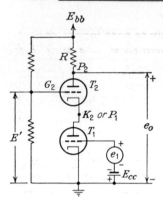

FIG. 17-14. The cascode amplifier.

load for T_1 is the effective impedance looking into the cathode of T_2; namely, $R_L \equiv (R + r_p)/(\mu + 1)$. For large values of μ this may be very small and to a first approximation can be considered as a short circuit. Hence, the plate potential of T_1 is constant. The definition of the transconductance is

$$g_m \equiv \left(\frac{\Delta i_b}{\Delta e_c}\right)_{E_b \text{ const.}}$$

Hence, the signal current is $\Delta i_b = g_m \Delta e_c = g_m e_1$, where e_1 is the signal input voltage. The gain is $A = -R \Delta i_b/e_1 = -g_m R$, which is the expression for the gain of a pentode.

Another point of view is the following: The plate d-c voltage E_{b1} of T_1 is determined by the grid-to-ground voltage E' of T_2. Actually, $E_{b1} = E' - E_{c2}$, where E_{c2} is the drop from grid to cathode of T_2 and is a negative number. The value of E_{c2} may vary between zero and the cutoff voltage, but this is small compared with the value of E' (which may be one or several hundred volts). Hence, E_{b1} is essentially constant, and the d-c tube current is also constant since it is determined by E_{b1} and the bias E_{cc}. Hence, a curve of d-c plate current vs. d-c voltage from the plate of T_2 to ground resembles the constant-current characteristic of a pentode. From this discussion it is clear that E' takes the place of the screen voltage in a pentode. The cascode amplifier has the advantage over the pentode in that no screen current need be supplied and in that it has the low noise of a triode (Sec. 15-12).

The exact expression for the amplification is found by replacing T_2 by an impedance $(R + r_p)/(\mu + 1)$ and T_1 by a generator $\mu \mathbf{E}_1$ in series with an impedance r_p. The result is

$$\mathbf{A}_1 = \frac{-(\mu)(\mu + 1)R}{R + (\mu + 2)r_p} \tag{17-27}$$

If $(\mu + 2)r_p \gg R$ and if $\mu \gg 1$, then this is approximately

$$\mathbf{A}_1 \cong \frac{-\mu R}{r_p} = -g_m R$$

which is the result obtained by the qualitative arguments given above.

It is possible to apply an a-c signal voltage $\mathbf{E}_2$ (in addition to the bias voltage E') to the grid of T_2. Under these circumstances T_1 acts as an impedance of magnitude r_p in the cathode of T_2. The voltage gain for this signal $\mathbf{E}_2$ is

$$\mathbf{A}_2 = \frac{-\mu R}{R + (\mu + 2)r_p} \tag{17-28}$$

If sinusoidal signals are applied simultaneously to both inputs, then, by the principles of superposition, the output $\mathbf{E}_o$ will be $\mathbf{E}_o = \mathbf{A}_1\mathbf{E}_1 + \mathbf{A}_2\mathbf{E}_2$.

The cascode circuit is sometimes used as a feedback amplifier by applying the external signal $\mathbf{E}_s$ to the grid of T_2 and the feedback voltage to the grid of T_1. Under these circumstances the gain with feedback is given by

$$\mathbf{A}_f \equiv \frac{\mathbf{E}_o}{\mathbf{E}_s} = \frac{\mathbf{A}_2}{1 - \mathbf{A}_1\beta} \tag{17-29}$$

where $\mathbf{A}_1$ and $\mathbf{A}_2$ are the gains without feedback (but with the feedback network in place) for signals $\mathbf{E}_1 = \mathbf{E}_f$ and $\mathbf{E}_2 = \mathbf{E}_s$, respectively. If the β network does not load the amplifier, then $\mathbf{A}_1$ and $\mathbf{A}_2$ are given by Eqs. (17-27) and (17-28), respectively.

The quiescent operating current in a cascode amplifier is found by the method of successive approximations. The method converges very rapidly and is best illustrated by a numerical example.

Example. Find the quiescent current in the cascode amplifier of Fig. 17-14 if $R = 20$ kilohms, $E_{bb} = 300$ volts, $E' = 125$ volts, and $E_{cc} = 4$ volts. The tube is a 6SN7.

Solution. If T_2 is not to draw grid current, then K_2 must be at a higher potential than G_2. However, it cannot be at too high a potential or T_2 will be cut off. Let us take as a first approximation $E_{c2} = -5$ and hence $E_{b1} = 125 + 5 = 130$ volts. Corresponding to this value of E_{b1} and to $E_{c1} = -4$, the plate current I_b is found from the 6SN7 characteristics to be 4.2 ma. Hence $E_{b2} = E_{bb} - I_b R - E_{b1} = 300 - (4.2)(20) - 130 = 86$ volts. For $E_{b2} = 86$ volts and $I_{b2} = 4.2$ ma, we find that $E_{c2} = -2$ volts.

The second approximation is $E_{b1} = 125 + 2 = 127$. Corresponding to this value of E_{b1} and to $E_{c1} = -4$ volts, we find that $I_b = 4.0$ ma. Hence, $E_{b2} = 300 - (4.0)(20) - 130 = 90$ volts. Corresponding to this E_{b2} and to $I_{b2} = 4.0$ ma, we find $E_{c2} \cong -2.3$ volts.

The third approximation to E_{b1} is $125 + 2.3 = 127.3$ volts, which is close enough to the previous value of 127 so as not to affect the value of the current appreciably. Hence, $I_b = 4.0$ ma.

17-9. Feedback and Stability.[5]

Negative feedback for which $|1 - \mathbf{A}\beta| > 1$ has been considered in some detail in the foregoing sections. If $|1 - \mathbf{A}\beta| < 1$, then the feedback is termed *positive* or *regenerative*. Under these circumstances, the resultant gain $\mathbf{A}_f$ will be greater than $\mathbf{A}$, the nominal gain without feedback, since $|\mathbf{A}_f| = |\mathbf{A}|/|1 - \mathbf{A}\beta| > |\mathbf{A}|$. Regeneration as an effective means of increasing the amplification of an amplifier was first suggested by Armstrong.[6] Because of the reduced stability of an amplifier with positive feedback, this method is seldom used.

To illustrate the instability in an amplifier with positive feedback, consider the following situation: No signal is applied, but because of some transient disturbance a voltage E_o appears at the output terminals. A portion of this voltage βE_o will be fed back to the input circuit and will appear in the output as an increased voltage $A\beta E_o$. If this term just equals E_o, then the spurious output has regenerated itself. In other words, if $A\beta E_o = E_o$ (that is, if $A\beta = 1$), the amplifier will oscillate (Chap. 18). Hence, if an attempt is made to obtain large gain by making $A\beta$ almost equal to unity, there is the possibility that the amplifier may break out into spontaneous oscillation. This would occur if, because of variation in supply voltages, aging of transistors or tubes, etc., $A\beta$ becomes equal to unity. There is little point in attempting to achieve amplification at the expense of stability. In fact, because of all the advantages enumerated in Sec. 17-2, feedback in amplifiers is almost always negative.

If an amplifier is designed to have negative feedback in a particular range but breaks out into oscillation at some high or low frequency, it is naturally useless as an amplifier. Hence, in the design of a feedback amplifier it must be ascertained that the circuit is stable at *all* frequencies and not merely over the frequency range of interest. In the sense used here, the system is stable if a transient disturbance results in a response which dies out. A system is unstable if a transient disturbance persists indefinitely and increases until it is limited only by some nonlinearity in the circuit. Thus the question of stability may be considered to involve a study of the transient response of the system. If Laplace transform notation is used, the transfer function $E_o/E_s = A_f$ is a function of the complex frequency $s = \sigma + j\omega$. The poles of the transfer function determine the transient behavior of the network. If a pole exists with a positive value of σ, this will result in a disturbance increasing exponentially with time. Hence, the condition which must be satisfied, if a system is to be stable, is that the poles of the transfer function must all lie in the left-hand half of the complex frequency plane. If the system without feedback is stable, then the poles of A do lie in the left-hand half plane. It follows from Eq. (17-2), therefore, that the stability condition requires that the zeros of $1 - A\beta$ must all lie in the left-hand half plane.

Nyquist[7] has obtained an alternative but equivalent criterion for stability which may be expressed in terms of the steady-state, or frequency response, characteristic. It will be given here without proof. Since the loop gain $A\beta$ is a complex number it may be represented as a point in the complex plane, the real component being plotted along the X axis, and the j component along the Y axis. Furthermore, $A\beta$ is a function of the frequency. Consequently, points in the complex plane are obtained for the values of **Aβ** corresponding to all values of f from zero to $+\infty$. The locus of all these points forms a closed curve. The criterion of Nyquist is that *the amplifier is unstable if this curve encloses the point $1 + j0$ and the amplifier is stable if the curve does not enclose this point*.

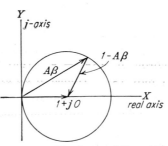

FIG. 17-15. The locus of $|1 - \mathbf{A}\beta|$ = 1 is a circle of unit radius.

The criterion for positive or negative feedback may also be represented in the complex plane. From Fig. 17-15 we see that $|1 - \mathbf{A}\beta| = 1$ represents a circle of unit radius with its center at the point $1 + j0$. If, for any frequency, **Aβ** extends outside this circle, the feedback is negative, since then $|1 - \mathbf{A}\beta| > 1$. If, however, **Aβ** lies within this circle, then $|1 - \mathbf{A}\beta| < 1$, and the feedback is positive. In the latter case the system will not oscillate unless Nyquist's criterion is satisfied.

As a first application of the criterion of stability, consider one stage of a simple RC-coupled amplifier with voltage feedback. The analysis of this circuit in Sec. 15-6 shows that the nominal gain **A** is real and negative

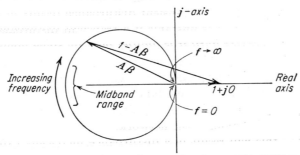

FIG. 17-16. The locus in the complex plane for all values of frequency of the loop gain **Aβ** of an RC-coupled amplifier is a circle.

(a phase angle of 180 deg) over most of the audio range. For the high and low frequencies, it is found that the gain falls to zero, and the phase approaches ± 90 deg. If the voltage feedback factor **β** is independent of the frequency, then **Aβ** varies as **A**. The locus of **Aβ** for all frequencies when plotted in the complex plane can be shown to be a circle plotted as indicated in Fig. 17-16. It should be noted that under these circumstances this curve is simply a polar plot of the gain **A** of the circuit. Furthermore, since this curve does not enclose the point $1 + j0$, the amplifier is stable and the feedback is negative for all frequencies. Alternatively, it is noticed from the diagram that $|1 - \mathbf{A}\beta| > 1$ for all frequencies, which is the condition for negative feedback.

As a second specific illustration, suppose that the polar plot of a given amplifier has the form illustrated in Fig. 17-17. The feedback is negative for this amplifier in the frequency range from 0 to f_1. Positive feedback exists in the frequency range from f_1 to ∞. Note, however, that the locus of $\mathbf{A}\beta$ does not enclose the point $1 + j0$. Hence, according to the Nyquist criterion, oscillations will not occur.

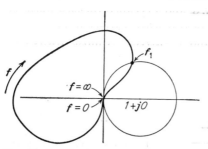

FIG. 17-17. The locus of $\mathbf{A}\beta$ in the complex plane for a circuit which exhibits negative feedback for low frequencies and positive feedback for high frequencies.

Often it is difficult to apply either of the above criteria for stability to a practical amplifier. It should be clear from the foregoing discussion that *no oscillations are possible if the magnitude of the loop gain $|\mathbf{A}\beta|$ is less than unity when its phase angle is zero*. This condition is sought for in practice to ensure that the amplifier will be stable.

Consider, for example, a three-stage RC-coupled amplifier with voltage feedback from the output to the input, as in Fig. 17-3. There is a definite maximum value of the feedback fraction $\beta = R_1/R_g$ allowable for stable operation.[8] To see this, note that if all capacitors are disregarded there is 180-deg phase shift in each stage, and 540 deg or, equivalently, 180 deg, for the three stages. At high frequencies there is an additional phase shift due to the shunting capacitances, and at the frequency for which the phase shift per stage is 60 deg the total phase shift around the loop is zero. If the gain at this frequency is called A_{60}, then β must be chosen such that $A_{60}\beta$ is less than unity, if the possibility of oscillations is to be avoided. Similarly, because of the phase shift introduced by the blocking capacitors, there is a low frequency for which the phase shift per stage is also 60 deg, and hence there is the possibility of oscillation at this low frequency also unless the maximum value of β is restricted as outlined above.

17-10. The Operational Amplifier.[9] This is a special type of voltage-feedback amplifier which is of great importance, particularly in electronic analog computers. It can be made to perform many operations such as sign changing or inverting, scale changing, phase shifting, adding, integrating, and differentiating.

The operational amplifier is shown in Fig. 17-18 and has an important advantage over the circuit of Fig. 17-1 in that the former has one terminal (2) of the external signal source in common with an amplifier output terminal (4). In other words, there is a common ground between the

input and output circuits. The feedback is now obtained from the impedance Z' between the ungrounded output (3) and input (1) terminals.
There is also an impedance Z between the ungrounded terminal of the
signal source and the input (1).

The amplifier between terminals 1, 2, 3, and 4 is called the *base amplifier*
and may be of either the vacuum-tube or transistor variety having a mid-
band amplification **A** which is real and negative. Almost always the

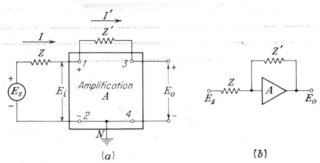

FIG. 17-18. Two representations of an operational amplifier.

amplifier consists of several common-cathode or common-emitter stages
in cascade. The input terminal is the grid or base. The output is usually taken from the plate or collector. Hence this type of feedback is
sometimes called *plate-to-grid* or *collector-to-base feedback*. This latter
configuration as a method of stabilizing the operating point of a transistor
was discussed in Sec. 9-12. Because of its small size, low power consump-
tion, and long life, the transistor is an excellent circuit element for use in
a computer.[10]

We shall now find an equivalent circuit of the operational amplifier.
Let us calculate the impedance which is presented by the amplifier at its
input terminals 1 and 2 in Fig. 17-18. The voltage across Z' is

$$\mathbf{E}_i - \mathbf{E}_o = \mathbf{E}_i - \mathbf{A}\mathbf{E}_i = \mathbf{E}_i(1 - \mathbf{A})$$

where $\mathbf{A} = \mathbf{E}_o/\mathbf{E}_i$ is the amplification without feedback but with $\mathbf{Z}'$ in
place (**A** is called the *open-loop loaded gain*). The impedance seen look-
ing into the input terminals is

$$\frac{\mathbf{E}_i}{\mathbf{I}} = \frac{\mathbf{E}_i}{\mathbf{E}_i(1 - \mathbf{A})/\mathbf{Z}'} = \frac{\mathbf{Z}'}{1 - \mathbf{A}}$$

An equivalent circuit which gives the same input current **I** from the
source $\mathbf{E}_s$, the same amplifier input voltage $\mathbf{E}_i$, and consequently the same
output voltage as in Fig. 17-18 is indicated in Fig. 17-19. The input
impedance $\mathbf{Z}_i$ of the amplifier which, for simplicity, was neglected in the

above discussion has been added to Fig. 17-19. From this figure we see that if

$$\left| \frac{\mathbf{Z}'}{1 - \mathbf{A}} \right| \ll |\mathbf{Z}_i| \tag{17-30}$$

then $\mathbf{I}' \cong \mathbf{I}$. Under these circumstances the output voltage is

$$\mathbf{E}_o = \mathbf{A}\mathbf{E}_i = \mathbf{A}\mathbf{I} \frac{\mathbf{Z}'}{1 - \mathbf{A}} \tag{17-31}$$

Even for a transistor, for which the input impedance is much smaller than that for a vacuum-tube amplifier, the inequality (17-30) will be satisfied provided that the amplification A is made sufficiently large. As $A \to \infty$

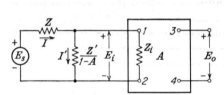

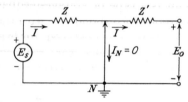

FIG. 17-19. An equivalent circuit of the operational amplifier.

FIG. 17-20. Virtual ground in the operational amplifier.

the impedance across terminals 1 and 2 approaches zero (a short circuit) and $\mathbf{I} \cong \mathbf{E}_s/\mathbf{Z}$. Also, as $A \to \infty$, we see from Eq. (17-31) that the output is

$$\mathbf{E}_o \cong -\mathbf{I}\mathbf{Z}' = -\frac{\mathbf{Z}'}{\mathbf{Z}}\mathbf{E}_s$$

and the over-all gain is

$$\mathbf{A}_f = -\frac{\mathbf{Z}'}{\mathbf{Z}} \tag{17-32}$$

The operation of the circuit may now be described in the following terms. At the input to the amplifier proper there exists a *virtual short circuit* or *virtual ground*. The term "virtual" is used to imply that, while the feedback serves to keep the voltage $\mathbf{E}_i$ at zero, no current actually flows through this short. The situation is depicted in Fig. 17-20, where the virtual ground is represented by the arrow. The current furnished by the generator $\mathbf{E}_s$ continues past this virtual short through the impedance $\mathbf{Z}'$.

Since the resultant gain is independent of the amplifier and depends only upon the two impedances $\mathbf{Z}$ and $\mathbf{Z}'$, it is clear that the advantages listed in Sec. 17-2 for the voltage-feedback amplifier are also valid for the operational amplifier.

Equation (17-32) is strictly valid only if $\mathbf{A}$ is infinite. It is sometimes important to consider the effect of a finite voltage gain. If $A_f = E_o/E_s$ is calculated from Fig. 17-19 we obtain the following exact expression:

$$A_f = \frac{-Y}{Y' - (1/A)(Y' + Y + Y_i)} \qquad (17\text{-}33)$$

where the Y's are the admittances corresponding to the Z's (for example, $Y' = 1/Z'$). Note that as $A \to \infty$

$$A_f = -\frac{Y}{Y'} = -\frac{Z'}{Z}$$

in agreement with Eq. (17-32).

17-11. Operational Amplifier—Another Viewpoint. The operational circuit is a type of voltage-feedback amplifier which does not fall into a one-to-one correspondence with the voltage-feedback arrangement of Fig. 17-1. It is to be observed, for example, that in Fig. 17-18, if the gain of the amplifier proper were reduced to zero, an output signal would still appear, following the path from input to output through the path of the impedances Z and Z'. In Fig. 17-1 such an alternative path is not present. This coupling between input and output around the amplifier would vanish if the output impedance of the amplifier were zero.

Let us attempt to obtain an equivalent circuit of the form indicated in Fig. 17-1b. Taking the input admittance Y_i into account in Fig. 17-18 we have, from the principle of superposition,

$$E_i = \frac{Y}{Y' + Y + Y_i} E_s + \frac{Y'}{Y' + Y + Y_i} E_o \qquad (17\text{-}34)$$

Thus the input consists of a linear combination of E_o and E_s in a manner which is independent of any external load, as is required for voltage feedback. On the basis of Eq. (17-34), the circuit of Fig. 17-18 may be replaced by an equivalent circuit, as shown in Fig. 17-21. This figure is now identical to Fig. 17-1b except that we have taken

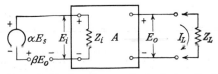

FIG. 17-21. Another equivalent circuit of an operational amplifier.

into account that the external signal E_s is attenuated by the ratio $\alpha \equiv Y/(Y' + Y + Y_i)$ before application to the amplifier. The feedback factor $\beta \equiv Y'/(Y' + Y + Y_i)$ so that the gain with feedback is

$$A_f = \frac{\alpha A}{1 - \beta A} = \frac{YA/(Y' + Y + Y_i)}{1 - Y'A/(Y' + Y + Y_i)}$$

which readily reduces to Eq. (17-33).

The output impedance with feedback Z_f is related to the output imped-ance without feedback Z_o by Eq. (17-3). For a high-gain amplifier, Z_f may be extremely small, perhaps only a fraction of an ohm.

17-12. Basic Uses of Operational Amplifiers.[11,12] An operational amplifier may be used to perform many mathematical operations. Among the basic configurations are the following:

Sign Changer or Inverter. If $Z = Z'$, then $A_f = -1$, and the sign of the input signal has been changed. Hence such a circuit acts as a phase inverter. If two such amplifiers are connected in cascade, the output from the second stage equals the signal input without change of sign. Hence, the outputs from the two stages are equal in magnitude but oppo-site in phase, and such a system is an excellent paraphase amplifier.

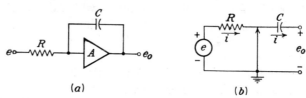

(a)   (b)

FIG. 17-22. (a) Operational integrator.   (b) Equivalent circuit.

Scale Changer. If the ratio $Z'/Z = k$, a real constant, then $A_f = -k$, and the scale has been changed by a factor $-k$. Usually, in such a case of multiplication by a constant, -1 or $-k$, Z and Z' are selected as resistors.

An interesting analogy may be drawn here between the amplifier and a lever. The virtual ground is represented by the fulcrum of the lever. If the ratio of the lengths of the lever arms is k, then a displacement of the end of one arm causes a displacement of the end of the other arm in the opposite direction which is k times as large. In Fig. 17-20, the volt-ages E_s and E_o represent the lever displacements.

Phase Shifter. Assume Z and Z' are equal in magnitude but differ in angle. Then the operational amplifier shifts the phase of a sinusoidal input voltage while at the same time preserving its amplitude. Any phase shift from 0 to 360 deg (or ± 180 deg) may be obtained.

Integrator. If $Z = R$ and a capacitor C is used for Z', as in Fig. 17-22a, we can show that the circuit performs the mathematical operation of inte-gration. The input need not be sinusoidal and hence will be represented by the lower-case symbol $e = e(t)$. (The subscript s will now be omitted, for simplicity.) Correspondingly the current as a function of time is designated by $i = i(t)$. In Fig. 17-22b (analogous to Fig. 17-20) the arrow represents a virtual ground. Hence $i = e/R$ and

$$e_o = -\frac{1}{C} \int i \, dt = -\frac{1}{RC} \int e \, dt \qquad (17\text{-}35)$$

The amplifier, therefore, provides an output voltage proportional to the integral of the input voltage. It must be remembered that the above considerations are based upon the approximate equivalent circuit of Fig. 17-20 which is strictly valid only for an amplifier having infinite gain. The higher the amplification of the base amplifier, the more accurate will be the integration.

If the input voltage is a constant $e = E$, then the output will be a ramp voltage $e_o = -(E/RC)t$. Such an integrator makes an excellent sweep circuit for a cathode-ray-tube oscilloscope and is called a *Miller integrator* or *Miller sweep*.[13]

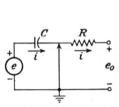

FIG. 17-23. Equivalent circuit of operational differentiator.

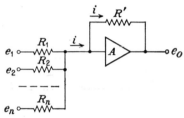

FIG. 17-24. Operational adder or summing amplifier.

Differentiator. If Z is a capacitor and $Z' = R$, then we see from the equivalent circuit of Fig. 17-23 that $i = C(de/dt)$ and

$$e_o = -Ri = -RC\frac{de}{dt} \qquad (17\text{-}36)$$

so that the output is proportional to the time derivative of the input.

Adder or Summing Amplifier. The arrangement of Fig. 17-24 may be used to obtain an output which is a linear combination of a number of input signals. Here

$$i = \frac{e_1}{R_1} + \frac{e_2}{R_2} + \cdots + \frac{e_n}{R_n}$$

and

$$e_o = -R'i = -\left(\frac{R'}{R_1}e_1 + \frac{R'}{R_2}e_2 + \cdots + \frac{R'}{R_n}e_n\right) \qquad (17\text{-}37)$$

If $R_1 = R_2 = \cdots = R_n$, then

$$e_o = -\frac{R'}{R_1}(e_1 + e_2 + \cdots + e_n) \qquad (17\text{-}38)$$

and the output is proportional to the sum of the inputs. In the more general case of Eq. (17-37) the scale of each input signal may be adjusted before adding.

There are, of course, many other methods which may be used to combine signals. The present method has the advantage that it may be extended to a very large number of inputs requiring only one additional resistor for each additional input. The result depends, in the limiting case of large amplifier gain, only on the resistors involved, and because of the virtual ground there is a minimum of interaction between input sources.

If in Fig. 17-24 the resistor R' is replaced by a capacitor C, the circuit will simultaneously integrate and add. The output will be given by

$$e_o = -\frac{1}{C} \int i\, dt = -\frac{1}{CR_1} \int e_1\, dt \cdots - \frac{1}{CR_n} \int e_n\, dt \quad (17\text{-}39)$$

The General Case. In the important cases considered above, $\mathbf{Z}$ and $\mathbf{Z}'$ have been simple elements such as a single R or C. In general, they may be any series or parallel combinations of R, L, or C. Using the methods of operational calculus or Laplace-transform analysis, $\mathbf{Z}$ and $\mathbf{Z}'$ can be written in their operational form as $\mathbf{Z}(s)$ and $\mathbf{Z}'(s)$, where s is the complex frequency variable. In this notation the reactance of an inductor is written formally as Ls and that of a capacitor as $1/sC$. The current $\mathbf{I}(s)$ is then $\mathbf{E}(s)/\mathbf{Z}(s)$, and the output is

$$\mathbf{E}_o(s) = -\frac{\mathbf{Z}'(s)}{\mathbf{Z}(s)}\, \mathbf{E}(s) \quad\quad (17\text{-}40)$$

The amplifier thus solves this operational equation.

17-13. Electronic Analog Computation.[9,12] The operational amplifier is the fundamental building block in an electronic analog computer. As an illustration, let us consider how to program the differential equation

$$\frac{d^2e}{dt^2} + K_1 \frac{de}{dt} + K_2 e - e_1 = 0 \quad\quad (17\text{-}41)$$

where e_1 is a given function of time and K_1 and K_2 are real positive constants.

We begin by assuming that d^2e/dt^2 is available in the form of a voltage. Then by means of an integrator a voltage proportional to de/dt is obtained. A second integrator gives a voltage proportional to e. Then an adder (and scale changer) gives $-K_1(de/dt) - K_2 e + e_1$. From the differential equation (17-41) this equals d^2e/dt^2, and hence the output of this summing amplifier is fed to the terminals where we had assumed d^2e/dt^2 was available in the first place.

The procedure outlined above is carried out in Fig. 17-25. The voltage d^2e/dt^2 is assumed to be available at an input terminal. The integrator (1) has a time constant $RC = 1$ sec, and hence its output at terminal 1 is $-de/dt$. This voltage is fed to a similar integrator (2) and the voltage at terminal 2 is $+e$. The voltage at terminal 1 is fed to the inverter and scale changer (3), and its output at terminal 3 is $+K_1(de/dt)$. This same operational amplifier (3) is used as an adder. Hence, if the given voltage $e_1(t)$ is also fed into it as shown, the output at terminal 3 also contains the term $-e_1$, or the net output is $+K_1(de/dt) - e_1$. Scale changer-adder (4) is fed from terminals 2 and 3 and hence delivers a resultant voltage $-K_2e - K_1(de/dt) + e_1$ at terminal 4. By Eq. (17-41) this must equal d^2e/dt^2, which is the voltage that was assumed to exist at the input terminal. Hence, the computer is

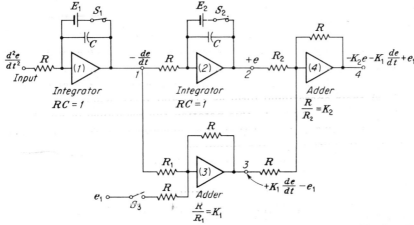

FIG. 17-25. A block diagram of an electronic analog computer.

completed by connecting terminal 4 to the input terminal. (This last step is omitted from Fig. 17-25 for the sake of clarity of explanation.)

The specified initial conditions (the values of de/dt and e at $t = 0$) must now be inserted into the computer. We note that the voltages at terminals 1 and 2 in Fig. 17-25 are proportional to de/dt and e, respectively. Because of the virtual ground at the input of an operational amplifier the voltage across the capacitor C of an integrator equals the output voltage. Hence, initial conditions are taken care of by applying the correct voltages E_1 and E_2 across the capacitors in integrators 1 and 2, respectively.

The solution is obtained by opening switches S_1 and S_2 and simultaneously closing S_3 (by means of relays) at $t = 0$ and observing the wave form at terminal 2. If the derivative de/dt is also desired, its wave form is available at terminal 1. The indicator may be a cathode-ray tube (with a triggered sweep), a Brush recorder, or, for qualitative analysis with slowly varying quantities, a vacuum-tube voltmeter.

The solution of Eq. (17-41) can also be obtained with a computer which contains differentiators instead of integrators. However, integrators are

<u>almost invariably preferred over differentiators in analog-computer applications for the following reasons.</u> Since the gain of an integrator decreases with frequency whereas the gain of a differentiator increases nominally linearly with frequency, it is easier to stabilize the former than the latter with respect to spurious oscillations. As a result of its limited band width, an integrator is less sensitive to noise voltages than a differentiator. Further, if the input wave form changes very rapidly, the amplifier of a differentiator may overload. Finally, as a matter of practice, it is very convenient to introduce initial conditions in an integrator.

REFERENCES

1. BLACK, H. S., "Stabilized Feed-back Amplifiers," *Elec. Eng.*, **53**, 114–120, January, 1934.
   PETERSON, E., J. G. KREER, and L. A. WARE, "Regeneration Theory and Experiment," *Bell System Tech. J.*, **13**, 680–700, October, 1934.
   TERMAN, F. E., "Feedback Amplifier Design," *Electronics*, **10**, 12–15, January, 1937.
   DAY, J. R., and J. B. RUSSELL, "Practical Feedback Amplifiers," *ibid.*, **10**, 16–19, April, 1937.
2. HUNTER, L. P. (ed.), "Handbook of Semiconductor Electronics," Sec. 11-7, McGraw-Hill Book Company, Inc., New York, 1956.
3. MILLMAN, J., and H. TAUB, "Pulse and Digital Circuits," pp. 88–89, McGraw-Hill Book Company, Inc., New York, 1956.
4. VALLEY, G. E., Jr., and H. WALLMAN, "Vacuum Tube Amplifiers," Radiation Laboratory Series, Vol. 18, Chap. 11, McGraw-Hill Book Company, Inc., New York, 1948.
5. TERMAN, F. E., "Feedback Amplifier Design," *Electronics*, **10**, 12–15, January, 1937.
6. ARMSTRONG, E. H., "Some Recent Developments in the Audion Receiver," *Proc IRE*, **3**, 215–247, September, 1915.
7. NYQUIST, H., "Regeneration Theory," *Bell System Tech. J.*, **11**, 126–147, January, 1932.
8. ARGUIMBAU, L. B., and R. B. ADLER, "Vacuum-tube Circuits and Transistors," pp. 405–408, John Wiley & Sons, Inc., New York, 1956.
9. RAGAZZINI, J. R., R. H. RANDALL, and F. A. RUSSELL, "Analysis of Problems in Dynamics by Electronic Circuits," *Proc. IRE*, **35**, 444–452, May, 1947.
10. BLECHER, F. H., "Transistor Circuits for Analog and Digital Systems," *Bell System Tech. J.*, **35**, 295–332, March, 1956.
    CURTIN, W. A., "Application of Junction Transistors to Carrier-frequency Computing Amplifiers," *Trans. AIEE, Communications and Electronics*, January, 1957.
11. CHANCE, B., et al., "Waveforms," Radiation Laboratory Series, Vol. 19, Chap. 2, McGraw-Hill Book Company, Inc., New York, 1949.
12. KORN, G. A., and T. M. KORN, "Electronic Analog Computers," McGraw-Hill Book Company, Inc., New York, 1952.
13. MILLMAN, J., and H. TAUB, "Pulse and Digital Circuits," pp. 212–219, McGraw-Hill Book Company, Inc., New York, 1956.

CHAPTER 18

SINUSOIDAL OSCILLATORS

THERE are many different circuit configurations which deliver an essentially sinusoidal output wave form even without an input signal voltage. The basic principles governing all these oscillators will be investigated. In addition to determining the conditions required for oscillations to take place, the frequency and amplitude stability will also be studied. First vacuum-tube and then transistor oscillators will be considered in some detail.

18-1. General Considerations. In Fig. 18-1 is shown an amplifier and feedback network with the feedback voltage not yet connected to the amplifier input. The amplifier provides an output voltage e_o as a consequence of the externally applied input voltage e_s. Suppose that it should happen that matters are adjusted in such a way that the feedback voltage e_f is *identically* equal to the externally applied input voltage e_s. Since the amplifier has no means of distinguishing the source of the input signal applied

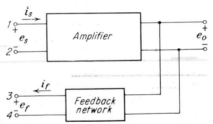

FIG. 18-1. An amplifier and feedback network not yet connected to form a closed loop.

to it, it would appear that, if the external source were removed and the output terminals 3 and 4 of the feedback network were connected to the amplifier input terminals 1 and 2, the amplifier would continue to provide the same output voltage e_o as before. Note, of course, that the statement $e_f = e_s$ means that the instantaneous values of e_f and e_s are exactly equal at all times. Note also that, since in the above discussion no restriction was made on the wave form, it need not be sinusoidal. The amplifier need not be linear, and the wave shape need not preserve its form as it is transmitted through the amplifier, provided only that when it emerges finally from the feedback coupling circuit the voltage has been restored to its original wave shape. And the wave form which is available from such a circuit and its frequency will be precisely whatever the

473

wave form and frequency are required to be in order that the fundamental condition $e_s = e_f$ shall be met.

Now we shall be concerned in the present section with a discussion of oscillators in which the entire circuit operates linearly and the amplifier or feedback network or both contain reactive elements. Under such circumstances, the only periodic wave form which will preserve its form is the sinusoidal wave form, and such a circuit should be expected to serve as a source of a sinusoidal voltage. So long, then, as we are dealing with sinusoidal wave forms the condition $e_s = e_f$ is equivalent to the condition that the *amplitude, phase,* and *frequency* of e_s and e_f be identical. Since the phase shift introduced in a signal in being transmitted through a reactive network is invariably a function of the frequency and since usually there will be only a single frequency for which e_f and e_s will be in phase with one another, we have the following important principle:

The frequency at which a sinusoidal oscillator will operate is the frequency for which the total phase shift introduced as a signal proceeds from the input terminals, through the amplifier and feedback network, and back again to the input is precisely zero (*or, of course, an integral multiple of 2π*). *Stated more simply, the frequency of a sinusoidal oscillator is determined by the condition that the loop phase shift is zero.*

While other principles may be formulated which may serve equally to determine the frequency, these other principles may always be shown to be identical to that stated above. It might be noted parenthetically that it is not inconceivable that the above condition might be satisfied for more than a single frequency. In such a contingency there is the possibility of simultaneous oscillation at several frequencies or an oscillation at a single one of the allowed frequencies, depending on the circumstances.

The condition given above determines the frequency, provided that the circuit will oscillate at all. Another condition which must clearly be met if the oscillator is to function is that the magnitude of e_s and e_f must be identical. This condition is then embodied in the following principle:

An oscillator will not function if at the oscillator frequency the magnitude of the product of the gain of the amplifier and the feedback factor of the feedback network (*the loop gain*) *is less than unity.*

Both of the above principles are consistent with the feedback formula $\mathbf{A}_f = \mathbf{A}/(1 - \beta\mathbf{A})$. For if $\beta\mathbf{A} = 1$ then $\mathbf{A}_f \to \infty$, which may in turn be interpreted that there exists an output voltage even in the absence of an externally applied signal voltage. And the condition $\beta\mathbf{A} = 1$ implies, of course, both that $\beta A = 1$ and that the phase of $\beta\mathbf{A}$ is zero.

The condition of *unity loop gain* $\mathbf{A}\beta = 1$ is called the *Barkhausen criterion.*

Referring again to Fig. 18-1, it appears that if βA at the oscillator frequency is precisely unity then with the feedback voltage connected to the input terminals the removal of the external generator will make no difference.   If βA is less than unity, the removal of the external generator will immediately result in a cessation of oscillations.   But now suppose that βA is greater than unity.   Then 1 volt appearing initially at the input terminals will, after a trip around the loop and back to the input terminals, appear there as a voltage larger than 1 volt.   This larger voltage will then reappear as a still larger voltage and so on.   It seems, then, that if βA is larger than unity the amplitude of the oscillations will continue to increase without limit.   But, of course, such an increase in the amplitude can continue only as long as it is not limited by the onset of nonlinearity of operation in the active devices associated with the amplifier.   Such a nonlinearity becomes more marked as the amplitude of oscillations increases.   This onset of nonlinearity to limit the amplitude of oscillations is an essential feature of the operation of all practical oscillators, as the following considerations will show.   The condition $\beta A = 1$ does not give a range of acceptable values of βA but rather a single and precise value.   Now suppose that initially it were even possible to satisfy this condition.   Then because circuit components and, more importantly, vacuum tubes and transistors change characteristics (drift) with age, temperature, voltage, etc., it is clear that, if the entire oscillator is left to itself, in a very short time either βA will become less than or larger than unity.   In the former case the oscillator simply stops, and in the latter case we are back to the point of requiring nonlinearity to limit the amplitude.   An oscillator in which the loop gain is exactly unity is an abstraction which is completely unrealizable in practice.   It is accordingly necessary, in the adjustment of a practical oscillator, always to arrange to have βA somewhat larger (say 5 per cent) than unity in order to ensure that, with incidental variations in transistor, tube, and circuit parameters, βA shall not fall below unity.   While the first two principles stated above must be satisfied on purely theoretical grounds, we may add a third general principle dictated by practical considerations, *i.e.*:

In every practical oscillator the loop gain is slightly larger than unity, and the amplitude of the oscillations is limited by the onset of nonlinearity.

The treatment of oscillators, taking into account the nonlinearity, is very difficult on account of the innate perverseness of nonlinearities generally.   In many cases the extension into the range of nonlinear operation is small.   For the present, we shall simply neglect these nonlinearities altogether.

In the above discussion we started with an externally applied signal which was a voltage wave form.   We could equally well have assumed a current signal at the amplifier input.   We often adopt this point of view when dealing with transistor oscillators.   A little thought will show that the conclusions reached above with respect to the conditions for oscillation remain valid if we interpret "loop gain" to mean "current gain around the loop." If in Fig. 18-1 the input impedance R_i is not infinite, we must imagine R_i to be placed across terminals 3 and 4 (since indeed the feedback network will be loaded down by the impedance R_i once the loop is closed). The current loop gain is given by i_f/i_s.

18-2. The Phase-shift Oscillator.[1] We select the so-called *phase-shift oscillator* (Fig. 18-2) as a first example because it exemplifies very simply the principles set forth above. Here an amplifier of conventional design is followed by three cascaded arrangements of a capacitor C and a resistor R, the output of the last RC combination being returned to the grid.

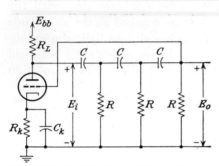

FIG. 18-2. An RC phase-shift oscillator.

The amplifier shifts by 180 deg the phase of any voltage which appears on the grid, and the network of resistors and capacitors shifts the phase by an additional amount. At some frequency the phase shift introduced by the RC network will be precisely 180 deg, and at this frequency the total phase shift from the grid around the circuit and back to the grid will be exactly zero. This particular frequency will be the one at which the circuit will oscillate provided that the magnitude of the amplification is sufficiently large.

From classical network analysis we find for the transfer function of the RC network, which is also the feedback factor,

$$\beta = \frac{E_o}{E_i} = \frac{1}{1 - 5\alpha^2 - j(6\alpha - \alpha^3)} \tag{18-1}$$

where $\alpha \equiv 1/\omega RC$. The phase shift is 180 deg for $\alpha^2 = 6$ or $f = 1/(2\pi RC \sqrt{6})$. At this frequency of oscillation $\beta = -\frac{1}{29}$. In order that βA shall not be less than unity, it is required that A be at least 29. The oscillator then cannot be made to work with a tube like the 12AU7 ($\mu = 20$). It will work with a 12AX7 ($\mu = 100$), and not infrequently the tube employed is a pentode like a 6AC7 or 6AU6.

In the above discussion the loading of the amplifier by the network was neglected. If the network input impedance is not high compared with the amplifier output impedance, the phase shift through the amplifier is not 180 deg. Under these circumstances the above results must be modified somewhat. But this is not a serious matter.

It is possible to use more than three RC sections in the phase-shifting network but no clear advantage results from so doing. However, it is not possible to use fewer than three sections since, if, say, two sections were used, each would have to provide 90 deg of phase shift. In this case the attenuation would be infinite.

The phase-shift oscillator is particularly suited to the range of frequencies from several cycles to several hundred thousand cycles and so includes the range of audio frequencies. At frequencies in the range of megacycles it has no marked advantage over circuits employing a tuned LC network, and besides at the higher frequencies it turns out, as a matter of practice, that the impedance of the phase-shifting network may become quite small and the loading of the amplifier by the phase-shifting network may become serious enough to require methods of correction which will add complications. On the other hand, if R and C are made large but still well within the range of commercially available values, frequencies of the order of one or two cycles are easily attained. Inductors suitable for use in LC tuned oscillators for this frequency range may well become impractical.

The frequency of the oscillator may be varied by changing the value of any of the impedance elements in the phase-shifting network. But if circuit components are varied without discrimination the impedance looking into the phase-shifting network and the magnitude of the transfer function will change. As a consequence there is the possibility that βA will fall below unity and the circuit will stop oscillating. On the other hand, if βA should continue to increase beyond unity the excursion of tube voltages must be farther and farther into the range of nonlinear operation in order to succeed in limiting the amplitude of oscillation, and as a result the amplitude must increase. Hence, a change in frequency occasioned by an arbitrary variation of circuit parameters will most usually affect the amplitude. Still, for quite small variations of frequency a variation of any single circuit component is quite feasible. But for variations of frequency over a large range the three capacitors C must be varied simultaneously. Such a variation will keep the input impedance to the phase-shifting network constant (Prob. 18-2) and keep constant also the magnitude of β. A variation of all three resistors R simultaneously will keep β constant but the impedance will vary. Such a variation of the impedance will vary **A** and consequently β**A** as well. It is possible to reduce the attenuation of the phase-shifting network by using more than three sections in the phase-shifting network or by removing the restrictions that all the capacitors be equal and that all the resistors be equal, but each of these methods complicates the matter of obtaining variable frequency operation.

The phase-shift oscillator is usually operated in Class A in order to keep distortion to a minimum. Self-bias is obtained from the cathode $R_k - C_k$ combination in Fig. 18-2.

18-3. Resonant-circuit Oscillators. Figure 18-3 shows the *tuned-plate oscillator* in which a resonant circuit is used to determine the frequency. Other oscillators of this type are considered in Sec. 18-5. In Fig. 18-3 r represents a resistance in series with the plate winding (of inductance L) in order to account for the losses in the transformer. If these losses are negligible so that r can be neglected, then at the frequency $\omega = 1/\sqrt{LC}$ the impedance of the resonant circuit is arbitrarily large and purely resistive. In this case the voltage drop across the inductor from plate to ground is precisely 180 deg out of phase with the applied input voltage to the vacuum tube, independently of the size of the tube plate resistance. If the direction of the winding of the secondary of the transformer (connected to the grid) is such as to introduce an additional phase shift of 180 deg (it is assumed that the secondary is not loaded), the total loop phase shift is exactly zero. At this frequency, then, the phase-shift condition for oscillation will have been satisfied. Again, since the transformer is considered to be unloaded, the ratio of the amplitude of the secondary to the primary voltage is M/L, where M is the mutual inductance. Since $A = \mu$ for an amplifier with an infinite load impedance, the condition $\beta A = 1$ is equivalent to $\mu = L/M$. More exactly, taking into account the finite size of the resistance r, we find

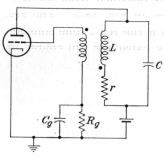

FIG. 18-3. A tuned-plate oscillator.

$$\omega^2 = \frac{1}{LC}\left(1 + \frac{r}{r_p}\right) \tag{18-2}$$

as the frequency-determining condition and

$$g_m = \frac{\mu r C}{\mu M - L} \tag{18-3}$$

as the condition which is equivalent to $\beta A = 1$.

The above considerations emphasize that the criteria stated in Sec. 18-1 with respect to the loop phase shift and the loop gain are the conditions which characterize the operation of the circuit. In particular, note that in the general case the frequency of oscillation is in the neighborhood of, but in no way simply related to, the frequency of a "natural" oscillation which might be excited in the resonant circuit. Nor is there any a priori connection between the oscillation frequency and the steady-state "resonance" frequency. The frequency of oscillation is determined solely by the consideration that the loop phase shift be zero. In this sense, the suggestive near-agreement of the frequency of the oscillator and the frequency of a natural oscillation or steady-state resonance is to be considered, superficially at least, as a pure coincidence. In the light of these last remarks it appears, too, that the designation of the oscillator of Sec. 18-2 as a "phase-shift oscillator," as opposed to the present designation "resonant-circuit oscillator," is entirely artificial. All oscillators, those discussed above as well as those to be considered below, could be called "phase-shift oscillators."

The bias for a resonant-circuit oscillator is obtained from an $R_g C_g$ parallel combination in series with the grid, as in Fig. 18-3. The grid and cathode of the tube act as a rectifier, and if the $R_g C_g$ time constant is large compared with one cycle the grid leak capacitor will charge up essentially to the peak grid swing. This voltage across C_g acts as the bias, and the grid is therefore driven slightly positive only for a short interval at the peak of the swing. The voltage at the grid is a large sinusoid, and since its peak value is approximately at ground potential we say that the grid is "clamped" to ground.[2] Since the grid base of the tube is traversed in a small fraction of one cycle the operation is Class C.

When the circuit is first energized the grid bias is zero and the tube operates with a large g_m, one greater than that given by Eq. (18-3). The loop gain is therefore greater than unity, and the amplitude of oscillation starts to grow. As it does so, grid current is drawn, clamping takes place, and the bias automatically adjusts itself so that its magnitude equals the peak value of the grid voltage. As the bias becomes more negative, the value of g_m decreases, and finally the amplitude stabilizes itself at that value for which the loop gain for the fundamental is reduced to unity. This phenomenon is discussed in more detail in Sec. 18-8. Since the operation is Class C, the use of the linear equivalent circuit is at best a rough approximation. In view of the above discussion, the value of g_m in Eq. (18-3) may be considered to be the minimum value required at zero bias in order for oscillations to start. It may also be interpreted as the average value of transconductance which determines the amplitude of oscillation.

18-4. Bridge Oscillators.[3] In a bridge circuit the output is in phase with the input at the balance frequency ω_0. Hence, this circuit may be used as the β network for an oscillator, provided that the phase shift through the amplifier is zero. This condition requires a two-stage amplifier. However, the output of a balanced bridge is zero at $\omega = \omega_0$ and therefore $\beta = 0$ and $A\beta = 0$ at $\omega = \omega_0$. In order to satisfy the Barkhausen condition $A\beta = 1$ it is necessary to unbalance the bridge but in such a way that the phase shift remains zero. The method of accomplishing such an unbalance will be illustrated with reference to the Wien bridge of Fig. 18-4.

E_1 is the input voltage to the bridge (the output of the amplifier) and E_2 is the output voltage of the bridge (the input to the amplifier). Two auxiliary voltages E_a and E_b are indicated such that $E_2 = E_b - E_a$. Clearly, $E_a = E_1 R_2/(R_1 + R_2)$ is in phase with E_1. Now $E_b = E_1 Z_2/(Z_1 + Z_2)$, and at the balance frequency E_b must be in phase with E_1. It is not difficult to show that Z_2 and Z_1 have the same phase angle at the

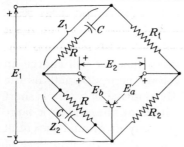

FIG. 18-4. A Wien-bridge network.

angular frequency $\omega_0 \equiv 1/RC$ and that at this frequency $Z_1 = (1 - j)R$ and $Z_2 = (1 - j)R/2$. Hence, $E_b = \frac{1}{3}E_1$ at $\omega = \omega_0$. If a null is desired, then R_1 and R_2 must be chosen so that $E_a = \frac{1}{3}E_1$ in order that $E_2 = E_b - E_a = 0$. Thus $R_2/(R_1 + R_2) = \frac{1}{3}$, or $R_1 = 2R_2$.

In the present case where the bridge is to be used as the β network for an oscillator we must keep the phase shift zero but the magnitude of β must not be zero. This is accomplished by taking the ratio $R_2/(R_1 + R_2)$ smaller than $1/3$. For example, let

$$\frac{E_a}{E_1} = \frac{R_2}{R_1 + R_2} = \frac{1}{3} - \frac{1}{\delta} \tag{18-4}$$

where δ is a number larger than 3. Then

$$\beta = \frac{E_2}{E_1} = \frac{E_b - E_a}{E_1} = \frac{E_b}{E_1} - \frac{1}{3} + \frac{1}{\delta} \tag{18-5}$$

At $\omega = \omega_0$, $E_b/E_1 = \frac{1}{3}$ and $\beta = 1/\delta$. The condition $A\beta = 1$ is now satisfied by making $A = \delta$. Note that the frequency of oscillation is precisely the null frequency of the balanced bridge, namely, $f_0 = 1/2\pi RC$. Note also that, at any other frequency, E_b is not in phase with E_1 and that therefore $E_2 = E_b - E_a$ is not in phase with E_1 so that the condition $A\beta = 1$ is satisfied only at the one frequency f_0.

Figure 18-5 is the schematic diagram of a simple Wien-bridge oscillator. The majority of the audio-frequency laboratory oscillators are of this type with the exception that in these commercial units pentode amplifiers are used. The advantage of the higher amplifier gain attainable with pentodes will be discussed later. In Fig. 18-5 the coupling capacitors are made large enough so that they introduce no appreciable phase shifts even at the lowest frequencies of operation. The resistor R_2 serves both as an element of the bridge and also as a cathode resistor for the first tube. The lower of the two resistors R serves also a dual purpose of bridge element and grid resistor.

Continuous variation of frequency is accomplished by varying simulta-

neously the two capacitors C (ganged variable air capacitors).   Changes
in frequency range are accomplished by switching in different values for
the two identical resistors R.

Practical frequency limits are determined from the following considerations: Ganged variable resistors which track with the same precision as
do ganged variable air capacitors are not readily available.   If, then,
variable air capacitors are to be used, they are necessarily relatively small
in capacity.   Hence, to attain low frequencies requires that large resistances R be used.   Large values of R (remember that one of the R's is
also a grid leak resistor) cause difficulty first because of the possibility that

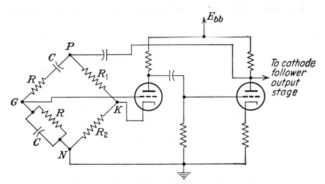

Fig. 18-5. A Wien-bridge oscillator.

the vacuum tube will block and secondly because if the impedance from
grid to ground is very large it becomes increasingly difficult to shield the
grid against stray 60-cycle voltages from the power supply.   With the
exercise of care, resistors R of the order of 10 megohms may be employed
and the frequency pushed as low as two cycles.   Again at low frequencies
the problem of selecting adequately large coupling condensers becomes
more difficult.   At the higher frequencies difficulties are encountered on
account of the fact that a reduction in size of the resistances R decreases
the impedance looking into the input terminals of the Wien bridge and
so increases the loading on the amplifier.   Even if the loading is not
adequate to stop the oscillation, it will have an adverse effect on the
stability of amplitude of oscillation with change of frequency range.

We consider an ingenious modification of the circuit of Fig. 18-5 which
serves to stabilize the amplitude against variations not only due to range
switching but also due to fluctuations occasioned by the aging of tubes,
components, etc.   The modification consists simply in replacing the
resistor R_2 by a tungsten-filament light bulb.   For the circuit of Fig.
18-5 a 110-volt 3-watt lamp is appropriate.

As was noted above, the amplitude of oscillation is determined by the
extent to which βA is greater than unity.   If β is fixed, the amplitude is

then determined by A, increasing as A increases until further increase is limited by the vacuum-tube nonlinearity. The regulation mechanism introduced by the tungsten bulb operates by automatically changing β in such a direction as to keep βA more nearly constant if, as when the loading of the amplifier changes, the value of A should change. It will be recalled that the resistance of a tungsten filament increases with temperature, and the temperature is in turn determined by the root-mean-square value of the current which passes through it. If the root-mean-square value of the current changes, then, because of the thermal lag of the tungsten filament, the temperature will be determined by the average value over a large number of cycles of the root-mean-square value of the current.

Consider now that the amplitude has decreased because A has decreased. The value of R_2 will decrease, and as a consequence $\beta = 1/\delta$ will increase, as indicated by Eq. (18-4). Or to put the matter another way, as A changes, the extent to which the Wien bridge is unbalanced will adjust itself in such a manner as to keep βA more nearly constant. An important fact to keep in mind about the mechanism just described is that, because of the thermal lag of the filament, the resistance of the filament during the course of a single cycle is very nearly absolutely constant. Therefore at any fixed amplitude of oscillation the tungsten filament behaves entirely like an ordinary linear resistor. If it should happen that the frequency is very low ($\cong 2$ cycles) it may be that the thermal lag of a tungsten filament is not adequate. In such a case a thermistor might be employed which has a large enough bulk to provide an adequate thermal lag. Since the thermal coefficient of the thermistor is negative (decreasing resistance with increasing temperature), the thermistor would be used in place of R_1 rather than R_2.

Other types of bridge networks besides the Wien bridge may be used as feedback elements to form an oscillator. The twin-T and bridge-T networks have been used for this purpose. The general principles enunciated above are applicable to these bridge-type oscillators although the practical details are different.

Whether the circuit of Fig. 18-5 is an oscillator or a frequency-selective feedback amplifier depends on the setting of R_1. If R_1 is set so that at the frequency ω_0 the bridge is balanced, the circuit is that of an amplifier. If the bridge is unbalanced in the manner indicated above, the circuit is an oscillator. If it should be desired that the circuit be used as an amplifier, then an appropriate and convenient means of introducing the external signal must be found.

18-5. A General Form of Circuit. Many r-f oscillator circuits fall into the general form shown in Fig. 18-6. The condition for oscillation may be found by considering this to be a feedback amplifier with the output taken from plate to cathode and with input terminals G and K. The load impedance $\mathbf{Z}_L$ consists of $\mathbf{Z}_2$ in parallel with the series combination of $\mathbf{Z}_1$ and $\mathbf{Z}_3$. The gain without feedback is $\mathbf{A} = -\mu\mathbf{Z}_L/(\mathbf{Z}_L + r_p)$. The feedback factor is $\beta = \mathbf{Z}_1/(\mathbf{Z}_1 + \mathbf{Z}_3)$. The loop gain is found to be

$$\mathbf{A}\beta = \frac{-\mu\mathbf{Z}_1\mathbf{Z}_2}{(r_p)(\mathbf{Z}_1 + \mathbf{Z}_2 + \mathbf{Z}_3) + (\mathbf{Z}_2)(\mathbf{Z}_1 + \mathbf{Z}_3)} \tag{18-6}$$

Another approach is to assume an input voltage $\mathbf{E}_{gk}$ between grid and cathode but with the junction point G' of $\mathbf{Z}_1$ and $\mathbf{Z}_3$ not connected to the

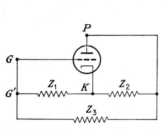

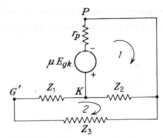

FIG. 18-6. The basic configuration for many resonant-circuit oscillators.

FIG. 18-7. The linear equivalent circuit of Fig. 18-6.

grid G. The loop gain is then the voltage developed across $\mathbf{Z}_1$ divided by $\mathbf{E}_{gk}$. The equivalent circuit is shown in Fig. 18-7. The loop voltage equations are

$$\mu\mathbf{E}_{gk} + \mathbf{I}_1(r_p + \mathbf{Z}_2) - \mathbf{I}_2\mathbf{Z}_2 = 0 \tag{18-7a}$$

and

$$-\mathbf{I}_1\mathbf{Z}_2 + \mathbf{I}_2(\mathbf{Z}_1 + \mathbf{Z}_2 + \mathbf{Z}_3) = 0 \tag{18-7b}$$

The loop gain is defined by $\mathbf{E}_{g'k}/\mathbf{E}_{gk} = \mathbf{I}_2\mathbf{Z}_1/\mathbf{E}_{gk}$, and solving for $\mathbf{I}_2$ from Eqs. (18-7a) and (18-7b) gives the result (18-6).

If the impedances are pure reactances (either inductive or capacitive) then $\mathbf{Z}_1 = jX_1$, $\mathbf{Z}_2 = jX_2$, and $\mathbf{Z}_3 = jX_3$. For an inductor $X = \omega L$, and for a capacitor $X = -1/\omega C$. Then

$$\mathbf{A}\beta = \frac{+\mu X_1 X_2}{(jr_p)(X_1 + X_2 + X_3) - (X_2)(X_1 + X_3)} \tag{18-8}$$

In order for the loop gain to be real (zero phase shift)

$$X_1 + X_2 + X_3 = 0 \tag{18-9}$$

and

$$\mathbf{A}\beta = \frac{\mu X_1 X_2}{-(X_2)(X_1 + X_3)} = \frac{-\mu X_1}{X_1 + X_3} \tag{18-10}$$

From Eq. (18-9) we see that the circuit will oscillate at the resonant frequency of the series combination of X_1, X_2, and X_3.

Using Eq. (18-9) in Eq. (18-10) yields

$$\mathbf{A\beta} = \frac{+\mu X_1}{X_2} \qquad (18\text{-}11)$$

Since $A\beta$ must be positive and at least unity in magnitude, then X_1 and X_2 must have the same sign.   In other words, they must be the same kind of reactance, either both inductive or both capacitive.   Then, from Eq. (18-9), $X_3 = -(X_1 + X_2)$ must be inductive if X_1 and X_2 are capacitive, or vice versa.

If X_1 and X_2 are capacitors and X_3 is an inductor the circuit is called a *Colpitts oscillator*.   If X_1 and X_2 are inductors and X_3 is a capacitor the circuit is called a *Hartley oscillator*.   In this latter case, there may

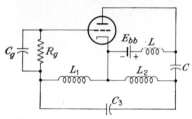

FIG. 18-8. A Hartley oscillator.

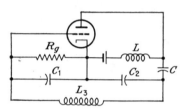

FIG. 18-9. A Colpitts oscillator.

be mutual coupling between X_1 and X_2 (and the above equations will then not apply).   If X_1 and X_2 are tuned circuits and X_3 represents the grid-to-plate interelectrode capacitance, the circuit is called a *tuned-plate, tuned-grid oscillator*.   The above theory indicates that both grid and plate circuits must be tuned to the inductive side of resonance.

A practical form of a Hartley oscillator is shown in Fig. 18-8.   The B-supply voltage is applied to the plate through the inductor L whose reactance is high compared with X_2.   The capacitor C has a low react-ance at the frequency of oscillation.   However, at zero frequency it acts as an open circuit.   Without this capacitor the B-supply voltage would be short-circuited by L in series with L_2.   The parallel combination of C_g and R_g acts to supply the bias.   The circuit operates in Class C and the grid current charges up C_g as explained in Sec. 18-3.

For a low-power oscillator it is possible to use series feed instead of the shunt feed indicated in Fig. 18-8.   The B supply is placed between the cathode (ground) and L_2.   This eliminates the use of L and C but now L_2 must be insulated from ground by a voltage equal to the B supply plus the peak a-c voltage developed across L_2.

A modified form of the Hartley circuit employs mutual coupling between L_1 and L_2 and places C_3 in parallel with L_2.

The practical form of the Colpitts circuit is shown in Fig. 18-9.   Simi-lar remarks to those made above with regard to L and C also apply here.

This circuit operates in Class C, and C_1 serves the double purpose of a frequency-determining element and a grid leak capacitor. Some ultra-high-frequency oscillators are also of the form given in Fig. 18-6. The impedances are not lumped elements but rather distributed (transmission-line) elements so adjusted that they appear as pure reactances.

18-6. Crystal Oscillators. If a piezoelectric crystal, usually quartz, has electrodes plated on opposite faces and if a potential is applied between these electrodes, forces will be exerted on the bound charges within the crystal. If this device is properly mounted then deformations take place within the crystal and an electromechanical system is formed which will vibrate when properly excited. The resonant frequency and the Q depend upon the crystal dimensions, how the surfaces are oriented with respect to its axes, and how the device is mounted.[4] Frequencies ranging from a few kilocycles to a few megacycles and Q's in the range from several thousand to several hundred thousand are commercially available. These extraordinarily high values of Q and the fact that the characteristics of quartz are extremely stable with respect to time and temperature account for the exceptional frequency stability of oscillators incorporating crystals (Sec. 18-7).

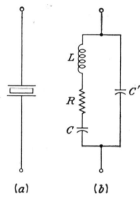

(a) **(b)**

Fig. 18-10. A piezoelectric crystal. (a) Symbol (b) Electrical equivalent circuit.

The electrical equivalent circuit of a crystal is indicated in Fig. 18-10. The inductor L, capacitor C, and resistor R are the analogs of the mass, the compliance (the reciprocal of the spring constant), and the viscous damping factor of the mechanical system. Typical values[5] for a 90-kc crystal are $L = 137$ henrys, $C = 0.0235$ $\mu\mu$f, and $R = 15$ kilohms, corresponding to $Q = 5,500$. The dimensions of such a crystal are 30 by 4 by 1.5 mm. Since C' represents the electrostatic capacitance between electrodes with the crystal as a dielectric, its magnitude ($\cong 3.5$ $\mu\mu$f) is very much larger than C.

If we neglect the resistance R, the impedance of the crystal is a reactance jX whose dependence upon frequency is given by

$$jX = -\frac{j}{\omega C'}\frac{\omega^2 - \omega_s^2}{\omega^2 - \omega_p^2} \tag{18-12}$$

where $\omega_s^2 = 1/LC$ is the series resonant frequency (the zero impedance frequency) and $\omega_p^2 = (1/L)(1/C + 1/C')$ is the parallel resonant frequency (the infinite impedance frequency). Since $C' \gg C$, then $\omega_p \cong \omega_s$. For the crystal whose parameters are specified above, the parallel frequency is only three-tenths of 1 per cent higher than the series frequency. For $\omega_s < \omega < \omega_p$ the reactance is inductive and outside this range it is capacitive, as indicated in Fig. 18-11.

A variety of crystal oscillator circuits are possible. If in the basic configuration of Fig. 18-6 a crystal is used for $\mathbf{Z}_1$, a tuned LC combination

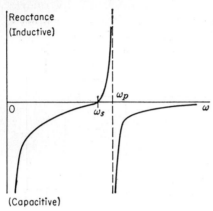

for $\mathbf{Z}_2$, and the capacitance C_{pg} between plate and grid for $\mathbf{Z}_3$, the resulting circuit is as indicated in Fig. 18-12. From the theory given in the preceding section the crystal reactance as well as that of the LC network must be inductive. In order for the loop gain to be greater than unity we see from Eq. (18-11) that X_1 cannot be too small. Hence, the circuit will oscillate at a frequency which lies between ω_s and ω_p but close to the parallel-resonance value. Since $\omega_p \cong \omega_s$, the oscillator frequency is essentially determined by the crystal and

FIG. 18-11. The reactance function of a crystal (whose resistance has been neglected).

not by the rest of the circuit. Figure 18-12 is the crystal version of the tuned-plate tuned-grid oscillator.

If in Fig. 18-6 $\mathbf{Z}_1$ is grid input capacitance, $\mathbf{Z}_2$ is the plate output capacitance, and $\mathbf{Z}_3$ is a crystal, the result is the circuit of Fig. 18-13,

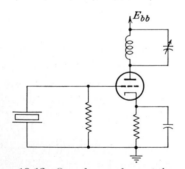

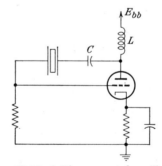

FIG. 18-12. One form of crystal oscillator.

FIG. 18-13. A Pierce crystal oscillator.

called the *Pierce crystal oscillator*. The crystal reactance must be inductive. Figure 18-13 is the crystal version of the Colpitts oscillator. The r-f choke L and the blocking capacitor C serve the same functions as they did in Fig. 18-9. This circuit has the merit of not requiring any tuning as one crystal is replaced by another if it is desired to change the frequency.

The Meacham crystal oscillator[6] is a bridge-type circuit and is indicated in Fig. 18-14. The crystal operates at its series-resonant frequency. The behavior of this circuit should be clear from the discussion of the Wien-bridge oscillator of Sec. 18-4. This circuit has excellent amplitude stability because of the lamp and exceptional frequency stability because of the crystal.

18-7. Frequency Stability. An oscillator, having initially been set at a particular frequency, will invariably not maintain its initial frequency but will instead drift and wander about in frequency sometimes uniformly

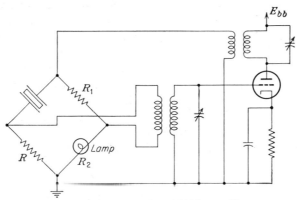

FIG. 18-14. Meacham crystal bridge oscillator.

in one direction, sometimes quite erratically. The *frequency stability* of an oscillator is a measure of its ability to maintain as nearly a fixed frequency as possible over as long a time interval as possible. These deviations of frequency arise because the values of the circuit features, on which the oscillator frequency depends, do not remain constant in time. (We use here the term "circuit features" to include circuit components, tube parameters, supply voltages, stray capacities, etc.) Accordingly, an obvious but clearly useless solution of the problem of making a frequency-stable oscillator is to keep constant all the circuit features. In the first place, the number of circuit features is very large, in general; secondly, some of the circuit features such as tube parameters are inherently unstable and extremely difficult to keep constant; and thirdly, it is hard enough to know where stray circuit elements and couplings are located and how to estimate their magnitudes without having to devise schemes to maintain them constant.

But we recognize also that in every oscillator circuit there are a relatively few circuit features on which the frequency is sensitively dependent while the frequency dependence of the far larger number of remaining features is comparatively slight. For example, in the circuit of Fig. 18-2 the frequency is for the most part determined by R and C, and the other features of the circuit affect the frequency to a much smaller extent.   We shall then have taken a long step in the direction toward frequency stability if we take pains to ensure the stability, at least, of these relatively few passive elements which influence the frequency markedly.   The principal cause of drift in these is the variation of temperature.   Means for maintaining the temperature constant and means for balancing the temperature-induced variation in one such element against that in another can be taken.[7]

In looking now to the other quite numerous but less important features of the circuit we might select from these the worst offenders with regard to their influence on frequency stability and take steps either to stabilize them or to readjust the circuit in such a manner that instability in these features reflects to a smaller extent in the frequency.   As an example of the former case, if it should be found that variations in the B-supply voltage had a marked effect on the frequency, one might employ a regulated power supply.   As an example of the latter case we have the introduction into the plate circuit of a large resistor to minimize the effect of plate-resistance instability.   But all these special procedures are, at best, palliative measures, suitable in one circuit and not in another and influencing, at most, one or two of the many features which have some effect on the frequency.

Now there is a principle, which can be employed in the design of oscillators where frequency stability is of prime importance, which will, at one blow, eliminate to a large extent the dependence of the frequency on all but a very restricted number of circuit elements.   The principle is as follows:

If in an oscillator there exists one set of elements which has the property that at the oscillation frequency these components introduce a large variation of phase with frequency, then $d\theta/d\omega$ serves as a measure of the independence of the frequency of all other features of the circuit.   The frequency stability becomes more marked as $d\theta/d\omega$ increases.   In the limit, as $d\theta/d\omega$ becomes infinite, the oscillator frequency depends only on this set of elements and becomes completely independent of all other features of the circuit.

This principle is of great value in serving as a guide in the design of oscillators when frequency stability is of importance, in providing a convenient and easy comparison of the relative frequency stability of two or more different oscillators, and in permitting easy approximations to be made of the influence on the frequency of a variation of features of an oscillator on which the frequency is only slightly dependent.   The proof of the principle is almost self-evident and is readily arrived at from the following considerations: Suppose that a variation takes place in some one feature of the oscillator *other than one of the components of the set of elements described above.*   Then if initially the phase condition for oscillation was satisfied at the frequency of oscillation it will, in general, no longer be satisfied after the alteration of the circuit feature. The frequency must accordingly shift in order once again to restore the loop phase shift to the exact value zero. If, however, there is a set of elements which, at the nominal oscillator frequency, produces a large phase shift for a small frequency change (that is, $d\theta/d\omega$ large), then it is clear that the frequency shift required to restore the circuital phase shift to zero need be only very small.

In a parallel-resonant circuit the impedance changes from an inductive to a capacitive reactance as the frequency is increased through the resonant point. If the Q is infinite (an ideal inductor with zero series resistance), this change in phase is abrupt, $d\theta/d\omega \to \infty$. Hence, a tuned-circuit oscillator will have excellent frequency stability provided that Q is sufficiently high and provided that L and C are stable (independent of temperature, current, etc.).

These ideas about tuned-circuit oscillators can be carried over to account for the exceptional frequency stability of crystal oscillators. From Fig. 18-11 we see that for a crystal with infinite Q the phase changes discontinuously from -90 to $+90$ deg as the frequency passes through ω_s and then abruptly back again from $+90$ to -90 deg as ω passes through ω_p. Of course, infinite Q is unattainable, but since commercially available crystals have values of Q of tens or hundreds of thousands, very large values of $d\theta/d\omega$ are realizable. Hence, if a crystal is incorporated into a circuit (such as those of Figs. 18-12, 18-13, and 18-14) an oscillator is obtained whose frequency depends essentially upon the crystal itself and nothing else. The crystal frequency does, however, still depend somewhat on the temperature, and constant-temperature ovens must be employed where the highest stability is required. The U.S. Bureau of Standards has been able to maintain crystals at frequencies constant to better than 1 part in 10^8 for periods of many months.

Let us compare the frequency stability of the phase-shift oscillator with the Wien-bridge oscillator. In order to do so we must evaluate $d\theta/d\omega$ for each circuit. From Eq. (18-1) it follows that θ for the phase-shift oscillator is given by

$$\tan \theta = \frac{6\alpha - \alpha^3}{1 - 5\alpha^2} = \frac{6/\alpha^2 - 1}{1/\alpha^3 - 5/\alpha} \tag{18-13}$$

Since $\alpha = 1/\omega RC$, then

$$\tan \theta = \frac{6\omega^2 R^2 C^2 - 1}{\omega^3 R^3 C^3 - 5\omega RC} \tag{18-14}$$

Some of the tedious algebra involved in finding $d\theta/d\omega$ may be avoided if we generalize the procedure as follows: For any oscillator, $\tan \theta$ may be written as the ratio of two polynomials in ω, or

$$\tan \theta = \frac{N(\omega)}{D(\omega)} \tag{18-15}$$

Differentiating this equation yields

$$\sec^2 \theta \, d\theta = \frac{dN}{D} - \frac{N \, dD}{D^2} \tag{18-16}$$

If the phase shift through the amplifier is either zero or π, then the phase shift θ through the feedback network must also be either 0 or π at the resonant frequency ω_0. In either case,

$$\tan \theta = 0 \qquad \sec^2 \theta = 1 \qquad N(\omega_0) = 0 \tag{18-17}$$

Hence, for $\omega = \omega_0$, Eq. (18-16) reduces to

$$d\theta = \frac{dN}{D} \tag{18-18}$$

Let us now apply this general result to the phase-shift oscillator for which, from Eq. (18-14),

$$N = 6\omega^2 R^2 C^2 - 1 \qquad D = \omega^3 R^3 C^3 - 5\omega RC \tag{18-19}$$

From Eq. (18-18),

$$\frac{d\theta}{d\omega} = \frac{12\omega R^2 C^2}{\omega^3 R^3 C^3 - 5\omega RC} \tag{18-20}$$

Remembering that $\omega_0 RC = 1/\sqrt{6}$, we find

$$\left(\omega \frac{d\theta}{d\omega}\right)_{\omega=\omega_0} = \frac{\frac{12}{6}}{(1/\sqrt{6})^3 - 5/\sqrt{6}} = -1.01 \tag{18-21}$$

Since $\omega \dfrac{d\theta}{d\omega} = \dfrac{d\theta}{d\omega/\omega}$, this equation is interpreted to mean that the change in phase in radians equals -1.01 times the fractional change in frequency.

The transfer function of a balanced Wien bridge is

$$\beta = \frac{-\frac{1}{3}}{1 - j[3\rho/(\rho^2 - 1)]} \tag{18-22}$$

where $\rho \equiv \omega/\omega_0$. It is seen that the phase changes discontinuously from $+90$ to -90 deg as ω is increased through ω_0. Such a system is ideal from the frequency-stability point of view, but unfortunately, as already pointed out, a balanced bridge cannot be used in an oscillator circuit. If the bridge is unbalanced by an amount $1/\delta$ then the transfer function is

$$\beta = \frac{1}{\delta} - \frac{\frac{1}{3}}{1 - j[3\rho/(\rho^2 - 1)]} \tag{18-23}$$

As indicated in Sec. 18-4, the gain A must equal δ if the circuit is to oscillate. If the phase angle θ of β is calculated and differentiated with respect to ω by proceeding as above, we find that

$$\left(\omega \frac{d\theta}{d\omega}\right)_{\omega=\omega_0} \equiv -\frac{2}{9} A \tag{18-24}$$

Equation (18-24) indicates that a Wien bridge will have excellent frequency stability provided that the bridge is unbalanced only slightly and a correspondingly large value of gain is used. Of course, care must be taken to use stable elements in the bridge and to maintain these at constant temperature. Comparison of this result with Eq. (18-21) shows that a Wien-bridge oscillator with a gain greater than 4.5 has a better frequency stability than a phase-shift oscillator.

18-8. Amplitude Stability and Distortion. Up to the present, we have neglected entirely the deviations from linear operation of the vacuum tubes which are associated with a sinusoidal oscillator. We have, however, recognized that distortion due to nonlinearity is an essential feature of the operation of any practical oscillator and that it is the onset of distortion with increasing signal amplitude which provides the mechanism to stabilize the amplitude of oscillation.

In a single stage of amplification the maximum allowable negative excursion of the input signal is limited by the occurrence of cutoff. On the other hand, the maximum allowable positive excursion is determined by the point at which grid current starts to flow. If the input signal is larger than the grid base, then one or the other of these maximum excursions is exceeded and harmonics must be generated.

There are four methods of obtaining amplitude stability in an oscillator. These are (1) grid-leak biasing, as in the Class C resonant-circuit oscillator; (2) grid limiting and/or cutoff limiting, as in a Class A phase-shift oscillator; (3) control of the feedback factor by a thermosensitive element, as in the bridge-type oscillator; and (4) variation of the bias and hence gain by means of a rectified output.

To proceed further to take into account the effect of the harmonic voltages which are generated, we must divide oscillators into two classes, those incorporating a resonant circuit and those which have no such highly selective circuit.

Consider the resonant-circuit oscillator first. Assume that the input voltage to the tube is sinusoidal but of amplitude large enough to produce harmonic currents within the tube. The output voltage, however, will consist, for the most part, of the fundamental frequency because of the filtering action of the resonant circuit itself. The filtering action will become more pronounced as the Q of the circuit increases. Hence we have the result that high Q values which contribute to good frequency stability also contribute to good wave form. Also because of the filtering action the feedback voltage returned to the input will be almost entirely of the fundamental frequency so that our initial premise that the input is sinusoidal is justified. Since it is the circuit which does the filtering independently of the tube, the tube may be permitted to make wide excursions into the range of nonlinearity before the output will be appreciably distorted. For example, the input voltage may easily be so large that if the plate load were a pure resistance the output would be a good square wave. Nevertheless, because of the filtering of the resonant circuit, the output will actually be of good sinusoidal wave form.

Our picture of the operation of a resonant-circuit oscillator is the following: A sinusoidal voltage E_i appears at the input of the oscillator, and as a consequence there appears at the output a fundamental sinusoidal voltage A_1E_i plus some harmonics. Because of the filtering action of the resonant circuit, the harmonics vanish and the sinusoidal voltage $\beta_1A_1E_i$ is returned to the input. (The subscript 1 on β and A refers to the fundamental.) It should now be clear that the amplitude of the oscillation should be determined by the condition $\beta_1A_1 = 1$.

Resonant-circuit oscillators usually operate in Class C, and bias is obtained from a parallel R_gC_g combination in series with the grid, as in Fig. 18-3. When the power is first turned on, the bias is zero and the gain is much greater than unity. The amplitude starts to increase and is soon large enough so that grid current is drawn near the peak of the sinusoid. Because of the clamping[2] action at the grid a bias voltage builds up across C_g. In accordance with the discussion given above, an equilibrium bias is reached which limits the amplitude to that value for which the loop gain for the fundamental is unity.

The situation is somewhat different for phase-shift or bridge oscillators where no resonant circuit is present to act as a strong filter to attenuate the harmonics generated within the tube. In order to obtain as pure a wave form as possible with these oscillators they are operated in Class A. Self-bias by means of a cathode resistor is usually employed. The loop gain is adjusted to be only 5 or 10 per cent greater than unity and hence the excursion into the region of cutoff or of positive grid voltages is small.

The output of an oscillator may be taken from either the plate or the grid. At which point is the purer wave form obtained? The nth harmonic voltage at the grid is β_n times that at the plate, where β_n is the feedback fraction for the nth harmonic. Similarly, the fundamental voltage at the grid is β_1 times that at the plate. Hence,

β_n/β_1 *is a measure of the ratio of the percentage distortion at the grid to that at the plate for a given circuit. If the magnitude of this fraction is less than unity the purer wave form is at the grid.*

It is sometimes desirable to compare different feedback circuits with respect to their effects on harmonics. If the same amplitude output is obtained with two different feedback networks, then the harmonics generated within the tube are the same. However, since feedback is employed, the nth harmonic at the plate is cut down by the factor $1/(1 - \mathbf{A}\beta_n)$. Hence,

$\mathbf{H}_n \equiv 1/(1 - \mathbf{A}\beta_n)$ *is a measure of the nth harmonic at the plate due to different types of feedback circuits.*

As an extension of the above logic, we conclude that

$\mathbf{K}_n \equiv (\beta_n/\beta_1)[1/(1 - \mathbf{A}\beta_n)]$ *is a measure of the nth harmonic at the grid due to different types of feedback circuits.*

In the case of bridge oscillators let us call the feedback factor of the unbalanced bridge β and that of the balanced bridge β'. Then from Eq. (18-5)

$$\beta = \frac{E_b}{E_1} - \frac{1}{3} + \frac{1}{\mathbf{A}} = \beta' + \frac{1}{\mathbf{A}} \tag{18-25}$$

At the null frequency $\beta' = 0$ but at any other frequency it is not zero. Thus $\mathbf{A}\beta_n = \mathbf{A}\beta_n' + 1$ and

$$\mathbf{H}_n = \frac{1}{1 - \mathbf{A}\beta_n} = -\frac{1}{\mathbf{A}\beta_n'} \tag{18-26}$$

The equation shows the advantage with respect to purity of wave form of unbalancing the bridge only slightly and making the gain correspondingly large. We thus see again that purity of wave form and stability of frequency are closely allied.

18-9. Negative Resistance in Oscillators. Our study of oscillators thus far has been based upon a steady-state analysis, the Barkhausen criterion. It is instructive to consider an alternative but usually much more complicated approach based upon a transient analysis. In this method the oscillator is replaced by its linear equivalent circuit and the differential equations are written for the resultant network. The solution for the output voltage (or for one of the mesh currents) will be of the form $K\epsilon^{\sigma t} \sin(\omega t + \varphi)$, where $\mathbf{s} = \sigma \pm j\omega$ are the roots of the characteristic equation ($\mathbf{s}$ is also the complex frequency or the Laplace transform variable). The symbols K and φ are constants of integration. Since the excitation to an oscillator is zero, then in order for an output to build up it is necessary that σ be a positive number. If σ were negative, any spurious voltage introduced into the circuit would quickly be damped out. If σ is positive, this spurious signal will cause the output amplitude to increase exponentially with time provided that the system remains linear. However, as we have already emphasized, the oscillator must enter a nonlinear region as its amplitude grows. As it does so, σ must decrease, and when the stable amplitude is reached $\sigma = 0$ so that the steady-state output is given by $K \sin(\omega t + \varphi)$.

Let us apply the above method of analysis to the resonant-circuit oscillator of Fig. 18-3. Using Norton's form (Sec. 8-5) the equivalent

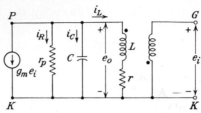

FIG. 18-15. The linear equivalent circuit of the resonant-circuit oscillator of Fig. 18-3

circuit may be drawn as indicated in Fig. 18-15. Kirchhoff's current law yields

$$g_m e_i + i_R + i_C + i_L = 0 \qquad (18\text{-}27)$$

Since

$$i_R = \frac{e_o}{r_p} \qquad i_C = C\frac{de_o}{dt} \qquad (18\text{-}28)$$

and

$$e_o = L\frac{di_L}{dt} + ri_L \qquad e_i = -M\frac{di_L}{dt} \qquad (18\text{-}29)$$

then Eq. (18-27) reduces to

$$CL\frac{d^2 i_L}{dt^2} + \left(-g_m M + \frac{L}{r_p} + Cr\right)\frac{di_L}{dt} + \left(1 + \frac{r}{r_p}\right)i_L = 0 \quad (18\text{-}30)$$

This is a second-order differential equation whose roots may be written in the form $\sigma \pm j\omega$, as we predicted. The expression for σ is

$$\sigma = \frac{g_m M - L/r_p - Cr}{2CL} = \frac{(\mu M - L)(g_m/\mu) - Cr}{2CL} \qquad (18\text{-}31)$$

According to the theory outlined above, in order for the oscillations to get started σ must be positive or

$$g_m > \frac{Cr\mu}{\mu M - L} \qquad (18\text{-}32)$$

As the amplitude of the oscillations grows and the tube enters its non-linear region, then g_m decreases and σ is reduced to zero. The steady-state amplitude is obtained when the average value of g_m is given by

$$g_m = \frac{Cr\mu}{\mu M - L} \qquad (18\text{-}33)$$

in agreement with Eq. (18-3). With this value of g_m, $\sigma = 0$ and Eq.

(18-30) reduces to

$$CL \frac{d^2i_L}{dt^2} + \left(1 + \frac{r}{r_p}\right) i_L = 0 \qquad (18\text{-}34)$$

This equation represents simple harmonic motion, a single-frequency oscillation whose angular value is given by

$$\omega^2 = \frac{1}{LC}\left(1 + \frac{r}{r_p}\right) \qquad (18\text{-}35)$$

This expression agrees with Eq. (18-2) obtained from the Barkhausen criterion.

A transient excited in a circuit containing resistance must die down with time because of the losses in the resistor. Hence, an interesting interpretation of the fact that the amplitude first builds up in an oscillator is that during this process the circuit exhibits a *negative* resistance. In order to carry this concept further, consider the parallel RLC circuit of Fig. 18-16 with no external excitation. The differential equation for the voltage e across this combination is

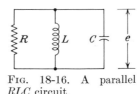

Fig. 18-16. A parallel RLC circuit.

$$LC \frac{d^2e}{dt^2} + \frac{L}{R}\frac{de}{dt} + e = 0 \qquad (18\text{-}36)$$

For this equation we find

$$\sigma = -\frac{1}{2RC} \qquad \omega^2 = \frac{1}{LC} - \frac{1}{4R^2C^2} \qquad (18\text{-}37)$$

Hence, in order for σ to be positive (for a positive C) it is necessary that R be negative. In an oscillator circuit R is not a constant, but as the amplitude builds up the tube enters its nonlinear region and $R \to \infty$, $\sigma \to 0$, and $\omega^2 \to 1/LC$.

On the basis of this discussion, we can conclude that *all* oscillators might be called "negative-resistance oscillators." This classification is no more useful than it is to designate all oscillators as "phase-shift oscillators" because the Barkhausen condition requires that the steady-state phase shift around the loop be zero. Perhaps the term "negative-resistance oscillator" should be reserved for use in connection with a two-terminal device which because of its internal physics exhibits a negative resistance.[8] One such device is the tetrode with the external terminals considered to be the plate and cathode. The volt-ampere characteristic is given in Fig. 11-2. We see that over a portion of the characteristic the current decreases as the voltage increases and hence this device exhibits negative resistance (because of secondary electron emission). If a circuit consisting of a resistor R_1, a capacitor C, and an inductor L in parallel is connected across the device whose negative resistance has a magnitude R_2 the circuit of Fig. 18-16 results, where R represents R_1 and R_2 in parallel and hence is given by

$$R = \frac{-R_1 R_2}{R_1 - R_2} \qquad (18\text{-}38)$$

If $R_1 > R_2$, then R is negative and oscillations can build up. The amplitude increases until the nonlinear portion of the volt-ampere characteristics is reached. The steady-state output is obtained when the average

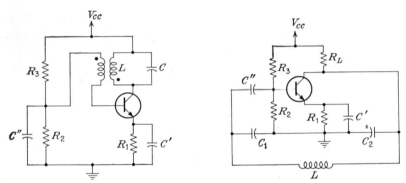

Fig. 18-17. Transistor resonant-circuit oscillator.

Fig. 18-18. Transistor Colpitts oscillator.

value of R_2 has increased so that it equals R_1. Under these circumstances $R = \infty$, $\sigma = 0$, and the frequency is given by $f = 1/(2\pi \sqrt{LC})$. This device is called a *dynatron*. Such oscillators are little used because of the unstable nature of the negative-resistance characteristic.

18-10. Transistor Oscillators. The general theory developed for vacuum-tube oscillators is equally valid for transistor sinusoidal generators. In particular, the Barkhausen criteria, the ideas involved in the building up of oscillations, the limiting of the amplitude due to non-linearities, and the methods of improving the frequency stability discussed earlier in this chapter may be applied to transistor oscillators. Even the specific circuit arrangements using vacuum tubes have their transistor counterparts. For example, the transistor resonant-circuit oscillator of Fig. 18-17 is analogous to the vacuum-tube resonant-circuit oscillator of Fig. 18-3. The transistor version of the Colpitts oscillator is given in Fig. 18-18 and the phase-shift oscillator in Fig. 18-19. Similarly, transistor analogs of the bridge-type oscillator, the Hartley oscillator, crystal oscillator, etc., can be constructed.[9] In these circuits the d-c operating bias is established by the resistors R_1, R_2, and R_3 (Sec. 9-12).

There are two fundamental properties of the transistor which make a

quantitative study of this device in an oscillator circuit much more difficult than the corresponding vacuum-tube analysis. The first is the
internal phase shift due to the reactive components of the transistor
parameters. The second is the low input impedance of the transistor
which will cause the feedback network to be heavily loaded by this device.

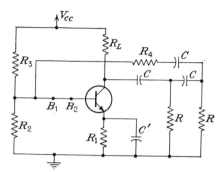

FIG. 18-19. Transistor phase-shift oscillator.

Let us now apply the Barkhausen conditions to the phase-shift oscillator of Fig. 18-19. The resistor $R_4 = R - R_i$, where R_i is the input
impedance at the base. This choice makes the three RC sections of the
phase-shifting network alike and simplifies the calculations. We shall
assume that the biasing resistors R_1, R_2, and R_3 have no effect on the
a-c operation and shall neglect these in the following analysis. We wish
to evaluate the current gain around the loop. Hence we shall imagine

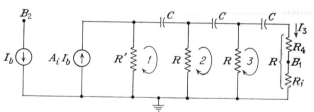

FIG. 18-20. The Norton's equivalent circuit for the transistor phase-shift oscillator.

the loop broken at the base between B_1 and B_2 but in order not to change
the loading on the feedback network we place R_i from B_1 to ground. If
we assume a current I_b to enter the base at B_2 the equivalent circuit is as
drawn in Fig. 18-20. The resistor R' represents the output impedance
R_o in parallel with R_L. The short-circuit current gain is $A_i = -a_e =$
$-[a/(1 - a)]$. The loop current gain equals I_3/I_b and is found by writing
Kirchhoff's voltage equation for the three meshes. The Barkhausen condition that the phase of I_3/I_b must equal zero leads to the following

expression for the frequency of oscillation:

$$f = \frac{1}{2\pi RC} \frac{1}{\sqrt{6 + 4k}} \tag{18-39}$$

where $k \equiv R'/R$. The requirement that the magnitude of I_3/I_b must exceed unity in order for oscillations to start leads to the inequality

$$a_e > 4k + 23 + \frac{29}{k} \tag{18-40}$$

The value of k which gives the minimum a_e turns out to be 2.7, and for this optimum value of R'/R we find $a_e = 44.5$ or $a = 0.978$. A transistor with a common-base short-circuit gain less than 0.978 cannot be used in a phase-shift oscillator.

REFERENCES

1. GINZTON, E. L., and L. M. HOLLINGSWORTH, *Proc. IRE*, **29**, 43–49, February, 1941.
   SHERR, S., "Generalized Equations for *R-C* Phase-shift Oscillators," *ibid.*, **42**(7), 1169–1172, July, 1954.
2. MILLMAN, J., and H. TAUB, "Pulse and Digital Circuits," pp. 119–126, McGraw-Hill Book Company, Inc., New York, 1956.
3. CLARKE, K. K., "Wein-bridge Oscillator Design," *Proc. IRE*, **41**(2), 246–249, February, 1953, and comment by J. M. DIAMOND, **42**(9), 1149, September, 1954.
   CHANCE, B., et al., "Waveforms," Radiation Laboratory Series, Vol. 19, pp. 115–123, McGraw-Hill Book Company, Inc., New York, 1949.
4. FAIR, I. E., "Piezoelectric Crystals in Oscillator Circuits," *Bell System Tech. J.*, **24**(2), 161–216, April, 1945.
   TERMAN, F. E., "Electronic and Radio Engineering," pp. 506–519, McGraw-Hill Book Company, Inc., New York, 1955.
5. VAN DYKE, K. S., "The Piezo-electric Resonator and Its Equivalent Network," *Proc. IRE*, **16**, 742–764, June, 1928.
6. MEACHAM, L. A., "The Bridge-stabilized Oscillator," *Proc. IRE*, **26**, 1278–1294, October, 1938.
7. CHANCE, B., et al., "Waveforms," Radiation Laboratory Series, Vol. 19, pp. 128–131, McGraw-Hill Book Company, Inc., New York, 1949.
8. HEROLD, E. W., "Negative Resistance and Devices for Obtaining It," *Proc. IRE*, **23**, 1201, October, 1935.
9. SHEA, R. F., et al., "Transistor Circuit Engineering," pp. 221–241, John Wiley & Sons, Inc., New York, 1957.
   HUNTER, L. P., "Handbook of Semiconductor Electronics," pp. 14-2 to 14-9, McGraw-Hill Book Company, Inc., New York, 1956.

CHAPTER 19

POWER SUPPLIES

A POWER supply must provide an essentially ripple-free source of power from an a-c line.   In Chap. 14 it is demonstrated that the output of a rectifier contains ripple components in addition to a d-c term.   Hence, it is necessary to include a filter between the rectifier and the load in order to attenuate these ripple components.   In this chapter we shall make a detailed study of such filters.

Because the rectifier is a nonlinear device, no simple exact method[1] of solution of the power-supply problem exists.   However, for each type of filter used a reasonable linear approximation will be made which will allow the circuit to be analyzed by the usual methods of a-c circuit theory.   Hence, the results to be obtained are not exact but do represent good engineering approximations.

19-1. The Harmonic Components in Rectifier Circuits.   An analytic representation of the output current wave of the single-phase half-wave rectifier is obtained by means of a Fourier series.   This series representation has the form

$$i = B_0 + \sum_{k=1}^{\infty} B_k \cos k\alpha + \sum_{k=1}^{\infty} A_k \sin k\alpha \qquad (19\text{-}1)$$

where $\alpha = \omega t$.   For convenience, the subscript b is dropped from i_b.   The coefficients that appear in the series are given by the following integrals:

$$
\begin{aligned}
B_k &= \frac{1}{\pi} \int_0^{2\pi} i \cos k\alpha \, d\alpha \\
A_k &= \frac{1}{\pi} \int_0^{2\pi} i \sin k\alpha \, d\alpha \\
B_0 &= \frac{1}{2\pi} \int_0^{2\pi} i \, d\alpha
\end{aligned}
\qquad (19\text{-}2)
$$

The constant term B_0 in the Fourier series is simply the average or d-c value of the current.

By performing the indicated integrations, using Eq. (14-2) for the explicit expressions for the current over the two specified intervals, there results

$$i = I_m \left[\frac{1}{\pi} + \frac{1}{2} \sin \omega t - \frac{2}{\pi} \sum_{k=2,4,6,\ldots} \frac{\cos k\omega t}{(k+1)(k-1)} \right] \qquad (19\text{-}3)$$

where

$$I_m = \frac{E_m}{r_p + R_L}$$

is the peak value of the current and where E_m is the maximum value of the transformer voltage. The lowest angular frequency that is present in this expression is that of the primary source of the a-c power. Except for this single term of angular frequency ω, all other terms in the final expression are even harmonics of the power frequency.

The corresponding expression for the output of the full-wave rectifier, which is illustrated in Fig. 14-6, may be derived from Eq. (19-3). By recalling that the full-wave circuit consists essentially of two half-wave circuits which are so arranged that one circuit conducts during one half cycle and the second operates during the second half cycle, then it is clear that the currents are functionally related by the expression $i_1(\alpha) = i_2(\alpha + \pi)$. The total load current $i = i_1 + i_2$ attains the form

$$i = I_m \left[\frac{2}{\pi} - \frac{4}{\pi} \sum_{\substack{k \text{ even} \\ k \neq 0}} \frac{\cos k\omega t}{(k+1)(k-1)} \right] \qquad (19\text{-}4)$$

where I_m has the same value as in Eq. (19-3) and where E_m is the maximum value of the transformer voltage to center tap. For convenience, E_m will be referred to simply as the "transformer maximum voltage."

We observe that the fundamental angular frequency ω has been eliminated from the equation, the lowest frequency in the output being 2ω, a second-harmonic term. This offers a definite advantage in the effectiveness of filtering of the output. A second desirable feature of the full-wave circuit is the fact that the current pulses in the two halves of the transformer winding are in such directions that the magnetic cycle through which the iron of the core is taken is essentially that of the alternating current. This eliminates any d-c saturation of the transformer core, which would give rise to additional harmonics in the output.

The Fourier series representation of the half-wave and the full-wave circuits using gas diodes can be obtained as above, although the form will be more complex. This greater complexity occurs because the conduction begins at some small angle α_1 and ceases at the angle $\pi - \alpha_1$, when it is assumed that the breakdown and the extinction potentials are equal. But since the angle α_1 is usually small under normal operating conditions, we will assume that Eqs. (19-3) and (19-4) are valid for circuits with either vacuum or gas diodes.

19-2. Inductor Filters. The operation of the inductor filter depends on the fundamental property of an inductor to oppose any change of current. As a result, any sudden changes that might occur in a circuit without an inductor are smoothed out by the presence of an inductor in the circuit.

Suppose that an inductor or "choke" filter is connected in series with the load in a single-phase half-wave circuit, as illustrated in Fig. 19-1. For simplicity in the

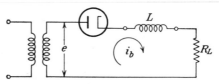

Fig. 19-1. Half-wave rectifier with choke filter.

analysis, suppose that the tube and choke resistances are negligible. Then the controlling differential equation for the current in the circuit during the time that current flows is

$$e = E_m \sin \omega t = L \frac{di_b}{dt} + R_L i_b \qquad (19\text{-}5)$$

An exact solution of this differential equation may be effected subject to the initial condition that $i_b = 0$ at $t = 0$. The solution is valid only as

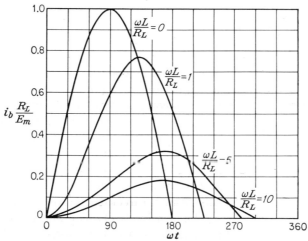

Fig. 19-2. The effect of changing the inductance on the wave form of the output current in a half-wave rectifier with an inductor filter. The load resistance R_L is assumed constant.

long as it yields a positive value of current since the diode can conduct only in one direction. The time at which the current falls to zero is called the "cutout point." The solution is given in Prob. 19-1, and the results are illustrated graphically in Fig. 19-2 with $\omega L/R_L$ as a parameter. The effect of changing the inductance on the wave form of the current is clearly seen. The simple inductor filter is seldom used with a half-wave circuit.

Suppose that a choke input filter is applied to the output of a single-phase full-wave rectifier. The circuit is given in Fig. 19-3. The wave forms obtained with and without an inductor are shown in Fig. 19-4.

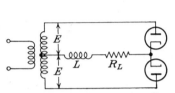

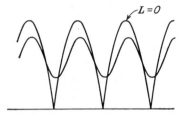

FIG. 19-3. The schematic wiring diagram of a full-wave choke-input-filtered rectifier.

FIG. 19-4. The load voltage in a single-phase full-wave rectifier circuit with a simple inductor filter. The load voltage with the inductor shorted out is also shown.

An exact solution of the circuit differential equation can be effected (Prob. 19-2). However, since no cutout occurs in the load current, it is now simpler to proceed by finding an approximate solution. The results will be sufficiently accurate for most applications and will be in a much more useful form than the exact solution.

The voltage that is applied to the circuit comprising the load resistor and the inductor filter is that given in Eq. (19-4), with the current replaced by the voltage (I_m is replaced by E_m). The amplitudes of the a-c terms beyond the first are small compared with the amplitude of the first term in the series. Thus, the fourth-harmonic-frequency term is only 20 per cent of the second-harmonic term. Further, since the impedance of the inductor increases with the frequency, better filtering action for the higher-harmonic terms results. It is therefore expected that the

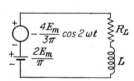

FIG. 19-5. The equivalent circuit of a full-wave choke-input-filtered rectifier.

wave form in the output will be principally of second-harmonic frequency, and we may neglect all harmonics except the first a-c term. That is, the equivalent circuit of the rectifier under these circumstances is assumed to be that illustrated in Fig. 19-5. For the sake of simplicity and because they introduce little error, the tube drop and the tube resistance will be neglected in the ripple calculations of this chapter. In addition, the resistance and leakage inductance of the transformer and the resistance of the inductor will likewise be neglected.

We note that only linear elements exist in the equivalent circuit and that the input voltage consists of a battery $2E_m/\pi$ in series with an a-c source whose emf is $(-4E_m/3\pi)\cos 2\omega t$. The load current will then be, in accordance with elementary circuit theory,

$$i_L = \frac{2E_m}{\pi R_L} - \frac{4E_m}{3\pi} \frac{\cos(2\omega t - \psi)}{\sqrt{R_L^2 + 4\omega^2 L^2}} \tag{19-6}$$

where

$$\tan \psi \equiv \frac{2\omega L}{R_L} \tag{19-7}$$

The load voltage curve in Fig. 19-4 is expressed by Eq. (19-6) (multiplied by R_L).

The ripple factor, defined in Eq. (14-19), becomes

$$r = \frac{\dfrac{4E_m}{3\pi \sqrt{2}} \dfrac{1}{\sqrt{R_L^2 + 4\omega^2 L^2}}}{2E_m/\pi R_L} = \frac{2R_L}{3\sqrt{2}} \frac{1}{\sqrt{R_L^2 + 4\omega^2 L^2}}$$

which may be expressed in the form

$$r = \frac{2}{3\sqrt{2}} \frac{1}{\sqrt{1 + 4\omega^2 L^2/R_L^2}} \tag{19-8}$$

This expression shows that filtering improves with decreased circuit resistance or, correspondingly, with increased currents. At no load, $R_L = \infty$, whence the filtering is poorest, and $r = 2/(3\sqrt{2}) = 0.47$. This result that applies when no choke is included in the circuit should be compared with Eq. (14-26), which gives 0.482. The difference arises from the higher-order terms in the Fourier series that have been neglected in the present calculation.

If the ratio $4\omega^2 L^2/R_L^2$ is large compared with unity, then the ripple factor reduces to

$$r = \frac{1}{3\sqrt{2}} \frac{R_L}{\omega L} \tag{19-9}$$

This result shows that at any load the ripple varies inversely as the magnitude of the inductance. Also, the ripple is smaller for small values of R_L, that is, for high currents.

The d-c output voltage is given by

$$E_{dc} = I_{dc}R_L = \frac{2E_m}{\pi} = 0.637E_m = 0.90E_{\text{rms}} \tag{19-10}$$

where E_{rms} is the transformer secondary voltage measured to the center tap. Note that under the assumptions made in the analysis the output voltage is a constant, independent of the load; *i.e.*, perfect regulation exists. Because of the effect of the choke resistance, the resistance of the tube, and the resistance of the transformer winding, the foregoing represents the output only at no load. The output voltage will decrease as the current increases in accordance with the equation

$$E_{dc} = \frac{2E_m}{\pi} - I_{dc}R \qquad (19\text{-}11)$$

where R is the total resistance in the circuit, exclusive of the load.

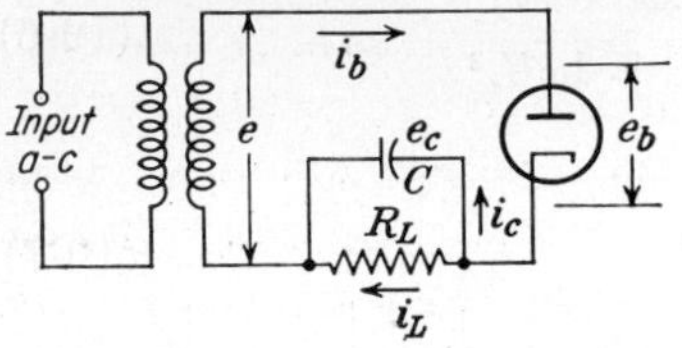

FIG. 19-6. A single-phase half-wave capacitor-filtered rectifier.

19-3. Capacitor Filters.[2] Filtering is frequently effected by shunting the load with a capacitor. The action of this system depends upon the fact that the capacitor stores energy during the conduction period and delivers this energy to the load during the inverse, or nonconducting, period. In this way, the time during which the current passes through the load is prolonged, and the ripple is considerably decreased.

Consider the half-wave capacitive rectifier of Fig. 19-6. Suppose first that the load resistor $R_L = \infty$. The capacitor will charge to the potential E_m, the transformer maximum value. Further, the capacitor will maintain this potential, for no path exists by which this charge is permitted to leak off, since the tube will not pass a negative current. The tube resistance is infinite in the inverse direction, and no charge can flow during this portion of the cycle. Consequently, the filtering action is perfect, and the capacitor voltage e_c remains constant at its peak value, as is seen in Fig. 19-7.

The voltage e_c across the capacitor is, of course, the same as the voltage e_L across the load resistor, since the two elements are in parallel. The tube voltage e_b is given by

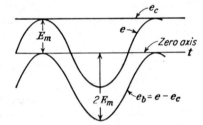

FIG. 19-7. Voltages in a single-phase half-wave capacitor-filtered rectifier *at no load*. The output voltage e_c is a constant, indicating perfect filtering. The tube voltage e_b is negative for all values of time, and the peak inverse voltage is $2E_m$.

$$e_b = e - e_c \qquad (19\text{-}12)$$

We see from Fig. 19-7 that the tube voltage is always negative and that the peak inverse voltage is twice the transformer maximum. Hence, the presence of the capacitor causes the peak inverse voltage to increase from a value equal to the transformer maximum when no capacitor filter is used to a value equal to twice the transformer maximum value when the filter is used.

Suppose, now, that the load resistor R_L is finite. Without the capacitor input filter, the load current and the load voltage during the conduction period will be sinusoidal functions of the time. The inclusion of a capacitor in the circuit results in the capacitor charging in step with the applied voltage. Also, the capacitor must discharge through the load resistor, since the tube will prevent a current in the negative direction. Clearly, the diode acts as a switch which permits charge to flow into the capacitor when the transformer voltage exceeds the capacitor voltage, and then acts to disconnect the power source when the transformer voltage falls below that of the capacitor.

The analysis will now proceed in two steps. First the conditions during conduction will be considered, and then the situation when the tube is nonconducting will be investigated.

Diode Conducting. If the tube drop is neglected, then the transformer voltage is impressed directly across the load. Hence, the output voltage is $e_L = E_m \sin \omega t$. The question immediately arises: Over what interval of time is this equation applicable? In other words, over what portion of each cycle does the diode remain conducting? The point at which the diode starts to conduct is called the "cutin point," and that at which it stops conducting is called the "cutout point." The latter will first be found in the same manner as that indicated for obtaining the cutout point for a half-wave inductor filter. The expression for the tube current is found, and the instant where this current falls to zero is the cutout time.

The expression for the tube current can be written down directly. Since the transformer voltage is sinusoidal and is impressed directly across R_L and C in parallel, then the phasor current $\mathbf{I}_b$ is found by multiplying the phasor voltage $\mathbf{E}$ by the complex admittance $(1/R_L) + j\omega C$. Hence

$$\mathbf{I}_b = \left(\frac{1}{R_L} + j\omega C \right) \mathbf{E}$$

$$= \left[\sqrt{\left(\frac{1}{R_L} \right)^2 + \omega^2 C^2} \ \underline{/\tan^{-1} \omega C R_L} \right] \mathbf{E} \qquad (19\text{-}13)$$

Since $\mathbf{E}$ has a peak value E_m, then the instantaneous current is

$$i_b = E_m \sqrt{\omega^2 C^2 + \frac{1}{R_L^2}} \sin (\omega t + \psi) \qquad (19\text{-}14)$$

where

$$\psi \equiv \tan^{-1} \omega C R_L \qquad (19\text{-}15)$$

This expression shows that the use of a large capacitor in order to improve the filtering for a given load R_L is accompanied by a high peak tube current i_b. The tube current has the form illustrated in Fig. 19-8. For a specified average load current, the tube current will become more peaked, and the conduction period will decrease as the capacitor is made larger.

It is to be emphasized that the use of a capacitor filter may impose serious duty conditions on the rectifying diode, since the average current may be well within the current rating of the tube, and yet the peak current may be excessive. If a current in excess of the temperature saturated value is specified by Eq. (19-14), the analysis must be modified, as this saturation value imposes a physical limitation on the output. In this case, the tube current pulse will flatten out, and the time duration will increase. The analysis to follow is not valid under these conditions. In the case of gas tubes, if a current higher than the saturation value is required by the circuit, even for very short intervals of time, the tube drop will increase and positive-ion bombardment of the cathode will be the result. If the tube drop exceeds the disintegration voltage of the cathode, the cathode may be permanently injured. It is for this reason that large capacitor input filters should not be used with rectifiers that employ gas diodes, without a careful check of the peak current demands.

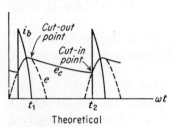

Fig. 19-8. Sketch of tube current and load voltage in a single-phase half-wave capacitor-filtered rectifier.

The cutout time t_1 is found by equating the tube current to zero at this time. Thus, from Eq. (19-14),

$$0 = \sin (\omega t_1 + \psi)$$

or

$$\omega t_1 + \psi = n\pi$$

where n is any positive or negative integer. The value of t_1 indicated in Fig. 19-8 in the first half cycle corresponds to $n = 1$ or

$$\omega t_1 = \pi - \psi = \pi - \tan^{-1} \omega C R_L \qquad (19\text{-}16)$$

Diode Nonconducting. In the interval between the cutout time t_1 and the cutin time t_2, the diode is effectively out of the circuit and the capacitor discharges through the load resistor with a time constant $C R_L$. Thus, the capacitor voltage (equal to the load voltage) is

$$e_c = A \epsilon^{-t/C R_L} \qquad (19\text{-}17)$$

To determine the value of the constant A appearing in this expression, it is noted from Fig. 19-8 that at the time $t = t_1$, the cutout time,

$$e_c = e = E_m \sin \omega t_1$$

whence

$$A = (E_m \sin \omega t_1) \epsilon^{+t_1/C R_L} \qquad (19\text{-}18)$$

Equation (19-17) thus attains the form

$$e_c = (E_m \sin \omega t_1)\epsilon^{-(t-t_1)/CR_L} \tag{19-19}$$

Since t_1 is known from Eq. (19-16), then e_c can be plotted as a function of time. This exponential curve is indicated in Fig. 19-8, and where it intersects the sine curve $E_m \sin \omega t$ (in the following cycle) is the cutin point t_2. The validity of this statement follows from the fact that at an instant of time greater than t_2, the transformer voltage e (the sine curve) is greater than the capacitor voltage e_c (the exponential curve). Since the tube voltage is $e_b = e - e_c$, then e_b will be positive beyond t_2 and the tube will become conducting. Thus, t_2 is the cutin point.

The output voltage consists of a section of the input sine curve followed by an exponential section. The cutin time t_2 cannot be given by an explicit analytic expression but must be found graphically by the method outlined above.

In principle at least, the foregoing results permit a complete analysis of the capacitor filter to be effected. For given values of ω, R_L, C, and E_m the tube current is given by Eq. (19-14). If $\alpha \equiv \omega t$, $\alpha_1 \equiv \omega t_1$, and $\alpha_2 \equiv \omega t_2$, the output potential is given by

$$\left.\begin{aligned}
e_c &= E_m \sin \alpha && \text{for } \alpha_2 < \alpha < \alpha_1 \\
\text{and by Eq. (19-19)} \\
e_c &= (E_m \sin \alpha_1)\epsilon^{-(\alpha-\alpha_1)/\omega CR_L} && \text{for } \alpha_1 < \alpha < 2\pi + \alpha_2
\end{aligned}\right\} \tag{19-20}$$

In these equations α_1 and α_2 represent the cutout and cutin angles *in the first half cycle*, respectively. The cutout angle is found from Eq. (19-16).

The d-c output voltage, the ripple factor, the peak tube current, etc., may then be calculated. These quantities can be plotted as functions of the parameters ω, R_L, C, and E_m. Such an analysis is quite involved, but it has been carried out,[3] and the results are given in graphical form.

It is possible to make several reasonable approximations which permit an analytic solution to the problem. This approximate solution possesses the advantage that it clearly indicates the dependence of the d-c output voltage and ripple factor upon the circuit component values. This approximate analysis is sufficiently accurate for most engineering applications and is carried out in the next section.

19-4. Approximate Analysis of Capacitor Filters. We shall assume that the output-voltage wave form for a full-wave circuit with a capacitor filter may be approximated by a broken curve which is made up of portions of straight lines, as shown in Fig. 19-9. The peak value of this wave is E_m, the transformer maximum voltage. If the total capacitor discharge voltage is denoted by E_r, then, from the diagram, the average value of the voltage is

$$E_{dc} = E_m - \frac{E_r}{2} \tag{19-21}$$

The instantaneous ripple voltage is obtained by subtracting E_{dc} from the instantaneous load voltage.   The result is shown in Fig. 19-10.   The

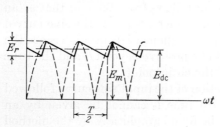

FIG. 19-9. The approximate load-voltage wave form in a full-wave capacitor-filtered rectifier.

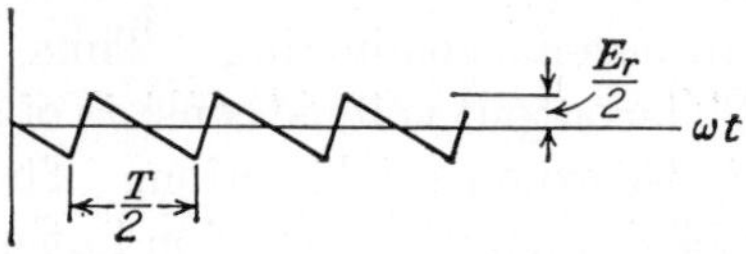

FIG. 19-10. The approximate wave form of the ripple voltage in a full-wave capacitor-filtered rectifier.

rms value of this "triangular wave" is independent of the slopes or lengths of the straight lines and depends only upon the peak value.   Calculation of this rms ripple voltage yields

$$E_{\text{rms}}' = \frac{E_r}{2\sqrt{3}} \tag{19-22}$$

The two most important characteristics of the capacitor filter circuit, the regulation and the ripple, are contained in Eqs. (19-21) and (19-22), respectively.   It is necessary, however, to express E_r as a function of the load current and the capacitance.   If T_2 represents the total nonconducting time, then the capacitor, when discharging at the constant rate I_{dc}, will lose an amount of charge $I_{dc}T_2$.   Hence, the change in capacitor voltage is $I_{dc}T_2/C$ or

$$E_r = \frac{I_{dc}T_2}{C} \tag{19-23}$$

The value of T_2 is found from Fig. 19-11.   This is the same diagram as in Fig. 19-9 except that the time origin is taken at the peak of the wave for convenience.   It is also assumed that the rising straight-line section passes through the zero and the peak values of the sine curve.   Although this approximation is a crude one, it leads to a simple solution which agrees fairly well with experimental results.   From the geometry of Fig. 19-11, it follows that

$$\frac{T'}{T/4} = \frac{E_m - E_r}{E_m}$$

and

$$T_2 = T' + \frac{T}{4} = \left(1 - \frac{E_r}{E_m}\right)\frac{T}{4} + \frac{T}{4} = \frac{2E_m - E_r}{E_m}\frac{T}{4}$$

Using Eq. (19-21), this reduces to

$$T_2 = \frac{E_{dc}}{E_m}\frac{T}{2} \qquad (19\text{-}24)$$

Hence, from Eq. (19-23)

$$E_r = \frac{I_{dc}}{C}\left(\frac{E_{dc}}{E_m}\frac{T}{2}\right) = \frac{I_{dc}}{2fC}\frac{E_{dc}}{E_m} \qquad (19\text{-}25)$$

where $f = 1/T$ is the power supply frequency.

The d-c output is given by Eq. (19-21),

$$E_{dc} = E_m - \frac{E_r}{2} = E_m - \frac{I_{dc}}{4fC}\frac{E_{dc}}{E_m}$$

or

$$E_{dc} = \frac{E_m}{1 + I_{dc}/4fCE_m} \qquad (19\text{-}26)$$

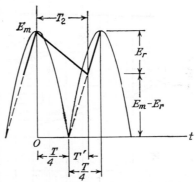

FIG. 19-11. The charging of the output capacitor is assumed to take place along a straight line passing through the zero and the peak values of the input sine curve.

Figure 19-12 gives graphs of this equation for $f = 60$ cps, $C = 4$ μf, and $E_m = 300\sqrt{2}$ and also $E_m = 450\sqrt{2}$. The experimentally measured values for the 5T4 and the 5U4-G tubes are taken from the RCA tube manual and are also indicated on the same graph. The maximum deviation between experiment and theory is less than 10 per cent. This is satisfactory agreement, particularly in view of the simplifying assumptions made in the derivation.

From the graphs of Fig. 19-12 it is seen that the regulation of a capacitor filter is poor. The larger the capacitance, the better will be the regulation.

The ripple factor is given by

$$r = \frac{E_{rms}'}{E_{dc}} = \frac{E_r}{2\sqrt{3}E_{dc}} = \frac{I_{dc}}{4\sqrt{3}fCE_m} \qquad (19\text{-}27)$$

where use has been made of Eqs. (19-22) and (19-25). The ripple is seen to vary directly with the load current and inversely with the capacitance.

In order to keep the ripple low and to ensure good regulation, very large capacitors (of the order of tens of microfarads) must be used. The most common type of capacitor for this rectifier application is the electrolytic capacitor. These capacitors are polarized, and care must be taken to insert them into the circuit with the terminal marked + to the positive side of the output.

If a half-wave circuit is used, then the nonconduction time will be one-half a cycle longer, or

$$T_2 = \frac{T}{2} + \frac{T}{2}\frac{E_{dc}}{E_m} \quad (19\text{-}28)$$

Using this expression, the ripple and the output voltages are found to be given by the equations

$$r = \frac{I_{dc}}{4fC\sqrt{3}}\left(\frac{1}{E_m} + \frac{1}{E_{dc}}\right) \quad (19\text{-}29)$$

and

$$E_{dc} = \frac{E_m - I_{dc}/4fC}{1 + I_{dc}/4fCE_m} \quad (19\text{-}30)$$

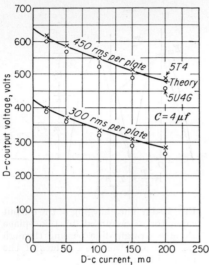

FIG. 19-12. Load voltage vs. load current for a capacitor input filter. $C = 4$ μf. The crosses and circles are the experimentally measured points for a 5T4 and a 5U4-G, respectively. These are taken from the RCA manual. The curves are plotted from Eq. (19-26).

A careful inspection of these equations reveals that the ripple of the half-wave circuit is approximately double that of the full-wave circuit. Also, the drop in voltage from no load to a given load for a half-wave circuit is approximately twice that for a full-wave circuit.

The desirable features of rectifiers employing capacitor input filters are the small ripple and the high voltage at light load. The no-load voltage is equal, theoretically, to the maximum transformer voltage. The disadvantages of this system are the relatively poor regulation, the high ripple at large loads, and the peaked currents that the tubes must pass.

We see from Fig. 19-6 that for a half-wave circuit the voltage across the tube on the inverse cycle is approximately twice the transformer maximum. In the full-wave circuit the inverse voltage across each tube is also twice the maximum transformer voltage measured from the midpoint to either end. This result is independent of the form of the filter used and is a property of the full-wave circuit itself, and not of the filter system.

19-5. L-section Filter. The two types of filtering action considered above may be combined into a single L-section filter. This filter combines the decreasing ripple with increasing load of the series inductor with the increasing ripple with increasing load of the shunt capacitor. Such a filter is illustrated in Fig. 19-13. The inductor offers a high series impedance to the harmonic terms, and the capacitor offers a low shunt impedance to them. The resulting current through the load is smoothed out much more effectively than with either L or C alone in the circuit.

The d-c voltage and the ripple factor are readily calculated by taking, for the voltage impressed at the terminals AB of the filter of Fig. 19-13, the first two terms in the Fourier series representation of the output voltage of the rectifier, viz.,

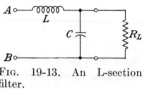

FIG. 19-13. An L-section filter.

$$e = \frac{2E_m}{\pi} - \frac{4E_m}{3\pi} \cos 2\omega t \qquad (19\text{-}31)$$

Thus, the two tubes are replaced by a battery in series with an a-c source having twice the power line frequency. This is the same equivalent circuit that was used in Sec. 19-2 for a full-wave inductor filter. If the resistance in series with the inductance is neglected, then the d-c output voltage equals the d-c input voltage, or

$$E_{dc} = \frac{2E_m}{\pi}$$

If the sum of the tube, transformer, and choke resistances is R, then

$$E_{dc} = \frac{2E_m}{\pi} - I_{dc}R \qquad (19\text{-}32)$$

The ripple will now be calculated. Since the object of the filter is to suppress the harmonic components in the system, the reactance of the choke must be large compared with the combined parallel impedance of capacitor and resistor. The latter combination is kept small by making the reactance of the capacitor much smaller than the resistance of the load. Very little error will be introduced, therefore, by assuming that the entire alternating current passes through the capacitor and none through the resistor. Under these conditions the net impedance across AB is approximately $X_L = 2\omega L$, the reactance of the inductor at the second-harmonic frequency. The alternating current through the circuit is

$$I_{rms}' = \frac{4E_m}{3\sqrt{2}\pi} \frac{1}{X_L} = \frac{\sqrt{2}}{3} E_{dc} \frac{1}{X_L} \qquad (19\text{-}33)$$

where the resistance R in Eq. (19-32) has been neglected. The a-c voltage across the load (the ripple voltage) is the voltage across the capacitor. This is

$$E_{rms}' = I_{rms}'X_C = \frac{\sqrt{2}}{3} E_{dc} \frac{X_C}{X_L} \qquad (19\text{-}34)$$

where $X_C = 1/2\omega C$ is the reactance of the capacitor at the second-harmonic frequency. The ripple factor is then given by

$$r = \frac{E_{\mathrm{rms}}'}{E_{dc}} = \frac{\sqrt{2}}{3}\frac{X_C}{X_L} = \frac{\sqrt{2}}{3}\left(\frac{1}{2\omega C}\right)\left(\frac{1}{2\omega L}\right) \tag{19-35}$$

which is, at 60 cps,

$$r = \frac{0.83}{LC} \tag{19-36}$$

with C in microfarads and L in henrys.

It is noticed that the effect of combining the decreasing ripple arising with a simple inductor filter and the increasing ripple arising with a simple capacitor filter for increasing loads is a constant ripple independent of load.

The foregoing analysis assumes that a current flows through the circuit at all times. If any cutout points of the type discussed in the previous section exist, this analysis is no longer valid. Consider the conditions that exist when no inductor is used. As already found, current will flow in the tube circuit for a small portion of the cycle and the capacitor will become charged to the peak transformer voltage in each cycle. Suppose that a small inductance is now inserted in the line. Although the time over which tube current will exist will be somewhat lengthened, cutout may still occur. As the value of the inductance is increased, a value will be reached for which the tube circuit supplies current to the load continuously, and no cutout occurs. This value of inductance is referred to as the *critical inductance L_c*. Under these circumstances, each tube conducts for one-half of the cycle, and the input voltage to the filter circuit has the form given by Eq. (19-31). It is only under these circumstances that the above-developed L-section filter theory is applicable.

FIG. 19-14. The tube current in a single-phase full-wave circuit when an L-section filter is used.

Referring to Fig. 19-14, we see that, if the rectifier is to pass current throughout the entire cycle, the peak ($\sqrt{2}\,I_{\mathrm{rms}}'$) of the a-c component of the current must not exceed the direct current, $I_{dc} = E_{dc}/R_L$. Therefore, for the tube current to exist during the entire cycle, it is necessary that

$$\frac{E_{dc}}{R_L} \geq \sqrt{2}\,I_{\mathrm{rms}}' = \frac{2E_{dc}}{3}\frac{1}{X_L}$$

where use has been made of Eq. (19-33). Hence,

$$X_L \geq \frac{2R_L}{3} \tag{19-37}$$

and the value for the critical inductance is given by

$$L_c = \frac{R_L}{3\omega} \qquad (19\text{-}38a)$$

For a 60-cps input frequency, this becomes

$$L_c = \frac{R_L}{1,130} \qquad (19\text{-}38b)$$

where R_L is expressed in ohms and L_c is in henrys.

It must be remembered that these values of critical inductance have been based not upon the true input voltage but rather upon an approximate voltage that is made up of the d-c term and the first a-c harmonic term in the Fourier series of the true input voltage. It was shown in Sec. 19-2 that this approximation introduced very little error in the calculation of the ripple factor. However, the neglect of the higher harmonic terms introduces an appreciable error in the calculation of the critical inductance.* It is advisable for conservative design to increase the values

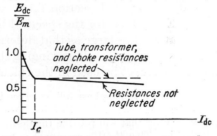

FIG. 19-15. The regulation curve of a rectifier with an L-section filter.

of L_c calculated from Eq. (19-38) by about 25 per cent.

The effect of the cutout is illustrated in Fig. 19-15, which shows a regulation curve of the system for constant L and a varying load resistor. Clearly, when the current is zero (R_L is infinite) the filter is of the simple capacitor type, and the output voltage is E_m. With increasing load current, the voltage falls, until at $I = I_c$ (the current at which $L = L_c$) the output potential is that corresponding to the simple L filter with no cutout, or $0.636E_m$. For values of I greater than I_c, the change in potential results from the effects of the resistances of the various elements of the circuit.

It is not possible to satisfy the conditions of Eq. (19-37) for all values of load, since at no load this would require an infinite inductance. If good voltage regulation is essential, it is customary to use a "bleeder"

---

* If A represents the amplitude of the first a-c term in the Fourier series of a wave and $B = 0.1A$ represents the amplitude of the second term, then $A + B = 1.1A$. A 10 per cent error is made if B is neglected in calculating the sum. It is this general process that is involved in the calculation of L_c. However, the calculation of the ripple factor requires an evaluation of an expression of the form $\sqrt{A^2 + B^2} = \sqrt{A^2 + (0.1A)^2} = 1.005A$. Hence, if B is neglected, this results in an error of only 0.5 per cent.

resistor in parallel with the load so as to maintain the conditions of Eq. (19-37), even if the useful current is small.

A more efficient method than using a small bleeder resistor, with its consequent power dissipation, is to make use of the fact that the inductance of an iron-core reactor depends, among other things, upon the magnitude of the direct current in the winding. Reactors for which the inductance is high at low values of direct current and decreases markedly with increased direct currents are called "swinging chokes." Typically, such a reactor might have an inductance which drops from 30 henrys at zero current to 4 henrys at 100 ma. A choke whose inductance is constant at 30 henrys requires much more iron in order to avoid saturation and hence is bulkier and more expensive than the swinging choke.

In designing an L-section filter, an inductor must be chosen so as to satisfy Eq. (19-38) for the specified bleeder resistor. Then a capacitor is chosen at least as large as that determined from Eq. (19-36) for the specified tolerable ripple. If a swinging choke is used, the minimum value of its inductance must be used in the calculation of the capacitor value needed.

Example. A single-phase full-wave rectifier is to supply 100 ma at 350 volts with a ripple that must be less than 10 volts. Specify the elements of a rectifier using a single L-section filter that will provide the desired results.

Solution. The effective resistance of the load is

$$R_L = \frac{350}{0.100} = 3,500 \text{ ohms}$$

The ripple factor is

$$r = \tfrac{10}{350} = 0.0286$$

According to Eq. (19-38b), the critical inductance for such a filter is

$$L_c = \frac{3,500}{1,130} = 3.1 \text{ henrys}$$

According to Eq. (19-36), the product LC must be at least as large as

$$LC = \frac{0.830}{0.0286} = 29$$

These calculations specify the minimum values of L and LC that may be used to accomplish the desired filtering. The actual values that will be used are determined by the commercially available inductors and capacitors. The desirability of using standard commercial merchandise is dictated both by availability and by economic considerations.

Since 10-henry chokes having the desired current rating are readily available, such an inductor will be chosen. The capacitor must therefore be about 3 μf. Since a 4-μf capacitor is readily available commercially, it will be chosen.

A search through a tube manual reveals several rectifier tubes having the proper ratings. One such tube is the 5Y3-GT with a maximum d-c output current rating of 125 ma, a maximum plate voltage per plate of 500 volts rms, and a peak inverse voltage of 1,400 volts. The plate characteristic of this tube (Fig. A9-5) shows that tho tube voltage is 50 volts at 100 ma, corresponding to a resistance of approximately 500 ohms.

The resistance of a 10-henry choke capable of carrying 100 ma is found in a manufacturer's catalogue. A reasonable value is 200 ohms. Similarly, a reasonable value for the transformer resistance is 200 ohms. Hence the total resistance in series with the inductor is $R = 500 + 200 + 200 = 900$ ohms. From Eq. (19-32) the peak transformer voltage is

$$E_m = \frac{\pi}{2}(E_{dc} + I_{dc}R) = \frac{\pi}{2}[350 + (0.1)(900)] = 690 \text{ volts}$$

and

$$E_{rms} = \frac{690}{\sqrt{2}} = 488 \text{ volts}$$

A stock transformer would be purchased whose current rating is at least 100 ma and whose voltage to center tap is close to 488 volts, say 500 volts. If the exact value of choke and transformer resistances were known, a more accurate calculation of the transformer voltage needed could be made.

The peak inverse voltage is $2E_m = (2)(690) = 1,380$ volts. Since the rated peak inverse voltage of the 5Y3-GT tube is 1,400 volts, it is safe to use this tube in this application.

If the load should be removed accidentally, the circuit will behave as if it has a capacitor input filter and the voltage will rise to the peak transformer voltage to center tap or to 690 volts. Hence the insulation rating of the filament heating transformer should be at least this high.

The inequalities used in the derivation of the expression for the ripple factor will now be checked. $R_L = 3,500$; $X_L = 4\pi fL = 7,540$; and $X_C = 1/4\pi fC = 332$ ohms. Hence $X_C \ll R_L$, $X_L \gg X_C$, thus verifying the inequalities assumed.

19-6. Multiple L-section Filters. The filtering may be made much more complete through the use of two L-section filters in cascade, as shown in Fig. 19-16. An approximate solution that is sufficiently accurate for practical purposes can be obtained by proceeding according to the development in Sec. 19-5.

It is assumed that the reactances of all the chokes are much larger than the reactances of the capacitors. Also, it is as-

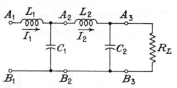

FIG. 19-16. A multiple (two-section) L-section filter.

sumed that the reactance of the last capacitor is small compared with the resistance of the load. Under these circumstances, the impedance between A_3 and B_3 is effectively X_{C_2}. The impedance between A_2 and B_2 is effectively X_{C_1}, and the impedance between A_1 and B_1 is effectively X_{L_1}. The alternating current I_1 is approximately

$$I_1 = \frac{\sqrt{2} \, E_{dc}}{3} \frac{1}{X_{L_1}}$$

The a-c voltage across C_1 is approximately

$$E_{A_2 B_2} = I_1 X_{C_1}$$

The alternating current I_2 is approximately

$$I_2 = \frac{E_{A_2 B_2}}{X_{L_2}}$$

The a-c voltage across the load is approximately

$$I_2 X_{C_2} = I_1 \frac{X_{C_2} X_{C_1}}{X_{L_2}} = \frac{\sqrt{2} E_{dc}}{3} \frac{X_{C_2}}{X_{L_2}} \frac{X_{C_1}}{X_{L_1}}$$

The ripple factor is given by dividing this expression by E_{dc}. Hence

$$r = \frac{\sqrt{2}}{3} \frac{X_{C_1}}{X_{L_1}} \frac{X_{C_2}}{X_{L_2}} \qquad (19\text{-}39)$$

A comparison of this equation with Eq. (19-35) indicates the generalization which should be made in order to obtain an expression valid for any number of sections. For example, a multiple L filter of n similar sections has a ripple factor that is given by

$$r = \frac{\sqrt{2}}{3} \left(\frac{X_C}{X_L} \right)^n = \frac{\sqrt{2}}{3} \frac{1}{(16\pi^2 f^2 LC)^n} \qquad (19\text{-}40)$$

For a multiple L filter of n similar sections, the product LC for a specified ripple factor may be evaluated from Eq. (19-40). The result is, at 60 cps,

$$LC = 1.76 \left(\frac{0.471}{r} \right)^{1/n} \qquad (19\text{-}41)$$

To the approximation that the impedance between A_1 and B_1 is simply X_{L_1}, the critical inductance is the same for the first inductor of a multi-section filter as for a single-section unit. The remaining inductors may have any values, since they play no part in determining the cutout condition.

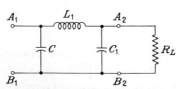

FIG. 19-17. A Π-section filter.

19-7. Π-section Filters. A very smooth output may be obtained by using a filter that consists of two capacitors separated by an inductor, as shown in Fig. 19-17. Such filters are characterized by highly peaked tube currents and by poor regulation as for the simple capacitor input filter. They are used if, for a given transformer, higher voltage than can be obtained from an L-section filter is needed and if lower ripple than can be obtained from a simple capacitor or an L-section filter is desired.

The action of a II-section filter can best be understood by considering the inductor and the second capacitor as an L-section filter that acts upon the triangular output-voltage wave from the first capacitor. The output potential is then approximately that from the input capacitor [Eq. (19-26)], decreased by the d-c voltage drop in the inductor. The ripple contained in this output is reduced by the L-section filter.

The ripple voltage can be calculated by analyzing the triangular wave of Fig. 19-10 into a Fourier series and then multiplying each component by X_{C_1}/X_{L_1} for this harmonic. This leads to rather involved expressions. An upper limit to the ripple can, however, be more easily obtained. If it is assumed that cutout takes place for the entire half cycle (for a full-wave rectifier), then Fig. 19-10 becomes a triangular wave with vertical sides. The Fourier analysis of this wave form is given by

$$ e = E_{dc} - \left(\frac{E_r}{\pi}\right) \left(\sin 2\omega t - \frac{\sin 4\omega t}{2} + \frac{\sin 6\omega t}{3} - \cdots \right) \quad (19\text{-}42) $$

From Eq. (19-23), $E_r = I_{dc}T_2/C$, and since it has now been assumed that $T_2 = T/2$, this reduces to

$$ E_r = \frac{I_{dc}T}{2C} = \frac{I_{dc}}{2fC} $$

The rms second harmonic voltage is

$$ E_2' = \frac{E_r}{\pi \sqrt{2}} = \frac{I_{dc}}{2\pi fC \sqrt{2}} = \sqrt{2}\, I_{dc} X_C \quad (19\text{-}43) $$

where X_C is the reactance of C at the second harmonic frequency.

A second method of obtaining the same result, due to Arguimbau,[4] is instructive. If the instantaneous current to the filter is i, then the rms second harmonic current I_2' is given by the Fourier component

$$ \sqrt{2}\, I_2' = \frac{1}{\pi} \int_0^{2\pi} i \cos 2\alpha \, d\alpha $$

The current i is in the form of pulses near the peak value of the cosine curve, and hence not too great an error is made by replacing $\cos 2\alpha$ by unity. Since the maximum value of the cosine is unity, this will give the maximum possible value of I_2'. Thus,

$$ \sqrt{2}\, I_2' \leq \frac{1}{\pi} \int_0^{2\pi} i \, d\alpha = 2I_{dc} $$

because, by definition,

$$ I_{dc} \equiv \frac{1}{2\pi} \int_0^{2\pi} i \, d\alpha $$

Hence, the upper limit of the rms second harmonic voltage is

$$E_2' = I_2'X_C = \sqrt{2}\, I_{dc}X_C$$

which agrees with the first method of analysis in which it was assumed that the cutout took place over the complete half cycle. If this were true, then the charging current could exist only for an infinitesimally small time near the peak of the input voltage or at the points for which $\cos 2\alpha = 1$. This shows the consistency of the two methods of attack.

The voltage E_2' is impressed on an L section, and by using the same logic as in Sec. 19-5 the output ripple is $E_2'X_{C_1}/X_{L_1}$. Hence, the ripple factor is

$$r = \frac{E_{\text{rms}}'}{E_{dc}} = \frac{\sqrt{2}\, I_{dc}X_C}{E_{dc}} \frac{X_{C_1}}{X_{L_1}} = \sqrt{2}\, \frac{X_C}{R_L} \frac{X_{C_1}}{X_{L_1}} \tag{19-44}$$

where all reactances are calculated at the second harmonic frequency. This expression gives the second harmonic ripple but, just as for the simple inductor filter, very little error is made in neglecting the higher harmonics, and we may consider this as the total ripple.

For 60 cps Eq. (19-44) reduces to

$$r = \frac{3{,}300}{CC_1L_1R_L} \tag{19-45}$$

where the capacitances are in microfarads, the inductances in henrys, and the resistances in ohms.

If the Π section is followed by an L section whose parameters are L_2 and C_2, then the above reasoning leads to the expression

$$r = \sqrt{2}\, \frac{X_C}{R_L} \frac{X_{C_1}}{X_{L_1}} \frac{X_{C_2}}{X_{L_2}} \tag{19-46}$$

This analysis can be extended in an obvious fashion to include any number of sections.

If a half-wave circuit is used, then it can be shown that Eqs. (19-44) and (19-46) are still valid provided that all reactances are calculated at the fundamental instead of the second harmonic frequency. Thus, for a single Π section, the half-wave ripple is eight times that for a full-wave circuit. The d-c output voltage is that corresponding to the half-wave simple capacitor filter [Eq. (19-30)], minus the d-c voltage drop in the inductor.

Example. Design a power supply using a Π-section filter to give d-c output of 250 volts at 50 ma with a ripple factor not to exceed 0.01 per cent.
Solution. The load resistance is $R_L = 250/(50 \times 10^{-3}) = 5{,}000$ ohms. From Eq. (19-45), with $C = C_1$, $r = 3{,}300/C^2LR_L$ or

$$C^2L = \frac{3{,}300}{10^{-4} \times 5{,}000} = 6{,}600$$

There is no unique way of solving this equation for C and L. A reasonable commercially available value of L will be chosen, and then C will be calculated. The Thordarson choke type T20C53 has an inductance of 20 henrys at 50 ma. Its d-c resistance is 375 ohms. If this is used, then the corresponding capacitors required have values

$$C = \left(\frac{6,600}{20}\right)^{\frac{1}{2}} = 18.1 \ \mu f$$

Electrolytic capacitors are available in this range. For example, the Cornell-Dubilier type BR 2045 has a rating of 20 μf at 450 volts d-c and would be suitable.

The d-c voltage drop in the choke is $(50 \times 10^{-3})(375) = 19$ volts. Hence, the d-c voltage across the first capacitor is $250 + 19 = 269$ volts. The peak transformer voltage to center tap E_m is given by Eq. (19-26),

$$E_{dc} = \frac{E_m}{1 + I_{dc}/4fCE_m}$$

or

$$269 = \frac{E_m{}^2}{E_m + \dfrac{50 \times 10^{-3}}{4 \times 60 \times 20 \times 10^{-6}}} = \frac{E_m{}^2}{E_m + 10.4}$$

Solving, $E_m = 278$ and $E_{\text{rms}} = E_m/\sqrt{2} = 196$. Hence a 200-0-200-volt transformer would be used. A suitable tube for this application would be the 6X5-GT. It is rated at 70 ma maximum output current and a peak inverse voltage of 1,250. The peak inverse for this circuit is $2E_m = 556$, which is well within the tube rating.

19-8. Π-section Filter with a Resistor Replacing the Inductor. This type of filter is analyzed in the same manner as above. The d-c output is the value given in Eq. (19-26) for a simple capacitor filter minus the $I_{dc}R$ drop in the resistor. The ripple factor is given by Eq. (19-44) with X_L replaced by R. Thus, for a single section

$$r = \sqrt{2}\,\frac{X_C}{R_L}\frac{X_{C_1}}{R} \tag{19-47}$$

Hence, if the resistor R is chosen equal to the reactance of the choke which it replaces, the ripple remains unchanged. Since this means a saving in the expense, weight, and space of the choke, it is desirable to use the resistor wherever possible. Such a replacement of a resistor for an inductor is often practical only for low-current power supplies. Thus, for example, if in a full-wave circuit with an output current of 100 ma, a 20-henry choke is to be replaced by a resistor to give the same ripple, its value must be $R = X_L = 4\pi fL = 15,000$ ohms. The voltage drop in this resistor would be $(15,000)(0.1) = 1,500$ volts! The d-c power dissipated would be $I_{dc}{}^2R = (0.1)^2(15,000) = 150$ watts! Hence such a substitution would not be a sensible one. However, if the rectifier is to furnish only 10 ma (perhaps for a cathode-ray-tube supply) then the drop in the resistor is only 150 volts and the power loss in this resistor is 1.5 watts. The resistor rather than the inductor should be used in such an application.

Since very large capacitances (100 μf or more) are now available, the II-section filter with a resistor replacing the inductor is becoming quite popular even for high current supplies. Consider, for example, a load current of 100 ma at 300 volts. If $R = 100$ ohms, the drop in this resistor is 10 volts and the power loss is 1 watt, which are reasonable values. The load resistance is $R_L = 3,000$ ohms. If two 100-μf capacitors are used, then we calculate from Eq. (19-47) that the ripple is 0.083 per cent, which may be satisfactory for some purposes.

19-9. Summary of Filters. Table 19-1 contains a compilation of the more important information relating to the various types of filters, when used with single-phase full-wave circuits. In all cases, tube, transformer, and filter-element resistances are considered negligible, and a 60-cycle power line is assumed. C is expressed in farads, L in henrys, and R in ohms.

TABLE 19-1

SUMMARY OF FILTER INFORMATION

Filter	None	L	C	L section	II section
E_{dc}—no load	$0.636E_m$	$0.636E_m$	E_m	E_m	E_m
E_{dc}—load I_{dc}	$0.636E_m$	$0.636E_m$	$\dfrac{E_m}{1 + \dfrac{I_{dc}}{240CE_m}}$	$0.636E_m$	$\dfrac{E_m}{1 + \dfrac{I_{dc}}{240CE_m}}$
Ripple factor r	0.48	$\dfrac{R_L}{1,600L}$	$\dfrac{I_{dc}}{416CE_m}$	$\dfrac{0.83 \times 10^{-6}}{LC}$	$\dfrac{3,330 \times 10^{-12}}{CC_1L_1R_L}$
Peak inverse	$2E_m$	$2E_m$	$2E_m$	$2E_m$	$2E_m$

19-10. Regulated Power Supplies. An unregulated power supply consists of a transformer, a rectifier, and a filter. There are two reasons why such a simple system is not good enough for some applications. The first is its poor regulation; the output voltage is far from constant as the load varies. The second is that the d-c output voltage varies directly with the a-c input. In many locations the line voltage (of nominal value 115 volts) may vary over as wide a range as 90 to 130 volts, and yet it is necessary that the d-c voltage remain essentially constant. An electronic feedback or control circuit is used in conjunction with an unregulated power supply to overcome the above two shortcomings. Such a system is called a *regulated power supply*.

If a power supply has poor regulation it possesses a high internal impedance. This difficulty may be avoided by using a cathode follower to convert from high to low internal impedance. Refer to Fig. 19-18. If the internal impedance of the unregulated supply is called r, then the output impedance R_o after the cathode follower has been added is, from Fig. 17-6b,

$$R_o = \frac{r + r_p}{\mu + 1} \qquad (19\text{-}48)$$

A reasonable value of r is 1,000 ohms (100-volt drop for each 100-ma change in load). If the control tube is a 6AS7 with $r_p = 300$ ohms and $\mu = 2$, then

$$R_o = \frac{1,000 + 300}{2 + 1} = 430 \text{ ohms}$$

which is an improvement over the 1,000-ohm output impedance of the unregulated power supply.

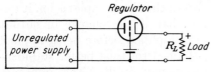

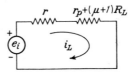

FIG. 19-18. A cathode-follower regulator for a power supply.

FIG. 19-19. Equivalent circuit of Fig. 19-18 for calculating the effect of variations in a-c input voltage.

Let us see if the simple cathode-follower regulator has also helped to stabilize the d-c output voltage against a-c input changes. If the change in the open-circuit d-c voltage of the unregulated supply is called $\Delta E_i \equiv e_i$ then, looking back into this supply, the equivalent circuit is a generator e_i in series with a resistor r. Looking into the plate of the cathode follower, the equivalent impedance is (see Fig. 17-7b) $r_p + (\mu + 1)R_L$ because R_L is the cathode resistor. The change in load current $\Delta I_L \equiv i_L$ due to e_i is found from the equivalent circuit of Fig. 19-19. Thus

$$i_L = \frac{e_i}{r + r_p + (\mu + 1)R_L} \qquad (19\text{-}49)$$

The *voltage stabilization ratio* S is defined as the ratio of the voltage change e_i of the unregulated power supply to the voltage change $\Delta E_o \equiv e_o = i_L R_L$ of the regulated power supply. Thus

$$S \equiv \frac{e_i}{e_o} \qquad (19\text{-}50)$$

The larger the numerical value of S, the better the stability. The input voltage change may be due to a change in a-c line voltage or may be ripple due to inadequate filtering.

For a simple cathode-follower regulator it follows from Eq. (19-49) that

$$S = \frac{r + r_p + (\mu + 1)R_L}{R_L} = \mu + 1 + \frac{r + r_p}{R_L} \qquad (19\text{-}51)$$

For a 6AS7, $\mu = 2$ and $r_p = 300$. For $r = 1,000$ and $R_L = 3,000$ ohms (300 volts at 100 ma), then $S = 2 + 1 + 1,300/3,000 = 3.3$. This means that a 1-volt change in d-c voltage at the unregulated side becomes only a $\frac{1}{3}$-volt change at the regulated output.

The physical reason for the improvement noted above lies in the fact that a large fraction of any increase in input voltage appears across the control tube so that the output voltage tries to remain constant. If the input increases, the output must also increase (but to a much smaller extent), because it is this increase in output that acts to bias the control tube more negatively. This additional bias causes an increase in plate-to-cathode voltage which tends to compensate for the increased input.

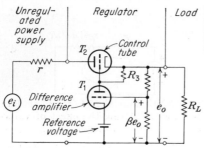

FIG. 19-20. A regulated power supply obtained by adding an amplifier to the circuit of Fig. 19-18.

From the above explanation it follows that if the change in output were amplified before being applied to the control tube better stabilization would result. The improvement will be demonstrated with reference to Fig. 19-20. An approximate expression for S (sufficiently accurate for most applications) is obtained as follows: The input voltage change e_i is very much larger than the output change e_o. If e_o is very small, then the change in current is very small. Hence, to a first approximation we can neglect the current change, and the a-c voltage across r may be taken as zero. Furthermore, from the definition of μ it follows that the change in plate voltage across the control tube is μ times the change in grid voltage. If β is the fraction of the output voltage e_o fed to the grid of the amplifier T_1, the output of the amplifier is $A_1 \beta e_o$, where A_1 is the *magnitude* of the amplification of T_1. Since the amplifier output is approximately the grid-to-cathode voltage of T_2, then the plate-to-cathode voltage of T_2 is $\mu_2 A_1 \beta e_o$. This voltage is approximately equal to e_i. Hence

$$S = \frac{e_i}{e_o} = \mu_2 A_1 \beta \qquad (19\text{-}52)$$

For a single-pentode amplifier an amplification of 150 is reasonable. If $\beta = 0.5$ and $\mu_2 = 2$, then $S = 150$ so that any input voltage change is divided by 150 before it appears at the output. This value represents a very considerable improvement over that obtained with the simple cathode follower.

To find the output impedance of the power supply, assume a voltage e_o applied to the output (with $e_i = 0$) and find the current i_o drawn from e_o.

The current in R_3 may be neglected because R_3 is very high ($\cong 1$ megohm) compared with the output impedance ($\cong 10$ ohms). From the equivalent circuit of Fig. 19-21 we have

$$-e_o + \mu_2 e_{gk2} + i_o(r_{p2} + r) = 0 \quad (19\text{-}53)$$

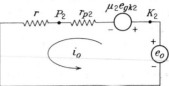

Since

$$e_{gk2} = -A_1\beta e_o \quad (19\text{-}54)$$

where A_1 is the magnitude of the amplification of T_1, then

$$(1 + \mu_2 A_1\beta)e_o = i_o(r_{p2} + r) \quad (19\text{-}55)$$

Fig. 19-21. Equivalent circuit for finding R_o of Fig. 19-20.

Because $\mu_2 A_1\beta = S \gg 1$, then the output impedance $R_o \equiv e_o/i_o$ is given by

$$R_o = \frac{r_{p2} + r}{S} \quad (19\text{-}56)$$

For the numerical values used above, $r_{p2} = 300$ ohms, $r = 1,000$ ohms, and $S = 150$, we find $R_o = 1,300/150 = 8.7$ ohms, which should be compared with the value of 430 ohms for the cathode-follower regulator.

Sometimes it is necessary to connect R_3 to the input (unregulated) side of the power supply in order to maintain adequate gain of T_1 as the grid-to-cathode voltage of T_2 approaches zero. The voltage stabilization will now be calculated for such a connection. The plate of T_1 drops an amount $\beta A_1 e_o$ because of e_o, as noted above, and rises an amount γe_i, where $\gamma \equiv r_{p1}/(r_{p1} + R_3)$ because of e_i. Hence, the grid of T_2 which is tied to the plate of T_1 drops an amount $\beta A_1 e_o - \gamma e_i$. The plate-to-cathode voltage of T_2 changes μ_2 times as much (the small change in output voltage at the cathode of T_2 is neglected). Hence

$$e_i = \mu_2(\beta A_1 e_o - \gamma e_i) \quad (19\text{-}57)$$

and

$$\beta = \frac{\mu_2\beta A_1}{1 + \mu_2\gamma} \quad (19\text{-}58)$$

This connection gives a smaller stabilization ratio (perhaps by a factor of 2) than that considered above with R_3 connected to the output side [compare with Eq. (19-52)]. The gain A_1 is somewhat higher when R_3 is connected to the input side because of the higher input voltage and correspondingly higher quiescent current.

The output impedance with R_3 connected to the input side is found to be given approximately by Eq. (19-56), and hence if S is half as large with R_3 on the input side then R_o is now twice as large.

A practical form of an electronic regulated power supply is indicated in Fig. 19-22. Specific numerical values for components and voltages are available in the literature.[5] The important components in the circuit will now be discussed.

1. The reference voltage, which in the preceding diagrams was shown as a battery, is usually a VR tube (Sec. 13-12) connected to the regulated output through a dropping resistor. This resistor is picked so that the tube current is in the normal-glow region. The 0.1-μf capacitor across the VR tube tends to prevent high-frequency oscillations. The most stable reference tube available is the 5651.

2. The amplifier must have high gain, and hence a pentode (6AK5, 6SJ7, 6SH7) is used. If better stabilization is desired, a multistage direct-coupled difference amplifier is used.

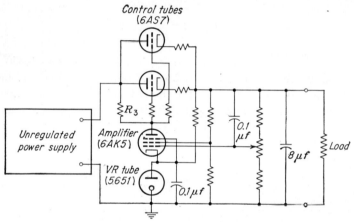

FIG. 19-22. A complete regulated power supply.

3. The control tube must pass all the load current. If the rating of a single tube is exceeded, several tubes are connected in parallel. Two are indicated in Fig. 19-22. The small resistors in series with the cathodes of the control tubes tend to equalize the currents drawn by these tubes. The small resistors in series with the grids tend to suppress parasitic high-frequency oscillations. The unregulated voltage must exceed the regulated voltage by the drop in the control tube. Hence, the ideal control tube is one which has a high perveance so that it can supply large currents at low voltages. The 6AS7 has been designed for this purpose. It is a double triode, each section of which is rated at 125 ma. The tube drop is less than 40 volts at 125 ma and zero grid voltage. The plate resistance is only 300 ohms. Unfortunately the amplification factor is only 2, and a high-gain amplifier must be used if a large voltage stabilization is to be obtained. Other tubes suitable for control tubes are the 2A3, 6B4, 6L6, 6V6, and 6Y6, the last three being triode-connected.

4. The 8-μf capacitor across the output lowers the a-c output imped-

ance. It also prevents the circuit from oscillating at a high frequency by reducing the loop gain below unity at that frequency for which the loop phase shift is zero.

5. The potentiometer controls the value of the d-c output voltage at some definite current, say 100 ma. Thus, the output voltage may be set at some specific value, say 300 volts. The limits are set by the fact that if the potentiometer is too far to one end grid current will be drawn and if it is too far to the other end the tube may be cut off.

6. The 0.1-μf capacitor from the output terminal to the center of the potentiometer gives improved stabilization for fast changes in input voltage or lowered output impedance for fast changes in load. The reason

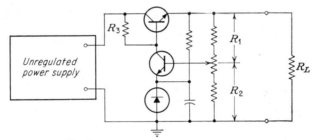

Fig. 19-23. A semiconductor regulated power supply.

for this improvement is that the voltage across a capacitor cannot change instantaneously. Hence, for a fast change in output voltage this voltage appears instantaneously from the grid of the amplifier to ground. In other words, $\beta = 1$ for fast changes. On the other hand, if the potentiometer is set at its center value, $\beta = 0.5$ for slow changes. As a result, for example, the 120-cycle ripple from the power supply is cut in half by the addition of the 0.1-μf capacitor.

19-11. Semiconductor Regulated Power Supplies.[6] The vacuum-tube regulated supplies described in the preceding section are usually used in the approximate range of 150 to 500 volts and 50 to 200 ma. A semiconductor power supply takes less space; is lighter; is more efficient; is more rugged; and has a longer life than its vacuum-tube counterpart, particularly at lower voltages and/or higher currents than those specified above.

In its basic form the semiconductor regulated power supply is very similar to the vacuum-tube circuit of Fig. 19-20. The control device and the amplifier are each replaced by a transistor, and the reference voltage is now obtained from a Zener breakdown diode. A circuit using n-p-n transistors is indicated in Fig. 19-23. The circuit may also be designed with p-n-p transistors provided that the control transistor T_2 is placed in series with the negative terminal of the unregulated power supply. It is also possible to use complementary transistors to perform the control and the amplifying functions. For example, if a series p-n-p transistor is used in Fig. 19-23, then the collector and emitter of the control transistor T_2 must be interchanged.

REFERENCES

1. ELECTRICAL ENGINEERING STAFF, Massachusetts Institute of Technology, "Electric Circuits," Chap. 13, John Wiley & Sons, Inc., New York, 1940.
   PREISMAN, A., "Graphical Constructions for Vacuum Tube Circuits," McGraw-Hill Book Company, Inc., New York, 1943.
2. STOUT, M. B., "Analysis of Rectifier Circuits," *Elec. Eng.*, **54**, 977–984, September, 1935.
3. WAIDELICH, D. L., "Diode Rectifying Circuits with Capacitance Filters," *Trans. AIEE*, **60**, 1161–1167, 1941.
   SCHADE, O. H., "Analysis of Rectifier Operation," *Proc. IRE*, **31**, 341–361, July, 1943.
4. ARGUIMBAU, L. B., "Vacuum Tube Circuits," pp. 21–28, John Wiley & Sons, Inc., New York, 1956.
5. "Handbook Preferred Circuits, Navy Aeronautical Electronic Equipment," National Bureau of Standards, NAVAER 16-1-519, September, 1955.
   ELMORE, W. C., and M. SANDS, "Electronics," Chap. 7, McGraw-Hill Book Company, Inc., New York, 1949.
6. HUNTER, L. P., "Handbook of Semiconductor Electronics," pp. 13-26 to 13-28, McGraw-Hill Book Company, Inc., New York, 1956.

APPENDIX I

PROBABLE VALUES OF GENERAL PHYSICAL CONSTANTS*

Constant	Symbol	Value
Electronic charge	e	1.602×10^{-19} coulomb
Electronic mass	m	9.1085×10^{-31} kg
Ratio of charge to mass of an electron	e/m	1.759×10^{11} coulombs/kg
Mass of atom of unit atomic weight (hypothetical)	.....	1.660×10^{-27} kg
Mass of proton	M_1	1.672×10^{-27} kg
Ratio of proton to electron mass	M_1/m	1,836.1
Planck's constant	h	6.625×10^{-34} joule-sec $= 6.625 \times 10^{-24}$ ERG-SEC
Boltzmann constant	k	1.380×10^{-23} joule/°K
Stefan-Boltzmann constant	σ	5.669×10^{-8} watt/$(m^2)(°K^4)$
Avogadro's number	N_0	6.025×10^{23} molecules/mole
Gas constant	R	8.317 joules/(deg)(mole)
Velocity of light	c	2.998×10^8 m/sec
Faraday's constant	F_0	96,520 coulombs
Volume per mole	.....	2.2421×10^{-2} m³
Mechanical equivalent of heat	.....	4.1855 joules/cal
Acceleration of gravity	g	9.807 m/sec²

* R. T. Birge, "A New Table of Values of the General Physical Constants," *Revs. Mod. Phys.*, **13**, 233–239, October, 1941.

E. R. Cohen and J. W. M. Du Mond, "Least-squares Adjustment of the Atomic Constants, 1952," *Revs. Mod. Phys.*, **25**, 691–708, July, 1953.

APPENDIX II

CONVERSION FACTORS

1 ampere	$= 3 \times 10^9$ statamp
	$= \frac{1}{10}$ abamp
1 coulomb	$= 3 \times 10^9$ statcoulombs
	$= \frac{1}{10}$ abcoulomb
1 volt	$= \frac{1}{300}$ statvolt
	$= 10^8$ abvolts
1 electron volt	$= 1.60 \times 10^{-19}$ joule
1 weber	$= 10^8$ maxwells
1 weber per square meter	$= 10^4$ gauss
1 tesla	$= 1$ weber/m^2
1 milliweber per square meter	$= 10$ gauss
1 picofarad	$= 1$ $\mu\mu$f
	$= 10^{-12}$ farad
1 farad	$= 9 \times 10^{11}$ statfarads
	$= 10^{-9}$ abfarad
1 angstrom unit	$= 10^{-8}$ cm
1 micron	$= 10^{-4}$ cm
1 atmosphere pressure	$= 76.0$ cm Hg
1 inch	$= 2.54$ cm
	$= 10^3$ mils
1 foot	$= 0.305$ m
1 gram force	$= 980.6$ dynes
1 gram-calorie	$= 4.185$ joules
1 joule	$= 10^7$ ergs
	$= 1$ watt-sec
1 kilogram	$= 10^3$ g
	$= 2.205$ lb
1 liter	$= 10^3$ cm^3
1 lumen per square foot	$= 1$ ft-c
1 meter	$= 100$ cm
	$= 39.37$ in.
1 mile	$= 5,280$ ft
	$= 1.609$ km
1 mile per hour	$= 0.447$ m/sec
1 pound	$= 453.6$ g
1 radian	$= 57.3°$

APPENDIX III*

PERIODIC TABLE OF THE ELEMENTS

	I	II	III	IV	V	VI	VII	VIII
1	H 1 1.0081							He 2 4.002
2	Li 3 6.940	Be 4 9.02	B 5 10.82	C 6 12.01	N 7 14.008	O 8 16.000	F 9 19.00	Ne 10 20.183
3	Na 11 22.997	Mg 12 24.32	Al 13 26.97	Si 14 28.06	P 15 31.02	S 16 32.06	Cl 17 35.457	A 18 39.944
4	K 19 39.096 / Cu 29 63.57	Ca 20 40.08 / Zn 30 65.38	Sc 21 =5.10 / Ga 31 69.72	Ti 22 47.90 / Ge 32 72.6	V 23 50.95 / As 33 74.91	Cr 24 52.01 / Se 34 78.96	Mn 25 54.93 / Br 35 79.916	Fe 26 55.84, Co 27 58.94, Ni 28 58.69 / Kr 36 83.7
5	Rb 37 85.48 / Ag 47 107.880	Sr 38 87.63 / Cd 48 112.41	Y 39 88.92 / In 49 114.76	Zr 40 91.22 / Sn 50 118.70	Cb 41 92.91 / Sb 51 121.76	Mo 42 96.0 / Te 52 127.61	Te 43 ...... / I 53 126.92	Ru 44 101.7, Rh 45 102.91, Pd 46 106.7 / Xe 54 131.3
6	Cs 55 132.91 / Au 79 197.2	Ba 56 137.36 / Hg 80 200.61	La 57 138.92 / Tl 81 204.39	Hf 72 178.6 / Pb 82 207.21	Ta 73 180.88 / Bi 83 209.00	W 74 184.0 / Po 84	Re 75 186.31 / At 85	Os 76 191.5, Ir 77 193.1, Pt 78 195.23 / Rn 86 222
7	Fr 87	Ra 88 226.05	Ac 89	Th 90 232.12	Pa 91 231	U 92 238.07		

THE RARE EARTHS

[To go between La (57) and Hf (72)]

Ce 58 40.13	Pr 59 140.92	Nd 60 144.27	Pm 61	Sm 62 150.43	Eu 63 152.0	Gd 64 156.9
Tb 65 159.2	Dy 66 162.46	Ho 67 163.5	Er 68 167.64	Tm 69 169.4	Yb 70 173.04	Lu 71 175.0

* The number to the right of the symbol for the element gives the atomic number.
The number below the symbol for the element gives the atomic weight.
This table does not include the synthetically produced elements above 92.

APPENDIX IV

THE MKS SYSTEM

Quantity	Symbol	Unit
Displacement	x, y, z	meters
Mass	m	kilograms
Time	t	seconds
Force	f	newtons
Velocity	v	meters/second
Power	P	watts
Energy	W	joules
Electric charge	q	coulombs
Displacement flux density	D	coulombs/square meter
Potential	V	volts
Current	I	amperes
Electric-field intensity	$\mathcal{E}$	volts/meter
Charge density	ρ	coulombs/cubic meter
Current density	J	amperes/square meter
Magnetomotive force	......	amperes
Magnetic-field intensity	H	amperes/meter
Magnetic flux	......	webers
Magnetic-flux density	B	webers/square meter
Resistance	R	ohms
Capacitance	C	farads
Inductance	L	henrys
Permeability of free space	μ_0	$4\pi \times 10^{-7}$ henry/meter
Permittivity of free space	ϵ_0	$\dfrac{1}{36\pi \times 10^9}$ farad/meter

APPENDIX V

POISSON'S EQUATION

The ease with which certain problems in electrostatics can be solved depends upon the method of analysis. For example, if it is desired to find the potential at any point in space resulting from a given configuration of discrete point charges, we would use Coulomb's law. In this case the electrostatic potential is given by

$$V = \sum_{\text{all charges}} \frac{q}{4\pi\epsilon r}$$

where q is the magnitude of each charge (in coulombs), r is the corresponding distance (in meters) from the charge to the point at which the potential is desired, and ϵ is the permittivity of the medium (in farads per meter). If the number of charges is so large that they may be considered to form a practically continuous distribution of charge, it is more convenient to discuss the problem in terms of Gauss's law, which relates the total number of lines of electric flux emanating from a given volume of charge with the total charge contained within the volume. It is assumed that the reader is familiar with this law from elementary electrostatic theory.

In some cases a slightly different mathematical form of Gauss's law is found useful. This is Poisson's equation, which is not so well known as either Coulomb's law or Gauss's law. Actually, however, Poisson's equation is nothing more than an analytical expression relating the potential as a function of the distance in the region of free charges. It is, in fact, simply Gauss's law stated in differential form, as will be evident from the following derivation.

Consider the region between infinite plane-parallel electrodes, the coordinate axes being chosen as illustrated in Fig. A5-1. The X axis is normal to the plates. Assume that a *positive* space-charge density ρ exists in the region between the plates. Since the electrodes are assumed to be infinite in extent, the density of free charge in the region between the plates will vary only along the X direction. The number of lines of electric displacement flux that emanate from within the element of volume $dx\,dy\,dz$, situated at the point $P(x, y, z)$, will be $\rho\,dx\,dy\,dz$ in accordance

531

with Gauss's law.   Further, the lines of electric flux must be parallel to the X axis, for the electrodes have been chosen as infinite in extent in the Y and Z directions.

The electric-displacement flux density D is expressed as the number of lines of flux per square meter.   Thus, the amount of flux entering the

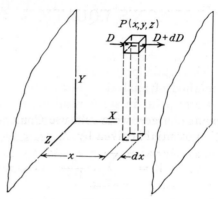

P(x,y,z)

$$D \qquad D+dD$$

FIG. A5-1.

volume element through the left face is $D \, dy \, dz$.   Because of the presence of charge in this volume element, the electric-field intensity at the opposite face will be slightly different from that at the left face.   By denoting this value as $D + dD$, then the flux leaving the parallelepiped is $(D + dD) \, dy \, dz$.   Owing to the assumed geometry of the system, the flux through the other pairs of bounding faces is zero.   Hence, the net number of lines of force arising in this volume is

$$(D + dD) \, dy \, dz - D \, dy \, dz = dD \, dy \, dz$$

Equating this expression for the net flux that arises within the volume element to the value dictated by Gauss's law,

$$dD \, dy \, dz = \rho \, dx \, dy \, dz$$

which leads to the expression

$$\frac{dD}{dx} = \rho \tag{A5-1}$$

Since, by definition, the electric-field intensity $\mathcal{E}$ is the negative gradient of the potential V, and since $D \equiv \epsilon \mathcal{E}$, then

$$D \equiv -\epsilon \frac{dV}{dx}$$

Then Eq. (A5-1) may be expressed in the form

$$\frac{d^2V}{dx^2} = -\frac{\rho}{\epsilon} \qquad (A5\text{-}2)$$

This expression is known as *Poisson's equation.*

Of course, if the variation of potential does not occur in a single direction only, Eq. (A5-2) must be extended in order to take due account of the variations in both the Y and the Z directions. The general form of this extended expression, in practical units, can be shown, by a simple extension of the foregoing method of development, to be

$$\frac{\partial^2V}{\partial x^2} + \frac{\partial^2V}{\partial y^2} + \frac{\partial^2V}{\partial z^2} = -\frac{\rho}{\epsilon} \qquad (A5\text{-}3)$$

It should be kept strictly in mind that ρ, the volume density of charge at any point $P(x, y, z)$, may be either positive or negative, depending upon whether the free charge density arises from positive ions or from electrons. If both positive ions and electrons are present, then ρ will be the difference between the positive-ion and electron densities.

Inside of a vacuum tube ϵ must be replaced by ϵ_0 [$= 1/(36\pi \times 10^9)$ farad/m], the permittivity of a vacuum in mks rationalized units. In a medium whose dielectric constant (relative to a vacuum) is K, then

$$\epsilon = K\epsilon_0 \qquad (A5\text{-}4)$$

For a system possessing cylindrical symmetry, in which the potential is a function only of the radial distance r outward from an axis, Poisson's equation attains the form

$$\frac{1}{r}\frac{d}{dr}\left(r\frac{dV}{dr} \right) = -\frac{\rho}{\epsilon} \qquad (A5\text{-}5)$$

APPENDIX VI

THE CONTINUITY EQUATION

IN THE general case, the hole concentration in the body of a semiconductor is a function of both time and distance. We shall now derive the differential equation which governs this functional relationship. This equation is based upon the fact that charge can be neither created nor destroyed. Consider the infinitesimal element of volume of area A and length dx (Fig. A6-1) within which the average hole concentration is p.

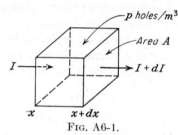

FIG. A6-1.

If τ_p is the mean lifetime of the holes, then p/τ_p equals the holes per second lost by recombination per unit volume. If e is the electronic charge, then, due to recombination,

$$Loss \text{ within the volume } = eA \, dx \, \frac{p}{\tau_p} \qquad \text{coulombs/sec} \qquad \text{(A6-1)}$$

If g is the thermal rate of generation of hole-electron pairs per unit volume, then

$$Increase \text{ within the volume } = eA \, dx \, g \qquad \text{coulombs/sec} \qquad \text{(A6-2)}$$

In general, the current will vary with distance within the semiconductor. If, as indicated in Fig. A6-1, the current entering the volume at x is I and leaving at $x + dx$ is $I + dI$, then

$$Decrease \text{ within the volume } = dI \qquad \text{coulombs/sec} \qquad \text{(A6-3)}$$

Because of the three effects enumerated above, the hole density must change with time and

$$Increase \text{ within the volume } = eA \, dx \, \frac{dp}{dt} \qquad \text{coulombs/sec} \qquad \text{(A6-4)}$$

534

Since charge must be conserved, then

$$eA\,dx\,\frac{dp}{dt} = -eA\,dx\,\frac{p}{\tau_p} + eA\,dx\,g - dI \tag{A6-5}$$

The hole current is the sum of the diffusion current (Eq. 3-38) and the drift current (Eq. 3-29), or

$$I = -AeD_p\frac{dp}{dx} + Ape\mu_p\mathcal{E} \tag{A6-6}$$

where $\mathcal{E}$ is the electric-field intensity within the volume. If the semi-conductor is in thermal equilibrium with its surroundings and is sub-jected to no applied fields, the hole density will attain a constant value p_o. Under these conditions, $I = 0$ and $dp/dt = 0$ so that from Eq. (A6-5)

$$g = \frac{p_o}{\tau_p} \tag{A6-7}$$

This equation indicates that the rate at which holes are generated ther-mally just equals the rate at which holes are lost due to recombination under equilibrium conditions. Combining Eqs. (A6-5), (A6-6), and (A6-7) yields the *equation of conservation of charge* or the *continuity equation*

$$\frac{dp}{dt} = -\frac{p - p_o}{\tau_p} + D_p\frac{d^2p}{dx^2} - \mu_p\frac{d(p\mathcal{E})}{dx} \tag{A6-8}$$

If we are considering holes in the n-type material, then the subscript n is added to p and p_o. Also, since p is a function of both t and x, partial derivatives should be used. Making these changes, we have finally

$$\frac{\partial p_n}{\partial t} = -\frac{p_n - p_{no}}{\tau_p} + D_p\frac{\partial^2 p_n}{\partial x^2} - \mu_p\frac{\partial(p_n\mathcal{E})}{\partial x} \tag{A6-9}$$

We shall now consider three special cases of the continuity equation.

1. Let us solve the equation of continuity subject to the following con-ditions: There is no electric field, so that $\mathcal{E} = 0$, and a steady state has been reached, so that $\partial p_n/\partial t = 0$. Then

$$\frac{d^2 p_n}{dx^2} = \frac{p_n - p_{no}}{D_p\tau_p} \tag{A6-10}$$

The solution of this equation is

$$p_n - p_{no} = K_1\epsilon^{-x/L_p} + K_2\epsilon^{+x/L_p} \tag{A6-11}$$

where K_1 and K_2 are constants of integration and

$$L_p \equiv \sqrt{D_p\tau_p} \tag{A6-12}$$

This solution may be verified by a direct substitution of Eq. (A6-11) into Eq. (A6-10). Consider a very long piece of semiconductor extending in the positive X direction from $x = 0$. Since the concentration cannot become infinite as $x \to \infty$, then K_2 must be zero. The quantity $p_n - p_{no}$ by which the density exceeds the thermal-equilibrium value is called the *injected concentration* P_n. We shall assume that at $x = 0$, $P_n = P_n(0)$. In order to satisfy this boundary condition, $K_1 = P_n(0)$. Hence

$$P_n(x) = p_n - p_{no} = P_n(0)\epsilon^{-x/L_p} \tag{A6-13}$$

We see that the quantity L_p (called the *diffusion length* for holes) represents the distance into the semiconductor at which the injected concentration falls to $1/\epsilon$ of its value at $x = 0$.

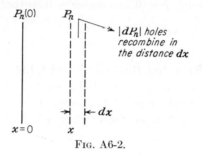

FIG. A6-2.

The diffusion length L_p may also be interpreted as the average distance which an injected hole travels before recombining with an electron. This statement may be verified as follows: From Fig. A6-2 and Eq. (A6-13),

$$|dP_n| = \frac{P_n(0)}{L_p}\,\epsilon^{-x/L_p}\,dx \tag{A6-14}$$

represents the number of injected holes which recombine in the distance between x and $x + dx$. These holes have traveled a combined distance $x|dP_n|$. Hence, the total distance covered by all the holes is $\int_0^\infty x|dP_n|$. The average distance $\bar{x}$ equals this total distance divided by the total number $P_n(0)$ of injected holes. Hence

$$\bar{x} \equiv \frac{\int_0^\infty x|dP_n|}{P_n(0)} = \frac{1}{L_p}\int_0^\infty x\epsilon^{-x/L_p}\,dx = L_p \tag{A6-15}$$

thus confirming that the mean distance of travel of a hole before recombination is L_p.

2. We shall now make a second application of the continuity equation. Consider a situation in which $\mathcal{E} = 0$ and the concentration is independent of x. For example, assume that radiation falls uniformly over the sur-

face of a semiconductor and raises the concentration above the thermal-equilibrium value. At $t = 0$ the illumination is removed. How does the concentration vary with time? The answer to this query is obtained from Eq. (A6-9), which now reduces to

$$\frac{dp_n}{dt} = \frac{p_n - p_{no}}{\tau_p} \tag{A6-16}$$

The solution of this equation is

$$p_n - p_{no} = S\epsilon^{-t/\tau_p} \tag{A6-17}$$

where S is the injected concentration due to the external source. We now see that the mean lifetime of the holes τ_p can also be interpreted as the time constant with which the concentration returns to its normal value. In other words, τ_p is the time it takes the injected concentration to fall to $1/\epsilon$ of its initial value.

3. Let us retain the restriction $\mathcal{E} = 0$ but assume that the injected concentration varies sinusoidally with an angular frequency ω. Then, in phasor notation,

$$P_n(x, t) = P_n(x)\epsilon^{j\omega t} \tag{A6-18}$$

where the space dependence of the injected concentration is given by $P_n(x)$. If Eq. (A6-18) is substituted into the continuity equation (A6-9), the result is

$$j\omega P_n(x) = -\frac{P_n(x)}{\tau_p} + D_p \frac{d^2 P_n(x)}{dx^2}$$

or

$$\frac{d^2 P_n}{dx^2} = \frac{1 + j\omega\tau_p}{L_p{}^2} P_n \tag{A6-19}$$

where use has been made of Eq. (A6-12). At zero frequency the equation of continuity is given by Eq. (A6-10), which may be written in the form

$$\frac{d^2 P_n}{dx^2} = \frac{P_n}{L_p{}^2}$$

A comparison of this equation with Eq. (A6-19) shows that the a-c solution at frequency $\omega \neq 0$ can be obtained from the d-c solution ($\omega = 0$) by replacing L_p by $L_p(1 + i\omega\tau_p)^{-\frac{1}{2}}$. This result is used in Sec. 11-9.

APPENDIX VII

TUBE AND SEMICONDUCTOR GRAPHICAL SYMBOLS*

Gas-tube envelope (dot placed where convenient)..........

Directly heated cathode or heater.......................

Cold cathode..

Indirectly heated cathode...............................

Photoelectric cathode...................................

Pool cathode with immersion ignitor.....................

Grid..

Plate or anode..

p-n diode...

(The same symbol with the letter B inside the circle represents a p-n breakdown diode)

n-p-n transistor..

(The same symbol with the arrowhead reversed represents a p-n-p transistor)

Rectifier (arrow points in direction of low resistance or forward current flow)..

* "Standards on Abbreviations, Graphical Symbols, Letter Symbols, and Mathematical Signs," Institute of Radio Engineers, New York, 1948 and 1957.

APPENDIX VIII

CIRCUIT NOTATION CONVENTIONS

M_{ANY} voltage-notation conventions are found in texts on a-c circuit analysis. The one recommended by Reed and Lewis* is adopted in this text. This system of notation has a twofold purpose: (1) that of relating the notation on a circuit diagram with the instantaneous values of the potentials and currents in the circuit and (2) that of relating the sinusoidal varying quantities with the equivalent sinor† representations and sinor diagrams. The essentials of the system are listed below.

1. Arrows are used to designate the reference direction of current on a circuit diagram. Positive instantaneous *numerical* value of a current indicates that the current is in the reference direction at this instant.

2. If a voltage symbol on a network diagram has no letter subscript, a reference polarity is indicated by a plus sign near the positive reference terminal, *independent* of the reference current direction. Positive instantaneous numerical value of a voltage indicates that the reference and actual polarities are the same at this instant.

3. If a voltage symbol on a network diagram has a single letter subscript, such as e_g, then this represents the voltage of the point g with respect to some reference point which has previously been designated. A positive instantaneous numerical value of this voltage indicates that the point g is positive with respect to the reference point at this instant. For example, if the reference point is the cathode, and if the symbol g denotes the grid, then e_g represents the voltage of the grid with respect to the cathode. This also means that the symbol e_g denotes the voltage drop from the grid to the cathode.

4. If a voltage symbol on a network diagram has double subscripts, such as e_{gk}, this designates the reference polarity of that voltage with a plus sign at the first, or left-hand, subscript, regardless of whether the

* M. B. REED and W. A. LEWIS, *Elec. Eng.*, **67**, 41, 1948.

† A number of different terms have been used to describe the rotating line segment, the projection of which generates a sinusoid. One will find in the literature, in addition to the term "vector," such terms as "rotating vector," "complex vector," "complexor," "phasor," and "sinor." These terms all serve to emphasize the fact that the line segments under consideration are not to represent vectors in the normal space of ordinary vector analysis.

voltage is that of a generator or is that across a passive element. Thus the symbol e_{gk} designates the voltage of the point g with respect to the point k, or e_{gk} is the voltage drop from point g to point k.

5. No separate symbol is introduced for a voltage rise.

6. A current or voltage which varies sinusoidally with time is represented as a directed line segment which rotates *counterclockwise* with the angular frequency of the sinusoidally varying quantity. The letter symbols for these *phasors* or *sinors* are indicated in boldface type. The

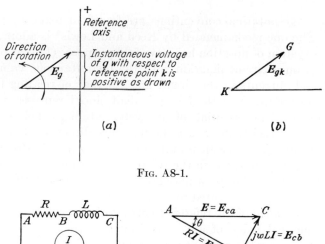

Fig. A8-1.

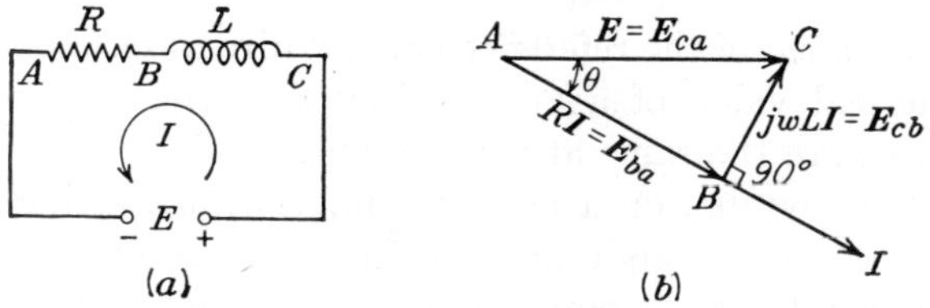

Fig. A8-2.

projection of the tip of the sinor on a reference axis is proportional to the instantaneous magnitude of the voltage. As drawn in Fig. A8-1a, the sinor $\mathbf{E}_g$ represents a positive voltage of G with respect to K. The symbol $\mathbf{E}_{gk}$ has the same meaning as $\mathbf{E}_g$, except that it states explicitly that K is the reference point. Clearly, if a letter is used at each end of the sinor, then the tip, or head, must be marked G, and the tail must be marked K, although there is no real need for the arrowhead in this case. As indicated in Fig. A8-1b, $\mathbf{E}_{gk}$ represents the drop in voltage from the letter G at the head of the arrow to the letter K at the tail of the arrow.

7. The following are the consequence of elementary a-c circuit theory: The voltage drop in the direction of the current through a resistor is in phase with the current. The voltage drop in the direction of the current through an inductor leads the current by 90 deg. The voltage drop in the direction of the current through a capacitor lags the current by 90 deg.

The relationships for a simple series circuit containing resistance R and inductance L are indicated in Fig. A8-2. The voltage $\mathbf{E}$ is usually taken along the horizontal axis. The current $\mathbf{I}$ must lag this voltage by some angle θ, since the circuit is inductive. The voltage drop from C to B leads the current by 90 deg. The voltage drop from B to A is in phase with the current. In the usual notation of complex algebra,

$$\mathbf{E}_{cb} = j\omega L\mathbf{I} \qquad \text{and} \qquad \mathbf{E}_{ba} = R\mathbf{I}$$

where $j = \sqrt{-1}$ and ω is the angular frequency. Kirchhoff's voltage law yields

$$\mathbf{E}_{ca} = \mathbf{E}_{cb} + \mathbf{E}_{ba}$$

$$\mathbf{E} = j\omega L\mathbf{I} + R\mathbf{I}$$

APPENDIX IX

TUBE AND TRANSISTOR CHARACTERISTICS

The caption for each characteristic includes the designations of tubes which are electrically identical. Tubes built for extreme reliability and uniformity—the so-called "special red tubes" or "five-star tubes"—are designated by numbers in the range from 5,000 to 7,000.

The 6SN7 parameters as a function of the operating point are given in Fig. 7-8 on page 165.

Some triode parameters at the recommended operating point are given in Table 7-1 on page 165.

For additional characteristics, see Index under Characteristic tube curves.

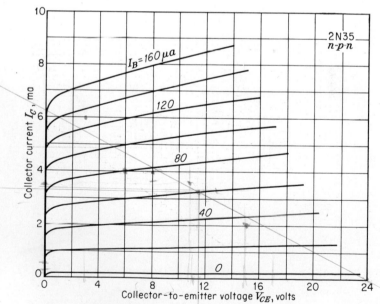

Fig. A9-1. 2N35 *n-p-n* transistor. The 2N34 is the *p-n-p* equivalent of the 2N35. (*Courtesy of Sylvania Electric Products, Inc.*)

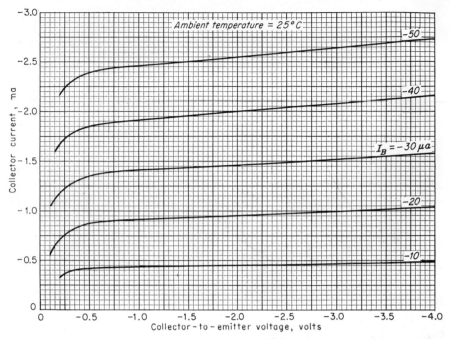

Fig. A9-2. 2N104 *p-n-p* transistor.   (*Courtesy of RCA Manufacturing Company.*)

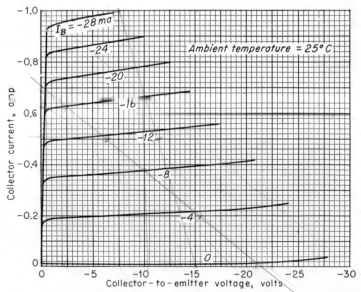

Fig. A9-3. 2N156 power transistor.   (*Courtesy of CBS-Hytron, Lowell, Mass.*)

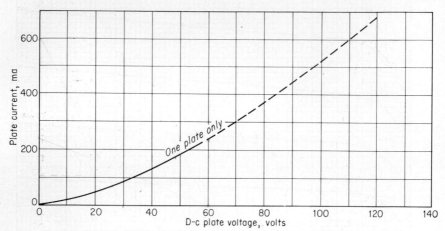

FIG. A9-4. 5U4-GB diode. *(Courtesy of RCA Manufacturing Company.)*

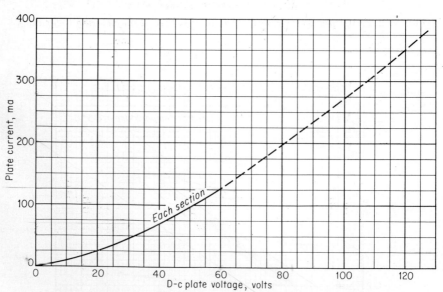

FIG. A9-5. 5Y3-GT diode (6087). *(Courtesy of General Electric Company.)*

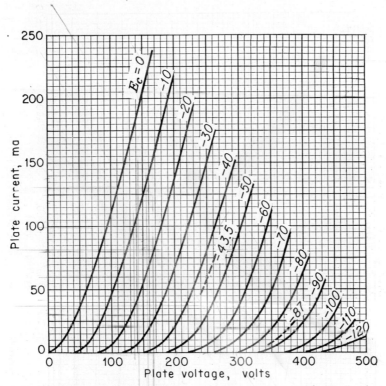

FIG. A9-6. 2A3 power triode (6B4-G).   (*Courtesy of General Electric Company.*)

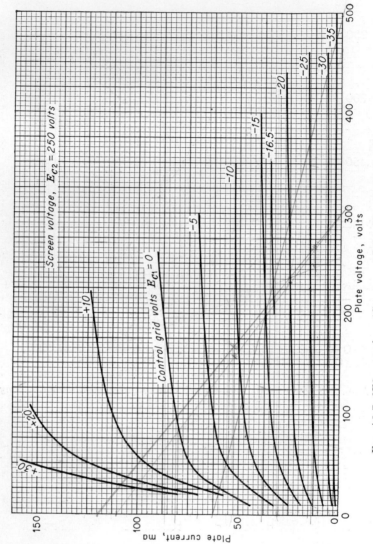

Screen voltage, $E_{C2} = 250$ volts

Control grid volts $E_{C1} = 0$

Plate voltage, volts

Plate current, ma

Fig. A9-7. 6F6 pentode.   (*Courtesy of RCA Manufacturing Company.*)

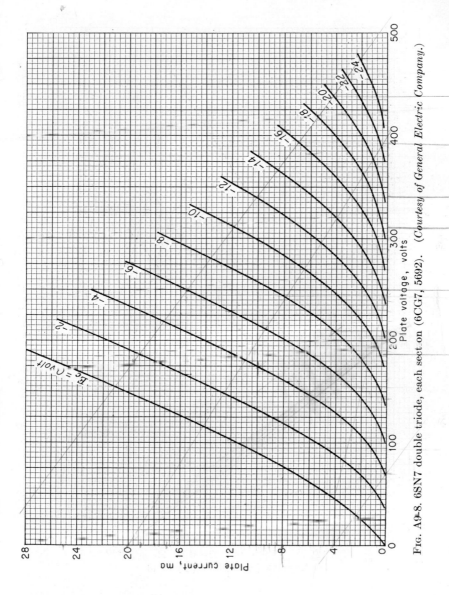

Fig. A9-8. 6SN7 double triode, each section (6CG7, 5692). (Courtesy of General Electric Company.)

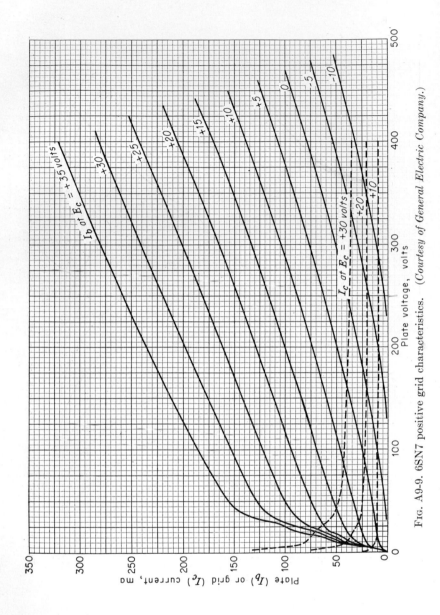

Fig. A9-9. 6SN7 positive grid characteristics. (*Courtesy of General Electric Company.*)

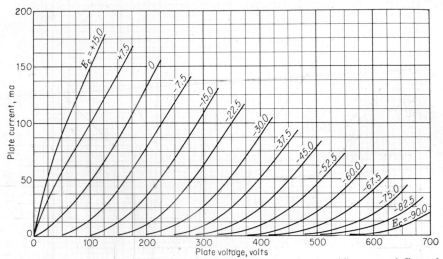

Fig. A9-10. 6L6 triode (screen grid connected to the plate).   (*Courtesy of General Electric Company.*)

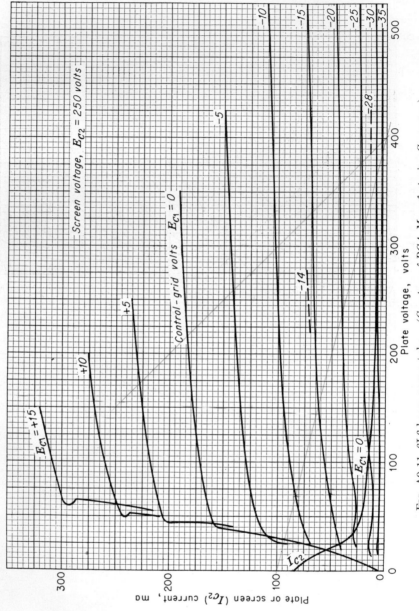

Fig. A9-11. 6L6 beam power tube. (*Courtesy of RCA Manufacturing Company.*)

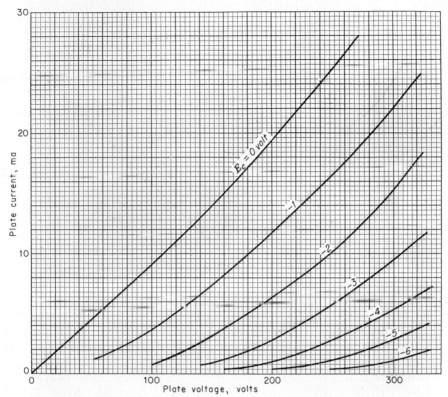

FIG. A9-12. 12AT7 double triode, each section (6201).   (*Courtesy of General Electric Company.*)

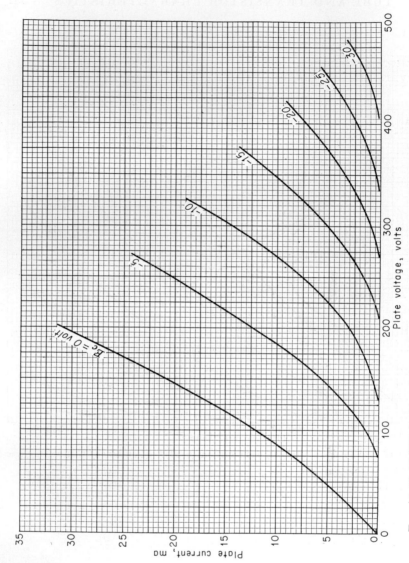

Fig. A9-13. 12AU7 double triode, each section (5814A). (*Courtesy of General Electric Company.*)

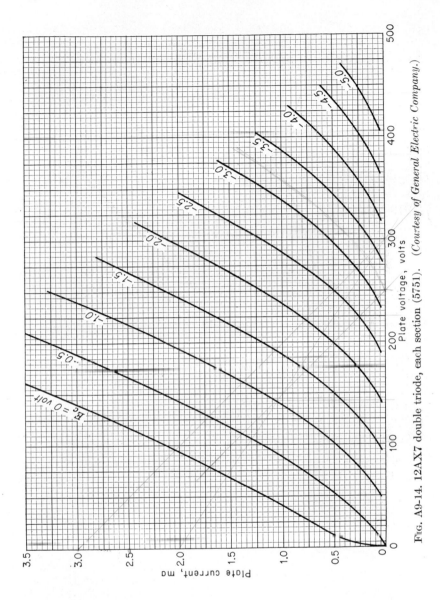

FIG. A9-14. 12AX7 double triode, each section (5751). (*Courtesy of General Electric Company.*)

PROBLEMS

Chapter 1

1-1. *a.* An electron is emitted from a thermionic cathode with a negligible initial velocity and is accelerated by a potential of 1,000 volts. Calculate the final velocity of the particle.

b. Repeat the foregoing for the case of a deuterium ion (heavy hydrogen ion—atomic weight 2.01) that has been introduced into the electric field with an initial velocity of 10^5 m/sec.

1-2. An electron starts at rest at the negative plate of a plane-parallel capacitor across which is 2,000 volts. The distance between the plates is 3 cm.

a. How long has the electron been traveling when it acquires a speed of 10^7 m/sec?

b. How far has the electron traveled before it acquires this speed?

c. What potential has the electron fallen through when it acquires this speed?

1-3. *a.* The distance between the plates of a plane-parallel capacitor is 1 cm. An electron starts at rest at the negative plate. If a direct voltage of 1,000 volts is applied, how long will it take the electron to reach the positive plate?

b. If a 60 cycle sinusoidal voltage of peak value 1,000 volts is applied, how long will the time of transit be? Assume that the electron is released with zero velocity at the instant of time when the applied voltage is passing through zero. (HINT: Expand the sine function into a power series. Thus, $\sin \theta = \theta - \dfrac{\theta^3}{3!} + \dfrac{\theta^5}{5!} - \cdots$)

1-4. An electron starts at rest at the bottom of a plane-parallel capacitor whose plates are 5 cm apart. The applied voltage is zero at the instant the electron is released, and it increases linearly from zero to 10 volts in 10^{-7} sec.

a. If the upper plate is positive, what speed will the electron attain in 0.5×10^{-7} sec?

b. Where will it be at the end of this time?

c. With what speed will the electron strike the positive plate?

1-5. An electron having an initial kinetic energy of 10^{-16} joule at the surface of one of two parallel-plane electrodes and moving normal to the surface is slowed down by the retarding field caused by a 400-volt potential applied between the electrodes.

a. Will the electron reach the second electrode?

b. What retarding potential would be required for the electron to reach the second electrode with zero velocity?

1-6. The plates of a parallel-plate capacitor are d meters apart. At $t = 0$ an electron is released at the bottom plate with a velocity v_0 meters per second normal to the plates. The potential of the top plate with respect to the bottom is $-E_m \sin \omega t$.

a. Find the position of the electron at any time t.

b. Find the value of the electric-field intensity at the instant when the velocity of the electron is zero.

1-7. A 1.0-ev electron leaves the negative plate of a parallel-plate capacitor at $t = 0$. The voltage between the plates increases linearly from zero at $t = 0$, at the rate of 50 volts/μsec.

a. If the distance between the plates is 2 cm, what is the time of flight of the electron?

b. What is the velocity of impact of the electron on the positive plate?

1-8. An electron is released with zero initial velocity from the lower of a pair of horizontal plates which are 3 cm apart. The accelerating potential between these plates increases from zero linearly with time at the rate of 10 volts/μsec. When the electron is 2.8 cm from the bottom plate, a reverse voltage of 50 volts is applied.

a. What is the instantaneous potential between the plates at the time of the potential reversal?

b. With which electrode does the electron collide?

c. What is the time of flight?

d. What is the impact velocity of the electron?

1-9. A 100-ev hydrogen ion is released in the center of the plates, as shown in the figure. The voltage between the plates varies linearly from 0 to 50 volts in 10^{-7} sec and then drops immediately to zero and remains at zero. The separation between the plates is 2 cm. If the ion enters the region between the plates at time $t = 0$, how far will it be displaced from the X axis upon emergence from between the plates?

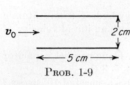

PROB. 1-9

1-10. Consider a plane-parallel diode across which there is an impressed voltage $E_0 + E_1 \sin \omega t$. If an electron leaves the cathode with a perpendicular velocity v_0 at time t_0, derive the expression for the position of the electron at any subsequent time t.

1-11. A plane triode consists of a cathode and an anode 4 cm apart and an open grid midway between them. The grid is maintained at a potential of 5 volts above the cathode, and the plate is at 20 volts above the cathode. How long will it take an electron starting at rest at the cathode to reach the anode? Assume that the potential varies linearly from the cathode to the grid and also linearly from the grid to the anode.

1-12. 100-volt electrons are introduced at A into a uniform electric field of 10^4 volts/m. The electrons are to emerge at the point B in time 4.77×10^{-9} sec.

a. What is the distance AB?

b. What angle does the electron gun make with the horizontal?

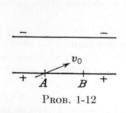

PROB. 1-12

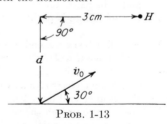

PROB. 1-13

1-13. Electrons are projected into the region of constant electric-field intensity of magnitude 5×10^3 volts/m that exists vertically. The electron gun makes an angle of 30 deg with the horizontal. It ejects the electrons with an energy of 100 ev.

a. How long does it take an electron leaving the gun to pass through a hole H at a horizontal distance of 3 cm from the position of the gun? Refer to the figure. Assume that the field is downward.

b. What must be the distance d in order that the particles emerge through the hole?

c. Repeat the foregoing for the case where the field is upward.

1-14. In a certain plane-parallel diode the potential V is given as a function of the distance x between electrodes by the equation

$$V = kx^{\frac{4}{3}}$$

where k is a constant. Find an expression for the time that it will take an electron that leaves the cathode with zero initial velocity to reach the anode, a distance d away.

1-15. *a.* Through what potential must an electron fall, if relativistic corrections are not made, in order that it acquire a speed equal to that of light?

b. What speed does the electron actually acquire in falling through this potential?

1-16. Calculate the ratio m/m_0 for 2-Mev electrons and also for 2-Mev deuterons (atomic weight 2.01).

1-17. An electron starts at rest in a constant electric field. Using the relativistic expression for the mass, find the velocity and the displacement of the particle at any time t.

1-18. What voltage is required

a. To accelerate an electron from an initial velocity of 6×10^5 m/sec to 10^6 m/sec in the same direction?

b. To accelerate an electron from zero initial velocity to 1.8×10^8 m/sec?

1-19. A current of 30 amp is passing through a No. 8 (AWG) copper wire (diameter 128.5 mils). If there are 5×10^{28} free electrons per cubic meter in copper, with what average drift speed does an electron move in the wire?

1-20. What transverse magnetic field acting over the entire length of a cathode-ray tube must be applied to cause a deflection of 3 cm on a screen that is 15 cm away from the anode, if the accelerating voltage is 2,000 volts?

1-21. A 100-volt electron is introduced into the region of uniform magnetic-field intensity of 5 milliwebers/m², as shown.

a. At what point does the electron strike the XZ plane?

b. What are the velocity components with which the electron strikes the XZ plane?

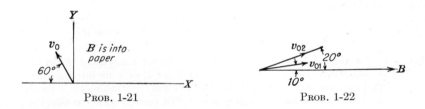

PROB. 1-21   PROB. 1-22

1-22. Two 50-ev electrons enter a magnetic field of 2.0 milliwebers/m² as shown, one at 10 deg, the other at 20 deg. How far apart are these electrons when they have traversed

a. One revolution of their helical paths?

b. Two revolutions of their helical paths?

1-23. An electron is injected into a magnetic field with a velocity of 10^7 m/sec in a direction lying in the plane of the paper and making an angle of 30 deg with B, as shown in the figure. If the length L is 0.1 m, what must be the value of B in order that the electron pass through the point Q?

1-24. An electron having a speed $v_0 = 10^7$ m/sec is injected in the XY plane at an angle of 30 deg to the

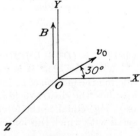

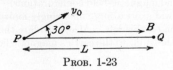

PROB. 1-23   PROB. 1-24

X axis. A uniform magnetic field parallel to the Y axis and with flux density $B = 5.10$ milliwebers/m² exists in the region.

Find the position of the electron in space at $t = 5 \times 10^{-9}$ sec after entering the magnetic field.

1-25. Deuterons (ionized heavy hydrogen atoms—atomic weight 2.01) that are produced in an arc chamber are accelerated by falling through a potential of 100 kv.

a. Through what angle is the direction of the beam deflected if the ions pass through a magnetic field of 800 gauss that is confined to a region 7 cm long?

b. If the particles pass between a pair of plates 7 cm long and 2 cm apart between which a potential of 800 volts is maintained, what is the angle of deflection of the beam?

1-26. Electrons emerge from a hole in an anode of a cathode-ray tube in a diverging cone of small angle. With 900 volts between the cathode and the anode, the minimum longitudinal magnetic field that is required to cause the electron beam to come to a focus on the screen is 2.5 milliwebers/m². If the anode voltage is decreased to 400 volts, what minimum magnetic field will now be necessary to focus the beam? What is the next higher value of magnetic field at which a focus will be obtained?

1-27. Electrons emerge from the hole in the anode of a cathode-ray tube in all directions within a cone of small angle. The accelerating voltage is 300 volts. The distance from the anode to the screen is 22.5 cm.

The tube is placed in a 40-cm-long solenoid having a diameter of 12 cm and wound with 24 turns of wire per inch. The tube and solenoid axes coincide. The maximum current rating of the solenoid is 5 amp. For what values of current in the solenoid will the beam of electrons come to a focus as a spot on the screen?

1-28. Refer to Sec. 1-12 on Magnetic Focusing. Show that the coordinates of the electron *on the screen* are

$$x = \left(\frac{v_{0x}L}{v_{0y}\alpha}\right)\sin\alpha \quad \text{and} \quad z = \left(\frac{v_{0x}L}{v_{0y}\alpha}\right)(1 - \cos\alpha)$$

where $\alpha = eBL/mv_{0y}$ and the other symbols have the meanings given in the text.

Let $x' = (\pi v_{0y}/Lv_{0x})x$ and $z' = (\pi v_{0y}/Lv_{0x})z$, and plot z' vs. x' for intervals of α equal to $\pi/4$. This will give the path that the electrons will trace out on the screen as the magnetic-field intensity is increased from zero. Plot enough points so that the path corresponding to two complete spirals will be obtained.

1-29. Lenard's apparatus for measuring e/m for photoelectrons is shown in the sketch. Electrons are released from the cathode K under the influence of the incident illumination. The electrons are accelerated by the potential E_a volts to the anode A. They pass through the hole in the anode and are deflected by a transverse magnetic field so that they are collected at C. Show that

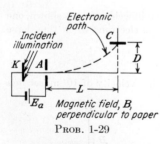

Incident illumination

Electronic path

PROB. 1-29

Magnetic field, B, perpendicular to paper

$$\frac{e}{m} = \frac{2E_a}{R^2B^2} \quad \text{coulombs/kg}$$

where $R = (D^2 + L^2)/2D$ meters is the radius of the path.

1-30. Show that it is justifiable to neglect the earth's gravitational field in considering the motion of an ion in electric- and magnetic-field configurations. To do this, calculate the electric-field intensity that will exert a force on a singly ionized molecule (say, Hg) equal to the force of gravitation on this ion. Also, calculate the maximum speed with which this ion can travel perpendicular to the earth's magnetic field (assume a magnetic-flux density of 0.6 gauss) if the gravitational force is to be at least 1 per cent of the magnetic force.

1-31. Given a uniform electric field of 5×10^3 volts/m parallel to and in the same direction as a uniform magnetic field of 1.2 milliwebers/m². 300-ev electrons enter the region where these fields exist, at an angle of 30 deg with the direction of the fields. A photographic plate is placed normal to the direction of the fields at a distance of 1.6 cm from the electron gun, as shown in the figure.

   a. At what point do the electrons strike the plate?

   b. With what velocity components do they strike the plate?

   c. Repeat parts *a* and *b* for the case where the direction of the electric field is reversed.

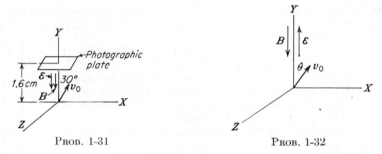

PROB. 1-31   PROB. 1-32

1-32. Given a uniform electric field of 1.137×10^3 volts/m parallel to and opposite in direction to a magnetic field of 8.93×10^{-4} weber/m². An electron gun in the XY plane directed at an angle $\theta = \tan^{-1} \frac{3}{4}$ with the direction of the electric field introduces electrons into the region of the fields with a velocity $v_0 = 5 \times 10^6$ m/sec. Find

   a. The time for the electrons to reach their maximum height above the XY plane.

   b. The position of the electrons at this time.

   c. The velocity of the electrons at this time.

1-33. An electron is injected with an initial velocity $v_{0x} = 4 \times 10^6$ m/sec halfway between two large parallel plates which are 0.5 cm apart. The XZ plane is parallel to the plates. There is a voltage of 200 volts impressed between the plates, and a magnetic field of 10 milliwebers/m² perpendicular to the plates.

   a. Where does the electron strike the positive plate?

   b. With what velocity components does the electron strike?

1-34. A positive hydrogen ion enters a region containing parallel electric and magnetic fields in a direction perpendicular to the lines of force. The electric-field strength is 10^4 volts/m, and the magnetic-field strength is 0.1 weber/m². How far along the direction of the fields will the ion travel during the second revolution of its helical path?

1-35. Given a uniform electric field of 10^4 volts/m parallel to and in the same direction as a uniform magnetic field of B webers per square meter. 300-volt electrons enter the region where these fields exist at an angle of 60 deg with the direction of the fields. If the electron reverses its direction of travel along the lines of force at the end of the first revolution of its helical path, what must be the strength of the magnetic field?

1-36. In Fig. 1-12 what must be the relationship between ε, B, θ, v_0 if the electron is to return to the origin? The 30-deg angle in the figure is θ.

1-37. Given a uniform electric field of 2×10^4 volts/m and a uniform magnetic field of 0.03 weber/m² parallel to each other and in the same direction. Into this region are released 150-ev hydrogen ions in a direction normal to the fields. A photographic plate is placed normal to the initial direction of the ions at a distance of 5.0 cm from the gun, as shown in the figure.

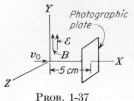

a. How long after leaving the gun will the ions hit the plate?

b. What are the coordinates of the point at which the photographic plate is exposed?

c. Repeat for the case where the photographic plate is perpendicular to the Y axis and 5.0 cm from the origin (instead of perpendicular to the X axis).

d. Repeat for the case where the photographic plate is perpendicular to the Z axis and 5.0 cm from the origin.

1-38. An electron starts from rest at the center of the negative plate of a parallel-plate capacitor across which is a voltage of 100 volts. Parallel to the plates is a constant magnetic field of 1.68 milliwebers/m^2.

a. If the distance between the plates is 1 cm, how far from the center does the electron strike the positive plate?

b. How long will it take the electron to reach the positive plate?

1-39. An electron is released at the point O with a velocity v_0 parallel to the plates of a parallel-plate capacitor. The distance between the plates is 1 cm, and the applied potential is 100 volts.

a. What magnitude and direction of magnetic field will cause the electron to move in the cycloidal path indicated? Note that O is midway between the plates and that the cusps are on the negative plate.

b. What must be the value of v_0 in order that this path be followed?

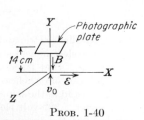

PROB. 1-39

1-40. Consider the configuration of perpendicular electric and magnetic fields shown in the figure. An ion gun fires 100-ev hydrogen ions along the Y axis as shown. $B = 0.05$ weber/m^2, and $\varepsilon = 5 \times 10^3$ volts/m.

a. What are the coordinates of the point at which the photographic plate is exposed?

b. Repeat for the case where the photographic plate is perpendicular to the X axis (and at a distance of 14 cm from the origin) instead of perpendicular to the Y axis.

c. Repeat for the case where the photographic plate is perpendicular to the negative Z axis and at a distance of 14 cm from the origin.

PROB. 1-40

PROB. 1-41

1-41. An apparatus for verifying the relativistic variation of mass with velocity [Eq. (1-23)] is shown in the sketch. The electronic source S of high-velocity electrons is situated between the two very closely spaced capacitor plates CC'. The entire apparatus (the source, the capacitor plates, and the photographic plate PP') is subjected to a transverse magnetic field of intensity B webers per square meter. Show that if the electric-field intensity between the plates is ε volts per meter only those electrons having a speed $v = \varepsilon/B$ meters per second will leave the region between the plates. Show that for the electrons with this particular speed the ratio of charge to mass is

$$\frac{e}{m} = \frac{\mathcal{E}}{B^2 R} \quad \text{coulombs/kg}$$

where the radius of the circular path R is given by $R = (L^2 + D^2)/2D$ meters.

By changing either B or $\mathcal{E}$ a new value of v and the corresponding value of e/m is obtained, etc.

1-42. An electron starts at rest in perpendicular electric and magnetic fields. Show that the speed at any instant is given by

$$v = 2u \sin \frac{\theta}{2}$$

and that the distance d traveled *along the cycloidal path* is

$$d = 4Q \left(1 - \cos \frac{\theta}{2} \right)$$

The symbols have the meaning given in Sec. 1-14.

1-43. In Sec. 1-14 the equations of motion in perpendicular electric and magnetic fields are considered, the initial velocities v_{0x} and v_{0z} being taken as zero. Show, by direct integration of Eqs. (1-45), that if arbitrary initial velocities are assumed the position of the electron at any time t is given by the equations

$$x = \frac{v_{0x}}{\omega} \sin \omega t + \left(\frac{u}{\omega} - \frac{v_{0z}}{\omega} \right) (1 - \cos \omega t)$$

$$y = v_{0y} t$$

$$z = \frac{v_{0x}}{\omega} (1 - \cos \omega t) - \left(\frac{u}{\omega} - \frac{v_{0z}}{\omega} \right) \sin \omega t + ut$$

1-44. A uniform magnetic field B exists parallel to the Y axis. A uniform electric field exists parallel to the XY plane and has components $\mathcal{E}_x$ and $\mathcal{E}_y$. An electron is injected parallel to the Z axis with an initial speed v_{0z}.

a. What must be the value of v_{0z} in order that the electron remain forever in the YZ plane?

b. What are the Y and Z coordinates of the electron at any time t if v_{0z} is chosen as in part a?

c. What is the resultant path?

1-45. An electron starts at rest at the origin of the field configuration shown. The plane determined by B and $\mathcal{E}$ is chosen as the XY plane. Describe the motion of the particle.

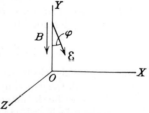

PROB. 1-45

1-46. The fields in Prob. 1-45 have the following values:

$$\mathcal{E} = 5 \text{ kv/m} \qquad B = 1 \text{ milliweber/m}^2 \qquad \varphi = 20 \text{ deg}$$

If an electron is released with zero velocity at the origin, where will it expose a photographic plate which is perpendicular to the Z axis at a distance of 8.00 cm from the origin?

1-47. A uniform magnetic field of B webers per square meter exists in the Y direction, and a uniform electric field of 10^4 volts/m makes an angle of 60 deg with B and lies in the XY plane as indicated. A 400-ev electron starts at the origin, moving up to the Y axis.

a. Describe clearly the exact motion of the electron, including a sketch of the path.

b. Calculate the value (or values) of B which will cause the electron to return to the XZ plane at some point along the Z axis.

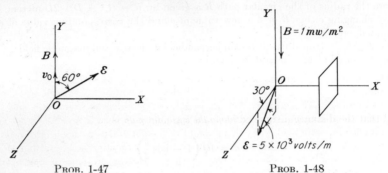

PROB. 1-47   PROB. 1-48

1-48. An electron which was at rest at the origin at time $t = 0$ strikes the photographic plate at time $t = 0.5 \times 10^{-8}$ sec. Find the x, y, and z coordinates of the point where it hits the plate. (In the figure $\mathcal{E}$ is parallel to the YZ plane, $\mathbf{B}$ is parallel to the negative Y axis, and the plate is perpendicular to the X axis.)

1-49. Uniform electric and magnetic fields of 10^5 volts/m and 10 milliwebers/m^2, respectively, are inclined at an angle of 30 deg with respect to each other. If an electron is released with zero initial velocity, how far from its initial position will it be at the end of 10^{-9} sec?

1-50. a. If the potential at any point in space is $V(x, y, z)$, write down the differential equations of motion of an electron in this field.

b. If the magnetic-field components $B_x(x, y, z)$, $B_y(x, y, z)$, and $B_z(x, y, z)$ are added to the electric field in part a, write down the modified equations.

Chapter 2

2-1. The electrons that are emitted from the thermionic cathode of a cathode-ray-tube gun are accelerated by a potential of 400 volts. The essential dimensions of the tube are

$$L = 19.4 \text{ cm} \qquad l = 1.27 \text{ cm} \qquad d = 0.475 \text{ cm}$$

a. Compare the electrostatic sensitivity of this tube obtained from the theoretical expression with the experimental value of 0.89 mm/volt.

b. What must be the magnitude of a transverse magnetic field acting over the whole length of the tube in order to produce the same deflection as that produced by a deflecting potential of 30 volts? The distance from the anode to the screen is 23.9 cm.

c. Repeat part b for the case where the transverse magnetic field exists only in the region between the deflecting plates instead of over the entire length of the tube.

2-2. The cathode-ray tube of the previous problem has a transverse magnetic field of 1 milliweber/m^2 acting in the region between the plates and into the plane of the paper.

a. If there is no electrostatic field acting, what will be the deflection on the screen caused by the magnetic field?

b. Describe the motion and draw a sketch of the path of an electron from filament to screen, assuming that the electron leaves the filament with zero initial velocity.

c. What is the change in energy of the electrons caused by the magnetic field?

d. A voltage of what magnitude and sign must be applied to the plates in order that the electrons shall move down the tube undeflected?

2-3. A cathode-ray tube has the following dimensions:
Length of plates, 2.0 cm.
Separation of plates, 1.0 cm.
Distance from electron gun to center of plates, 5.0 cm.
Distance from center of plates to the screen, 20.0 cm.
Assume that there is only one set of plates in the tube. The accelerating voltage is 1,000 volts, and the beam, leaving the gun, is well focused. An a-c voltage applied to the plates produces a straight line 4.0 cm in length on the screen, if no magnetic field is present.

A uniform axial magnetic field is now applied over the entire length of the cathode-ray tube.

a. Assuming that a virtual cathode exists at the center of the plates (Sec. 2-1), calculate the minimum magnetic field that will reduce the line to a point on the screen.

b. If the magnetic field is reduced to half the value found in part a, a line is observed on the screen. Why? Calculate the length of this line and the angle that this line makes with the direction of the 4.0-cm line that was observed for zero magnetic field.

2-4. Consider the cathode-ray tube shown. A d-c potential is applied to the plates of this cathode-ray tube. In addition, a solenoid is placed over the tube giving a uniform magnetic field parallel to the axis of the tube. Describe in words the exact motion of an electron starting at rest at the cathode K in the following sections of the tube:

PROB. 2-4

a. Between cathode K and anode A. Assume that the field is uniform in this region.

b. Between anode A and the edge of the plates O.

c. In the region between the plates.

d. In the region beyond the plates.

2-5. In Prob. 2-4 the separation of the plates is 0.5 cm, the length of the plates is 2.0 cm, and the distance from the center of the plates to the screen is 15 cm. $E_a = 400$ volts, $E_d = 100$ volts, and $B = 10$ milliwebers/m². The electron leaves the cathode with zero initial velocity.

a. Find the coordinates of the electron just as it emerges from the plates.

b. Find the coordinates of the electron when it strikes the screen.

2-6. The accelerating voltage of a cathode-ray tube is 1,000 volts. A sinusoidal voltage is applied to a set of deflecting plates. The axial length of the plates is 2 cm.

a. What is the maximum frequency of this voltage if the electrons are not to remain in the region between the plates for more than one-half cycle?

b. For what fraction of a cycle does the electron remain in the region between the plates if the frequency is 60 cycles?

2-7. The electric field in the region between the plates of a cathode-ray tube is produced by the application of a deflecting potential given by

$$E_d = 60 \sin (2\pi \times 10^8 t) \quad \text{volts}$$

The important tube dimensions are

$$L = 19.4 \text{ cm} \qquad l = 1.27 \text{ cm} \qquad d = 0.475 \text{ cm}$$

The accelerating voltage is 200 volts. Where will an electron strike the screen if it enters the region between the plates at an instant when the phase of the deflecting voltage is zero?

2-8. Solve Prob. 2-7 if the applied deflecting potential is given by

$$E_d = 4 \times 10^{10}t \qquad \text{volts}$$

2-9. *a.* A sinusoidal voltage of frequency ω is applied to the deflecting plates of a cathode-ray tube. The transit time between the plates is τ. The length of the line on the screen is A. If A_0 is the line length when the transit time is negligible compared with the period of the applied voltage, show that

$$A = A_0 \frac{\sin (\omega\tau/2)}{\omega\tau/2}$$

b. If $E_a = 1,000$ volts and $l = 1$ cm, at what frequency will $A/A_0 = 0.9$?

2-10. Consider in detail the movement of an electron through a cathode-ray tube when electric fields are applied to both pairs of deflecting plates. Show that the vector displacement on the screen is approximately proportional to the vector sum of the electric-field intensities.

2-11. Prove that, if the accelerating voltage E_a is high enough so that relativistic corrections must be made, the deflection of an electron in a cathode-ray tube will be

$$D = D_0 \frac{1 + \Psi}{1 + \frac{1}{2}\Psi}$$

where D_0 is the nonrelativistic deflection, and

$$\Psi = \frac{eE_a}{m_0c^2} = \frac{v_N{}^2}{2c^2}$$

where the symbols have the meanings given in the text. Show that, if $\Psi \ll 1$, then D reduces to

$$D = D_0(1 + \tfrac{1}{2}\Psi)$$

How much error is made if the nonrelativistic instead of the correct formula is used for an 80,000-volt cathode-ray tube?

— **2-12.** A cathode-ray tube is equipped with a pair of plates that are inclined at an angle 2β with each other, as shown in the diagram. An electron is accelerated by the anode voltage E_a so that it enters the region between the plates with a velocity v_{0x}. Neglect the effects of fringing, and assume that the lines of flux are vertical.

a. Prove that the vertical component of velocity is given by

$$v_y = \frac{eE_d}{2mv_{0x} \tan \beta} \ln \left(1 + \frac{2x \tan \beta}{d}\right)$$

where E_d is the deflecting voltage.

HINT: Make use of the relationship

$$\frac{dv_y}{dt} = \frac{dv_y}{dx}\frac{dx}{dt} = v_x \frac{dv_y}{dx}$$

b. What is the slope (tan θ) of the path at the point where the electron leaves the region of the plates?

c. The distance from the center of the plates to the screen is L. If $L \gg l$, then little error will be made in assuming that the deflection on the screen is $D = L \tan \theta$. Under these conditions show that

$$D = \frac{E_d L}{4E_a \tan \beta} \ln \left(1 + \frac{2l}{d} \tan \beta\right)$$

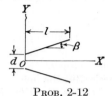

PROB. 2-12   PROB. 2-13

2-13. Consider two cathode-ray tubes, one containing parallel deflecting plates and the other inclined plates as shown in the diagram. If the tubes are identical in all other respects prove that

a. The maximum possible deflection on the screen is the same for both tubes.

b. The sensitivity of the tube with the inclined plates is 38 per cent greater than that of the tube with the parallel plates.

NOTE: Use the result of the previous problem.

2-14. A cathode ray tube that is provided with a postaccelerating anode has the following dimensions:

$$l = 1.6 \text{ cm} \qquad L = 18.2 \text{ cm} \qquad d = 0.50 \text{ cm}$$

The distance from the center of the plates to the ring R (Fig. 2-3) is 4.0 cm. The intensifier is 1.6 cm from the screen.

a. When used as an ordinary cathode-ray tube, the postaccelerating anode is connected to the accelerating anode. Calculate the deflection on the screen under these circumstances if $E_d = 50$ volts and $E_a = 1,200$ volts.

b. If one-half the accelerating voltage is applied after deflection between the anode and the intensifier electrode, what is the new deflection? See Fig. 2-3, where $E_{a1} = E_{a2} = 600$ volts. Assume that the intensifier field is axial and exists only in the region between R and I. 2,01 cm

c. If $E_{a1} = E_{a2} = 1,200$ volts, what is the new deflection? Compare with part *b* and discuss. 1,09 cm

2-15. The following experiment is performed on a cathode-ray tube that has all its plates brought out separately: An alternating voltage is applied to the (Y) plates nearest the gun. The other two (X) plates are tied together. Describe what happens to the vertical line as the potential between the X set of plates and the anode is varied positively and negatively.

2-16. Linear sweep circuits are applied simultaneously to the horizontal and vertical plates of a cathode-ray tube. One plate of each set is tied to the second anode. What pattern will appear on the screen if

a. The frequency applied to the vertical plates is five times the frequency applied to the horizontal plates?

b. The frequency applied to the horizontal plates is five times the frequency applied to the vertical plates?

2-17. A mixture of Li^6 and Li^7 singly ionized atoms are produced in an ion source. These ions are accelerated by a potential difference of 1,000 volts between the source and an exit probe. The ions pass through a hole in the probe into a uniform transverse magnetic field of 1,000 gauss. A photographic plate is placed normal to the direction of the ions at the point where they enter the region of the magnetic field (see Fig. 2-13). What is the separation of the two lines on the photographic plate?

NOTE: The superscripts give the atomic weights of the isotopes.

2-18. A mixture of K^{39}, K^{40}, and K^{41} singly ionized atoms are produced in an ion source. These ions are accelerated by a potential difference of 1,500 volts between the source and an exit probe. The ions pass through a hole in the probe into a uniform transverse magnetic field. If the K^{39} line formed on a photographic plate that is oriented perpendicular to the original direction of the ions is 38.20 cm from the source, calculate the separation of the three lines on the photographic plate (see Fig. 2-13).

NOTE: The superscripts give the atomic weights of the isotopes.

2-19. A helium leak-detector mass spectrometer accelerates the ions through 500 volts and then bends them in a circle of radius 4.0 cm. What is the value of the magnetic field used in the instrument?

2-20. The position of a certain strong β line of a sample of radium B which is placed at the origin of a magnetic spectrograph corresponds to a radius of curvature of 16.0 cm when the magnetic-field intensity is 120.5 gauss.

a. What would the speed be if the mass of the electrons did not change with velocity?

b. What is the true speed of the particles?

c. What is the ratio m/m_0?

(See M. M. Rogers, A. W. McReynolds, and F. T. Rogers, Jr., *Phys. Rev.*, **57**, 379, 1940.)

2-21. Given uniform electric and magnetic fields parallel to one another. Ions enter the region where these fields exist with velocities at right angles to the fields. *For small values of magnetic field*, prove that a photographic plate placed normal to the initial direction of the ions will, on development, show a series of parabolas, each parabola indicating a different value of the ratio e/m of the ion. Show that each point on a given parabola corresponds to a different value of initial velocity. This is the principle of the positive-ray spectrograph.

2-22. Electrons having an initial velocity $\mathbf{v}_0$ along the X axis enter a uniform magnetic field $\mathbf{B}$ (into the paper) at P. The magnetic field is sharply terminated outside the region MN. A plate with a hole H is placed in the XZ plane as shown.

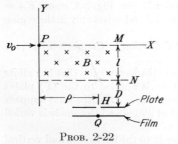

PROB. 2-22

It is required that only those electrons having an initial speed $v_{0x} = \mu$ should enter *vertically* through the hole H and expose the photographic plate at the point Q, vertically below H. Assuming that μ, ρ, and D are known and are not zero, find

a. The strength of the magnetic field required.

b. The distance l.

c. The time required for the electrons to reach H from the instant of arrival at P.

d. The velocity of the electrons at H.

2-23. The magnetic-field strength is 0.9 weber/m² in a certain cyclotron. Light hydrogen ions (protons) are used.

a. What must be the frequency of the oscillator supplying the power to the dees?

b. If each passage of the ions across the accelerating gap increases the energy of the ion by 60,000 volts, how long does it take for the ion introduced at the center of the spiral to emerge at the rim of the dee with an energy of 6 Mev?

c. Calculate the radius of the last semicircle before emergence.

2-24. Protons are accelerated in the MIT cyclotron. The magnetic-field strength is 1.3 webers/m², and the radius of the last semicircle is 0.5 m.

a. What must be the frequency of the oscillator supplying the power to the dees?

b. What is the final energy acquired by the proton?

c. If the total transit time of the proton is 3.3 μsec, how much energy is imparted to the particle in each passage from one dee to the other?

2-25. Explain what would happen if protons were used instead of electrons in the General Electric Co. 100-Mev betatron. In particular, calculate

a. The maximum energy that the proton would acquire.

b. The average energy acquired per trip around the doughnut.

c. The number of revolutions that the proton would make.

2-26. Prove that the 1:2 stability condition for the betatron is satisfied at any radius if the magnetic-field intensity decreases as $1/r$ from the origin.

2-27. A betatron at the University of Illinois operates with a peak magnetic-field strength of 0.12 weber/m² at the orbit and accelerates electrons to a final energy of 2.2 Mev. The average energy acquired per revolution is 10 ev.

a. What is the ratio m/m_0?

b. What is the orbital radius?

c. At what rate does the magnetic field vary?

d. What is the average transit time?

e. What is the total path length?

2-28. A cylindrical diode consists of a long, straight filament of radius r_k and a concentric anode of radius r_a between which is applied a potential E_b. Owing to the filament current I, a magnetic field surrounds the cathode, the lines of flux being circular and concentric with the filament.

If the electron starts from rest at the filament, describe its motion qualitatively. Show that there is a critical cutoff filament current above which no plate current exists, for a given plate voltage.

2-29. Sinusoidal voltages of the same amplitude and frequency are applied to both the horizontal and the vertical deflecting plates of a cathode-ray tube. If the phase angle between these two voltages is θ, plot the pattern that will appear on the screen, if

a. $\theta = 0$.

b. $\theta = \pi/4$.

c. $\theta = \pi/2$.

d. $\theta = \pi$.

This problem illustrates the use of the cathode-ray tube as a phase-measuring device.

2-30. A voltage $E_x = A \sin \omega_1 t$ is applied to the horizontal plates, and a voltage $E_y = A \sin (\omega_2 t + \theta)$ is applied to the vertical plates of a cathode-ray tube. Plot the pattern that will be observed on the screen, if

a. $\omega_2/\omega_1 = 2$, $\theta = 0$.

b. $\omega_2/\omega_1 = 2$, $\theta = \pi/2$.

c. $\omega_2/\omega_1 = 3$, $\theta = 0$.

d. $\omega_2/\omega_1 = 3$, $\theta = \pi/2$.

e. $\omega_2/\omega_1 = \frac{3}{2}$, $\theta = 0$.

f. $\omega_2/\omega_1 = \frac{3}{2}$, $\theta = \pi/2$.

These patterns are called Lissajous figures. This problem illustrates the use of the cathode-ray tube as an instrument for comparing an unknown frequency with a given standard. (See *RCA Pamphlet* TS-2, "Cathode-ray Tubes and Allied Types," 1935.)

Chapter 3

3-1. Prove that the concentration n of free electrons in a metal is given by

$$n = \frac{d\nu}{AM} = \frac{A_0 d\nu \times 10^3}{A} \qquad \text{electrons/m}^3$$

where d = density, kg/m³
ν = valence, free electrons per atom
A = atomic weight
M = weight of atom of unit atomic weight, kg (see Appendix I)
A_0 = Avogadro's number, molecules/mole

3-2. Compute the conductivity of copper for which $\mu = 34.8$ cm²/volt-sec and $d = 8.9$ g/cm³. Use the result of Prob. 3-1.

3-3. Compute the mobility of the free electrons in aluminum for which the density is 2.70 g/cm³ and the resistivity is 3.44×10^{-6} ohm-cm. Assume that aluminum has three valence electrons per atom. Use the result of Prob. 3-1.

3-4. The resistance of No. 18 copper wire (diameter = 1.03 mm) is 6.51 ohms per 1,000 ft. The concentration of free electrons in copper is 8.4×10^{28} electrons per cubic meter. If the current is 2 amp, find the

a. Drift velocity.
b. Mobility.
c. Conductivity.

3-5. A diode consists of a plane emitter and a plane-parallel anode separated by a distance of 0.5 cm. The anode is maintained at a potential of 10 volts negative with respect to the cathode.

a. If an electron leaves the emitter with a speed of 10^6 m/sec and is directed toward the anode, at what distance from the cathode will it intersect the potential-energy barrier?

b. With what speed must the electron leave the emitter in order to be able to reach the anode?

3-6. A particle when displaced from its equilibrium position is subject to a linear restoring force $f = -kx$, where x is the displacement measured from the equilibrium position. Show, by the energy method, that the particle will execute periodic vibrations with a maximum displacement which is proportional to the square root of the total energy of the particle.

3-7. A particle of mass m kilograms is projected vertically upward in the earth's gravitational field with a speed v_0 meters per second.

a. Show by the energy method that this particle will reverse its direction at the height of $v_0^2/2g$ meters, where g is the acceleration of gravity in meters per second per second.

b. Show that the point of reversal corresponds to a "collision" with the potential-energy barrier.

3-8. A triode consists of plane-parallel elements. The grid is located 0.2 cm, and the anode is 1.0 cm from the cathode. The grid is maintained at a potential of -1.0 volt and the plate at a potential of 100 volts with respect to the cathode. Assume that the potential varies linearly from the cathode to the grid and also linearly from the grid to the plate. Assume that the grid offers no mechanical hindrance to the flow of electrons.

a. If the electron leaving the cathode surface in the perpendicular direction collides with the potential-energy barrier after it has traveled a distance of 0.05 cm, with what energy was it emitted?

b. With what energy must it leave the emitter in order to be able to reach the anode? The foregoing assumptions are not strictly valid in a practical triode.

3-9. *a.* If the cathode and plate of the previous problem are maintained at zero potential and if the potential of the grid is 4 volts (positive), will the electron collide with a potential-energy barrier at any point of its path, if its initial velocity is zero?

b. How long will it take the particle to reach the anode?

c. With what velocity will the electron strike the plate?

3-10. Consider the following model of an atom: The nucleus consists of a positive point charge Ze, where Z is the atomic number and e is the numerical value of the charge of the electron. This is surrounded by Z electrons of which $Z - 1$ may be considered to be located on the surface of an imaginary sphere of radius r_0.

a. If the potential at infinity is taken as zero, show that the potential-energy function of the remaining (valence) electron is given by

$$4\pi\epsilon_0 U = -\frac{e^2}{r} \qquad \text{if } r > r_0$$

$$4\pi\epsilon_0 U = -\frac{Ze^2}{r} + (Z - 1)\frac{e^2}{r_0} \qquad \text{if } r < r_0$$

In the equations above r is expressed in meters, e in coulombs, U in joules, and ϵ_0 is the permittivity of free space in the mks rationalized system.

b. Consider three such atoms in a row. The first is separated from the second by a distance of $4r_0$, and the second is separated from the third by the same amount. Assuming that sodium atoms ($Z = 11$) are under consideration, plot to scale the potential energy of the valence electron. Make the transformations

$$y = \frac{4\pi\epsilon_0 U r_0}{e^2} \qquad \text{and} \qquad x = \frac{r}{r_0}$$

and plot y vs. x instead of U vs. r.

— **3-11.** How many electrons per cubic meter in metallic tungsten have energies between 8.5 and 8.6 ev

a. At 0°K?

b. At 2500°K?

3-12. *a.* Calculate the maximum energy of the free electrons in metallic aluminum at absolute zero. Assume that there are three free electrons per atom. The specific gravity of aluminum is 2.7.

b. Repeat part *a* for the electrons in metallic silver. The specific gravity of silver is 10.5. Assume that there is one free electron per atom.

— **3-13.** *a.* Show that the average energy E_{av} of the electrons in a metal is given by

$$E_{av} = \frac{\int E \, dN_E}{\int dN_E}$$

b. Prove that the average energy at absolute zero is $3E_M/5$.

3-14. If the emission from a certain cathode is 10,000 times as great at 2000° as at 1500°K, what is the work function of this surface?

— **3-15.** *a.* If the temperature of a tungsten filament is raised from 2300° to 2320°K, by what percentage will the emission change?

b. To what temperature must the filament be raised in order to double its emission at 2300°K?

3-16. By what percentage will the emission from a tungsten filament that is maintained at 2500°K change when the power input to the filament is changed by 5 per cent?

HINT: Use differentials to obtain fractional changes in current from the Dushman equation and fractional changes in power from the Stefan-Boltzmann equation.

3-17. If 10 per cent of the thermionic-emission current is collected (under space-charge-free conditions), what must be the retarding voltage at the surface of the metal? The filament temperature is 2000°K.

3-18. What fraction of the thermionic current will be obtained with zero applied voltage between the cathode and anode of a diode? The work function of the cathode is 4.50 volts, and the work function of the anode is 4.75 volts. The cathode temperature is 2000°K.

3-19. A plane cathode having a work function of 3.00 volts is connected directly to a parallel-plane anode whose work function is 5.00 volts. The distance between anode and cathode is 2.00 cm. If an electron leaves the cathode with a normal-to-the-surface velocity of 5.93×10^5 m/sec, how close to the anode will it come?

3-20. A diode has an oxide-coated cathode operating at a temperature of 1000°K With zero plate voltage the anode current is essentially zero, indicating that the contact potential is high enough to keep most of the electrons from reaching the plate. The applied voltage is increased so that a small current is drawn. Show that there is a tenfold increase in current for every 0.2-volt increase in voltage.

3-21. A diode, with plane-parallel electrodes, is operated at a temperature of 1500°K. The filament is made of tungsten, the area being such that a saturation current of 10 μa is obtained. The contact difference of potential between cathode and anode is 0.5 volt with the cathode at the higher potential.

a. What current is obtained with zero applied voltage?

b. What applied voltage will yield a current of 1 μa?

c. What fraction of the electrons emitted from this filament can move against an *applied retarding* field of 1 volt?

3-22. What accelerating field must be applied to the surface of a tungsten emitter operating at 2500°K in order to increase the zero-field thermionic emission by 1 per cent?

3-23. Calculate the electron-emission current density from the surface of a cold tungsten metal if the electric-field intensity is

a. 10^8 volts/m.

b. 10^9 volts/m.

c. 3×10^9 volts/m.

d. 10^{10} volts/m.

This problem illustrates how large an electric field is needed to obtain appreciable cold-cathode emission.

3-24. Indicate by letter which of the following statements are true:

a. The work function of a metal is always less than the potential barrier at the surface of a metal.

b. The potential barrier at the surface of a metal is a solid hill made up of the material of the metal.

c. The ionic structure of a metal shows that the inside of the metal is not an equipotential volume.

d. At absolute zero the electrons in a metal all have zero energy.

e. The energy method of analyzing the motion of a particle can be applied to uncharged as well as to charged particles.

f. The ionic structure of a metal shows that the surface of a metal is not a specific quantity.

g. For an electron to escape from a metal, the potential barrier at the surface of the metal must first be broken down.

h. The FDS distribution function for the electrons in a metal shows how many electrons are close to a nucleus and how many are far away.

i. The number of secondary electrons which leave a metal is always greater than the number of primary electrons striking the metal surface.

3-25. Indicate by letter which of the following statements are true:

a. The potential energy as a function of distance along a row of ions *inside* a metal varies very rapidly in the immediate neighborhood of an ion but is almost constant everywhere else inside the metal.

b. The potential-energy barrier at the surface of a metal *cannot* be explained on the basis of the modern crystal-structure picture of a metal, but it can be explained on the basis of classical electrostatics (image forces).

c. In order to remove any one of the free electrons from a metal, it is necessary only to give this electron an amount of energy equal to the work function of the metal.

d. The symbol E_M used in the energy distribution function represents the maximum number of free electrons per cubic meter of metal at absolute zero.

e. The area under the energy distribution curve represents the total number of free electrons per cubic meter of metal at any temperature.

f. The Dushman equation of thermionic emission gives the current that is obtained from a heated cathode as a function of applied plate voltage.

3-26. Consider intrinsic germanium at room temperature (300°K). By what per cent does the conductivity increase per degree rise in temperature?

3-27. Repeat Prob. 3-26 for intrinsic silicon.

3-28. *a.* Prove that the resistivity of intrinsic germanium at 300°K is 45 ohm-cm.

b. If a donor-type impurity is added to the extent of one atom per 10^8 germanium atoms, prove that the resistivity drops to 3.7 ohm-cm.

3-29. *a.* Find the resistivity of intrinsic silicon at 300°K.

b. If a donor-type impurity is added to the extent of one atom per 10^8 silicon atoms, find the resistivity.

3-30. *a.* Determine the concentration of free electrons and holes in a sample of germanium at 300°K which has a concentration of donor atoms equal to 2×10^{14} atoms per cubic centimeter and a concentration of acceptor atoms equal to 3×10^{14} atoms per cubic centimeter. Is this *p-* or *n*-type germanium? In other words, is the conductivity due primarily to holes or to electrons?

b. Repeat part *a* for equal donor and acceptor concentrations of 10^{15} atoms per cubic centimeter. Is this *p-* or *n*-type germanium?

c. Repeat part *a* for a temperature of 400°K, and show that the sample is essentially intrinsic.

3-31. Find the concentration of holes and of electrons in *p*-type germanium at 300°K if the conductivity is 100 (ohm-cm)$^{-1}$.

3-32. Repeat Prob. 3-31 for *n* type germanium if the conductivity is 0.1 (ohm-cm)$^{-1}$.

3-33. A sample of germanium is doped to the extent of 10^{14} donor atoms per cubic centimeter and 7×10^{13} acceptor atoms per cubic centimeter. At the temperature of the sample the resistivity of pure (intrinsic) germanium is 60 ohm-cm. If the applied electric field is 2 volts/cm, find the total conduction current density.

Chapter 4

4-1. At what temperature will a thoriated-tungsten filament give 5,000 times as much emission as a pure tungsten filament at the same temperature? The filament dimensions of the two emitters are the same.

4-2. The saturation current from a certain tungsen filament operated at 1840°K is 143 μa. What would be the emission from a thoriated-tungsten filament of the same area operating at the same temperature?

4-3. How much power must be supplied to an oxide-coated filament 1.8 cm² in area in order to maintain it at 1100°K? Assume that the heat loss due to conduction is

10 per cent of the radiation loss. Calculate the total emission current and the cathode efficiency of the cathode. Take $e_T = 0.7$; $E_W = 1.0$ ev; and $A_0 = 100$ amp/$(m^2)(°K^2)$.

4-4. The type 45 triode is provided with a ribbon filament of the W type; this filament is 0.014 by 0.004 in., and it is 4.5 in. long. Calculate the filament temperature and the total cathode emission expected from this oxide-coated cathode when operated under normal filament power (1.5 amp at 2.5 volts). Take the emissivity to be 0.3, and assume the following values for the thermionic-emission constants: $E_W = 1.0$ ev and $A_0 = 100$ amp/$(m^2)(°K^2)$.

4-5. A tungsten cathode is heated to a temperature of 2300°K. What must the retarding voltage be in order to limit the current density to 10^{-2} amp/m^2? Neglect contact potential.

4-6. Given a diode with zero voltage applied between cathode and anode. The work function of the anode is 4.75 volts. The cathode temperature is 2000°K. The plate current flowing is 23.5 per cent of the thermionic current. Presuming that space-charge effects can be neglected, what is the work function of the cathode?

4-7. Prove that the following relationships are valid for a plane-parallel diode operating under space-charge-limited conditions:

$$V = E_b \left(\frac{x}{d}\right)^{\frac{4}{3}}$$

$$v = v_b \left(\frac{x}{d}\right)^{\frac{2}{3}}$$

and

$$\rho = \rho_b \left(\frac{x}{d}\right)^{-\frac{2}{3}}$$

where $v_b = (2eE_b/m)^{\frac{1}{2}}$ is the speed with which the electrons strike the plate and $\rho_b = E_b/81\pi d^2 10^9$ is the charge density at the plate. The other symbols have the meanings assigned in the text.

4-8. Show that the transit time of an electron from the cathode to the anode of a plane-parallel space-charge-limited diode is $T = 3d/v_b$, where d is the cathode-anode spacing and $v_b = (2eE_b/m)^{\frac{1}{2}}$ is the speed with which the electron strikes the plate. The electron is assumed to leave the cathode with zero initial velocity.

Show that, if the space charge is negligibly small, the transit time is $T = 2d/v_b$. This is only two-thirds of the time taken under space-charge conditions.

4-9. Show that the tangent to the potential distribution curve at the anode of a plane-parallel space-charge-limited diode passes through the zero of potential at one-fourth the cathode-plate distance.

4-10. A diode having plane-parallel electrodes is operating under space-charge conditions. The plate current is 10 ma at 100 volts plate voltage.

a. What must be the plate voltage in order that the plate current be doubled?

b. What current will be obtained if the voltage is doubled ($E_b = 200$ volts)?

c. If another diode is constructed having half the cathode-anode spacing and twice the electrode area, what current will be obtained if a potential of 100 volts is applied?

4-11. A plane-parallel diode having a 2-cm spacing is operated under space-charge conditions. The plate voltage is 100 volts. What is the space-charge density at a point halfway between the cathode and anode?

4-12. In a plane-parallel vacuum diode the applied voltage is 50 volts. Under the assumption of zero emission velocity the minimum cathode temperature for which the field at the cathode is zero is 1000°K. If the cathode is heated to 1200°K, what is the maximum value of the plate voltage for which the field at the cathode is zero? Assume that the value of b_0 corresponding to the work function of the cathode is $b_0 = 12,000°K$.

4-13. The space-charge-limited current of a certain plane-parallel-type vacuum diode is 20 ma at a plate voltage of 100 volts. The temperature-limited current of the same type is 20 ma at a filament temperature of 2300°K.

Two identical diodes of this type are connected in series across a d-c supply with the proper polarity for both tubes to conduct. Find the plate current through the tubes and the voltage across each tube if the supply voltage is

a. 50 volts and if both tubes are operated at the same filament temperature of 2300°K.

b. 300 volts and if both tubes are operated at the same filament temperature of 2300°K.

c. 300 volts and if one tube is operated at a filament temperature of 2300°K while the other is operated at a filament temperature of 3000°K.

4-14. For a space-charge-limited diode the functional relationship between plate current and plate voltage is given by Eq. (4-14). Determine whether or not the diodes whose volt-ampere characteristics are plotted in Appendix IX satisfy this formula. Determine the exponent of E_b for each diode.

4-15. *a.* A plane-parallel diode with a cathode-anode spacing of 1 cm operates under space-charge-limited conditions at a plate voltage of 100 volts. How much power per square meter must the plate dissipate?

b. If the voltage is increased to 400 volts, by what factor is the dissipation multiplied?

c. If the emissivity of the anode material is 0.5, find the anode temperature in each case. Assume an ambient temperature of 20°C.

4-16. In a certain space-charge-limited diode a current of 5 ma results from the application of 100 volts. What is the maximum plate voltage that can be applied before the plate dissipation exceeds 16 watts?

4-17. The anode of a space-charge-limited diode is made of material whose emissivity is 0.7. When the plate voltage is 200 volts, the temperature of the anode is 50°C. The ambient temperature is 20°C. What is the plate current density?

4-18. Given a tungsten cathode and a cylindrical coaxial anode having the following dimensions:

$$\begin{aligned}
\text{Lighted length} &= 1.0 \text{ in.} \\
\text{Cathode diameter} &= 0.005 \text{ in.} \\
\text{Anode diameter} &= 0.5 \text{ in.}
\end{aligned}$$

The filament voltage is 2.5 volts. The filament current is 1.0 amp. The plate voltage is 200 volts. Take $e_T = 0.26$.

a. Calculate the space-charge-limited current.

b. Calculate the temperature-limited current.

c. Calculate the plate current. *is always the smaller of the above 2 (a) & (b)*

β **4-19.** Given a cylindrical tungsten filament whose lighted length is 1 in. and whose diameter is 4 mils. Coaxial with this emitter is a cylindrical plate whose diameter is 0.4 in. Take $e_T = 0.26$.

a. What must be the power input to the filament if it is to operate at 2000°K?

b. What is the saturation current obtainable from this tube?

c. What plate current is obtained at a plate voltage of 100 volts?

4-20. Calculate the maximum current from a straight tungsten wire 1 mm in diameter and 3 cm long to a cylindrical anode 4 cm in diameter when the potential difference between cathode and anode is 120 volts.

4-21. The tungsten filament of a high-vacuum rectifying diode has a diameter of 0.0085 in. and a lighted length of 1.00 in. The plate diameter is 0.75 in. Take $e_T = 0.26$.

a. If the filament input is 5.0 amp at 2.0 volts, what is the saturation current?

b. At what potential will the current become temperature-limited?

4-22. Prove that the current density at the plate of a cylindrical diode is the same as that in a plane diode if the cathode-anode spacing is the same in both tubes and if the anode radius is very much greater than the cathode radius.

4-23. Prove that the space-charge density ρ varies with distance r according to the factor $r^{-\frac{2}{3}} (\beta^2)^{-\frac{2}{3}}$, where β^2 is defined in Sec. 4-5.

— **4-24.** In either a plane or a cylindrical diode all the dimensions are enlarged by the same factor. If the voltage remains constant, show that the space-charge current is unchanged.

4-25. *a.* Evaluate the forward resistance R_f and the plate resistance r_p of the 5U4-GB diode at a plate voltage of 50 volts.

b. Repeat for the 5Y3-GT tube.

— **4-26.** *a.* A 5U4-GB tube in series with a 250-ohm load is excited from a 60-volt d-c source. What is the tube current? What is the tube voltage? Repeat if the load is

b. 50 ohms.

c. Zero.

d. Infinity.

4-27. The 120-volt d-c mains are impressed across a 5Y3-GT diode in series with a resistor R. Find the tube current and voltage if R equals

a. 500 ohms.

b. 200 ohms.

c. Zero.

d. Infinity.

4-28. Plot (from zero to 120 volts input) the dynamic characteristic of the 5U4-GB diode for a 250-ohm load.

— **4-29.** A plane-parallel diode, operating under space-charge-limited conditions, delivers a plate current of 100 ma at a plate voltage of 100 volts.

a. What are R_f and r_p at $E_b = 100$ volts?

b. What are R_f and r_p at 50 volts?

Chapter 5

— **5-1.** *a.* For what voltage will the reverse current in a *p-n* junction diode reach 90 per cent of its saturation value at room temperature?

b. What is the ratio of the current for a forward bias of 0.05 volt to the current for the same-magnitude reverse bias?

c. If the reverse saturation current is 10 μa, calculate the forward currents for voltages of 0.1, 0.2, and 0.3 volt, respectively.

5-2. *a.* Calculate and plot the volt-ampere characteristic of an ideal *p-n* junction diode at room temperature. The reverse saturation current is 10 μa. Assume input voltages in the range from -0.2 to $+0.2$ volt.

b. The diode has an ohmic resistance of 25 ohms. Plot the new volt-ampere diode characteristic, taking the ohmic drop into account. Use the same graph sheet and the same current range as in part *a.*

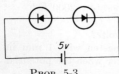

PROB. 5-3

◄ **5-3.** *a.* Two *p-n* junction diodes are connected in series opposing as indicated. A 5-volt battery is impressed upon this series arrangement. Find the voltage across each junction at room temperature. Assume that the magnitude of the Zener voltage is greater than 5 volts.

Note that the result is independent of the reverse saturation current. Is it also independent of temperature?

HINT: Assume that reverse saturation current flows in the circuit and then justify this assumption.

b. If the magnitude of the Zener voltage is 4.9 volts, what will be the current in the circuit? The reverse saturation current is 5 μa.

5-4. *a.* In the circuit of Prob. 5-3 the Zener breakdown voltage is 2.0 volts. The reverse saturation current is 5 μa. If the diode resistance could be neglected, what would be the current?

b. If the ohmic resistance is 100 ohms, what is the current?

5-5. A *p-n* junction diode at room temperature has a reverse saturation current of 10 μa, negligible ohmic resistance, and a Zener breakdown voltage of 100 volts. A 1-K resistor is in series with this diode, and a 30-volt battery is impressed across this combination. Find the current

a. If the diode is forward-biased.

b. If the battery is inserted into the circuit with the reverse polarity.

c. Repeat parts *a* and *b* if the Zener breakdown voltage is 10 volts.

5-6. An ideal silicon *p-n* junction diode has a reverse saturation current of 30 μa. At a temperature of 125°C find the dynamic resistance for a 0.2-volt bias in

a. The forward direction.

b. The reverse direction.

5-7. Calculate the barrier capacitance of a germanium *p-n* junction whose area is 1 mm by 1 mm and whose space-charge thickness is 2×10^{-4} cm. The dielectric constant of germanium (relative to free space) is 16.

5-8. For an alloy junction for which N_a is not negligible compared with N_d, verify that Eq. (5-12) remains valid provided that W is interpreted as the total space-charge width and that $1/N_a$ is replaced by $1/N_a + 1/N_d$.

5-9. The zero-voltage barrier height at an alloy germanium *p-n* junction is 0.2 volt. The concentration N_a of acceptor atoms in the *p* side is much smaller than the concentration of donor atoms in the *n* material, and $N_a = 3 \times 10^{20}$ atoms per cubic meter. Calculate the width of the depletion layer for an applied reverse voltage of

a. 10 volts.

b. 0.1 volt.

c. For a forward bias of 0.1 volt.

d. If the cross-sectional area of the diode is 1 mm² evaluate the space-charge capacitance corresponding to the above values of applied voltage.

5-10. *a.* Consider a grown junction for which the uncovered charge density ρ varies linearly as indicated in Fig. 5-7. If $\rho = ax$, prove that the barrier voltage E_B is given by

$$V_B = \frac{aW^3}{12\epsilon}$$

b. Verify that the barrier capacitance C_T is given by Eq. (5-14).

5-11. *a.* Prove that the maximum electric field $\mathcal{E}_m$ at an alloy junction is given by

$$\mathcal{E}_m = \frac{2V_B}{W}$$

b. It is found that Zener breakdown occurs when $\mathcal{E}_m = 2 \times 10^7$ volts/m $\equiv \mathcal{E}_Z$. Prove that Zener voltage V_Z is given by

$$V_Z = \frac{\epsilon \mathcal{E}_Z^2}{2eN_a}$$

Note that the Zener breakdown voltage can be controlled by controlling the concentration of acceptor ions.

5-12. *a.* Starting with Eq. (5-26), verify that the open-circuit barrier height V_0 is given by

$$V_0 = V_T \ln \frac{N_a N_d}{n_i{}^2}$$

b. Verify that this result can be put in the convenient form

$$V_0 = V_T \ln \frac{\sigma_n \sigma_p (b+1)^2}{\sigma_i{}^2 b}$$

where σ_n (σ_p) = conductivity of n (p) side
σ_i = conductivity of an intrinsic sample
$b = \mu_n/\mu_p$

5-13. *a.* Using the result of Prob. 5-12, evaluate V_0 for germanium at room temperature. Assume that both the n and p sides are doped to the extent of one atom per 10^8 germanium atoms. The physical constants of germanium and silicon are given in Table 3-1.

b. Repeat part *a* for silicon.

5-14. Starting with Eqs. (5-22) and (5-23), prove that the ratio of hole to electron current crossing a junction is given by

$$\frac{I_{pn}(0)}{I_{np}(0)} = \frac{\sigma_p L_n}{\sigma_n L_p}$$

where σ_p (σ_n) = conductivity of p (n) side. Note that this ratio depends upon the ratio of the conductivities. For example, if the p side is much more heavily doped than the n side, then the hole current will be much larger than the electron current crossing the junction.

5-15. Starting with Eq. (5-36), verify that the reverse saturation current is given by

$$I_0 = A V_T \frac{b \sigma_i{}^2}{(1+b)^2} \left(\frac{1}{L_p \sigma_n} + \frac{1}{L_n \sigma_p} \right)$$

where σ_n (σ_p) = conductivity of n (p) side
σ_i = conductivity of intrinsic material
$b = \mu_n/\mu_p$

5-16. Using the result of Prob. 5-15, find the reverse saturation current for a germanium p-n junction diode at room temperature, 300°K. The cross-sectional area is 4.0 mm², and

$$\sigma_p = 1.0 \text{ (ohm-cm)}^{-1} \qquad \sigma_n = 0.1 \text{ (ohm-cm)}^{-1} \qquad L_n = L_p = 0.15 \text{ cm}$$

Other physical constants are given in Table 3-1.

5-17. Find the ratio of the reverse saturation current in germanium to that in silicon, using the result of Prob. 5-15. Assume that $L_n = L_p = 0.1$ cm and $\sigma_n = \sigma_p = 1.0$ (ohm-cm)$^{-1}$ for germanium, whereas the corresponding values are 0.01 cm and 0.01 (ohm-cm)$^{-1}$ for silicon. See also Table 3-1.

5-18. *a.* Find the per cent increase in the reverse saturation current per degree rise in temperature at room temperature for germanium. HINT: Take the logarithm of Eq. (5-37) and then differentiate.

b. Repeat part *a* for silicon.

5-19. *a.* Prove that the reverse saturation current in germanium is multiplied by 2.80 for every 10°C rise in temperature near room temperature (300°K).

b. Prove that the reverse saturation current in silicon is multiplied by 4.45 for every 10°C rise in temperature near room temperature (300°K).

5-20. *a.* The voltage impressed on a junction diode is $V = V_1 + V_m \epsilon^{j\omega t}$. This expression represents a d-c voltage V_1 and a sinusoidal voltage of peak value V_m. Assume that $V_m \ll V_1$. The current may be expected to consist of a d-c term plus an a-c term. Hence, assume that the concentration is given by an expression of the form

$$p_n - p_{no} = p_{no}(\epsilon^{V_1/V_T} - 1)\epsilon^{-x/L_p} + F(x)V_m \epsilon^{j\omega t}$$

Show that this form satisfies the equation of continuity [Eq. (A6-9)] and that $F(x)$ is given by

$$F(x) = K\epsilon^{-(1+j\omega\tau_p)^{\frac{1}{2}}x/L_p}$$

b. At $x = 0$, $p_n - p_{no} = p_{no}\left(\exp\dfrac{V_1 + V_m \epsilon^{j\omega t}}{V_T} - 1\right)$. Show that if $V_m/V_T \ll 1$

$$p_n - p_{no} = p_{no}(\epsilon^{V_1/V_T} - 1) + p_{no}\frac{V_m}{V_T}\epsilon^{V_1/V_T}\epsilon^{j\omega t}$$

Comparing this expression with that given in part *a*, evaluate K.

c. Prove that the diffusion current at $x = 0$ is

$$I_{pn}(0) = I_1 + eD_pA\,\frac{p_{no}}{V_T L_p}\,\epsilon^{V_1/V_T}(1 + j\omega\tau_p)^{\frac{1}{2}}V_m \epsilon^{j\omega t}$$

where I_1 is the direct current corresponding to V_1.

d. If $\omega\tau_p \ll 1$, prove that

$$I_{pn}(0) = I_1 + g_p V_m \epsilon^{j\omega t} + j\omega C_{Dp}V_m \epsilon^{j\omega t}$$

where g_p is the zero-frequency conductance and $C_{Dp} = (\tau_p/2)g_p$ is the diffusion capacitance for holes.

e. If $\omega\tau_p \gg 1$, prove that

$$I_{pn}(0) = I_1 + g_p\left(\frac{\omega\tau_p}{2}\right)^{\frac{1}{2}}V_m \epsilon^{j\omega t} + j\omega C_{Dp}V_m \epsilon^{j\omega t}$$

where $C_{Dp} = (\tau_p/2\omega)^{\frac{1}{2}}g_p$.

Note that the conductance as well as the capacitance varies with frequency.

Chapter 6

6-1. Find the maximum speed with which the photoelectrons will be emitted (if at all) when radiation of wave length 5,893 A falls upon

a. A cesium surface, for which the work function is 1.8 volts.

b. A platinum surface, for which the work function is 6.0 volts.

c. Repeat parts *a* and *b* if the surfaces are illuminated with neon resonance radiation (743 A) instead of the yellow sodium line.

6-2. What is the minimum energy, expressed in joules and in electron volts, required to remove an electron from the surface of metallic potassium, the photoelectric threshold wave length of which is 5,500 A?

6-3. A cesium surface, for which the work function is 1.8 volts, is illuminated with argon resonance radiation (1,065 A). What retarding potential must be applied in order that the plate current in this photocell drop to zero? Assume that the contact potential is 0.50 volt, with the plate negative with respect to the cathode.

6-4. When a certain surface is irradiated by the 2,537-A mercury line, it is found that no current flows until at least 0.54 volt accelerating potential is applied. Assume that the contact potential is 1.00 volt, the cathode being positive with respect to the anode.

a. What is the work function of the surface?

b. What is the threshold wave length of the surface?

6-5. A certain photosurface has a spectral sensitivity of 6 ma/watt of incident radiation of wave length 2,537 A. How many electrons will be emitted photoelectrically by a pulse of radiation consisting of 10,000 photons of this wave length?

6-6. The photoelectric sensitivity of a PJ-22 photocell is 14 μa/lumen, when the anode potential is 90 volts. The window area of the photocell is 0.9 in.^{2} A 100-watt electric-light bulb has a mean horizontal candle power of 120 cp. What will be the photocurrent if the cell is placed 3 ft from the lamp? NOTE: 1 cp corresponds to a total light flux of 4π lumens.

6-7. The energy distribution curve of a light source is known. The spectral sensitivity curves of several of the commercially available photosurfaces are supplied by the tube manufacturer and are shown in Fig. 6-11. Explain exactly how to determine which tube should be used with this particular light source in order to obtain the maximum photocurrent.

6-8. Devise a circuit for determining automatically the correct exposure time in the photographic printing process. Use a photocell, a relay, and any other auxiliary apparatus needed. The blackening of a photographic emulsion is determined by the product of the luminous intensity falling on the plate and the time of exposure. The instrument must trip the relay at the same value of this product regardless of what light source is used.

6-9. Plot curves of photocurrent vs. light intensity for a PJ-23 for load resistances of 1 and 10 megohms, respectively. The supply voltage is held constant at 80 volts.

6-10. a. The intensity of illumination on a 929 phototube is constant at 0.1 lumen. An adjustable voltage supply in series with a 25-megohm resistance is applied to the tube. Plot a curve of anode current vs. supply voltage. From this curve, determine the wave shape of the photocurrent if the impressed voltage is sinusoidal and has a peak value of 250 volts.

b. Repeat part a if the load resistance is 50 megohms instead of 25 megohms.

c. Repeat part a if the impressed voltage consists of a 125-volt battery in series with an alternating voltage whose peak value is 125 volts.

6-11. In Fig. 6-13 the tube is a PJ-22, E_{bb} = 80 volts, and an electronic switch is placed across R_L. The switch closes at 20 volts or above and has an infinite input impedance.

a. What minimum light intensity is required to close the switch, if R_L = 2 megohms?

b. If the maximum voltage across the switch may not exceed 50 volts and if the maximum intensity of light is 208 ft-c, what is the maximum allowable value of R_L?

6-12. Calculate the number of stages required in a secondary-emission multiplier to give an amplification of 10^6 if the secondary-emission ratio is 3.5.

6-13. In a nine-stage secondary-emission phototube multiplier, the incident photocurrent is 10^{-8} amp and the output current from the multiplier is 0.1 amp. What is the secondary-emission ratio of the target material?

6-14. In the secondary-emission multiplier of Fig. 6-18, the distance between a target and its plate is 1.0 cm. The potential between these two elements is 100 volts. Assume that there is no field between targets and that the electrons leave each target with zero velocity so that the resultant motion is truly cycloidal.

a. Find the minimum magnetic field required in order that this tube operate properly.

b. If the tube were designed to operate with a field of 5 milliwebers/m^2, what would be the distance between centers of adjacent targets? Assume that the path remains cycloidal.

6-15. The photocurrent I in a p-n junction photodiode as a function of the distance x of the light spot from the junction is given in Fig. 6-23. Prove that if log I is plotted vs. x then a linear relationship is obtained on either side of the junction. Prove that the slopes of the lines are $-1/L_p$ and $-1/L_n$, respectively, on the n and p sides. Note that L_p represents the diffusion length for holes in the n material.

Chapter 7

7-1. *a.* From the plate characteristics of the 6SN7 triode (Appendix IX), obtain the transfer or mutual characteristics for $E_b = 100$, 200, and 300 volts.

b. Obtain the constant-current characteristics of the 6SN7. Plot e_b vs. e_c for $I_b = 6$, 12, and 18 ma.

7-2. *a.* From the plate characteristics of the 12AX7 triode (Appendix IX), obtain the mutual or transfer characteristics for $E_b = 100$, 200, and 300 volts.

b. Obtain the constant-current characteristics for the 12AX7. Plot e_b vs. e_c for $I_b = 0.7$, 1.4, and 2.1 ma.

7-3. If the plate current in a triode can be represented by Eq. (7-1), show that r_p is proportional to i_b^{-m} and that g_m is proportional to i_b^{m}, where $m = (n - 1)/n$. Note that if the three-halves-power law is valid, then $m = \frac{1}{3}$.

7-4. The plate resistance of a 6J5 triode or one unit of a 6SN7 is 7.7 K, and the transconductance is 2.6 millimhos.

a. If the plate voltage is increased by 50 volts, what is the increase in plate current? The grid voltage is maintained constant.

b. What change in grid voltage will bring the plate current back to its former value? The plate voltage is maintained at the value to which it was raised in part *a.*

7-5. The plate resistance of a triode is 10 K, and the amplification factor is 20. The tube is operated at the quiescent point $E_b = 250$ volts, $E_c = -8$ volts, and $I_b = 8$ ma.

a. To what value must the grid voltage be changed if the plate current is to change to 12 ma? The plate voltage is maintained at 250 volts.

b. To what value must the plate voltage be changed if the plate current is to be brought back to its previous value? The grid voltage is maintained constant at the value found in part *a.*

7-6. The plate current of a 6F6 tube connected as a triode can be expressed approximately by the equation $i_b = 41(e_b + 7e_c)^{1.41} \times 10^{-6}$ amp. The tube is operated with a grid bias of -20 volts, and the plate voltage is 250 volts. Calculate the following:

a. The tube current.

b. The plate resistance.

c. The transconductance.

7-7. *a.* Show that the volt-ampere curve for $E_c = -8$ volts of a type 6SN7 triode (Appendix IX) can be expressed by an equation of the form

$$i_b = k(e_b + 20e_c)^n$$

Determine k and n from a logarithmic plot.

Plot the curve expressed by this equation and the experimental curve on the same sheet of paper, and compare.

b. Calculate the values of r_p and g_m from this equation at the conditions $E_c = -8$ volts and $E_b = 250$ volts, and compare with the values given in Fig. 7-8.

7-8. *a.* Calculate μ, r_p, and g_m from the plate characteristics of the 6SN7 tube (Appendix IX) at the quiescent point $E_b = 250$ volts, $E_c = -8$ volts.

  b. Plot μ, r_p, and g_m for a 6SN7 as a function of I_b, with $E_b = 250$ volts.

  c. Plot μ, r_p, and g_m for a 6SN7 as a function of E_c, with $E_b = 250$ volts.

  7-9. Given the transfer characteristics of a triode. Explain clearly how to determine r_p, μ, and g_m at a specified quiescent point.

  7-10. Show that if the triode plate characteristic can be approximated by straight lines the equation of these lines is

$$i_b = \frac{1}{r_p}\,(\mu e_c + e_b - \epsilon)$$

where ϵ is the voltage intercept at zero current of the $e_c = 0$ curve.

  7-11. *a.* Starting with the definitions of g_m and r_p, show that if two identical tubes are connected in parallel g_m is doubled and r_p is halved. Since $\mu = r_p g_m$, then μ remains unchanged.

  b. If the two tubes are not identical show that

$$g_m = g_{m1} + g_{m2}$$

that

$$\frac{1}{r_p} = \frac{1}{r_{p1}} + \frac{1}{r_{p2}}$$

and that

$$\mu = \frac{\mu_1 r_{p2} + \mu_2 r_{p1}}{r_{p1} + r_{p2}}$$

  7-12. *a.* The circuit shown is used to measure grid current. Prove that the grid current I_c with the switch S open is given by

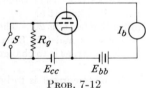

PROB. 7-12

$$I_c = \frac{\Delta I_b}{g_m R_g}$$

where ΔI_b is the change in plate current as the switch is closed and g_m is the transconductance of the tube.

  b. The foregoing method depends upon a knowledge of g_m. This limitation is removed as follows: The plate current I_b is noted with S open. The switch is then closed, and the bias is adjusted until the plate current is its previous value. Explain how this procedure allows the determination of I_c.

  7-13. When the grid is insulated from the cathode and the plate of a vacuum triode, it is said to be "floating." Describe an experimental method of determining this floating potential.

  7-14. An adjustable resistor R_L is connected in series with the plate of a 6SN7 triode and a plate supply of 250 volts. The grid is maintained at -4 volts with respect to the cathode. Determine by graphical methods, using the plate characteristics in Appendix IX,

  a. The plate current, when R_L has the following values: 0, 10, and 50 K.

  b. The plate voltage corresponding to the resistances in part *a.*

  c. The load resistance that will give a plate current of 10 ma.

  d. The voltage drop across R_L if the bias is changed to -8 volts and if the load resistance is 10 K.

  7-15. A 12AX7 triode is operated at the quiescent point $E_b = 250$ volts, $E_c = -2$ volts. The plate characteristics of this tube are given in Appendix IX.

  a. Calculate the plate supply voltage that must be used for the following values of load resistance: 50, 100, and 200 K.

b. If the grid excitation is sinusoidal with a peak value of 2 volts, find the maximum and minimum currents obtainable with each of the load resistances of part *a*.

c. Plot the dynamic transfer characteristic for $R_L = 100$ K.

7-16. For a 6SN7 tube (Appendix IX) evaluate r_c as a function of E_c with E_b as a parameter. Choose values of E_b of 250, 150, and 50 volts.

7-17. *a.* If $e = 0$, find e_o.

b. If $e = 100$, find e_o.

c. If the grid-to-cathode voltage is zero, find e_o.

d. If $e_o = 0$, find e.

7-18. Given a cathode follower with $E_{bb} = 250$ volts, $E_{cc} = 0$, and $R_k = 100$ K, the tube is one section of a 12AX7. Find the input voltage e and the output voltage e_o for

a. Cutoff.

b. Zero grid-to-cathode voltage.

c. Calculate and plot e_o vs. e for values between the extremes in parts *a* and *b*. Observe how linear this curve is.

d. Calculate the amplification.

7-19. *a.* The supply E_{cc} is adjusted from zero to 150 volts in 50-volt steps. Calculate the output voltage E_o for each value of E_{cc}.

b. Repeat part *a* if the grid-to-ground voltage is 50 volts instead of zero.

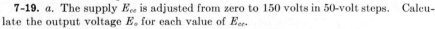

PROB. 7-17

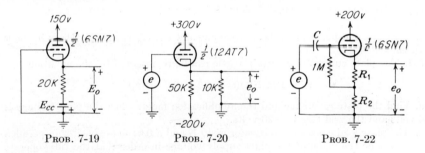

PROB. 7-19   PROB. 7-20   PROB. 7-22

7-20. What is

a. e when the output is zero?

b. e_o if $e = -100$ volts?

c. The grid-to-cathode voltage when $e_o = +50$ volts?

7-21. Design an a-c cathode follower using a 12AX7 tube and a 300-volt supply using self-bias. The circuit must operate quite linearly over an input voltage range of ± 75 volts.

7-22. The reactance of C and the impedance of the generator are both negligible. $R_1 + R_2 = 10$ K. The input signal e is symmetrical with respect to ground. Find R_1 and R_2 if the tube is to handle, without distortion and without drawing grid current, the largest possible amplitude of signal. What is the maximum signal the tube will handle in this case?

7-23. *a.* Find the quiescent plate current.

HINT: Apply Thévenin's theorem between the plate and ground to the elements external to the tube.

b. Find the quiescent output voltage E_o with respect to ground.

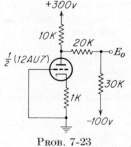

PROB. 7-23

Chapter 8

8-1. Figure 8-5, which shows the magnitude of the amplification A of an amplifier as a function of load resistance R_L, is based upon the assumption that μ and r_p remain constant as R_L is varied. Suppose that instead of operating the tube at a fixed Q point the plate and grid supply voltages are maintained constant as R_L is varied. The operating point and hence μ and r_p will now be functions of R_L.

Plot A vs. R_L for a 6SN7 tube operating under the conditions $E_{bb} = 400$ volts and $E_{cc} = -8$ volts. Choose values of load resistance that correspond to quiescent currents of from 1 to 16 ma. Plot Fig. 8-5 on the same graph sheet, and compare the two curves. The variations of μ and r_p as a function of load current are given in Fig. 7-8 for a 6SN7. The plate characteristics are given in Appendix IX.

8-2. The plate current of a certain triode can be represented by the equation

$$i_b = 0.002(e_c + 0.1e_b)^{\frac{3}{2}} \text{ amp}$$

a. Find the plate resistance when the plate voltage is 200 volts and the grid bias is -15 volts.

b. The plate load consists of a series circuit made up of a resistance of 10 K and an inductance of 2.0 henrys (of negligible resistance). What must be the value of the plate supply voltage in order that the tube operate under the conditions of part *a*?

c. If a 1-volt maximum 1,000-cps signal is impressed on the amplifier, calculate the output voltage across the inductor.

d. Calculate the phase angle between input and output voltages. Draw a sinor diagram.

8-3. The plate current of a certain triode can be represented by the equation

$$i_b = 4 \times 10^{-4}(e_c + 0.1e_b)^{1.5} \text{ amp}$$

a. Find the plate resistance and the amplification factor when the plate voltage is 450 volts and the grid bias is -20 volts.

b. The plate load consists of a resistor of 10 K and a 0.016-μf capacitor in parallel. What must be the value of the plate supply voltage in order that the tube operate under the conditions of part *a*?

c. If a 2-volt rms 1,000-cps signal is impressed on the amplifier, draw the equivalent circuit and calculate the output voltage across the load.

8-4. *a.* If e is a small a-c input signal, derive an expression for the a-c output voltage e_o.

b. Show that the Thévenin's equivalent circuit looking into the plate is a generator $-\mu e$ in series with an output impedance $R_o = r_p + (\mu + 1)R_k$.

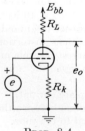

PROB. 8-4

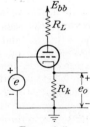

PROB. 8-5

8-5. *a.* If *e* is a small a-c input signal, derive an expression for the a-c output voltage e_o in the circuit shown.

b. Show that the Thévenin's equivalent circuit looking into the cathode is a generator $\mu e/(\mu + 1)$ in series with an output impedance $R_o = (r_p + R_L)/(\mu + 1)$.

8-6. If an a-c input signal E_s is impressed between the grid and ground, find the amplification $A = E_o/E_s$. The tube parameters are $\mu = 30$ and $r_p = 5$ K.

8-7. If in Prob. 8-6 the signal is impressed in series with the 40-K resistor (instead of from grid to ground), find A.

8-8. Find the voltage amplification $A = E_o/E_s$. The signal E_s is a 1,000-cps sinusoid of small amplitude. The triode parameters are $\mu = 100$ and $r_p = 50$ K.

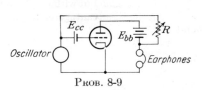

PROB. 8-6

8-9. The circuit shown can be used to measure the transconductance of a triode. Prove that, when a balance is obtained, $g_m = 1/R$ (see Ref. 2 of Chap. 8).

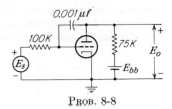

PROB. 8-8

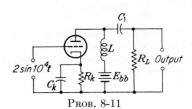

PROB. 8-9

8-10. A triode is operated as shown. Calculate the voltage gain at 1,000 cps. Draw a sinor diagram. $\mu = 20$, and $r_p = 10$ K.

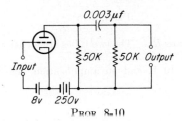

PROB. 8-10

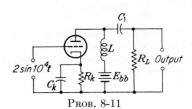

PROB. 8-11

8-11. A triode is used in the circuit shown. The circuit parameters have the following values: $L = 10$ henrys, $C_1 = 0.10$ μf, $C_k = 10$ μf, $R_L = 10$ K, $E_{bb} = 300$ volts, $\mu = 50$, $r_p = 50$ K. It is desired to have a direct current of 1.0 ma in the plate circuit and a grid voltage of -3 volts when the applied signal is zero. Determine the following:

a. Self-bias resistor R_k.

b. Voltage gain of the amplifier.

c. Phase shift between input and output voltage. Draw a sinor diagram.

Note that no grid battery is used in this circuit but that the voltage drop $I_b R_k$ acts as the grid bias.

8-12. The triode shown has a plate resistance of 2.5 K and an amplification factor of 5. If the rms-reading voltmeter V has a resistance of 10 K and negligible reactance, what will it read? The input signal E is 12 volts rms at a frequency of 1,000 cps. The reactance of the capacitor C may be neglected in comparison with the voltmeter resistance.

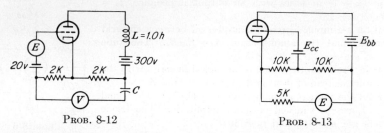

PROB. 8-12 PROB. 8-13

8-13. Draw the equivalent circuit and find the a-c plate current in the tube shown. The tube constants are $\mu = 10$ and $r_p = 5$ K. The 1,000-cycle oscillator E has an rms output of 0.2 volt.

8-14. Analyze the circuit shown, which is known as a *bootstrap* circuit. This provides the same gain but without the 180-deg phase reversal of a conventional amplifier. It has the disadvantage of requiring isolation of the input-signal source from ground.

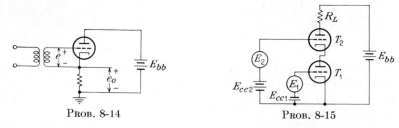

PROB. 8-14 PROB. 8-15

8-15. Find an expression for the a-c voltage across R_L. The two tubes are identical and have parameters μ, r_p, and g_m.

8-16. Each tube has a plate resistance $r_p = 10$ K and an amplification factor $\mu = 20$. Find the gain
a. e_o/e_1, if $e_2 = 0$.
b. e_o/e_2, if $e_1 = 0$.

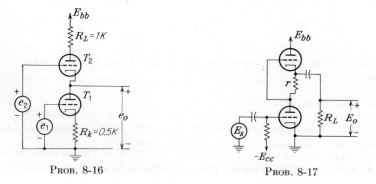

PROB. 8-16 PROB. 8-17

8-17. *a.* Prove that the magnitude of the signal current is the same in both tubes provided that

$$r = \frac{1}{g_m} + \frac{2R_L}{\mu}$$

Neglect the reactance of the capacitors.

b. If r is chosen as in part *a*, prove that the voltage gain is given by

$$A = \frac{-\mu^2}{\mu + 1} \frac{R_L}{R_L + r_p/2}$$

8-18. Calculate the signal current I in terms of the signal voltage E_1 and E_2. The parameters of each tube are $\mu = 70$ and $r_p = 44$ K.

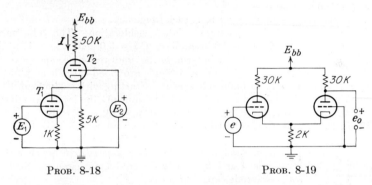

PROB. 8-18   PROB. 8-19

8-19. *a.* If $\mu = 19$ and $r_p = 10$ K for each tube, find the voltage gain $A = e_0/e$
b. Find the output impedance.

8-20. Derive the current-source equivalent circuit from the Taylor's series expansion, Eq. (8-19).

8-21. Analyze the Miller bridge circuit of Fig. 8-19 using the current-source equivalent circuit.

8-22. Verify the expression (8-23) for the gain of the grounded-grid amplifier, taking source impedance into account.

8-23. Prove that the input impedance for the grounded-grid amplifier is $(r_p + R_L)/(\mu + 1)$.

8-24. *a.* Given a cathode follower with the grid resistor R_g connected from grid to cathode. Prove that the input impedance Z_i is greater than R_g and is given by

$$Z_i = \frac{R_g}{1 - A}$$

where A is the voltage gain.

b. For a 12AU7 with $R_k = 20$ K and $R_g = 1$ megohm, find the value of Z_i.

8-25. Calculate the input impedance (the impedance seen by E_s) for the circuit of Prob. 8-8.

8-26. Solve Prob. 8-15 by replacing T_2 by its Thévenin's equivalent looking into its cathode (Prob. 8-5*b*).

8-27. Solve Prob. 8-16 by replacing T_1 by its Thévenin's equivalent looking into its plate (Prob. 8-4*b*) and by replacing T_2 by its Thévenin's equivalent looking into its cathode (Prob. 8-5*b*).

8-28. Solve Prob. 8-18 by the method suggested in Prob. 8-27.

8-29. Solve Prob. 8-19 by using the Thévenin's equivalent circuit looking into each cathode (Prob. 8-5*b*).

8-30. *a.* A 6SF5 triode works into a 100-kilohm resistive load.   Calculate the complex voltage gain and the input admittance of the system for frequencies of 100 and 100,000 cps.   Take the interelectrode capacitances into consideration.   The tube parameters are $\mu = 100$, $r_p = 66$ K, $g_m = 1.5$ millimhos, $C_{gk} = 4.0$ μμf, $C_{pk} = 3.6$ μμf, and $C_{gp} = 2.4$ μμf.

Compare these results with those which are obtained when the interelectrode capacitances are neglected.

b. Calculate the input resistance and capacitance.

8-31. Calculate the input admittance of a 6C5 triode at 10^3 and 10^6 cps when the total plate-circuit impedance is

a. A resistance of 50 K.

b. An inductive reactance of 50 K at each frequency.

Take the interelectrode capacitances into consideration.   The tube parameters are $\mu = 20$, $r_p = 10$ K, $g_m = 2.0$ millimhos, $C_{gk} = 3.0$ μμf, $C_{pk} = 11.0$ μμf, and $C_{gp} = 2.0$ μμf.   Express the results in terms of the input resistance and capacitance.

8-32. A 6J5 (6SN7) is incorporated in a simple grounded-cathode amplifier circuit. It is to be operated at the recommended point.   Starting with a zero load, how much resistance must be introduced as load in order to multiply the input capacitance by a factor of 6? $C_{pk} = 0.7$, $C_{gk} = 2.4$, $C_{gp} = 3.9$μμf, $\mu = 20$, $r_p = 7.7$K.

8-33. In the circuit shown the triode is used as an adjustable impedance element, by varying the d-c bias and thereby the g_m of the triode.

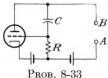

a. Assume that there is a generator E between the terminals A and B.   Draw the equivalent circuit.   Neglect interelectrode capacitances.

b. Show that the input admittance between A and B is

PROB. 8-33

$$Y_i = Y_p + (1 + g_m R) Y_{CR}$$

where Y_p is the admittance corresponding to r_p and Y_{CR} is the admittance corresponding to R and C in series.

c. If $g_m R \gg 1$, show that the effective input capacitance is

$$C_i = \frac{g_m \alpha}{\omega(1 + \alpha^2)}$$

and the effective input resistance is

$$R_i = \frac{(1 + \alpha^2) r_p}{1 + \alpha^2(1 + \mu)}$$

where $\alpha \equiv \omega C R$.

d. At a given frequency show that the maximum value of C_i (as either C or R is varied) is obtained when $\alpha = 1$ and

$$(C_i)_{\max} = \frac{g_m}{2\omega}$$

Also show that the value of R_i corresponding to this C_i is

$$(R_i)_{\max} = \frac{2r_p}{2 + \mu}$$

which, for $\mu \gg 2$, reduces to $(R_i)_{\max} = 2/g_m$.

e. The tube is a 6SN7 (see Fig. 7-8) operated at 5,000 cps. If the bias is adjusted so that the tube current can be varied over the range from 2 to 20 ma, over what range do $(C_i)_{max}$ and $(R_i)_{max}$ vary?

8-34. Solve for the analogous quantities to those asked for in Prob. 8-33, if the capacitor C is replaced by an inductor L.

8-35. Verify Eq. (8-49) for the gain of a cathode follower.

8-36. Verify Eq. (8-55) for the output impedance of a cathode follower.

8-37. A PJ-22 phototube and a 6SN7 amplifier are used in the circuit shown for counting certain objects. When no object is in the path of the incident beam, the intensity on the cell is 100 ft-c. Under this condition, it is desired that there be no current in the relay. When an object interrupts the light beam, the light intensity on the cell is 5 ft-c and it is desired that the relay should close. If the relay closes at 20 ma, for what range of values of R will the circuit operate properly? The relay resistance is 1 kilohm.

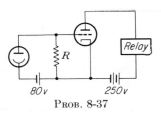

PROB. 8-37

8-38. In the circuit shown the illumination on the phototube is 50 ft-c. Calculate the current in each resistor.

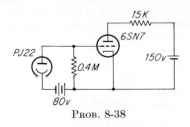

PROB. 8-38

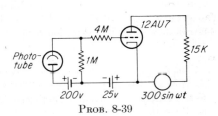

PROB. 8-39

8-39. In the figure shown the phototube controls the load current of the triode. As used in this circuit, the phototube current I_b as a function of the intensity j (in foot-candles) is given by the equation

$$I_b = \frac{j}{10}$$

where I_b is in microamperes.

a. Find the minimum illumination that will send current through the 15-K load.

b. If the illumination is fixed at 150 ft-c, what is the peak instantaneous load current?

c. Make a rough plot of the a-c input voltage as a function of time, and (using the same abscissa) make a rough plot of the instantaneous load voltage for the fixed illumination of 150 ft-c. In particular, indicate where the output voltage drops to zero.

8-40. Design a photocell circuit that will close a relay if the illumination exceeds 0.1 lumen and will open the relay if the illumination falls below 0.02 lumen. A type 929 photocell, a type 12AT7 amplifier, and a 1-K relay that closes at 10 ma and opens at 2 ma are to be used. The voltage source for each tube is the 120-volt d-c house supply.

a. Sketch the circuit.

b. Calculate the resistance needed to couple the phototube to the amplifier.

c. Calculate the grid bias that must be used.

Chapter 9

9-1. Verify Eqs. (9-16) starting with Eqs. (9-12) and (9-15).

9-2. *a.* A transistor is operating in the cutoff region with both the emitter and collector junctions reverse-biased by at least a few tenths of a volt. Prove that the currents are given by

$$I_E = \frac{I_{EO}(1 - \alpha_F)}{1 - \alpha_F \alpha_R}$$

$$I_C = \frac{I_{CO}(1 - \alpha_R)}{1 - \alpha_F \alpha_R}$$

b. Prove that the emitter-junction voltage required just to produce cutoff ($I_E = 0$ and the collector back-biased) is

$$V_E = V_T \ln(1 - \alpha_F)$$

c. Evaluate I_C, I_E, and I_B in part *a* and V_E in part *b* for an *n-p-n* 2N35 transistor for which (at room temperature) $\alpha_F = 0.98$, $I_{CO} = 2\ \mu$a, and $I_{EO} = 1.6\ \mu$a.

9-3. *a.* Given an *n-p-n* 2N35 transistor for which (at room temperature) $\alpha_F = 0.98$, $I_{CO} = 2\ \mu$a, and $I_{EO} = 1.6\ \mu$a. A common-emitter connection is used, and $V_{CC} = 12$ volts and $R_L = 4.0$ K. What is the minimum base current required in order that the transistor enter its saturation region?

b. Under the conditions in part *a* find the voltages across each junction and between each pair of terminals, if the base spreading resistance r_B is neglected.

c. Repeat part *b* if the base current is 200 μa.

d. How are the above results modified if $r_B = 250$ ohms?

9-4. Plot emitter current vs. emitter-to-base voltage for a 2N35 transistor if

a. $V_C = 0$.

b. V_C is back-biased by more than a few tenths of a volt. Neglect the base spreading resistance.

9-5. Plot carefully to scale the common-emitter characteristic I_C/I_B vs. V_{CE} for a transistor with $\alpha_F = 0.90 = \alpha_R$.

9-6. Derive the expression (9-32) for the parameters a_{21} and a_{22} in terms of the physical constants of the transistor.

9-7. *a.* If it is *not* assumed that $W/L_B \ll 1$, prove that Eqs. (9-29) and (9-31) remain valid provided that

$$a_{11} = Ae\left(D_p \frac{p_{no}}{L_B} \coth \frac{W}{L_B} + \frac{D_n n_{EO}}{L_E}\right)$$

$$a_{12} = a_{21} = -AeD_p \frac{p_{no}}{L_B} \operatorname{csch} \frac{W}{L_B}$$

$$a_{22} = Ae\left(D_p \frac{p_{no}}{L_B} \coth \frac{W}{L_B} + \frac{D_n n_{CO}}{L_C}\right)$$

b. Show that, if $W/L_B \ll 1$, these expressions reduce to those given by Eqs. (9-30) and (9-32).

9-8. Show that Eq. (9-34) follows from Eq. (9-33).

9-9. Using the results of Prob. 9-7, verify Eqs. (9-35) to (9-40).

9-10. Obtain the exact expression (9-36) for the transport factor β by carrying out the partial derivative in the definition of β in Eq. (9-43).

9-11. Obtain the exact expression (9-37) for the cathode efficiency γ by carrying out the partial derivative in the definition γ in Eq. (9-42).

9-12. *a.* A 2N104 transistor (Appendix IX) is used in a common-emitter circuit with $V_{CC} = 4$ volts and $R_L = 2$ K. If bias is obtained by connecting a 100-K resistor from collector to base, find the quiescent point.

b. Find the stability factor S if $\alpha_E = 44$.

9-13. *a.* In order to see how much less variable the circuit of Fig. 9-16 is than that of Fig. 9-15 to a change of transistor, consider that two 2N35 transistors are available, one with the characteristics in Fig. A9-1 and the second with the same shape but with I_B replaced by $I_B/2$. (For example, the curve marked $I_B = 40\,\mu$a for the first transistor is marked 20 μa for the second transistor.) Take $V_{CC} = 22.5$ volts, $R_L = 5.6$ K, $R_B = 250$ K for Fig. 9-16 and $R_B = 560$ K for Fig. 9-15 so that with transistor 1 both circuits are operating at $I_B = 40$ μa and $I_C = 2.2$ ma. Find I_C for each circuit for transistor 2.

b. Repeat part *a* for transistor 3, whose characteristics are obtained from transistor 1 by changing I_B to $2I_B$. In other words, the curve marked 40 μa is now called 80 μa.

9-14. For the two-battery transistor circuit shown prove that the stabilization factor S is given by

$$S = \frac{1}{1 - \alpha + \alpha R_1/(R_1 + R_2)}$$

9-15. *a.* Verify Eq. (9-56).

b. Show that S may be put in the form

$$S = \frac{G_1 + G_2 + G_3}{(1 - \alpha)G_1 + G_2 + G_3}$$

PROB. 9-14

where the G's are the conductances corresponding to the R's.

9-16. Determine the quiescent currents and the collector-to-emitter voltage for a 2N35 transistor in the self-biasing arrangement of Fig. 9-18. The circuit-component values are $V_{CC} = 20$ volts, $R_L = 2$ K, $R_1 = 0.1$ K, $R_2 = 5$ K, and $R_3 = 100$ K.

9-17. A *p-n-p* 2N104 transistor is used in the self-biasing arrangement of Fig. 9-18. The circuit-component values are $V_{CC} = 4.5$ volts, $R_L = 1.5$ K, $R_1 = 0.27$ K, $R_2 = 2.7$ K, and $R_3 = 27$ K.

a. If $\alpha_E = 44$, find the stabilization factor S.

b. Find the quiescent point.

c. Recalculate the above values if the base spreading resistance of 690 ohms is taken into account.

9-18. *a.* A 2N35 transistor is used in the self-biasing arrangement of Fig. 9-18 with $V_{CC} = 16$ volts and $R_L = 1.5$ K. The quiescent point is chosen to be $V_{CE} = 8$ volts and $I_C = 4$ ma. A stabilization factor $S = 12$ is desired. If $\alpha_B = 0.98$, find $R_1, R_2,$ and R_3.

b. Repeat part *a* for $S = 3$.

c. What is the "price" paid for the improved stability in part *b*?

9-19. *a.* A *p-n-p* 2N104 transistor is used in a common-collector circuit (Fig. 9-18 with $R_L = 0$). The circuit-component values are $V_{CC} = 3.0$ volts, $R_1 = 1$ K, $R_2 = R_3 = 5$ K. If $\alpha = 0.978$, find S.

b. Find the quiescent point.

c. Recalculate the above values, taking the base spreading resistance of 690 ohms into account.

Chapter 10

10-1. Verify the transformation equations in Table 10-1.

10-2. Verify the expression in Table 10-2 for A_i for a grounded-base amplifier

a. By direct evaluation of the short-circuit current divided by $I_g = V_g/R_g$.

b. By substituting A_v and R_o in Eq. (10-17).

10-3. Verify the expression in Table 10-2 for R_o for a grounded-base amplifier by evaluating the current I_a drawn from an auxiliary voltage V_a impressed across the output terminals (with zero input voltage and $R_L = \infty$). Then $R_o = V_a/I_a$.

10-4. Verify the expressions in Table 10-2 for A_v and R_o for a grounded-emitter configuration.

10-5. Repeat Prob. 10-2 for the common-emitter configuration.

10-6. Repeat Prob. 10-3 for the common-emitter configuration.

10-7. In Fig. 10-4b replace $r_m I_e$ by $-r_m(I_b + I_c)$ and convert the term containing I_b into a current generator. Show that this procedure results in the common-emitter T equivalent circuit of Fig. 10-9. NOTE: In Fig. 10-4b replace i by I.

10-8. Repeat Prob. 10-2 for the common-collector configuration.

10-9. Repeat Prob. 10-3 for the common-collector configuration.

10-10. Repeat Prob. 10-4 for the common-collector configuration.

10-11. Verify the expression in Table 10-2 for R_i for the common-collector configuration.

10-12. Draw a linear equivalent circuit for the common-collector configuration using a current generator proportional to

a. The input current.

b. The output current.

c. Is there an advantage in using one or the other of these circuits?

10-13. From the equivalent T circuit write down the common-emitter short-circuit current gain A_{ie} as the ratio of two currents, subject to the restriction that $R_g \gg R_i$. Do the same for the common-collector current gain A_{ic}. Show that $A_{ie} + A_{ic} = 1$. Check this relationship in Table 10-3.

10-14. Draw the equivalent circuits for the common-emitter and common-collector configurations subject to the restriction that $R_L = 0$. Show that the input impedances of the two circuits are identical. Verify this relationship in Table 10-2.

10-15. For a common-base amplifier with $R_g = 0$ prove that the voltage gain A is given approximately by Eq. (9-1), namely, $A \cong aR_L/r_e'$. Make the assumptions that the base spreading resistance is zero and that the load resistance is small enough so that $r_b R_L/r_c \ll r_e$. Make use of the relationships in Tables 10-3 and 10-1.

$\beta \quad T$
10-16. Given a grounded-emitter amplifier with the following parameters: $r_b = 750$ ohms, $r_e = 13$ ohms, $r_d = 20$ K, $a_e = 50$, $R_g = 1$ K, and $R_L = 2$ K. Draw the equivalent circuit and calculate the voltage gain. Check your result by using the solution given in Table 10-2.

10-17. *a.* Evaluate R_i for the three configurations for $R_L = 10$ K. Use the transistor parameter values given in Table 10-3.

b. Evaluate R_o for the three configurations for $R_g = 50$ K.

10-18. For the common-base configuration what is the maximum value of R_L for which R_i does not exceed 50 ohms? Use the transistor parameter values given in Table 10-3.

10-19. *a.* For a common-emitter configuration what is the maximum value of R_L for which R_i differs by no more than 10 per cent of its value for $R_L = 0$? Use the transistor values given in Table 10-3.

b. What is the maximum value of R_g for which R_o differs by no more than 10 per cent of its value for $R_g = 0$?

10-20. Repeat Prob. 10-19 for the common-collector configuration.

10-21. For a common-emitter configuration what parameter can be obtained

a. From the vertical spacing of the collector characteristics?

b. From the slope of these characteristics?

c. Evaluate these parameters for the 2N35 at the quiescent point $I_c = 1$ ma and $V_{CE} = 4$ volts.

10-22. Consider n identical common-emitter stages in cascade. If n is greater than unity, prove that the input impedance is given approximately by

$$R_i = r_b + \frac{r_e}{1 - a}$$

10-23. In the illustrative problem in Sec. 10-5 replace each stage by its equivalent T circuit. Solve the resultant four-mesh network for the output current in terms of the input voltage and then calculate the over-all voltage gain.

10-24. In the illustrative problem in Sec. 10-5 find the output impedance of the two stages in cascade under the assumption that the input is an ideal

  a. Current source.

  b. Voltage source.

10-25. *a.* In the circuit shown, the output terminals are collector and ground. Prove that the relationships given in Table 10-2 for the common-emitter configuration remain valid provided that r_e is replaced by $r_e + R_1$.

  b. Now take the output terminals between emitter and ground. Prove that the expressions given in Table 10-2 for the common-collector configuration remain valid provided that R_L is replaced by R_1, that r_c is replaced by $r_c + R_L$, but that r_m ($=ar_c$) is not altered.

  c. Show that R_i is the same for parts *a* and *b*.

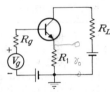

PROB. 10-25

10-26. *a.* The circuit of Prob. 10-25 has the following parameters: $R_L = 2$ K, $R_1 = 40$ ohms, $R_g = 0$, $r_e = 10$ ohms, $r_b = 1$ K, $r_c = 1$ megohm, and $a = 0.90$. Without using the results of Prob. 10-25, evaluate the voltage gain if the output is taken across R_1.

  b. Check your answer by using the results of Prob. 10-25*b*.

10-27. In the illustrative problem in Sec. 10-5 calculate the voltage gain of each stage by multiplying the short-circuit current gain by the effective load resistance R and dividing by the input resistance. The resistance R is the parallel combination of the actual load R_L, the output impedance R_o, and (except for the last stage) the input impedance R_i of the following stage.

10-28. Verify Eqs. (10-41) for the relationships between the H and the T parameters in the common-base configuration.

10-29. Verify Eqs. (10-45) for the relationships between the H and T parameters in the common-emitter configuration.

10-30. The HA7501 *p-n-p* silicon fused-junction transistor has the following common-base hybrid parameters:

$$h_i = 45 \text{ ohms} \qquad h_f = -0.88$$
$$h_r = 4 \times 10^{-4} \qquad h_o = 1.0 \ \mu\text{mho}$$

Find the parameters of the common-base and also of the common-emitter T-equivalent circuit.

10-31. The silicon transistor ST12 has the following hybrid parameters:

$$h_{fe} = 60 \qquad h_{ib} = 60 \text{ ohms}$$
$$h_{ob} = 0.4 \ \mu\text{mho} \qquad h_{rb} = 5 \times 10^{-4}$$

Find the parameters in the common-base and common-emitter T-equivalent circuits.

10-32. Given the following common-emitter hybrid parameters, find the common-base hybrid parameters:

$$h_{ie} = 2 \text{ K} \qquad h_{re} = 6 \times 10^{-4}$$
$$h_{fe} = 50 \qquad h_{oe} = 25 \ \mu\text{mhos}$$

10-33. Prove that the relationships between the common-base resistance parameters and the common-base equivalent-T parameters are

$$r_{11} = r_e + r_b \qquad r_{12} = r_b$$
$$r_{21} = r_b + ar_c \qquad r_{22} = r_c + r_b$$

10-34. Find the relationships between admittance parameters y_{11}, y_{21}, y_{13}, and y_{22} and the equivalent-T parameters for a common-emitter configuration.

Chapter 11

11-1. Draw the equivalent circuit of a pentode including *all* interelectrode capacitances. Show that to a very good approximation the input capacitance is equal to C_{gk} and C_{gs} in parallel and that the output capacitance is equal to C_{pk}, C_{ps}, and C_{p3} in parallel. The symbols are defined in Sec. 11-5.

11-2. From the plate characteristics of a 6F6 power pentode (see Appendix IX), draw the transfer characteristics for a screen voltage of 250 volts and the following values of plate voltage: $E_b = 80$, 160, 240, and 320 volts.

11-3. A 6F6 pentode (see Appendix IX) is operated at the quiescent point $E_c = -15$ volts, $E_b = 200$ volts. Draw the dynamic curves for the following values of load resistance: 1, 5.5, and 10 kilohms.

11-4. A 6AU6 pentode (Fig. 11-7) is operated at the quiescent point $E_{c1} = -2.0$ volts, $E_{c2} = 150$ volts, and $E_b = 200$ volts.

    a. Plot the transfer characteristic.

    b. Plot the dynamic characteristic for a load resistance of 20 K.

11-5. A 6AU6 pentode (Fig. 11-7) is operated at the quiescent point $E_{c1} = -2.5$ volts, $E_{c2} = 150$ volts, and $E_b = 200$ volts.

    a. What is the plate resistance r_p?

    b. What is the transconductance g_m for an increase in plate current?

    c. Repeat part *b* for a decrease in plate current.

    d. Find the average value of g_m.

    e. Find μ using the results of parts *a* and *d*. Why can μ not be found directly from the plate characteristics?

11-6. A 6AU6 amplifier (Fig. 11-7) used in the circuit shown has a voltage gain of 15. It is desired that the quiescent point be $E_{c1} = -1.0$ volt and $E_{c2} = 150$ volts. The capacitors may be considered to be arbitrarily large. The screen current is 0.4 of the plate current. Evaluate

    a. g_m.

    b. R_L.

    c. R_k.

    d. R_s.

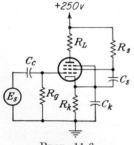

+250v

PROB. 11-6

11-7. *a.* Given a pentode amplifier with an unbypassed cathode resistor R_k. (In the figure of Prob. 11-6, $C_k = 0$.) Prove that the amplification A is approximately given by

$$A = \frac{g_m R_L}{1 + g_m R_k}$$

b. Note that if $g_m R_k \gg 1$ then $A \cong R_L/R_k$ independent of g_m. What is the significance of this result?

11-8. *a.* The circuit shown can be used as a d-c voltmeter with a very high input impedance. The two tubes are identical pentodes although shown as triodes for convenience. The indicating instrument has a resistance R_m. Draw the equivalent circuit, and show that the meter current will be

$$\frac{\mu R E}{(R_k + \mu R_k + R + r_p)(2R + R_m) - 2R^2}$$

where E is the d-c voltage to be measured.

b. The meter is a 1-ma milliammeter whose resistance is 100 ohms. $R = 10$ kilohms. The tubes are 6SJ7's for which $g_m = 1.65$ millimhos and $r_p = 1.0$ megohm, approximately. If $R_k \gg r_p/\mu = 1/g_m$, show that $I_m = E/2R_k$ approximately. For example, if $R_k = 50$ kilohms, full-scale reading will correspond to 100 volts. Note that the meter reading depends only upon R_k and hence the calibration will be stable, i.e., independent of the aging or the replacement of the tubes or voltage supply. Show

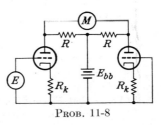

PROB. 11-8

that, in general, $I_m = E/2R_k$ provided that the following inequalities are true:

$$r_p \gg R \gg R_m, \qquad \mu \gg 1, \qquad \text{and} \qquad R_k \gg \frac{1}{g_m}$$

11-9. a. Prove that the short-circuit common-emitter current gain is

$$\mathbf{A}_i = \frac{\alpha \mathbf{Z}_c - \mathbf{Z}_e}{(1 - \alpha)\mathbf{Z}_c + \mathbf{Z}_e}$$

where $\mathbf{Z}_c$ is the parallel impedance of r_c' and C_c, and $\mathbf{Z}_e$ is the parallel impedance of r_e' and C_e.

b. Since $\mathbf{Z}_e \ll |(1 - \alpha)\mathbf{Z}_c|$, show that $\mathbf{A}_i = \dfrac{\alpha(\omega)}{1 - \alpha(\omega)}$.

11-10. Prove that the product of the zero-frequency current gain and the alpha cutoff frequency is the same for the common-emitter as for the common-base configuration.

11-11. a. Evaluate $\alpha(\omega_\alpha)$ from Eq. (11-23) with $\alpha_0 = 1$. Verify that its magnitude is 0.775 and its phase angle is 50 deg.

b. If ω_α is given by Eq. (11-24), verify that the magnitude of $\alpha(\omega_\alpha)$ is 0.707 and its phase is 58 deg.

11-12. For an n-p-n germanium transistor $W = 1$ mil and $\tau_n = 4$ μsec. Find

a. $f_{\alpha b}$.

b. $f_{\alpha e}$.

11-13. A silicon p-n-p transistor has an alpha cutoff frequency of 100 kc. What is the base thickness?

11-14. a. If $\gamma = 1$ and if $W^2/L_B^2 \ll 1$, prove that the common-emitter cutoff frequency is given by $\omega_{\alpha e} = 1/\tau_B$.

b. If W^2/L_B^2 is small but not negligible compared with unity, prove that

$$\omega_{\alpha e}\tau_B = 1 - \frac{1}{12}\frac{W^2}{L_B^2}$$

Chapter 12

12-1. Calculate the concentration of gas molecules in a "vacuum" tube at 10^{-6} mm Hg pressure and room temperature,

a. If the gas is nitrogen.

b. If the gas is neon.

12-2. If 1.0 g of argon gas is confined in a volume of 1 liter at 40°C, what is the pressure of the gas?

12-3. Obtain Eq. (12-2) directly from Eq. (12-1) without the use of Loschmidt's number. Convert the pressure from newtons per square meter to millimeters of Hg.

12-4. A gas tube contains argon at a pressure of 15 mm Hg and 25°C. How many molecules per cubic meter have energies within the range of 0.100 to 0.101 ev?

12-5. *a.* Prove that the average energy E_{av} of gas molecules is given by

$$E_{av} = \frac{\int_0^\infty E\rho_\eta \, d\eta}{\int_0^\infty \rho_\eta \, d\eta}$$

b. Verify that $E_{av} = \frac{3}{2}E_T$.

12-6. *a.* Calculate the mean free path of a mercury molecule in a rectifier operating at a mercury condensation temperature of 40°C. The pressure is 0.006 mm Hg. The radius of a mercury molecule is 1.82 A.

b. Calculate the number of collisions per second.

c. Calculate the random current density. Assume that $\frac{1}{10}$ of 1 per cent of the molecules are ionized.

12-7. Calculate the number of collisions per second made by a neon molecule, if the pressure is 1 mm Hg and the temperature is 100°C. The radius of a neon molecule is 1.17 A.

12-8. A gas photocell contains ionized argon (atomic radius $= 1.43 \times 10^{-10}$ m) at a pressure of 0.3 mm Hg and room temperature of 20°C. On an average, how many collisions are made by an ion in traveling a distance of 2 cm?

12-9. Show that the time for one revolution of the electron in the hydrogen atom in a circular path about the nucleus is

$$T = \frac{m^{\frac{1}{2}}e^2}{4\sqrt{2}\,\epsilon_0(-W)^{\frac{3}{2}}} \qquad \text{sec}$$

where the symbols are as defined in Sec. 12-3.

12-10. Bohr postulated that the stationary states are determined by the condition that *the angular momentum must be an integral multiple of $h/2\pi$*, where h is Planck's constant. For the hydrogen atom show that (in mks units)

a. The possible radii are given by

$$r = \frac{h^2\epsilon_0 n^2}{\pi m e^2} \qquad \text{meters}$$

where n is any integer but not zero. For the ground state ($n = 1$) show that the radius is 0.53 A.

b. The energy levels are given by

$$W_n = -\frac{me^4}{8h^2\epsilon_0^2}\frac{1}{n^2} \qquad \text{joules}$$

c. The reciprocal of the wave length (called the *wave number*) of the spectral lines is given by

$$\frac{1}{\lambda} = R\left(\frac{1}{n_2^2} - \frac{1}{n_1^2}\right) \qquad \text{waves/m}$$

where n_1 and n_2 are integers with n_1 greater than n_2 and $R = me^4/8\epsilon_0^2h^3c = 1.10 \times 10^7/m$ is called the *Rydberg constant*.

If $n_2 = 1$, this formula gives a series of lines in the ultraviolet called the *Lyman series*. If $n_2 = 2$, the formula gives a series of lines in the visible, called the *Balmer series*. Similarly the series for $n_2 = 3$ is called the *Paschen series*. These predicted lines are observed in the hydrogen spectrum.

12-11. Show that Eq. (12-15) follows from Eq. (12-14).

12-12. A photon of wave length 1,400 A is absorbed by cold mercury vapor, and two other photons are emitted. If one of these is the 1,850-A line, what is the wave length of the second photon?

12-13. Cold mercury vapor is bombarded with radiation, and as a result the fluorescent lines 2,537 A and 4,078 A appear. What wave length must have been present in the bombarding radiation?

12-14. The six lowest energy levels of hydrogen are 0, 10.19, 12.07, 12.73, 13.04, and 13.20 ev. If cold hydrogen vapor absorbs the ultraviolet 972-A line, what possible fluorescent lines may appear?

12-15. The seven lowest energy levels of sodium vapor are 0, 2.10, 3.19, 3.60, 3.75, 4.10, and 4.26 ev. A photon of wave length 3,300 A is absorbed by an atom of the vapor, and three other photons are emitted.

a. If one of these is the 11,380-A line, what are the wave lengths of the other two photons?

b. Between what energy states do the transitions take place in order to produce these lines?

12-16. What might happen if cold mercury vapor is bombarded with

a. One 5.00-ev photon?

b. One 5.00-ev electron?

c. One 5.46-ev photon?

12-17. *a.* With what speed must an electron be traveling in a sodium-vapor lamp in order to excite the yellow line whose wave length is 5,893 A?

b. Could electrons with this speed excite the 2,537-A line of Hg?

12-18. *a.* What is the minimum speed with which an electron must be traveling in order that a collision between it and an unexcited neon atom may result in ionization of this atom?

b. What is the minimum frequency that a photon can have and still be able to cause photoionization of a neon atom?

12-19. An X-ray tube is essentially a high-voltage diode. The electrons from the hot filament are accelerated by the plate supply voltage so that they fall upon the anode with considerable energy. They are thus able to effect transitions among the tightly bound electrons of the atoms in the solid of which the target (the anode) is constructed.

a. What is the minimum voltage that must be applied across the tube in order to produce X rays having a wave length of 0.5 A?

b. What is the minimum wave length in the spectrum of an X-ray tube across which is maintained 60 kv?

12-20. An electron, after falling through a potential of 10 volts, collides with a mercury atom that is in its lowest metastable state. As a result of the impact the atom is elevated to its 7.73-volt level. What is the energy in joules of the impinging electron after the collision? Assume that the kinetic energy of the atom is unaffected by the collision.

12-21. Argon resonance radiation falls upon sodium vapor. If a photon ionizes an unexcited sodium atom, with what speed is the electron ejected?

12-22. A metastable neon atom possessing 16.6 volts energy "collides" with an unexcited argon atom and ionizes this atom. If the atoms are at rest before and after the impact, calculate the energy with which the electron is emitted.

12-23. Consider a Townsend discharge in which there is zero concentration of electrons at the cathode (no photocurrent, and the γ emission is negligible). There is a constant volume ionization due to an external source of q ions per cubic meter per second. Show that the current density at any distance x is given by

$$J = \frac{qe}{\alpha} (\epsilon^{\alpha x} - 1)$$

where e is the electronic charge and α is the first Townsend coefficient.

12-24. In a gas photocell there is a pressure for which the current is a maximum at a given field intensity (or since the spacing is fixed, at a given voltage). Show that this is the pressure at which a line through the origin is tangent to the α/p curve.

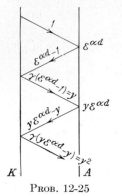

Prob. 12-25

12-25. Prove that an electron released at the cathode of a gas diode with plane-parallel electrodes will yield $\epsilon^{\alpha d}/(1 - y)$ electrons at the anode. This is essentially Eq. (12-20). The symbols have the meanings used in Sec. (12-14) with the added abbreviation $y = \gamma(\epsilon^{\alpha d} - 1)$.

Proceed by considering the sequence of events indicated in the sketch. One electron released at the cathode multiplies to $\epsilon^{\alpha d}$ electrons at the anode. Owing to this ionization, there are liberated $\epsilon^{\alpha d} - 1$ positive ions which travel to the cathode and there release $\gamma(\epsilon^{\alpha d} - 1) = y$ secondary electrons. These y electrons multiply by ionization to $y\epsilon^{\alpha d}$ at the anode. Hence $y\epsilon^{\alpha d} - y$ positive ions travel to the cathode and liberate $\gamma(y\epsilon^{\alpha d} - y) = y^2$ secondary electrons, etc. The total number of electrons at the anode is obtained by adding the number that reach the anode owing to each of the individual events, as outlined above. The result is a geometric series with an infinite number of terms.

12-26. Using plane-parallel electrodes in air at 1 mm Hg pressure and a constant electric-field intensity of 160 volts/cm, the following data were taken:

d, cm	0.5	1.0	1.5	2.0	2.5	3.0	3.5
$\dfrac{I_b}{I_e}$	2.42	5.87	14.4	35.1	88.2	250	915

a. Verify the theory of Sec. 12-14 by finding the value of α and γ.

b. What are the breakdown separation and the breakdown voltage?

NOTE: These data are based upon the results of F. H. Sanders, *Phys. Rev.*, **44**, 1020, 1933.

12-27. Given two cold-cathode tubes as shown, containing the same gas at the same pressure. The cathode of tube 2 has a much larger surface than that in tube 1. Sketch the volt-ampere characteristic of each tube. Give the reasons for your expected curves.

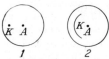

Prob. 12-27

12-28. The sparking-potential curves of a gas as a function of pressure for two different separations, d_1 and d_2, of the plane-parallel electrodes are illustrated. Which is the greater distance, and why?

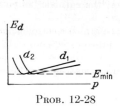

PROB. 12-28

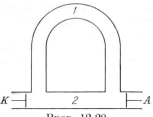

PROB. 12-29

12-29. It is found that as the voltage is increased from zero, a discharge takes place between the cathode and anode through the long path 1 instead of the short path 2 of the tube sketched. Explain.

12-30. Using the tube of Prob. 12-29 at a constant voltage between K and A, the pressure is gradually decreased. Explain why the discharge will first take the shorter path and then the longer path.

12-31. It is often said that a field of 3×10^6 volts/m is required for sparking in air at atmospheric pressure. Show that this is true only for a spacing of 1 cm. In particular, what is the breakdown field strength for 0.25 cm separation?

12-32. Given a gas at a constant pressure between plane-parallel electrodes. The breakdown curve as a function of separation of electrodes shows a minimum. Explain why this is to be expected physically.

12-33. Given a thermionic plane cathode and a plane-parallel collector a distance d apart in an envelope containing a gas at a high pressure. The mean free path is so small that each electron makes many collisions with the gas molecules and hence may be considered to be traveling with a steady drift velocity proportional to the electric-field intensity. (In a vacuum where there is no mechanical hindrance due to collisions with molecules the electron would move with constant acceleration and not constant velocity.) Assume that the energy per mean free path is less than the ionization potential so that the tube is operating under space-charge conditions. If the mobility is μ, then the drift speed v is given by

$$v = -\mu \mathcal{E} = \mu \frac{dV}{dx}$$

Show that the maximum current at a plate potential E_b is given by

$$I_b = \frac{S\mu E_b^{\frac{3}{2}}}{32\pi \times 10^9 d^3}$$

where S is the cathode area.

HINT: Proceed as in Sec. (4-4).

12-34. *a.* Consider a tube with plane-parallel electrodes between which there is a constant charge density ρ. Show that the potential at any point is given by the formula

$$V = \frac{E_b x}{d} + \frac{\rho x}{2\epsilon_0}(d - x)$$

where d is the cathode-anode separation, E_b is the anode potential, and ϵ_0 is the permittivity of free space in mks units.

b. Show that if ρ is positive there exists a potential maximum greater than the anode voltage. This corresponds to the electron trap of Fig. 12-11.

12-35. Show that the electric-field intensity at the cathode end of the cathode-fall region is equal to $4E_k/3d_k$, where E_k and d_k represent the cathode-fall potential and distance, respectively.

12-36. The cathode fall of potential for brass plane-parallel electrodes in air is 350 volts. Calculate the normal current density if the pressure is 1 mm Hg. Use an average molecular weight for air.

12-37. Plane-parallel barium-coated electrodes are sealed in a tube containing argon gas and connected as indicated in Fig. 12-6. The gas pressure inside the tube is 0.15 mm Hg. The distance between the electrodes is 10 cm. The sparking-potential curve for this tube is indicated. The supply voltage E_{bb} is increased until the tube conducts. The load is a 10-megohm resistor.

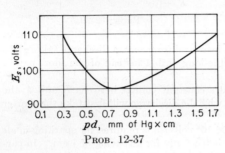

PROB. 12-37

a. At what minimum value of E_{bb} will the tube conduct?

b. If the voltage is held at this minimum value, what will be the tube current? Assume that the maintaining tube drop is equal to the Paschen's minimum.

c. Calculate the cathode area which is covered with glow for the current in part *b.*

12-38. In a certain mercury discharge the random ion current density is 6.0 amp/m². A probe is maintained 10.0 volts negative with respect to the plasma. Calculate the thickness of the positive-ion sheath.

Chapter 13

13-1. An 884 argon-filled triode is to be used as a sweep-circuit relaxation oscillator in the circuit of Fig. 13-9. If $E_{cc} = 25$ volts, $E_{bb} = 400$ volts, $C = 0.0025$ μf, $R = 1.0$ megohm, and the extinction voltage is 16 volts,

a. Calculate the frequency of oscillation.

b. Calculate the peak amplitude of the generated oscillations.

c. If the peak current rating of the tube is 0.5 amp, what is a suitable value for R'?

d. Plot the wave shape of the sweep voltage, assuming that the capacitor discharges through the tube in zero time.

Assume that Fig. 13-7 represents the critical grid characteristic of the tube.

13-2. An 885 thyratron is used as a relaxation oscillator in the circuit of Fig. 13-9. The critical grid curve for the tube is that given in Fig. 13-7. The extinction voltage is 15 volts. If the sweep-speed error is not to exceed 5 per cent, design a 60-cycle sweep whose amplitude is 25 volts. Specify reasonable values of E_{bb}, E_{cc}, R, and C, and give reasons for your choice.

13-3. The 884 thyratron is to operate as a saw-tooth oscillator with an amplitude of 100 volts at a frequency of 1,000 cps.

If the maintaining voltage is 15 volts find

a. E_{cc}.

b. C.

c. If the peak current rating of the tube is 0.5 amp, what is a suitable value for R?

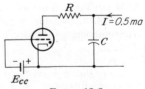

PROB. 13-3

13-4. A saw-tooth oscillator uses an 884 thyratron. A 450-volt power supply is available. A 500-cps saw-tooth wave is desired with a peak-to-peak amplitude of 45 volts. Assume that the maintaining voltage is 15 volts.

a. Draw and design a circuit using nominal components.

b. What is the slope error?

13-5. In the circuit of Fig. 13-9 a 929 phototube (Fig. 6-14) is used in place of the resistor R. Explain clearly why this circuit will now give a linear sweep output.

Design a 1,000-cycle 50-volt sweep. The intensity of the illumination on the photo-cell is 0.1 lumen. Specify E_{bb}, E_{cc}, and C. Assume that an 885 thyratron is used for which the maintaining voltage is 15 volts and the critical grid starting characteristic is that given in Fig. 13-7.

13-6. In the circuit sketched the 929 phototube controls the current in the 884 thyratron. For what range of values of light flux will the thyratron be nonconducting? Explain your analysis clearly.

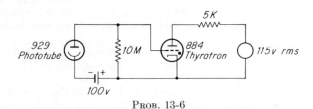

Prob. 13-6

13-7. The circuit of Fig. 13-9 is modified by replacing the resistor R by a 6AU6 pentode (Fig. 11-7).

a. Explain clearly why this will result in an approximately linear sweep. How can the amplitude of the sweep be controlled? How can the frequency be adjusted without changing the amplitude?

b. The screen voltage on the 6AU6 is 150 volts. The plate supply voltage is 300 volts. The capacitor is 0.1 μf. A 300-cycle 150-volt linear sweep is desired. Specify the grid voltages of the 6AU6 and the 884 tubes. Assume that the critical grid characteristic of the 884 is given in Fig. 13-7 and that $E_m = 15$ volts.

c. The screen voltage on the 6AU6 is 150 volts. The plate supply voltage is 300 volts. A 200-volt 5,000-cycle sweep is desired. Specify the grid voltages of the 6AU6 and the 884 tubes and also the value of the capacitance C.

13-8. *a.* Why would it be impossible to design an 80-volt 100-cycle linear sweep using a d-c power supply voltage of 250 volts, a 0.05-μf capacitor, an 884 thyratron (Fig. 13-7), and a 929 phototube (Fig. 6-14)?

b. Replace the phototube with a 6AU6 pentode (Fig. 11-7), and complete the design. Sketch the complete circuit, and give *all* battery voltages.

c. If the peak current rating of the 884 is 0.5 amp, what is a suitable value for the plate-current limiting resistance?

13-9. Design a 150-volt 10,000-cycle linear sweep using a d-c power supply voltage of 250 volts. Sketch the circuit and specify all tubes, all tube voltages, all resistors, capacitors, etc. Explain your analysis, and state clearly any assumptions you may make.

13-10. *a.* In Fig. 13-9 $E_{bb} = 250$ volts, $E_{cc} = 75$, $R = 1$ megohm, and $C = 0.01$ μf. The maintaining voltage is 15 volts. A single narrow pulse is applied across R_g. What is the minimum pulse amplitude which will fire the tube?

b. Sketch the wave form across C.

c. A train of narrow pulses of large amplitude whose repetition frequency is f is applied across R_g. What is the slope error if $f = 10$ kc?

d. For what value of f will the sweep amplitude be 50 volts?

13-11. Given two cylindrical glow-discharge tubes having cathode dimensions as shown. Both tubes have the same cathode material. The current range of T_1 is 5 to 50 ma.

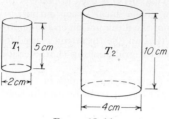

PROB. 13-11

a. If the tubes are filled with the same gas at the same pressure, what is the maximum current rating of T_2?

b. Suppose that the pressure in T_2 is twice that in T_1, what is the corresponding maximum current rating of T_2?

13-12. *a.* An OD3/150 and an OA3/75 tube are to be used in series to give a constant output voltage of 225 volts. The supply voltage is 300 volts. What is the value of the current-limiting resistor that must be used if the nominal load current is 25 ma and the nominal tube current is 15 ma?

b. If the load suddenly decreases by 5 ma, what will be the tube current?

c. The load is as in part *a.* If the supply voltage suddenly changes to 310 volts, what will be the tube current?

13-13. *a.* An OC3/105 voltage-regulator tube is used in the circuit of Fig. 13-17. The load fluctuates between 40 and 60 ma. If the supply voltage remains constant at 245 volts, find the value of R so that the load voltage is maintained fixed at 105 volts. Assume that the normal operating range of the tube is 5 to 40 ma.

b. With R set as in part *a* and with the load fixed at 50 ma, find the range over which the supply voltage may vary without affecting the output voltage.

13-14. An OC3/105 is used in the circuit shown as a simple relaxation oscillator. R and C are to be chosen to yield a recurrence frequency of 1,000 cps.

a. Calculate and plot the wave shape of the output, when $E_{bb} = 125$ volts. (Choose the starting voltage as 115 volts, extinction voltage at 103 volts.)

b. Repeat when $E_{bb} = 400$ volts.

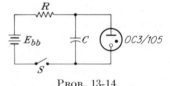

PROB. 13-14

c. Discuss the matter of linearity on the basis of these results. In particular, determine the voltage excursion over which the slope error is within 5 per cent in each case.

13-15. Show that the period of oscillation of a relaxation oscillator of the type illustrated in Fig. 13-9 and Prob. 13-14 is

$$T = RC \ln \frac{E_{bb} - E_e}{E_{bb} - E_d}$$

where E_d is the voltage at which the tube starts to conduct and E_e is the extinction voltage.

13-16. The tube used in the sweep circuit of Prob. 13-14 has a breakdown voltage of 160 volts, an extinction voltage of 140 volts, $E_{bb} = 300$ volts, and $RC = 0.02$ sec.

a. Find the sweep amplitude.

b. Find the sweep frequency.

c. Find the slope error.

d. If the sweep frequency and sweep amplitude are to remain constant, how can the deviation from linearity be reduced?

13-17. *a.* An OA4-G tube is used in the circuit of Fig. 13-19 with $E_{bb2} = 100$ volts and $E_{bb1} = 80$ volts. What is the largest value of grid-limiting resistor for which the current will transfer to the main anode? Assume that there is no input pulse.

b. What is the value of the load resistance needed to obtain full rated load current of 25 ma?

13-18. An OA4-G tube is to be used in the circuit of Fig. 13-19. The resistor in the control anode circuit is 2 megohms, and the load consists of a 1,500-ohm relay. Assume that there is no input pulse.

a. What is the maximum value of E_{bb2} for which the load current will not exceed the rated value of 25 ma?

b. What is the minimum value of E_{bb1} in order that the tube operate properly?

13-19. The circuit shown is a photocell-operated warning circuit.

a. What is the minimum photocell current which will operate the buzzer?

b. What is the maximum voltage across the photocell?

c. What is the maximum voltage across the buzzer coil?

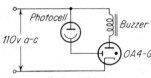

PROB. 13-19

d. During what fraction of a cycle does current flow through the buzzer if the photocell current is 50 μa?

13-20. *a.* In the neon spectrum, there are a number of levels grouped between 16.6 and 16.8 volts and another group between 18.3 and 18.9 volts. In what part of the spectrum are the lines emitted by transitions between these two groups of levels?

b. Other prominent lines in the spectrum originate on the 20.7-volt level and end on levels in the 18.3- to 18.9-volt group. To what spectral region do the emitted photons belong?

It is these transitions which are responsible for the characteristic color of a neon sign.

Explain why cold neon vapor is transparent to the red lines which give a neon sign its brilliance.

Chapter 14

14-1. A vacuum diode whose internal resistance is 200 ohms is to supply power to a 1,000-ohm load from a 300-volt (rms) source of supply. Calculate

a. The peak load current.
b. The d-c load current.
c. The a-c load current.
d. The d-c tube voltage.
e. The total input power to the plate circuit.
f. The efficiency of rectification.
g. The percentage regulation from no load to the given load.

14-2. Show that the maximum d-c output power in a half-wave single-phase circuit occurs when the load resistance equals the plate resistance.

14-3. Prove that the regulation of both the half-wave and the full-wave rectifier is given by

$$\% \text{ regulation} = \frac{r_p}{R_L} \times 100\%$$

14-4. A full-wave single-phase rectifier consists of a double-diode tube the internal resistance of each element of which may be considered to be constant and equal to 500 ohms. These feed into a pure resistance load of 2,000 ohms. The secondary transformer voltage to center tap is 280 volts rms. Calculate

a. The d-c load current.
b. The direct current in each tube.
c. The a-c voltage across each diode.
d. The d-c output power.

e. The efficiency of rectification.

f. The percentage regulation from no load to the given load.

14-5. Verify Eq. (14-33), which gives the ripple factor in a half-wave gas-tube circuit.

14-6. Show that the input power to the plate circuit of any rectifier circuit using gas diodes may be expressed in the form

$$P_i = I_{\text{rms}}^2 R_L + E_0 I_{dc}$$

where the symbols have the meanings used in the text.

14-7. Gas diodes are used in a full-wave circuit.

a. Show that the direct current is

$$I_{dc} = \frac{2E_m}{\pi R_L} \left[\cos \alpha_1 - \left(\frac{\pi}{2} - \alpha_1 \right) \sin \alpha_1 \right]$$

where $\sin \alpha_1 \equiv E_0/E_m$ and it is assumed that the maintaining and extinction voltages equal E_0.

b. Show that the efficiency of rectification is

$$\eta_r = \frac{4}{\pi} \frac{\left[\cos \alpha_1 - \left(\frac{\pi}{2} - \alpha_1 \right) \sin \alpha_1 \right]^2}{\frac{\pi}{2} - \alpha_1 - \sin \alpha_1 \cos \alpha_1} \times 100\%$$

14-8. A gas diode is used in a half-wave circuit to supply a 500-ohm resistor from the 220-volt a-c mains. The breakdown and maintaining voltages are constant at 10 volts. Calculate the readings of the following instruments:

a. A d-c ammeter in series with the load.

b. An a-c ammeter in series with the load.

c. A d-c voltmeter placed across the tube.

d. An a-c voltmeter placed across the tube.

e. A wattmeter whose current coil is in series with the load and whose voltage coil is across the input.

f. The efficiency of rectification.

14-9. A mercury-vapor diode is used in a half-wave circuit to supply power to a 15-ohm resistor from a 12-volt rms source of voltage. Assume that the breakdown and maintaining voltages of the tube are constant at 12 volts. Calculate

a. The peak load current.

b. The phase angles in each cycle at which conduction starts and stops.

c. The d-c load current.

d. The a-c load current.

e. The d-c load power.

f. The efficiency of rectification.

14-10. A high-pressure gaseous rectifier is used to charge a 6-volt battery at a 6-amp charging rate. The tube drop is constant at 10 volts. The filament input is 18 amp at 2.2 volts. If the 120-volt a-c mains are applied directly, calculate

a. The value of the series resistor needed.

b. The over-all efficiency.

If the 120-volt d-c lines are used instead of the a-c lines, calculate the quantities called for in parts a and b.

Assume that the battery resistance is constant at 0.05 ohm and that the battery voltage is constant at 6 volts throughout the charging process.

14-11. In the full-wave single-phase bridge, can the transformer and the load be interchanged? Explain carefully.

14-12. A 1-ma d-c meter whose resistance is 10 ohms is calibrated to read rms volts when used in a bridge circuit using copper oxide elements. The effective resistance of each element may be considered to be zero in the forward direction and infinite in the inverse direction. The sinusoidal input voltage is applied in series with a 5-K resistor. What is the full-scale reading of this meter?

14-13. Find the minimum insulation voltage required of each of the filament transformers in the voltage doubling circuit of Fig. 14-11 if

a. The positive side of the output is grounded.

b. The negative is grounded.

The peak alternating voltage is E_m.

14-14. The circuit shown is a half-wave voltage doubler. Analyze the operation of this circuit. Calculate

a. The maximum possible voltage across each capacitor.

b. The peak inverse voltage of each tube.

c. The cathode-to-ground insulation stress.

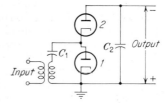

PROB. 14-14

Compare this circuit with the bridge voltage doubler of Fig. 14-11. In this circuit the output voltage is negative with respect to ground. Show that if the connections to the cathode and anode of each tube are interchanged, the output voltage will be positive with respect to ground.

14-15 The circuit of the preceding problem can be extended from a doubler to a quadrupler by adding two tubes and two capacitors as shown. (*a*) and (*b*) are alternative ways of drawing the same circuit.

a. Analyze the operation of this circuit.

b. Answer the same questions as those asked in Prob. 14-14.

c. Generalize the circuit of this and the preceding problem so as to obtain n-fold multiplication when n is any even number. In particular, sketch the circuit for six-fold multiplication.

d. Show that n-fold multiplication, with n odd, can also be obtained provided that the output is properly chosen.

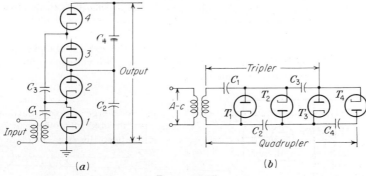

PROB. 14-15

14-16. By connecting two half-wave doublers of the type illustrated in Prob. 14-14 to the same input, show that it is possible to obtain a full-wave quadrupler. Explain the operation of this circuit.

14-17. Explain, with the aid of a circuit diagram, exactly what happens in a full-wave single-phase circuit employing two single-anode tank rectifiers when an arc-back occurs.

14-18. A controlled rectifier is adjusted so as to fire at an angle φ in each cycle. The peak of the applied alternating voltage is E_m, and the load resistor is R_L. Derive expressions for

    a. The rms tube current.

    b. The rms voltage drop across the tube.

    c. The total output power.

Assume that the tube drop is negligible in comparison with E_m.

14-19. The arc drop in a certain thyratron is 10 volts. The tube is operated from a 440-volt rms sinusoidal source. The load is a resistance of 100 ohms. Calculate the average value of the plate current

    a. When the grid and plate voltages are in phase.

    b. When the grid voltage lags the plate voltage by 30 deg.

    c. When the grid voltage leads the plate voltage by 30 deg.

Assume that the critical grid voltage is zero for all values of plate voltage.

14-20. The thyratron circuit of Fig. 14-20 is used to regulate the average current in a 250-ohm plate load resistor of an FG-27A tube. The voltage $E_{ab} = 220$ volts rms at 60 cps, Z_1 is a 1,000-ohm resistor, and Z_2 is a variable inductor whose resistance may be neglected.

    a. If the inductance is set at 2.65 henrys, draw a sinor diagram showing the grid and the plate voltages (before conduction starts in each cycle). Sketch these voltages approximately to scale as a function of $\alpha = \omega t$. Determine the angle at which the tube will fire.

    b. What is the magnitude of the d-c plate current that will be obtained with the conditions adjusted as in part *a*?

    c. As the inductance is varied, what are the maximum and minimum values of direct current that can be obtained?

    d. If the resistance R of the inductor is not negligible, discuss the modifications that must be made in the solution of this problem. In particular, redraw the sinor diagram, taking R into account.

    e. If Z_1 is a variable capacitor and Z_2 is a 1,000-ohm resistor, repeat parts *a*, *b*, and *c*. For part *a* the capacitance is adjusted to 1.53 μf.

14-21. Control of a thyratron is to be obtained with a fixed 1-μf capacitor and a variable resistor R. The tube drop is 15 volts.

    a. Draw a sinor diagram and determine whether Z_1 or Z_2 is to be R.

    b. If $R = 0$, what is the value of the direct current through the 500-ohm load?

    c. If R is adjusted so that the grid voltage lags the plate voltage by 90 deg, what will an a-c voltmeter across the tube read?

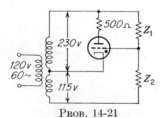

PROB. 14-21

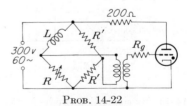

PROB. 14-22

14-22. In the thyratron circuit shown the transformer primary and secondary windings are so arranged that continuous phase shift control is obtained as R is varied.

a. Draw a sinor diagram showing the grid and plate voltages (before conduction starts in each cycle).

b. What is the plate current if R is extremely large?

c. What is the plate current if R is very small?

d. What is the plate current if $R = X_L$?

The transformer reactances may be considered to be infinite.

14-23. In the phase-shift-controlled thyratron circuit shown the reactance of the inductor is twice the reactance of the capacitor. The resistance of the choke coil may be neglected. The phase is varied by varying the resistance R.

a. Draw the sinor circle diagram showing the phase angle θ between the grid and plate voltage (before conduction starts in each cycle).

b. Prove that $\tan (\theta/2) = X/R$ and that the magnitude of the grid voltage equals the magnitude of the plate voltage.

c. Between what limits can the d-c load current be varied? To what values of R do these limits correspond?

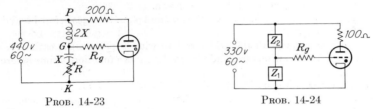

PROB. 14-23   PROB. 14-24

14-24. It is desired to control the current in the 100-ohm resistor in the plate circuit of the thyratron shown by means of the phase-shift method.

a. If a fixed 0.5-μf capacitor and an adjustable resistor R are available, which must be Z_1 and which must be Z_2? Show by a sinor diagram the reason for your choice.

b. What value of R will cause the largest d-c plate current? Calculate the value of this current.

c. What is the minimum value of the controlled direct current?

d. What must the value of R be in order that 70 per cent of the maximum possible current pass through the load?

e. Repeat parts *a*, *b*, *c*, and *d* if a 10-henry inductor (of negligible resistance) is available instead of the 0.5-μf capacitor.

14-25. *a.* In the thyratron circuit shown, a fixed inductor of 4 henrys and a variable resistor are used. With the aid of a sinor diagram, decide whether Z_1 or Z_2 must be the resistor in order to have control as R is varied.

b. What is the maximum reading of a d-c ammeter in series with the load, and for what value of R is this obtained?

c. The resistor is set at 1,000 ohms. Calculate the reading of an a-c voltmeter across the tube.

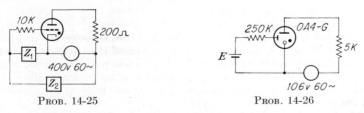

PROB. 14-25   PROB. 14-26

14-26. An OA4-G cold-cathode triode is used to control the current in a 5-K resistor. Use the transfer characteristics and maintaining voltages of Fig. 13-18.

a. The d-c control anode voltage E is highly positive and is slowly reduced toward zero.   At what value of E does the current in the 5-K resistor just drop to zero?

b. If E is just slightly larger than the value found in part *a*, sketch the wave shape of the plate current.

c. Calculate the reading of a d-c ammeter in the plate circuit if E is set as in part *b*.

14-27. An FG-27A thyratron is operated at a mercury condensation temperature of 35°.   The plate supply voltage is 440 volts rms.   The load is a 100-ohm resistor. Calculate the d-c plate current under the following conditions:

a. The grid bias is −5 volts.

b. An a-c voltage whose rms value is 5 volts is used instead of a battery in the grid circuit.   Assume that the grid lags the plate voltage by 90 deg.

c. The grid circuit is excited by the d-c and a-c voltages of parts *a* and *b* in series.

14-28. In Fig. 14-28, C is replaced by a 1,000-ohm resistor, and R is replaced by a 1.53-henry inductor.   The power line is 115 volts rms at 60 cps.   The load is a 250-ohm resistor.   Assume that the critical grid curve of the thyratron coincides with the zero voltage axis and that the tube drop is zero.

a. If $E_c = 0$, find the angle between the grid and plate voltages before breakdown by means of a sinor diagram.

b. If $E_c = 67$ volts (with the grid negative with respect to the cathode), draw a diagram of the instantaneous grid and plate voltages as a function of time before breakdown.

c. Under the conditions of part *b*, find the d-c plate current.

14-29. In Fig. 14-28 it is desired that the direct current through the load be varied from maximum current to 2 amp by means of the d-c bias.   The magnitude of the reactance X_C is twice the resistance R.   The power line is 240 volts at 60 cps, and the load resistor is 25 ohms.

a. What direct current is obtained when the d-c bias E_c is zero?

b. What is the maximum direct current, and at what bias is it obtained?

c. What bias must be supplied to reduce the direct current to 2 amp?

14-30. A thyratron is controlled by the bias phase method.   The plate supply is 400 volts rms, the load resistance is 1,000 ohms, and the a-c grid supply, which lags the plate supply by 30 deg, is 100 volts rms.   Plot roughly to scale the d-c load current as a function of the d-c bias from −200 to +200 volts.   In particular, calculate

a. The maximum current and the d-c bias at which it is obtained.

b. The current at zero d-c bias.

c. The bias at which the current will drop to zero.

14-31. Bias phase control is employed in a thyratron circuit.   The critical grid starting characteristic of the tube may be assumed to coincide with the zero voltage axis.   Sketch roughly to scale the ratio I_{dc}/I' as a function of the ratio of the d-c bias E_c to the peak a-c grid voltage E_{gm} for the following conditions:

a. The grid voltage lags the plate voltage by 90 deg.

b. The grid voltage leads the plate voltage by 90 deg.

c. The grid voltage lags the plate voltage by 150 deg.

d. The grid voltage leads the plate voltage by 150 deg.

e. For case *a* prove that the result is a straight line, as shown in Fig. 14-31.

14-32. An FG-33 positive-grid thyratron is operated at an ambient temperature of 35°.   The plate excitation is a sinusoidal voltage whose peak value is 400 volts.   The load is a 100-ohm resistor.   An a-c grid voltage of adjustable maximum value E_{gm} is applied in phase with the plate voltage.   Plot a curve showing the relationship between the average plate current I_{dc} and E_{gm}.

14-33. The peak sinusoidal voltage applied to the plate of an FG-27A thyratron,

operating at 35° ambient temperature, is 400 volts. The load is a 100-ohm resistor.
The a-c grid voltage lags the plate voltage by a fixed angle of 150 deg. The peak grid
voltage E_{gm} is adjustable. Plot the curve showing the relationship between the
average plate current I_{dc} and E_{gm}.

14-34. What fraction of the maximum plate current is obtained in the thyratron
circuit shown when the grid is connected to points A, B, and C, respectively? Draw
diagrams of instantaneous plate and grid voltages in each case.

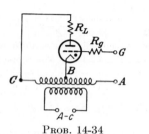

PROB. 14-34

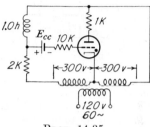

PROB. 14-35

14-35. *a.* Draw a sinor diagram for the circuit shown and state whether or not the
grid circuit has control over the plate current, with the connection shown. If not,
redraw the circuit correctly for control.

b. Find the d-c plate current when the grid bias voltage E_{cc} is 60 volts.

c. Find the maximum and minimum d-c plate current and the corresponding battery
bias voltages.

d. Make a list of any assumptions made in your calculations in parts *b* and *c*.

14-36. In the circuit shown the illumination on the phototube controls the direct
current in the FG-27A thyratron load R_L. Find the direct current in R_L when the
illumination is 100 ft-c.

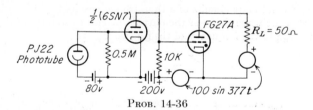

PROB. 14-36

14-37. Two FG-27A tubes operate at a temperature of 50°C in a full-wave controlled rectifier circuit.

a. If the firing angle is φ deg behind the anode voltage, sketch curves showing the
current wave shape in the load.

b. Derive expressions for the following:

1. Direct current in load.
2. Alternating current in load.
3. Efficiency of rectification.

14-38. FG-27A thyratrons are employed in the full-wave controlled rectifier illustrated. The tubes operate at 50°C.

a. The lines *a* and *b* of the control circuit are to be connected to the power lines 1 and 2. Show by a voltage diagram which lines are connected together for conduction to occur for less than a half cycle per tube.

b. Calculate the direct current in the load.

c. Calculate the total a-c power to the plate circuit.

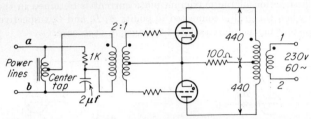

PROB. 14-38

14-39. Two thyratrons are operated in the full-wave circuit shown. Assume that the critical grid characteristic coincides with the zero-voltage axis. Neglect the tube drop. The load resistance is $R_L = 200$ ohms.

a. By means of a phasor diagram, decide how to interconnect the points P_1, P_2, P_3, and P_4 for bias phase control.

b. Find the d-c load current if the bias voltage E_{cc} is 50 volts.

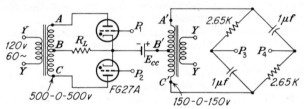

PROB. 14-39

14-40. The grid and plate circuits of a thyratron are excited by 115-volt sinusoidal voltages. Sketch the wave shape of the output current if the ratio of the frequency of the plate voltage to the frequency of the grid voltage is

a. 2.

b. $\frac{1}{2}$.

c. 3.

d. $\frac{1}{3}$.

14-41. Design a circuit using thyratrons so that the plate current will have the "chopped" sinusoidal wave shape shown. Such a wave shape is employed as the "heat" control of electric resistance welding, although welders require ignitrons in order to meet the current requirements.

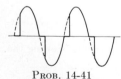

PROB. 14-41

14-42. An ignitron is used in the circuit of Fig. 14-33. The peak plate voltage is 500 volts, and the load is a 3-ohm resistor. Assume that conduction begins when the ignitor current exceeds 10 amp and that the ignitor rod acts as an ohmic resistance whose magnitude is 7 ohms. Calculate

a. The peak power taken by the rod.

b. The average power taken by the rod.

c. The d-c power supplied to the load.

d. The ratio of (*b*) to (*c*).

Neglect the tube drop of the diode in series with the ignitor rod. Neglect the ignitron tube drop. The frequency is 60 cps.

14-43. Sketch a single-phase full-wave rectifier circuit using ignitrons and any other auxiliary apparatus needed.

14-44. An ignitron is used as a half-wave rectifier. The ignitor is adjusted so that conduction commences 90 deg after the start of each cycle of applied voltage. The tube drop during conduction equals 20 volts. The applied voltage is 300 volts rms, and the load is a 50-ohm resistor. Calculate

 a. The d-c load current.
 b. The power taken by the tube.
 c. The total power delivered to the plate circuit.
 d. The rms load current.
 e. The total power taken by the load resistor. Obtain the solution to part e from that in part d, and check this against the result obtained by subtracting the solution to part b from that to part c.

14-45. An ignitron is used in a half-wave circuit to supply power to a 15-ohm resistor from a 320-volt rms source of supply. Breakdown occurs when the potential across the tube in the conduction direction is 225 volts. When the tube conducts, the potential drop across it is 15 volts. Calculate

 a. The reading of an a-c ammeter in series with the load.
 b. The reading of a d-c ammeter in series with the load.
 c. The reading of an a-c voltmeter across the tube.
 d. The reading of a d-c voltmeter across the tube.
 e. The reading of an a-c voltmeter across the load.
 f. The reading of a d-c voltmeter across the load.
 g. The power dissipated in the tube.
 h. The d-c load power.
 i. The average power supplied by the source.
 j. The efficiency of rectification.

14-46. Two ignitrons are operated in the *inverse-parallel* connection shown. The firing angle is set at 30 deg. Assume ideal transformers and a resistive load.

Draw diagrams showing the following wave shapes in the circuit.

 a. Voltage across ignitron.
 b. Voltage across welding transformer.

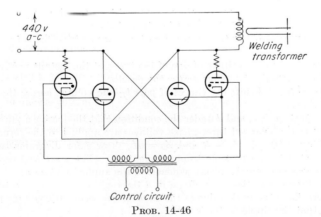

PROB. 14-46

14-47. *a.* In the circuit sketched, neither tube is conducting.   A positive pulse is applied to the grid of tube 1 and fires it.   Then a positive pulse is applied to the grid of tube 2.   This extinguishes tube 1 and fires tube 2.   Explain why.

If, now, another positive pulse is applied to tube 1, what will happen?

What is the limitation on the rapidity with which two succeeding pulses may be applied so as to cause the current to shift from one tube to the next?

b. The points 1 and 2 are connected together so that a positive pulse is applied simultaneously to the grids of both tubes.   Explain clearly what will happen as successive pulses are applied to the grids.

Note: It must be remembered that the critical grid starting characteristics vary slightly from tube to tube.

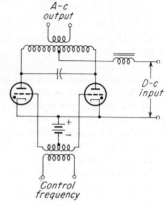

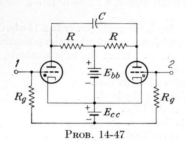

PROB. 14-47   PROB. 14-48

14-48. Consider the separately excited parallel inverter circuit sketched.   Derive an expression for the potential across the capacitor C, which is also the output potential, if a perfect output transformer is assumed.   If the time constant of the circuit is small compared with the time for one-half cycle, show that the voltage across C is a square wave whose amplitude is equal to the d-c input voltage minus the tube drop and whose frequency equals the control frequency.

14-49. A single-phase full-wave rectifier is set to operate with a 30-deg delay angle. The load consists of a resistor in series with an inductor, the inductance of which is so large that the load current may be considered to be constant.   The secondary transformer voltage to center tap is 230 volts rms.   The tube drop during conduction is constant and is equal to 20 volts.

a. Sketch the voltage of each plate and also of the cathodes (with respect to the transformer-secondary center tap) as a function of time.

b. Sketch—directly below the curves of part *a*—the anode voltage of each tube as a function of time.

c. Calculate the anode voltage of one of the tubes at the instant before it fires.

d. Calculate the output voltage across the resistor.

e. Sketch—directly below the curves of part *b*—the voltage across the choke as a function of time.

f. Repeat parts *a*, *b*, *c*, and *d* under the condition that the load is a pure resistance.

14-50. By error, balanced three-phase voltages are applied to the terminals *A*, *K*, and *B* of Fig. 14-20.   If $Z_1 = R$ and $Z_2 = \omega L$, draw sinor diagrams to determine whether or not it is still possible to obtain control.   (There are two such diagrams possible, depending upon the phase sequence of the applied voltages.)

14-51. *a.* Prove that the d-c voltage in a three-phase half-wave rectifier is $3\sqrt{3}\,E_m/2\pi$, where E_m is the peak value of the transformer secondary voltage per leg.

b. Prove that the ripple factor is 0.182.

14-52. Show that the transformer currents in the three-phase bridge circuit of Fig. 14-39 are as depicted in Fig. 14-40.

14-53. Find the voltage e_c across the commutating inductor of Fig. 14-41 graphically from the wave forms of Fig. 14-42. Show that the result is approximately a triangular wave form whose fundamental frequency is three times the input frequency.

14-54. Verify all the items in one of the columns of Table 14-1. (The column is to be designated by the instructor.)

14-55. If there is a large enough inductance in series with the load so that the load current may be considered to be constant, show that the efficiency of rectification is given by $E_{dc}/(E_{dc} + E_0)$ for those polyphase circuits in which a single tube conducts at a time.

Chapter 15

15-1. *a.* To show the effect of phase shift on the image seen on a cathode-ray screen, consider the following: The sinusoidal voltages applied to both sets of plates should be equal in phase and magnitude so that the maximum displacement in either direction on the screen is 2 in. Because of frequency distortion in the horizontal amplifier the phase of the horizontal voltage is shifted 5 deg, but the magnitude is changed inappreciably. Plot to scale the image that actually appears on the screen and compare with the image that would be seen if there were no phase shift.

b. If the phase shift in both amplifiers were the same, what would be seen on the cathode-ray screen?

15-2. It is desired that the voltage gain of an RC-coupled amplifier at 60 cycles should not decrease by more than 10 per cent from its mid-band value. Show that the coupling capacitance must be at least equal to $0.0055/R_g'$ μf if R_g' is expressed in megohms.

15-3. An RC-coupled amplifier stage uses a 12AX7 tube (Table 7-1) with $R_L = 15$ K, $R_g = 1$ megohm, $C_c = 0.02$ μf, and $C_s = 50$ $\mu\mu f$. Evaluate

    a. f_1.

    b. f_2.

    c. The mid-band voltage gain in decibels.

    d. The phase shift at 20 cps.

    e The phase shift at 200 kc.

15-4. An RC-coupled amplifier stage uses a 6SL7 tube with $\mu = 70$, $r_p = 44$ K, $R_L = 50$ K, and $R_g = 1$ megohm. Assume a total shunting capacitance of 100 $\mu\mu f$. Find

    a. The mid band amplification in decibels

    b. f_2.

    c. C_c if $f_1 = 50$ cps.

15-5. The band width of an amplifier extends from 20 cps to 20 kc. Find the frequency range over which the voltage gain is down less than 1 db from its mid-band value.

15-6. Prove that over the range of frequencies from $10f_1$ to $0.1f_2$ the voltage amplification is constant to within 0.5 per cent and the phase shift to within ± 0.1 rad.

15-7. Three cascaded stages have an over-all upper 3-db frequency of 20 kc and a lower 3-db frequency of 20 cps. What are f_1 and f_2 of each stage?

15-8. Two stages of an RC-coupled amplifier consist of a double triode 12AT7 (Table 7-1) with $R_L = 10$ K, $R_g = 0.5$ megohm, and $C_s = 50$ $\mu\mu f$ for each stage.

a. What must be the value of C_c in order that the frequency characteristic of each stage be flat within 1 db down to 10 cps?

b. Repeat part *a* if the over-all gain of both stages is to be down 1 db at 10 cps.

c. At what high frequency is the over-all gain down 1 db?

d. What is the over-all mid-band voltage gain?

15-9. A three-stage RC-coupled amplifier uses 6SN7 tubes (Table 7-1) with $R_L = 10$ K, $R_g = 0.1$ megohm, $C_c = 0.005$ μf, and $C_s = 60$ $\mu\mu$f for each stage.   Evaluate

a. The over-all mid-band voltage gain in decibels.

b. f_1.

c. The over-all lower 3-db frequency.

d. f_2.

e. The over-all upper 3-db frequency.

15-10. Given two RC-coupled stages connected as in Fig. 15-1 and using a 12AU7 double triode tube.   The circuit parameters are $E_{bb} = 300$ volts, $E_{cc} = -5$ volts, the quiescent current $= 10$ ma, $g_m = 2.2$ millimhos, $r_p = 7.7$ K, $R_g = 1$ megohm, $C_c = 0.01$ μf, $C_{pg} = 1.5$ $\mu\mu$f, $C_{gk} = 1.6$ $\mu\mu$f, $C_{pk} = 0.5$ $\mu\mu$f, and shunt wiring capacitance per stage $= 20$ $\mu\mu$f.   The output is taken at E_3.   Find

a. The load resistance.

b. The mid-band gain of each stage and the over-all gain.

c. The input capacitance.

d. f_1.

e. f_2 for each stage.   Why do the two stages have different values of f_2 whereas f_1 is the same for both stages?

f. How are the above results modified if the output is observed on an oscilloscope whose input impedance is a 1-megohm resistance in parallel with a 20-$\mu\mu$f capacitance?

15-11. An RC-coupled amplifier uses a 6AK5 pentode stage ($g_m = 5.1$ millimhos and $C_o + C_i = 6.8$ $\mu\mu$f).   The stray wiring capacitance from the signal lead to ground in each stage is 10 $\mu\mu$f.   If $R_g = 1$ megohm, $C_c = 0.01$ μf, and a voltage gain of 15 per stage is desired, calculate

a. R_L.

b. f_1.

c. f_2.

If 6SN7 (Table 7-1) triode tubes are used instead of the pentodes, repeat parts a, b, and c.   Assume $C_{op} = 3.9$ $\mu\mu$f, $C_{gk} = 2.4$ $\mu\mu$f, and $C_{pk} = 0.7$ $\mu\mu$f.

15-12. Justify Eq. (15-23) for the over-all voltage gain of cascaded transistor amplifier stages.

15-13. A two-stage grounded-base transistor amplifier is fed from an ideal current source.   The load impedance for each stage is 10 K.   The transistor parameters are $\alpha = 0.99$, $r_b = 1.5$ K, $r_c = 1$ megohm, and $r_e = 25$ ohms.

a. Calculate the input impedance of each stage.

b. Draw the Norton's equivalent circuit for each stage.

c. Calculate the voltage gain of each stage.

d. Calculate the over-all voltage gain.

15-14. In the two-stage transistor amplifier of Fig. 15-7 the circuit values are $R_L = 3$ K, $C_c = 10$ μf, $R_b = 50$ K, and $R_g = \infty$.   The transistor parameters are $\alpha = 0.95$, $r_e = 10$ ohms, $r_c = 1$ megohm, $r_b = 1$ K, and $f_\alpha = 200$ kc.   Evaluate f_1 and f_2.

15-15. For the circuit of Prob. 15-14 find in the mid-band region

a. The current gain of each stage.

b. The voltage gain of each stage.

c. The over-all voltage gain.

15-16. Prove that the low-frequency voltage gain of a transistor amplifier relative to the mid-band voltage gain is given by the same formula as for the current gain ratio, namely, Eq. (15-27).

15-17. *a.* Consider an amplifier with a cathode resistor R_k used for self-bias. If this resistor is bypassed with a capacitor C_k, prove that the low-frequency amplification $\mathbf{A}_1$ relative to the mid-band amplification $\mathbf{A}_0$ is

$$\frac{\mathbf{A}_1}{\mathbf{A}_0} = \frac{1 + j\omega R_k C_k}{B + j\omega R_k C_k}$$

where $B = 1 + (\mu + 1)R_k/(r_p + R_L)$.

b. Prove that the lower 3-db frequency is $f_1 = \sqrt{B^2 - 2}/2\pi R_k C_k$. What is the physical meaning of the condition $B < \sqrt{2}$?

15-18. Self-bias is used with an amplifier. The tube is a 6SN7 with $R_L = 15$ K and $E_{bb} = 300$ volts.

a. If the quiescent voltage is to be -8 volts, what must be the value of the cathode resistance R_k?

b. What is the amplification with and also without R_k bypassed?

c. What C_k is required if the lower 3-db point is to be 20 cps? HINT: Use the result of Prob. 15-17.

15-19. In Fig. 15-11 the pentode is a 6AU6 operating at the quiescent point $E_b = 150$ volts, $E_{c1} = -1.5$ volts, $E_{c2} = 150$ volts, $E_{c3} = 0$. The screen current is 0.4 of the plate current. If $E_{bb} = 350$ volts, find

a. R_L.

b. R_d.

c. R_k.

15-20. Design a two-stage RC-coupled amplifier using a 6SN7 double triode to meet the following specifications: $E_{bb} = 300$ volts and no other d-c voltage sources are available; the load on the second stage is 50 K in parallel with 100 $\mu\mu$f; the voltage amplification is to be at least 100 at 1 kc and not less than 70.7 at 20 cps and 100 kc; the output voltage is to be about 50 volts rms with as little distortion as possible.

Specify all resistance and capacitance values. Assume $C_{gp} = 3.9$ $\mu\mu$f, $C_{gk} = 2.4$ $\mu\mu$f, $C_{pk} = 0.7$ $\mu\mu$f, and a stray wiring capacitance of 10 $\mu\mu$f.

Chapter 16

16-1. Verify that the output power for the series-fed amplifier of Fig. 16-1 is a maximum for $R_L = r_p$. Also show that the power is at least 89 per cent of its maximum value for $0.5r_p \leq R_L \leq 2r_p$.

16-2. *a.* Nonlinear distortion results in the generation of frequencies in the output that are not present in the input. If the dynamic curve can be represented by Eq. (16-7) and if the input signal is given by

$$e_g = E_1 \cos \omega_1 t + E_2 \cos \omega_2 t$$

show that the output will contain a d-c term and sinusoidal terms of (angular) frequency ω_1, ω_2, $2\omega_1$, $2\omega_2$, $\omega_1 + \omega_2$, and $\omega_1 - \omega_2$.

b. Generalize the results of part *a* by showing that if the dynamic curve must be represented by higher-order terms in e_g the output will contain intermodulation frequencies which are given by the sum and difference of integral multiples of ω_1 and ω_2, for example, $2\omega_1 \pm 2\omega_2$, $2\omega_1 \pm \omega_2$, $3\omega_1 \pm \omega_2$, etc.

16-3. A type 6L6 tube is operated as a triode with a load resistance of 2.0 kilohms and a plate supply of 300 volts. The grid bias is -15 volts, and the peak grid signal is 15 volts.

a. What is the fundamental current output?

b. What is the percentage second harmonic distortion?

c. What is the direct current?

Use the plate characteristics in Appendix IX.

16-4. A 6SN7 (Table 7-1 and Fig. A9-8) is to be operated from a B-supply voltage of 240 volts. A voltage gain of approximately 10 is desired. The peak-to-peak 2,000-cycle sinusoidal input voltage is 12 volts. If the grid is never to swing positively, specify

a. The load resistance.

b. The bias voltage.

c. The quiescent current.

d. The per cent second harmonic distortion.

e. The fundamental voltage and power gains.

16-5. A type 6B4-G triode supplies power to a 4-K load from a 300-volt source of power. The bias voltage is set at -40 volts, and a 40-volt-peak sinusoidal signal is applied. Using the plate characteristics in Fig. A9-6, plot

a. One cycle of the output plate current as a function of the time for the sinusoidal input grid signal.

b. On the same curve sheet, plot the calculated output curve on the assumption that the output will consist of the fundamental and a second harmonic distortion component. The magnitude of the fundamental and second-harmonic terms must be found first.

16-6. A 6B4-G triode (Fig. A9-6; $\mu = 4.2$, $r_p = 800$ ohms) is operated as a simple power amplifier with a load resistance of 800 ohms. The grid bias is -45 volts.

a. If the quiescent current is to be 60 ma, what must be the plate supply voltage?

b. If a 1,000-cycle signal whose peak value is 4.0 volts is applied to the grid, what will be the peak value of the output voltage?

c. If a 1,000-cycle signal whose peak value is 40.0 volts is applied to the grid, what will be the peak value of the 1,000-cycle output voltage?

d. Under the conditions of part *c*, what will be the peak value of the 2,000-cycle component of the output voltage?

e. Under the conditions of part *c*, what will be the d-c component of the plate current?

16-7. A triode supplies 0.85 watt to a 4-K load. The zero-signal d-c plate current is 31 ma, and the d-c plate current with signal is 34 ma. Determine the per cent second harmonic distortion.

16-8. The grid excitation of an amplifier is $e_g = \sqrt{2}\, E_g \sin \omega t$. Prove that the output current can be represented by a Fourier series which contains only odd sine components and even cosine components.

16-9. Supply the missing steps in the derivation of Eq. (16-19).

16-10. Obtain a seven-point schedule by the Espley method. Determine B_0, B_1, B_2, B_3, B_4, B_5, and B_6 in terms of I_{max}, $I_{\frac{2}{3}}$, $I_{\frac{1}{3}}$, I_b, $I_{-\frac{1}{3}}$, $I_{-\frac{2}{3}}$, and I_{min}.

16-11. Obtain a five-point schedule for determining B_0, B_1, B_2, B_3, and B_4 in terms of I_{max}, $I_{0.707}$, I_b, $I_{-0.707}$, and I_{min}.

16-12. A power triode feeds a load resistance R_L through an ideal transformer of turns ratio n. Show that the voltage gain is

$$A = \frac{n\mu\delta}{n^2 + \delta}$$

where $\delta \equiv R_L/r_p$, μ is the amplification factor, and r_p is the plate resistance of the tube.

Show that for a fixed value of δ and μ the maximum gain is $n\mu/2$ and is obtained when the turns ratio is adjusted to equal $\delta^{\frac{1}{2}}$.

Show that under these conditions the load resistance reflected into the primary equals the plate resistance.

16-13. A 2A3 operates under the conditions $E_c = -45$ volts, $E_{bb} = 400$ volts, and $R_L = 2$ K. A 45-volt peak sinusoidal signal is applied to the grid.

a. Calculate the power output, the power dissipated in the tube, and the plate-circuit efficiency.

b. If an ideal shunt-feed system is used instead of the series-feed system, calculate the value of E_{bb} in order that the tube operate at the same quiescent point as in part *a*.

c. Determine the power output, the power dissipated in the tube, and the plate-circuit efficiency for the shunt-feed system.

16-14. Calculate the output power, the plate-circuit efficiency, and the percentage second harmonic distortion of a 6L6 connected as a triode when supplying power to an effective 4,000-ohm load from a 300-volt supply, with $E_c = -22.5$ volts, if

a. The load is series-fed.

b. The load is transformer-coupled to the tube.

A 22.5-volt peak sinusoidal signal is impressed on the grid of the tube.

16-15. Draw three triode plate characteristics to correspond to the grid voltages $E_c + E_{gm}$, E_c, and $E_c - E_{gm}$. Draw the load line through the point $i_b = 0$, $e_b = E_{bb}$, and the Q point $e_c = E_c$, $i_b = I_b$, and $e_b = E_b$. This corresponds to a series-fed resistance load.

a. Assuming that the input signal is zero, indicate on the i_b-e_b plane the areas that represent the total input power to the plate circuit, the plate dissipation, and the power loss in the load resistance.

b. Repeat part *a* if the input signal is sinusoidal with a peak value equal to E_{gm}. Also, indicate the area that represents the output power.

c. The ratio of what two areas gives the plate-circuit efficiency?

d. Repeat parts *a*, *b*, and *c* for a shunt-fed load. Assume that the static resistance is small but not zero.

16-16. Verify the equations in Sec. 16-5 for the frequency response of an output transformer.

16-17. Verify Eqs. (16-37).

16-18. Prove that for a series-fed load the plate-circuit efficiency is given by

$$\eta_p = \frac{25}{1 + r_p/R_L} \quad \%$$

16-19. A 6L6 power triode operates at $E_b = 250$ volts. The maximum allowable plate dissipation is 10 watts. Draw curves of power output and second harmonic distortion vs. R_L for the following values of R_L: 3, 4, 5, 6, and 7 K.

16-20. A 2A3 triode is to be used in a transformer-coupled Class A₁ power amplifier to supply an audio-frequency signal to a load having a resistance of 50 ohms. A plate supply voltage of 250 volts is available, and the signal input voltage to the grid is sinusoidal with an rms value of 1.0 volt. The plate dissipation (for zero signal voltage) is 15.0 watts.

a. What output-transformer turns ratio will give maximum power output (assuming an ideal transformer)?

b. What is the a-c power output?

c. What is the plate-circuit efficiency?

d. Repeat parts *a*, *b*, and *c* if the magnitude of the grid signal is not restricted to 1.0 volt but rather any required voltage is available. The distortion is not to exceed 5 per cent. (Figure 16-10 will be helpful.)

16-21. A 6B4-G power triode is used with an output transformer. The plate supply voltage is 250 volts. Assume that any required grid swing is available. The distortion is not to exceed 5 per cent. Under this condition (case 2 in Sec. 16-6) the maximum power is obtained if $R_L = 2r_p$ ($= 1.6$ K). Find

a. The maximum power output.

b. The quiescent current.

c. The no-signal plate dissipation.

d. The maximum plate dissipation specified by the manufacturer is 15 watts. This value is used in Fig. 16-10 to determine the quiescent point. Discuss your results as compared with those indicated in Fig. 16-10.

16-22. a. A 6F6 pentode (Appendix IX) is operated at the quiescent point $E_c = -15$ volts, $E_b = 200$ volts. Draw the dynamic curves for the following values of load resistance: 1, 5.5, and 10 kilohms.

b. The grid signal voltage is sinusoidal with a peak value of 15 volts. Plot the output current as a function of time for each of the load resistances in part a.

c. Calculate the second, third, and fourth harmonic distortion for the 1- and the 10-K loads.

16-23. Calculate the distortion components in the output of a 6F6 tube connected as a pentode that supplies power to an effective 2-K load resistor. The screen is maintained at 250 volts, the grid bias is -20 volts, and the plate voltage at the quiescent point is 300 volts. The grid signal is sinusoidal and has a peak value of 20 volts.

16-24. a. A 6F6 pentode is operated with a screen voltage of 250 volts and a grid bias of -15 volts. The grid signal is sinusoidal and has a peak value of 15 volts. Calculate and plot as a function of the quiescent-plate voltage E_b the load resistance that must be used to give zero second harmonic distortion.

b. Calculate and plot as a function of E_b the third harmonic distortion for the conditions in part a.

16-25. Verify the data plotted in Fig. 16-13 for $R_L = 1$ K and for $R_L = 4$ K.

16-26. A 6L6 is operated at the quiescent point $E_{c1} = -14$, $E_b = 250$, and $E_{c2} = 250$. The peak grid swing is 14 volts. Use Fig. A9-11.

a. What must the load resistance be in order to eliminate second harmonic distortion?

b. For a load resistance of 2.5 kilohms, calculate the per cent third harmonic distortion.

16-27. A 6L6 operates at the quiescent point $E_{c1} = -15$ volts, $E_b = 200$ volts, $E_{c2} = 250$ volts. The grid signal is sinusoidal with a peak value of 15 volts. The load is shunt-fed.

a. Calculate the effective load resistance for which there will be zero second harmonic distortion.

With the load as determined in part a, calculate

b. The output power.

c. The power dissipated in the plate.

d. The plate-circuit efficiency.

16-28. A 6F6 operates as a pentode from a 250-volt screen supply, a 300-volt plate supply, and a 20-volt grid supply. An ideal output transformer having a turns ratio of 25:1 feeds a 4-ohm load. Calculate

a. The direct current if the input signal is zero.

b. The direct current if the input signal is sinusoidal having a peak value of 20 volts.

c. The percentage second and third harmonic distortion.

d. The fundamental power output.

e. The total power output.

16-29. Repeat Prob. 16-28 if the load has a value of 12 ohms instead of 4 ohms.

16-30. A voltage triode (one section of a 6SN7) with a 7.7-K load is RC-coupled to a 6B4-G power triode which feeds a 25-ohm load through an ideal transformer having a 10:1 turns ratio. The grid input resistance of each stage is 0.5 megohm. The quiescent operating point of the 6SN7 is $E_b = 250$ volts, $E_c = -8$ volts and of the 6B4-G is $E_b = 250$ volts, $E_c = -43.5$. The input signal voltage is 3 volts rms. The cathode bypass capacitors may be assumed arbitrarily large.

a. Draw the schematic wiring diagram.

b. Indicate the magnitudes of the self-biasing resistors and of the B-supply voltage for each tube.

c. Calculate the input voltage to the second stage.

d. Calculate the power delivered to the load.

e. Calculate the decibel gain (voltage and power) of each stage and of the entire system.

16-31. Design an audio amplifier capable of delivering at least 3 watts of undistorted power output to a 4-ohm load resistor. The largest input signal has an rms value of 0.3 volt and is capable of delivering very little power. Draw the schematic wiring diagram, using a 2A3 in the output stage. Indicate the values of all the circuit elements such as resistors, capacitors, and power supplies.

16-32. In a push-pull system the input to tube 1 is $e_{g1} = E_{gm} \cos \omega t$ and the input to tube 2 is $e_{g2} = -E_{gm} \cos \omega t$. The plate current in each tube may be expressed in terms of the grid excitation voltage by a series of the form

$$i_b = I_b + a_1 e_g + a_2 e_g{}^2 + a_3 e_g{}^3 + \cdots$$

With the aid of this series, show that the output current contains only odd cosine terms.

Show that the plate supply current contains only even harmonics, in addition to a d-c term.

16-33. Prove, without recourse to a Fourier series, that mirror symmetry [Eq. (16-44)] exists in a push-pull amplifier. Start with $i = k(i_{b1} - i_{b2})$ and make use of Eq. (16-41).

16-34. Two 6L6 triodes are operated in push-pull Class A from a 250-volt source of potential. The bias voltage is -22.5 volts.

a. Construct the composite static characteristics.

b. Plot the composite dynamic characteristic corresponding to a plate-to-plate load of 10 kilohms. On the same graph sheet, plot the dynamic characteristics of each tube. If the peak a-c signal is 45 volts grid to grid, calculate

c. The power output.

d. The third harmonic distortion.

e. The d-c supply current.

f. The plate-circuit efficiency.

16-35. Repeat the calculations of the preceding problem if the tubes are operated in Class AB₁. The bias is adjusted to -30 volts, and the peak a-c signal is 60 volts grid to grid. The B-supply voltage is maintained at 250 volts.

16-36. Two 2A3 triodes are operated in push-pull Class A from a 250-volt supply. The grid bias is -40 volts, and the peak a-c signal is 80 volts grid to grid. The plate-to-plate resistance is adjustable in 4-K steps from 2 to 14 K. Calculate and plot, as a function of resistance,

a. The power output.

b. The third harmonic current.

c. The d-c supply current.

d. The plate-circuit efficiency.

16-37. Two 6F6 pentodes are operated in push-pull Class A from a 300-volt source of potential. The screen voltage is 250 volts. The bias voltage is −15 volts.

a. Construct the composite static characteristics.

b. Plot the composite dynamic characteristic corresponding to a plate-to-plate load of 20,000 ohms. On the same graph sheet, plot the dynamic characteristic of each tube.

If the peak a-c grid-to-grid signal is 30 volts, calculate

c. The power output.

d. The third harmonic distortion.

e. The d-c supply current.

f. The plate-circuit efficiency.

16-38. A pair of 6F6 pentodes are operated in push-pull Class AB₁ to supply power to a pure resistor load of 6 ohms from a 300-volt power supply. The grid bias is fixed at −20 volts. The screen voltage is maintained at 250 volts. A 20-volt peak signal is applied to each tube.

a. Calculate the turns ratio of the output transformer if this power is to be a maximum.

b. Calculate the percentage distortion under these conditions.

c. Calculate the direct current from the plate supply.

16-39. A pair of 6L6 beam tubes are operated in Class AB₂ from a 400-volt supply. The screen voltage is maintained at 250 volts. The grid bias is −25 volts. The peak grid-to-grid a-c signal is 80 volts. The plate-to-plate resistance is 4 K. Calculate

a. The power output.

b. The third harmonic current.

c. The d-c supply current.

d. The plate-circuit efficiency.

16-40. Given a push-pull transformer with a primary that is not divided at the exact center as shown ($N_1 \neq N_1'$). Explain exactly how such a circuit could be

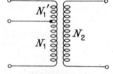

analyzed. In particular, take $N_1 = 2N_1'$, and carry through the analysis for a particular tube.

16-41. Show that for an ideal push-pull Class B amplifier the plate-circuit efficiency and the power output are given by the expressions in Eqs. (16-68).

16-42. Given an ideal Class B amplifier whose characteristics are given in Fig. 16-30. The *B*-supply voltage E_b and the effective load resistance R are fixed as the grid signal

Prob. 16-40

is varied. Show that the plate dissipation P_p increases from zero for no output ($I_m = 0$), passes through a maximum at $I_m = 2E_b/\pi R$, and then decreases. Plot a curve showing the variation of P_p vs. I_m.

If the grid is not driven positive, show that P_p does not pass through a maximum as indicated above unless $R > 2r_p/(\pi - 2)$.

16-43. A single tube is operating as an ideal Class B amplifier into a 1,000-ohm load. A d-c meter in the plate circuit reads 10 ma. How much a-c power is the tube delivering?

16-44. A 2N156 *p-n-p* power transistor (Fig. A9-3) in a common-emitter transformer-coupled configuration feeds an effective load of 30 ohms. The quiescent point is $I_B = -8$ ma, $V_{CE} = -10$ volts. The peak-to-peak input signal current is 16 ma. Find

a. The distortion components.

b. The output power.

c. The collector-circuit efficiency.

16-45. The shape of the collector characteristic of a transistor resembles somewhat those of the plate characteristics of a pentode. Explain carefully why it is *not* possible to eliminate second harmonic distortion in a transistor, whereas it is possible to do so with a pentode, by the proper choice of a load resistance.

16-46. A 2N156 p-n-p power transistor is used in the circuit of Fig. 16-32 at the quiescent point $I_B = -8$ ma, $V_{CE} = -10$ volts. Calculate and plot the power output and the second, third, and fourth harmonic distortions for load resistances of 10, 30, and 50 ohms. The peak-to-peak current is 16 ma.

16-47. A 2N156 power transistor is used in the Class B push-pull circuit of Fig. 16-34. If $V_{CC} = -15$ volts, peak $I_B = 28$ ma and $R_L' = 30$ ohms, calculate

a. The power output.

b. The collector-circuit efficiency.

c. The third harmonic distortion.

16-48. Sketch the circuit of a push-pull Class B transistor amplifier in the common-collector configuration

a. With an output transformer.

b. Without an output transformer.

16-49. Discuss the push-pull complementary circuit of Fig. 16-36. In particular, show that no even harmonics are present.

Chapter 17

17-1. Given a single-stage RC-coupled uncompensated amplifier with a mid-band gain of 1,000 (real and negative). It is made into a feedback amplifier with $\beta = \frac{1}{10}$ (real and positive).

a. As the frequency is varied, to what value does the gain of the amplifier without feedback fall before the gain of the amplifier with feedback falls 3 db?

b. What is the ratio of the half power frequencies with feedback to those without feedback?

c. If $f_1 = 20$ cps and $f_2 = 50,000$ cps for the amplifier without feedback, what are the corresponding values after feedback has been added?

17-2. An amplifier without feedback gives a fundamental output of 36 volts with 7 per cent second harmonic distortion when the input is 0.028 volt.

a. If 1.2 per cent of the output is fed back into the input in a degenerative circuit, what is the output voltage?

b. For an output of 36 volts with 1 per cent second harmonic distortion, what is the input voltage?

17-3. Assume that the parameters of the circuit are $r_p = 10$ K, $R_g = 1$ megohm, $R_1 = 40$ ohms, $R_L = 50$ K, and $\mu = 60$. Neglect the reactances of all capacitors. Find the gain and output impedance of the circuit at the terminals

a. AN.

b. BN.

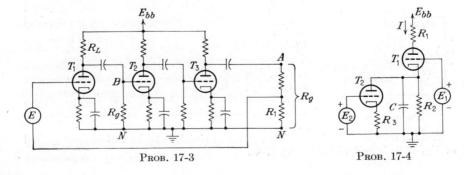

PROB. 17-3   PROB. 17-4

17-4. E_1 and E_2 are sinor input voltages. Draw the equivalent circuit from which to calculate the signal current I for the circuit shown.

17-5. A feedback amplifier has two sets of input terminals. The external signal is applied to input 1, and the gain for this signal is A_1. The feedback signal is applied to input 2, and the gain for this signal is A_2.

a. Show that for voltage feedback

$$A_f = \frac{A_1}{1 - \beta A_2} \quad \text{and} \quad Z_f = \frac{Z_o}{1 - \beta A_2}$$

b. Show that for current feedback

$$A_f = A_1 \quad \text{and} \quad Z_f = Z_o + (1 - A_2)Z_s$$

17-6. *a.* If the positive supply voltage changes by $\Delta E_{bb} = e_a$, how much does the plate-to-ground voltage change?

b. How much does the cathode voltage change, under the conditions in part *a*?

c. Repeat parts *a* and *b* if E_{bb} is constant but E_{cc} changes by $\Delta E_{cc} = e_k$.

d. If $R_L = 0$ so that the circuit is a cathode follower, show that, if $(\mu + 1)R_k \gg r_p$, the cathode voltage changes by $\dfrac{e_a}{\mu + 1}$ or $\dot{e}_k \dfrac{r_p/R_k}{\mu + 1}$. What is the physical significance of these results?

PROB. 17-6   PROB. 17-7

17-7. Each triode section is operated at a quiescent grid-to-cathode voltage of -2 volts and a quiescent plate-to-cathode voltage of 250 volts. Find the value of

a. The resistance R.

b. The grid-to-ground voltage of each section.

c. The effective cathode impedance R_{k1} of T_1.

d. If T_2 were replaced by a resistor of value R_{k1} (found in part *c*), calculate the negative supply voltage required to maintain the same quiescent current as above.

17-8. Each tube shown has a plate resistance $r_p = 10$ K and an amplification factor $\mu = 20$. Find the gain

a. e_o/e_1 if $e_2 = 0$.

b. e_o/e_2 if $e_1 = 0$.

17-9. Prove that the Thévenin's equivalent circuit between plate and ground of Fig. 17-8*a* is as depicted in Fig. 17-8*b*.

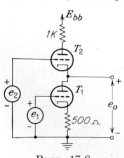

PROB. 17-8

17-10. Prove that the Thévenin's equivalent circuit between cathode and ground of Fig. 17-8*a* is as depicted in Fig. 17-8*c*.

17-11. If $R_1 = R_2 = R$ and if the two tubes have identical parameters, verify that the voltage amplification $e_o/e_s = -\mu/2$ and that the output impedance is $\frac{1}{2}[r_p + (\mu + 1)R]$.

17-12. In the circuit of Prob. 17-11 the triodes are the two sections of a 12AX7 with $r_p = 62$ K and $\mu = 100$. If $e_s = 5$ volts, $R_1 = 2$ K, and $R_2 = 1$ K, find the output voltage e_o and the output impedance.

17-13. The triodes are the two sections of a 5965 with $\mu = 47$ and $r_p = 7.2$ K. If the plate supply ripple voltage is $e_a = 1$ mv, what is the ripple voltage at the plate of T_2?

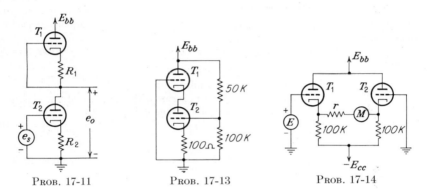

PROB. 17-11   PROB. 17-13   PROB. 17-14

17-14. *a.* The circuit shown is that of a d-c vacuum-tube voltmeter. The d-c meter M measures the input voltage E. The resistance r is used to adjust the range of the instrument. Compute the value of r such that a 200-μa meter will read full scale when the input voltage is 10 volts. The triodes are the two sections of a 6SN7 for which $\mu = 20$ and $r_p = 7.7$ K. First obtain an approximate solution by assuming that each triode is an ideal cathode follower. Then use the exact equivalent circuit looking into each cathode to obtain a more accurate value for r.

b. Consider that, because of aging, the g_m has increased by 10 per cent, the r_p has decreased by 10 per cent, and μ has remained constant. Compute the correction (in per cent) which must be applied to the instrument readings. HINT: Since the correction is small, use the binomial expansion and neglect higher-order terms.

17-15. Given a cathode follower with a cathode resistor of 25 K using a 6SN7. The input voltage swings over such a large range that the plate resistance varies between 24 and 8 K. Assume that μ is constant over this range. Prove that the gain remains constant to within about 3 per cent.

17-16. In a cathode follower consider the cathode resistor R_k as part of the amplifier and not as the external load. Evaluate A, β, and then A_f from Eq. (17-2).

17-17. In the cathode-coupled phase-inverter circuit of Fig. 17-11 solve for the current by drawing the equivalent circuit looking into the cathode of T_1. Then replace T_2 by the Thévenin's equivalent looking into its plate. The cathode resistor R_k may be taken arbitrarily large.

17-18. In the circuit of Fig. 17-11, $R_L = r_p = 10$ K, $R_k = 1$ K, and $\mu = 19$. If the output is taken from the plate of T_2, find

a. The voltage gain.

b. The output impedance.

17-19. *a.* Prove that in the phase-inverter circuit of Fig. 17-11 the signal current i_1 is always larger than i_2 in magnitude.

b. Prove that, if i_1 is to exceed i_2 by less than 10 per cent,

$$R_k > 10 \frac{r_p + R_L}{\mu + 1}$$

17-20. *a.* In the phase-inverter circuit of Fig. 17-11 show that the voltage across R_k is

$$\frac{1}{2} \frac{\mu e}{\mu + 1} \frac{1}{1 + (r_p + R_L)/2(\mu + 1)R_k} \cong \frac{e}{2}$$

b. Assume that the amplification factors of the two sections are identical and constant but that the plate resistances r_{p1} and r_{p2} are functions of plate current. Show that the single-ended gain at the plate of T_1, assuming that R_k is large compared with $(R_{L2} + r_{p2})/(\mu + 1)$, is

$$A \cong \frac{\mu R_{L1}}{R_{L1} + r_{p1} + r_{p2} + R_{L2}}$$

Explain why this circuit tends to keep amplitude distortion low.

17-21. *a.* A signal voltage e_a is applied in series with the plate of T_1. Assuming that R_k is very large, prove that the output voltage e_o is given by

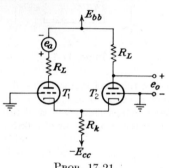

PROB. 17-21

$$e_o = \frac{R_L e_a}{2(R_L + r_p)}$$

b. Prove that the output impedance Z_o at the plate of T_2 is given by

$$Z_o = \frac{R_L(R_L + 2r_p)}{2(R_L + r_p)}$$

17-22. For the difference amplifier, verify
a. Eq. (17-23).
b. Eq. (17-24).
17-23. For the cascode amplifier, verify
a. Eq. (17-27).
b. Eq. (17-28).
c. Eq. (17-29).

17-24. In the cascode circuit of Fig. 17-14 the triodes are the two sections of a 12AT7, $R = 10$ K, $E' = 125$ volts, $E_{bb} = 250$ volts, and $E_{cc} = 2$ volts. Find the quiescent current and the voltage at K_2.

17-25. In the cascode circuit of Fig. 17-14 the tube is a 6SN7, $R = 10$ K, $E' = 200$ volts, $E_{bb} = 320$ volts, and $E_{cc} = 8$ volts. Find the quiescent current and the voltage at P_1.

17-26. *a.* Find the minimum value of E_{bb} so that the top tube does not draw grid current.

b. Plot i_b vs. E_{bb} from this minimum value of E_{bb} to $E_{bb} = 500$ volts and show that this volt-ampere characteristic resembles that of a pentode.

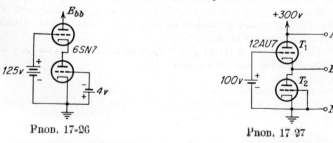

PROB. 17-26   PROB. 17-27

17-27. *a.* Find the quiescent current in the circuit shown.

b. Find the effective impedance seen between terminals A and N.

c. Between B and N.

17-28. Prove that the polar plot of the loop gain of an RC-coupled amplifier is a circle in the complex plane located as in Fig. 17-16.

17-29. *a.* The possibility of oscillation is to be avoided in the three-stage RC-coupled amplifier of Prob. 17-3. Prove that the mid-band loop gain must be kept below 8.

b. What is the maximum possible value of R_1 if all other component values are as specified in Prob. 17-3?

17-30. Derive the exact formula (17-33) for the voltage gain of an operational amplifier from the equivalent circuit of Fig. 17-19.

17-31. Design an operational amplifier whose output (for a sinusoidal signal) is equal in magnitude to its input and leads the input by 45 deg.

17-32. Consider a single-stage operational amplifier with a gain of 100. If $Z = R$ and $Z' = -jX_c$ with $R = X_c$, calculate the gain as a complex number.

17-33. Given an operational amplifier consisting of R and L in series for Z and C for Z'. If the input is a constant E, find the output e_o as a function of time. Assume an infinite open-loop gain.

17-34. For the circuit shown, prove that the output voltage is given by

$$-e_o = \frac{R_2}{R_1} e + \left(R_2 C + \frac{L}{R_1} \right) \frac{de}{dt} + LC \frac{d^2e}{dt^2}$$

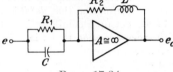

PROB. 17-34

17-35. Given an operational amplifier with Z consisting of a resistor R in parallel with a capacitor C and Z' consisting of a resistor R'. The input is a sweep voltage $e = \alpha t$. Prove that the output is a sweep voltage that starts with an initial step. Thus, show that

$$e_o = -\alpha R'C - \alpha \frac{R'}{R} t$$

Assume an infinite open-loop gain.

17-36. Sketch an operational amplifier circuit having an input e and an output which is approximately $-5e - 3de/dt$.

17-37. *a.* The input to the operational integrator of Fig. 17-22 is a step voltage of magnitude E. Prove that the output is

$$e_o = AE[1 - \epsilon^{-t/RC(1-A)}]$$

b. Compare this result with that obtained if the step voltage is impressed upon a simple RC integrating network (without the use of an amplifier). Show that for large values of RC both solutions represent a voltage which varies approximately linearly with time. Verify that if $A \gg 1$ the slope of the ramp output is approximately the same for both circuits. Also prove that the deviation from linearity for the amplifier circuit is $1/(1 - A)$ times that of the simple RC circuit.

17-38. *a.* The input to an operational differentiator whose open-loop gain A is finite is a ramp voltage $e = \alpha t$. Show that the output is

$$e_o = \frac{A}{1 - A} \alpha RC[1 - \epsilon^{-t(1-A)/RC}]$$

b. Compare this result with that obtained if the same input is impressed upon a simple RC differentiating network (without the use of an amplifier). Show that approximately the same final constant output $RC\,de/dt$ is obtained. Also show that the operational-amplifier output reaches this correct value of the differentiated input much more quickly than does the simple RC circuit.

17-39. Given an operational amplifier with Z consisting of R in series with C and Z' consisting of R' in parallel with C'. The input is a step voltage of magnitude E.

a. Show by qualitative argument that the output voltage must start at zero, reach a maximum, and then again fall to zero.

b. Show that if $R'C' \neq RC$ the output is given by

$$e_o = \frac{R'CE}{R'C' - RC}\,(\epsilon^{-t/RC} - \epsilon^{-t/R'C'})$$

17-40. Sketch in block-diagram form a computer using operational amplifiers to solve the differential equation

$$\frac{de}{dt} + 0.5e + 0.1\sin\omega t = 0$$

An oscillator is available which will provide a signal $1\sin\omega t$. Use only resistors and capacitors.

17-41. Set up a computer in block-diagram form to solve Eq. (17-41) by starting with the assumption that de/dt is available as a voltage between two terminals.

17-42. Set up a computer in block-diagram form to solve Eq. (17-41) by starting with the assumption that e is available as a voltage between two terminals.

17-43. An operational amplifier has a base amplifier whose *unloaded* open-loop gain and impedance are $\mathbf{A}_u$ and $\mathbf{Z}_u$, respectively. These are the values of gain and output impedance with the impedance $\mathbf{Z}'$ omitted. Assume zero input admittance.

a. Draw the equivalent circuit of the operational amplifier. Include an external impedance $\mathbf{Z}_L$ across the output terminals.

b. Find the expression for the ratio $\mathbf{E}_o/\mathbf{E}_i$ which gives the gain without feedback but with the amplifier loaded with $\mathbf{Z}'$.

c. From part *b* deduce that the open-loop loaded gain $\mathbf{A}$ and output impedance $\mathbf{Z}_o$ (with the base amplifier loaded by $\mathbf{Z}'$) are given by

$$\mathbf{A} = \mathbf{A}_u\,\frac{\mathbf{Z}' + \mathbf{Z}_u/\mathbf{A}_u}{\mathbf{Z}_u + \mathbf{Z}'} \quad\text{and}\quad \mathbf{Z}_o = \frac{\mathbf{Z}_u\mathbf{Z}'}{\mathbf{Z}_u + \mathbf{Z}'}$$

HINT: Write

$$\frac{\mathbf{E}_o}{\mathbf{E}_i} = \frac{\mathbf{A}\mathbf{Z}_L}{\mathbf{Z}_L + \mathbf{Z}_o}$$

d. Find the expression for $\mathbf{E}_o/\mathbf{E}_s$ which gives the gain with feedback. Write

$$\frac{\mathbf{E}_o}{\mathbf{E}_s} = \frac{\mathbf{A}_f\mathbf{Z}_L}{\mathbf{Z}_L + \mathbf{Z}_f}$$

and prove that $\mathbf{A}_f$ is given by Eq. (17-33) and that the output impedance with feedback $\mathbf{Z}_f$ is given by

$$\mathbf{Z}_f = \frac{\mathbf{Z}_o}{1 - \mathbf{A}\mathbf{Z}/(\mathbf{Z} + \mathbf{Z}')} = \frac{\mathbf{Z}_o}{1 - \mathbf{A}\beta}$$

Chapter 18

18-1. Verify Eq. (18-1) for the feedback factor of the phase-shift network of Fig. 18-2, assuming that this network does not load the amplifier. Prove that the phase shift is 180 deg for $\alpha^2 = 6$ and that at this frequency $\beta = \frac{1}{29}$.

18-2. *a.* For the network of Prob. 18-1 show that the input impedance is given by

$$Z_i = R \frac{1 - 5\alpha^2 - j(6\alpha - \alpha^3)}{3 - \alpha^2 - j4\alpha}$$

b. Show that the input impedance at the frequency of the oscillator, $\alpha = \sqrt{6}$, is $(0.83 - j2.70)R$.

Note that if the frequency is varied by varying C the input impedance remains constant. However, if the frequency is varied by varying R, the impedance is varied in proportion to R.

18-3. Design a phase-shift oscillator to operate at a frequency of 5 kc. Use one of the triodes in Table 7-1. The phase-shift network is not to load down the amplifier.

a. Which tubes in Table 7-1 can *not* be used?

b. Find the minimum value of R_L for which the circuit will oscillate.

c. Find the product RC.

d. Choose a reasonable value for R and find C.

18-4. *a.* A two-stage oscillator uses the phase-shifting network shown. Prove that

$$\beta = \frac{1}{3 + j(\omega RC - 1/\omega RC)}$$

b. Show that the frequency of oscillation is $f = 1/2\pi RC$ and that the gain must exceed 3.

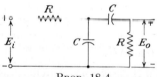

Prob. 18-4

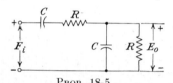

Prob. 18-5

18-5. *a.* Find the feedback factor for the network shown.

b. Sketch the circuit of a phase-shift oscillator using this feedback network.

c. Find the expression for the frequency of oscillation, assuming that the network does not load down the amplifier.

d. Find the minimum gain required for oscillation.

18-6. Consider the two-section RC feedback network shown. Find the transfer function β and verify that it is not possible to obtain 180-deg phase shift with a finite attenuation.

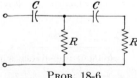

Prob. 18-6

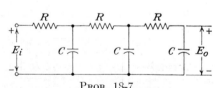

Prob. 18-7

18-7. For the feedback network shown find

a. The transfer function.

b. The input impedance.

c. If this network is used in a phase shift, find the frequency of oscillation and the minimum amplifier voltage gain. Assume that the network does not load down the amplifier.

18-8. Take into account the loading of the RC network in the phase-shift oscillator of Fig. 18-2. If R_o is the output impedance of the amplifier (assume that C_k is arbitrarily large), prove that the frequency of oscillation f and the minimum gain A are given by

$$f = \frac{1}{2\pi RC} \frac{1}{\sqrt{6 + 4(R_o/R)}}$$

$$A = 29 + 23\frac{R_o}{R} + 4\left(\frac{R_o}{R}\right)^2$$

18-9. Apply the Barkhausen criterion to the tuned-plate oscillator and verify Eqs. (18-2) and (18-3).

18-10. Show that the circuit of Prob. 18-4 is equivalent to a completely unbalanced Wien bridge, *i.e.*, one for which $R_2 = 0$.

18-11. Exercise your ingenuity to see in how many different ways you can introduce an external signal in the circuit of Fig. 18-5 considered to be adjusted to operate as a frequency selective amplifier. Discuss the relative merits of each possibility.

18-12. Consider the Wien-bridge oscillator of Fig. 18-5. Explain in a general way how it comes about that the total phase shift around the circuit and hence the frequency of oscillation depend on the following:

a. The plate resistance.

b. The coupling capacitance.

c. The grid leak resistance.

d. The cathode resistance.

e. The load resistance.

f. The supply voltage.

g. The filament heater voltage.

h. The stray capacitance across the outputs of the tubes.

18-13. In the bridge circuit of Fig. 18-5 add an inductor in series with R and C between points G and P. Also, replace the parallel combination of R and C by a resistor R_3. Find the frequency of oscillation and the minimum gain of the amplifier if

a. R_1 is infinite.

b. R_1 is finite.

18-14. *a.* At what frequency will the circuit shown oscillate, if at all?

b. Find the minimum value of R needed to sustain oscillations. The tube is a 6SL7 with $\mu = 70$ and $r_p = 44$ K.

HINT: Assume a voltage E from grid G_1 of T_1 to ground but with the point G' not connected to the grid G_1. Calculate the loop gain from the equivalent circuit obtained by looking into each cathode.

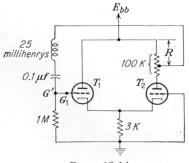

PROB. 18-14

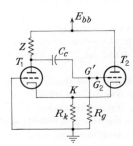

PROB. 18-15

18-15. In the cathode-coupled oscillator circuit shown Z represents a parallel RLC combination. Assume that R_k, R_g, and C_c are arbitrarily large.

a. At what frequency will the circuit oscillate, if at all?

b. Prove that the minimum value of R needed to sustain oscillations is $2r_p/(\mu - 1)$ $\cong 2/g_m$.

HINT: Assume a voltage E from the grid G_2 of T_2 to ground but with the point G' not connected to the grid G_2. Calculate the loop gain from the equivalent circuit obtained by looking into each cathode.

18-16. In the circuit of Prob. 18-15 the impedance Z consists of an inductor L in parallel with a capacitance C. The series resistance of the inductor is r. Prove that the frequency of oscillation is given by

$$\omega^2 = \frac{1}{LC}\left(1 - \frac{r^2 C}{L}\right)$$

and the minimum transconductance is given by

$$g_m = \frac{2\mu r C}{(\mu - 1)L}$$

18-17. Verify Eq. (18-6) by the two methods outlined in the text.

18-18. a. Consider the Colpitts oscillator, taking into account the resistance r in series with the inductor L. Prove that the frequency of oscillation is given by

$$\omega^2 = \frac{1}{L}\left[\frac{1}{C_1} + \frac{1}{C_2}\left(1 + \frac{r}{r_p}\right)\right]$$

b. If $r/r_p \ll 1$, prove that the minimum transconductance is given by

$$g_m = \frac{r\mu C_2(C_1 + C_2)}{L(\mu C_2 - C_1)}$$

18-19. Sketch the circuit of a tuned-plate tuned-grid oscillator using shunt feed.

18-20. a. Consider the Hartley oscillator of Fig. 18-8 with the addition of a cathode resistor R_k. If the resistances of the inductors are r_1 and r_2, respectively, find the frequency of oscillation.

b. Find the value of R_k for which the loop gain will just equal unity.

18-21. The Hartley oscillator of Fig. 18-8 is modified by placing C_3 across L_2 and by allowing a mutual inductance M between L_1 and L_2. Find the frequency of oscillation.

18-22. a. Verify Eq. (18-12) for the reactance of a crystal.

b. Prove that the ratio of the parallel- to series-resonant frequencies is given approximately by $1 + \frac{1}{2}C/C'$.

c. If $C = 0.04$ $\mu\mu$f and $C' = 2.0$ $\mu\mu$f, by what per cent is the parallel- greater than the series-resonant frequency?

18-23. A crystal has the following parameters: $L = 0.33$ henry, $C = 0.065$ $\mu\mu$f, $C' = 1.0$ $\mu\mu$f, and $R = 5.5$ K.

a. Find the series-resonant frequency.

b. By what per cent does the parallel-resonant frequency exceed the series-resonant frequency?

c. Find the Q of the crystal.

18-24. Verify Eq. (18-22) for the transfer function of the balanced Wien bridge.

18-25. Verify Eq. (18-24) for the frequency stability of a Wien-bridge oscillator.

18-26. For the phase-shifting network of Prob. 18-4 prove that

$$\left(\omega \frac{d\theta}{d\omega}\right)_{\omega \to \omega_0} = -\frac{2}{3}$$

18-27. Find the ratio of the per cent second harmonic distortion at the grid to that at the plate of the phase-shift oscillator of Fig. 18-2.

18-28. If an oscillator uses the feedback network of Prob. 18-4, is the wave form purer at the grid or at the plate?

18-29. Evaluate $|H_2|$ for the Wien bridge, with $A = 50$, for the network of Prob. 18-4 and for the phase-shift oscillator of Fig. 18-2. Which type of oscillator has the least second harmonic distortion at the plate?

18-30. Which has less second harmonic distortion at the grid, the phase-shift oscillator of Fig. 18-2 or the Wien-bridge oscillator with $A = 20$?

18-31. Verify Eqs. (18-39) and (18-40) for the transistor phase-shift oscillator.

18-32. Verify that the transistor phase-shift circuit of Fig. 18-19 will not oscillate if α is less than 0.978.

Chapter 19

19-1. *a.* Prove that the general solution of the differential equation in Eq. (19-5) is

$$i_b = \frac{E_m}{\sqrt{R_L{}^2 + \omega^2 L^2}} \left[\sin (\omega t - \Psi) + e^{-R_L t/L} \sin \Psi \right]$$

where $\tan \Psi = \omega L / R_L$.

b. The angle of cutout ωt_2 is that angle at which the current becomes zero. Show that at cutout

$$\sin (\omega t_2 - \Psi) + e^{-(R_L/\omega L)\omega t_2} \sin \Psi = 0$$

Plot a semilog curve of ωt_2 vs. $\omega L / R_L$, with $\omega L / R_L$ in the range from 0.1 to 1,000.

c. Verify the curves of Fig. 19-2. In particular, check the value for $\omega L / R_L = 5$.

19-2. A single-phase full-wave rectifier uses gas diodes. The tube drop and internal resistance of the tubes may be neglected. Assume an ideal transformer.

a. Prove that one tube conducts for one half cycle and that the other tube conducts for the remaining half cycle of the input line voltage, if the load consists of a resistor R in series with an inductor L.

b. Find the analytic expression for the load current in the interval

$$0 \leq \alpha = 2\pi f t \leq \pi$$

HINT: Set up the differential equation for the load current i in this interval. The solution of this equation will consist of a steady-state a-c term added to a "transient" term. Evaluate the arbitrary constant in the "transient" term by noting that the current repeats itself at intervals of π in α, so that $i(0) = i(\pi)$.

c. Evaluate the direct current I_{dc} by averaging the instantaneous current.

d. Evaluate the first term in the Fourier series for the current, and compare with Eq. (19-6).

Compare this method of attack with that used in Sec. 19-2.

19-3. Prove that the rms value of the triangular voltage depicted in Fig. 19-10 is given by Eq. (19-22).

19-4. A single-phase full-wave rectifier uses an 83 gas tube. The transformer voltage is 350 volts rms to center tap. The load consists of a 4-μf capacitor in parallel with a 2,500-ohm resistor. The tube drop and the transformer resistance and leakage reactance may be neglected.

a. Calculate the cutout angle.

b. Plot to scale the output voltage and the tube current (see Fig. 19-8). Determine the cutin point graphically from this plot, and find the peak tube current corresponding to this point.

c. Repeat parts a and b, using a 16- instead of a 4-μf capacitor.

19-5. a. Show that Eq. (19-26) reduces to

$$E_{dc} = E_m - \frac{I_{dc}}{4fC}$$

provided that

$$\frac{I_{dc}}{4fCE_m} \ll 1$$

b. Show that this result is obtained if it is assumed that the capacitor discharges for the complete half cycle $T/2$.

19-6. The circuit of Fig. 19-13 can be analyzed by the methods of elementary a-c theory without making the approximations used in Sec. 19-5. Assuming that the input voltage to the filter is given by Eq. (19-31), prove that the ripple factor is

$$r = \frac{\sqrt{2}/3}{\sqrt{\left(\frac{X_L}{R_L}\right)^2 + \left(\frac{X_L}{X_C} - 1\right)^2}}$$

Under what condition does this reduce to the simpler equation (19-35)?

19-7. By error the capacitor of an L-section filter is connected to the input side of the inductor. Examine this filter analytically, and derive an expression for

a. The regulation of the system.

b. The ripple factor.

Compare these results with those in Sec. 19-5.

19-8. The output of a full-wave rectifier is fed from a 400-0-400-volt transformer. The load current is 0.1 amp. Two 4-μf capacitors are available. The tube drop of each gas tube is 15 volts. The circuit resistance exclusive of the load is 500 ohms.

a. Calculate the value of inductance for a two-stage L-section filter. The inductances are to be equal. The ripple factor is to be 0.0001.

b. Calculate the d-c output voltage.

19-9. Given two equal capacitors C and two equal inductors L. Under what circumstances will it be better to use a double L-section filter than to use a single section with the inductors in series and the capacitors in parallel?

19-10. An L-section filter is used in the output of a full-wave rectifier that is fed from a 375-0-375-volt transformer. The load current is 0.2 amp. Two 4-μf capacitors and two 20-henry chokes are available. The drop in the gas rectifier tubes is 15 volts.

a. Calculate the 120-cycle ripple voltage, if a single-section filter is used, with the two chokes in series and the two capacitors in parallel.

b. Repeat part a for a two-section filter.

c. Calculate the 240-cycle ripple voltage if a single-section filter is used.

19-11. Design a power supply for a load varying from zero to 150 ma at a full-load output voltage of approximately 250 volts. Good regulation is desired. The ripple voltage is not to exceed 0.1 volt.

Specify the type of circuit, the type of filter, and the type of tube. Give nominal ratings of all the circuit elements used.

Assume

a. Vacuum-tube rectifiers have a plate resistance of 350 ohms.

b. Gas-tube rectifiers have a tube drop of 10 volts.

c. Power transformers are rated in steps of 50 volts (*i.e.*, you can buy a transformer whose total secondary voltage output is 50 volts, or 100 volts, or 150 volts, etc., rms).

d. The transformer secondary resistance totals 200 ohms.

e. Chokes are rated in steps of 5 henrys.

f. Each choke resistance is 200 ohms.

g. Capacitors are rated in 4-μf steps.

19-12. Design a power supply for a load that varies between the limits of 20 and 100 ma at a nominal voltage of 300 volts. The ripple factor is not to exceed 0.1 per cent, and good regulation is desired. Specify the type of circuit, the type of tube, and the type of filter to use. Give nominal ratings of all the circuit elements used. Make the same assumptions as in Prob. 19-11.

19-13. Given a full-wave rectifier circuit, a 375-0-375 volt transformer, $R_L = 2,000$ ohms, gas diodes with a 20-volt drop, two 20-henry chokes, and two 16-μf capacitors. The transformer resistance to center tap and each choke resistance is 200 ohms. Calculate the approximate output voltage and ripple factor under the following filter arrangements:

a. The two chokes are connected in series with the load.

b. The two capacitors are connected in parallel across the load.

c. A single-section L filter, consisting of the two inductors in series and the two capacitors in parallel.

d. A two-section L filter.

e. A Π-section filter, using both inductors.

19-14. Derive an expression for the ripple in a Π-section filter when used with a half-wave rectifier, subject to the same approximations as those in Sec. 19-7 for the full-wave case.

19-15. A full-wave single-phase rectifier employs a Π-section filter consisting of two 4-μf capacitors and a 20-henry choke. The transformer voltage to center tap is 300 volts rms. The load current is 50 ma. Calculate the d-c output voltage and the ripple voltage. The resistance of the choke is 200 ohms.

19-16. The voltage at the input capacitor of a Π-section filter is given to a close approximation by $e(t) = 525 - 40 \sin 754t$. The output capacitor of the filter is 10 μf. If the filter d-c output voltage is 500 volts for a 100-ma load with a ripple factor of 0.001, determine the inductance and d-c resistance of the filter choke.

19-17. Given a full-wave rectifier using ideal elements (*i.e.*, no resistance or leakage reactance in the transformer, no tube drop, and no resistance in the chokes). The voltage on each side of the center tap of the transformer is 300 volts rms.

Answer the questions below for *each* of the following types of filter:

1. No filter.
2. A 10-μf capacitor filter.
3. A 20-henry inductor filter.
4. An L-section filter consisting of a 10-μf capacitor and a 20-henry choke.

a. What is the no-load d-c voltage? (List your answers as *a*1, *a*2, *a*3, and *a*4.)

b. What is the d-c voltage at 100 ma?

c. Does the ripple increase, decrease, or stay constant with increasing load current?

d. What is the peak inverse voltage across each tube?

19-18. A single center-tapped transformer (350-0-350 volts) is to supply power at two different voltages for certain service. The negative is to be grounded on each system. The low voltage is full wave and is filtered with a two-section L filter. The high voltage is half wave and has a capacitor input filter. Show the schematic diagram for such a system. What is the nominal output voltage of each unit?

19-19. What voltages are available from the rectifier circuit shown?   A 425-0-425-volt transformer is used.   Label the polarities of the output voltages.

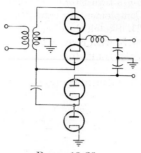

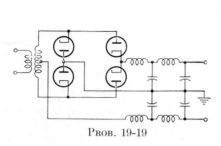

PROB. 19-19   PROB. 19-20

19-20. The circuit shown is to be used to supply power for an amplifier and also for the accelerating voltage of an associated cathode-ray tube.   What output voltages are obtained if a 350-0-350-volt center-tapped transformer is used?   (HINT: See Prob. 14-14.)

19-21. The circuit shown operates from a 300-0-300-volt transformer.

a. What are the magnitude and polarity of the d-c voltage at A? at B? under no load?

b. What is the peak inverse on each tube?

c. If the load current at A is 100 ma, what is the voltage at A?

d. If the load current at B is 20 ma, what is the voltage at B?

19-22. Prove that if no approximations are made in the derivation for the stabilization factor S in Eq. (19-52) the exact value of S is given by

$$S = \frac{r + r_{p2}}{R_L} + 1 + \mu_2 + \mu_2 A_1 \beta$$

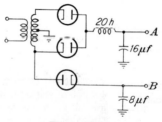

PROB. 19-21

19-23. In the regulated power supply of Fig. 19-20 the resistor R_3 is connected to the input side of the series tube.   Prove that the output impedance is given approximately by Eq. (19-56) with S defined by Eq. (19-58).

19-24. Given a regulated power supply with the following specifications:

Unregulated input voltage = 450 volts.

Regulated output voltage = 255 volts.

Load current is 200 ma.

Control tubes: three 6B4-G's (Fig. A9-6) in parallel.

Reference voltage: OC3/105.

Amplifier: a 6AU6 (Fig. 11-7) with the screen connected *directly* to the regulated output.   The plate load resistor is 100 K and is connected to the unregulated side.

a. Sketch the complete circuit and indicate reasonable values for all resistors and capacitors.

b. Calculate the plate voltage of the 6AU6 with respect to ground.

c. Calculate the grid voltage of the 6AU6 with respect to ground.

d. Calculate the voltage stabilization S.

19-25. In Fig. 19-23, $R_2 = 2R_1$, and the breakdown diode voltage is 10 volts. What is the approximate value of the regulated output voltage?

19-26. Sketch the circuit of a regulated semiconductor power supply whose output is positive with respect to ground, using
  a. p-n-p transistors.
  b. Complementary transistors.

19-27. Sketch the circuit of a regulated semiconductor power supply whose output is negative with respect to ground, using
  a. p-n-p transistors.
  b. n-p-n transistors.
  c. Complementary transistors.

INDEX